Twayne's Introductions to World Literature Series

A PROGRAM DESIGNED TO INTRODUCE
FOREIGN WRITERS OF MERIT
TO READERS OF ENGLISH

Jacob Steinberg, General Editor

Twayne's Introductions to World Literature Series

Introduction to Modern

GREEK

LITERATURE

An Anthology of
Fiction, Drama, and Poetry

Edited and Translated by

MARY P. GIANOS

Poetry translations by

KIMON FRIAR

TWAYNE PUBLISHERS, INC.

New York

To KIMON MOSCHOS

Acknowledgments

Acknowledgment is made to the following authors for permission to translate prose and drama included in this volume:

To Panayotis Kanellopoulos for the version of "Poetry and Truth in Neo-Hellenic Life," revised expressly for this anthology.

To I. M. Panayotopoulos for "Humble Life"; Lambis Myrivilis to Irvin Ziemann for Stratis Myrivilis' "The Cat's Eye"; Elias Venezis for "Mycenae"; Kosmas Politis for "A Double"; Petros Haris for "Lights on the Sea"; Takis Doxas for "The Traffic Officer of Phigalia"; Yiannis Manglis for "The Wedding"; Markos Lazaridis for "Fear"; Demetrios Yiakos for "The Path of Dawn"; Pandelis Prevelakis to André Michalopoulos for *The Last Tournament;* George Theotokas for *The Game of Folly vs. Wisdom;* and Mrs. Sylvia Akritas for Loukis Akritas' *Hostages.*

To the following for granting permission to Kimon Friar to translate the poetry:

Mrs. Anna Sikelianos for "Sparta" and "Unrecorded"; Takis Papatzonis for "The Unlooked-for Theme" and "The Sluggish of Mind"; George Seferis for "In the Manner of G. S.," "Our Own Sun," and "Stratis the Mariner by the Dead Sea"; George Themelis for "Appearance" and "Passing"; Zoë Karelli for "Worker in the Workshop of Time," "Presences," and "Kiss of Silence"; Andreas Embiricos for "Light on a Whale," "Spring as Always," and "The Euphrates"; George Thomas Vafopoulos for "The Night," "The Return of the Satyrs," and "The Mask"; Alexander Baras for "The *Cleopatra,* The *Semiramis,* and The *Theodora*"; George Sarandaris for "The Bride" and "Friendships"; Melissanthi for "Stage Set" and "Atonement"; Yannis Ritsos for "Guilty Conscience," "The First Sensual Delight," "Under Suspicion," "Degrees of Emotion," and "Builders"; Nikos Engonopoulos for "Mercurius Bouas," "Psychoanalysis of Phantoms," and "Poetry 1948"; Alexander Matsas for "Adventure of Psyche" and "Diver"; Odysseus Elytis for "Body of

Summer," "The Autopsy," and "This Wind That Loiters"; Nikiphoros Vrettakos for "To a Friend," "The Other Morning," and "The Flowering Dogwood"; Nikos Gatsos for excerpt from *Amorgos;* and Takis Varvitsiotis for "The Testimony of the Mirror" and "To Federico García Lorca."

To the following publishers and periodicals:

Aetos Publishing Co., Athens—for Alexandros Papadiamantis' "The Dreamer" in *Papadiamantis, Karkavitsas and Other Writers,* Basic Library No. 28, ed. by Theodoros Xidis, 1955; Konstantinos Theotokis' "Village Life" in *Konstantinos Theotokis,* Basic Library No. 31, ed. by Angelos Terzakis, 1955.

Diphros Publishing Co., Athens—for Markos Lazaridis' "Fear" in *Gazelle,* 1961.

I. D. Kollaros & Co., Inc., Athens—for Konstantinos Hadzopoulos' "Clara's Dream," and Emmanuel Roidis' "Psychology of a Husband from the Island of Syra" in *The Short Story Anthology,* ed. by H. N. Apostolidis, 1953, 1954, 1960; for Kostas Ouranis' "I Shall Die One Day on a Mournful Autumn Twilight" and "Stop Sending Now" in *Anthology, 1708-1959,* ed. by H. N. Apostolidis, 1963; for Constantine Cavafis' "Ithaca," "The City," "The God Forsakes Antony" and "He Swears" in *Anthology, 1708-1959,* ed. by H. N. Apostolidis, 1963; for Kostas Kariotakis' "Only," "Athens," and "Optimism" in *Anthology, 1708-1959,* ed. by H. N. Apostolidis, 1963; for Petros Haris' "Lights on the Sea" in *Lights on the Sea and Other Stories,* 1958; for Andreas Karkavitsas' "The Sea" in *Words of the Prow,* 1953; for Stratis Myrivilis' "The Cat's Eye" in *The Green Book,* 1956; for George Theotokas' *The Game of Folly vs. Wisdom* in *Theatrical Works, I,* 1965; for Elias Venezis' "Mycenae" in *Winds,* 2nd ed., 1959.

G. Kouris Publishing Co., Athens—for Yiannis Manglis' "The Wedding" and Kosmas Politis' "A Double" in *Anthology of the Greek Short Story, 1900-1963,* ed. by A. Nenedakis, 1963.

Nea Estia, Athens—for Loukis Akritas' *Hostages,* Nov. 1, 1956; Gregorios Xenopoulos' *Divine Dream,* Dec. 25, 1951.

Philological New Year, Athens—for Takis Doxas' "The Traffic Officer of Phigalia," 1964.

Intellectual Cyprus, Leucosia—for Demetrios Yiakos' "The Path of Dawn" in *The Path of Dawn,* 1963.

Simon & Schuster—for excepts from Nikos Kazantzakis' *The Odyssey, A Modern Sequel,* tr. by Kimon Friar, 1958.

Preface

Modern Greek prose and drama are not generally known to the American reader. The notable exception, certainly, is the prose and one or two plays of Nikos Kazantzakis, who has also won acclaim in this country as the poet of the monumental *The Odyssey: A Modern Sequel*, which according to Panayotis Kanellopoulos, is "one of the high points in our century." But Greek poets generally have fared better in translation. In recent years, many good collections of Greek poetry, including those of the Alexandrian poet, Constantine Cavafis, and of the Nobel Prize winner, George Seféris, have appeared; individual poets, as Sikelianós, Elytis, Gátsos, and others, have also been widely anthologized. But Modern Greek prose and drama deserve attention as well as poetry. Thus, one aim of this anthology is to present such translations. The other aim is to introduce Twayne's Greek Authors Series, the critical volumes devoted to individual writers, past through present.

The preparation of any anthology presents certain difficulties, compounded when translation is involved. One of the first considerations is the time span to be covered. This volume is arranged in chronological order of prose writers, dramatists, and poets born between the years 1850 and 1914, though many writers of the latter date produced their mature work in the thirties and forties. Political affiliations do not dictate choices, and early women writers are included only in the poetry section. Women writers today are producing meritorious prose and drama, and they will be included in the *Introduction to Contemporary Greek Literature*, along with the younger writers, the second volume now in preparation. Emanuel Roidis, though born before 1850 (d. 1904), contributed so greatly to reshaping the written language that I considered he should be the only exception in this volume of those born between the years decided upon as limits.

How does one, secondly, decide what is representative of Greek literature during a given period? Though an attempt has been made to select works of authors so often anthologized in Greek, much has to be eliminated from a volume whose size is necessarily limited by a decision to introduce a writer with a self-contained novelette, short story, or play. I, therefore, directed my attention to those authors who, more or less, were a greater influence on later writers and who also contributed to the development of Modern Greek literature. Kostis Palamas (1859–1943), one of the greatest men of Greek letters and an influence for nearly half a century, was omitted because he is almost untranslatable.

As the new Greek nation, freed from the bondage of nearly four centuries of Turkish rule, emerged to take its place on the European literary scene, and as translations of French, German, Russian, English, and Italian writers were being made available by those, like Konstantinos Hadzopoulos, who had studied abroad and had experienced the new literary trends, changes in Greek literature were inevitable. Yet, for all the foreign influences and for all the emphasis on changing social conditions in Greece, the writers speak of problems close to their own hearts.

The sea surrounding Greece—sometimes hostile, but more often the route to distant lands which promised fulfillment of dreams—inspired writers like Papadiamantis, Karkavitsas, Manglis, and Petros Haris. The harsh realities of daily existence, the restrictive and embittering social and moral taboos, the shattered dreams, the premature aging brought about by life in the provinces, are satirical themes of many Greek writers, including Konstantinos Theotokis and Takis Doxas, youngest of the group, and one of the best portrayers of provincial life in Greece today.

I. M. Panayotopoulos presents *Humble Life,* one of the most personal documents in Modern Greek literature, with warm humanity. In the midst of poverty, the inhabitants of a poor section of Piraeus, not radically altered to this day, find time to play and love. Even when tragedy strikes at the mill or the sea, when individuals are exploited by the new factory owners, these poor, forgotten souls carry on their daily lives without bitterness, but with a stoic resignation to their *moira* and a kind of faith in tomorrow.

As for drama, also included here for the first time, the plays selected exhibit a continuity with the classical structure of drama. The only exception is Pandelis Prevelakis' *The Last Tournament* (translated by André Michalopoulos). For his theme, Prevelakis returns to the glorious, yet tumultuous days of the Medici, whose concern and patronage preserved many Greek texts. Loukis Akritas presents the drama of the Occupation in recognizable classical structure, as classical as is Gregorios Xenopoulos' comedy *Divine Dream*. For *The Game of Folly vs. Wisdom*, George Theotokas chooses a Byzantine setting to satirize contemporary morality.

Spyros Melas, perhaps one of the greatest modern Greek playwrights of satirical comedy, has not been included. *The King and the Dog*, first produced in Athens in 1954, and the play most representative of his writings, is too lengthy; its inclusion would have eliminated other works. Nor are the novelists like Anghelos Terzakis, Photis Kontoglou, and others, included, because I feel that excerpted material is too scant for thorough knowledge of a man's work. The only essay translated is that by Dr. Panayotis Kanellopoulos, former Prime Minister of Greece, and the most significant philosophic writer of Greece in the last two decades. In his essay Kanellopoulos traces the historical development of Greek literature, naming all important writers and including writers from Cyprus as well.

To those who aided me in one way or another in preparing this anthology, I owe a great debt. Special gratitude is offered to Professors George A. Panichas, Charles Mitsakis, Chester Cable, and Mrs. June Henderson for valuable editorial comments, and to Miss Patricia Gingrich for reading portions of the manuscript and commenting on my translations. I am also indebted to Professor André Michalopoulos and to Mr. Irwin Ziemann for allowing me to use their translations for the first time in this volume.

My greatest debt, certainly, belongs to Mr. Kimon Friar for his own translations of poets represented here. Special acknowledgment is made to each writer for granting permission either to me or to Mr. Friar to translate his work, and to the Greek publishers who first printed the works here translated.

Contents

II DRAMA

III *POETRY*

Contents

Contents

PART I

FICTION

Panayotis Kanellopoulos

(1903–   )

Panayotis Kanellopoulos was born in 1903 in Patras. After completing the gymnasium there he went on to study law, social sciences, and philosophy at the Universities of Athens, Heidelberg, and Munich. Inspired by Shakespeare, Schiller, and Racine, he had already begun to write poetry and in 1918 had published his early poems in the *Numas*, an *avant-garde* literary periodical printed in Athens.

In 1926 he published his first book, *Society of Nations*, which coincided with his appointment as secretary-general to the Minister of National Economy. From 1929 to 1935 he taught sociology at the University of Athens, the first to occupy such a chair in Greece, and for a year, in 1934, he served as President of the Institution of Social Assurances, which had only then been established.

His early life became one of opposing interests. Philosophical meditation contrasted with public activity; solitude of an enclosed study contrasted with the expansiveness of society; literary publications contrasted with political responsibilities. The books he wrote while professor at the University of Athens were sociological in content but philosophical in tone. The most significant of these are: *History of Social Theories* (1929); *Karl Marx* (1930); *Society of Our Times* (1931); *Man and Social Conflicts* (1932); *Technology and Economics* (1934); *and Philosophical and Sociological Problems of History* (1935). A number of essays on these same problems were also published in foreign periodicals, but the essay which clearly formulates the early crystallizations of his thought is "Loneliness as a Sociological Problem."

The year 1935 was one of great military and political upheavals in Greece. Although Kanellopoulos was silenced politically for the next four years (1936–40), he remained actively engaged in writing the *History of the European Spirit*, one of his most significant literary contributions. Here, he traces the parallel paths of the journey of the spirit of Western man through philosophy, literature, and art. In 1938 he published a collection of poems under the pseudonym Aimos Aurelios, because public use of his name, as an exile, was prohibited.

Kanellopoulos served his country with the government-in-exile during

3

the occupation of Greece. He became Prime Minister for a time in 1945, and in all postwar elections his home province returned him to Parliament. He has served as a member of most cabinets within the last twenty years, and as Deputy Prime Minister in 1955 and again from 1959 to 1963, years of the greatest stability the Greek nation has ever known. Today, he is the leader of one of the two leading parties in Greece, the National Radical Union, though politically inactive.

Unceasing, vigorous political activities have not diminished his literary activities. These latter have, in effect, been intensified by a need to seek refuge in writing. Restricting his hours of sleep, foregoing all but the most essential of social appearances, he has made writing the antidote to the political turmoil of the day. As his political responsibilities become more burdensome, he devotes himself with greater concentration, during the hours of his solitude, to personal meditation and to literary endeavors. Some thirty books and numerous essays have established him as one of the major writers of Greece. The most significant works published after 1950 include: *The Twentieth Century* (1951); *Christianity and Our Times* (1953; three essays from this work have been translated into English under the title *Ascent to Faith*, 1966); *Prolegomena to Metaphysics* (1955); *The End of Zarathustra* (1956); *Five Athenian Dialogues* (1956); *I Was Born in 1402* (1957); *Cycle of Sonnets* (1957); *From Marathon to Pydna and to the Downfall of Corinth, 490–146 B.C.*, a three-volume historical account of the Hellenistic period (1963); and *Years of the Great War*, a documented, personal account of the author's experiences during the dramatic events of World War II.

Two small books, beautifully illustrated, were published for the *Little Art Books Series* of Knorr and Hirth Verlag in Germany. *Mistra, the Byzantine Pompeii* (1963) appeared in German and English editions, and *Athens* (1964) appeared in German, English, and French editions.

In 1959 Kanellopoulos became a permanent member of the Academy of Athens (Academy of Letters, Sciences, and Arts). He has been decorated for distinguished service not only in his own country, but in many foreign countries as well.

Poetry and Truth in Neo-Hellenic Life

What would Hyperion, the hero in Friedrich Hölderlin's masterpiece, have written to his friend Bellarmin had he been able to return to his beloved country today? What kind of men would he be encountering, and with whom would he be associating? How would he react to neo-Hellenic intellectual and moral reality? To what would he reply in the affirmative and to what in the negative?

Nearly one hundred eighty-five years have passed since Hyperion left his homeland to settle in Germany. He left soon after the Russo-Turkish War of 1768. The question of a possible return to Greece is somewhat dramatically bold, not because of the number of years that have elapsed, but because Hyperion would have remained the same, unchanged in every way. Hyperion would still be a most tender friend, as well as a most dreadful critic. He would be like his good friend Alabanda when talking about the sins of our times: a "fiery, severe, dreadful accuser."

Nature has remained the same in Greece. Hyperion would love the Greek landscape even today, just as he had loved it before. The Parthenon still stands; in fact, Hyperion would find it in part reconstructed. The old gate which separated (so Hölderlin says) the ancient city from the new one, no longer stands as it had in the days when Hyperion visited Greece: "dumb and deserted as a pond which must be drained." Thousands of people daily pass one another before this very gate. But what kind of people are they? When Hyperion faced the gate, he envisioned "thousands of attractive people who," in passing from the ancient city to the new, "greeted one another daily." Do these *attractive* people exist today?

The question is startling. Hyperion (otherwise Hölderlin) measured Hellenic beauty with absolute standards. He was the perfect Hellene of German descent. How is it possible, with such an absolute standard, to judge the contemporary Greek, or even contemporary man? I cannot verify that the best ancient Athenian could measure up to this standard, which is not only classical, but which is also elevated to the invisible loftiness of the *impossible* by the romantic nostalgia of the German Hölderlin.

The name Notaras still exists in Greece. Thus, even today, some good Notaras could guide Hyperion to a house in Salamis where the youth might face his Diotima for the first time. I would not want to exclude the possibility of the existence today, neither in Greece nor in any other country, of a lovely girl with Diotima's beautiful soul and courageous spirit. But it is doubtful that today's Diotima could speak as Hyperion's, though it is unessential that a true living being should speak with such perfection, for that would provoke boredom. Suffice it for me to suppose that women do exist today who, without speaking like Diotima, have intellectual purity and spiritual courage. Hyperion could meet such a woman today in Salamis. Undoubtedly, he could meet such a friend as Alabanda.

If Hyperion were to return to his homeland today, he would certainly find nature, women, friendship, and the Parthenon there before him. Beyond the eternal, however (and something of the eternal exists in nature, women, friendship, and the Parthenon), what would Hyperion find in Greece? What would he say about the contemporary spirit of the Greek people, about the contemporary poet, about the current attitude of the State and Society toward the poet and toward pure spirit?

When Hyperion left Greece for Germany, Goethe and Schiller, Kant and Herder, were living in that country; so was the spirit of Winkelmann and of Lessing. And with Bach and Mozart, a new world in man's spirit had been revealed. Even so, Hyperion spoke in the sharpest manner against Germany during her supreme hour. Forgetting that even rulers at that time were philosophizing, or that they respected and honored the philosopher and poet, he wrote that "poets live in the world as strangers in their own houses," that they resembled Odysseus, "who sat before his own door like a beggar while the shameless suitors revelled in the great hall and asked: who brought this beggar here to us?"

If Hyperion spoke in this manner about Germany during her greatest hour, what would he have said about our times? What would he have said about contemporary Greece, or Germany, or any other country?

Hyperion, certainly, never did say, as did Nietzsche, that the State, "the coldest of all monsters," had been invented for those who were a surplus in the world. Perhaps Nietzsche was reacting against Hegel, the friend of Hölderlin, who was at the opposite extreme in his over-estimation of the State. Hyperion-Hölderlin sufficed with observing that the State is "the rude surface around the kernel of life, and nothing more." This surface has become even more rude in our times, no longer dedicating itself to covering and protecting the kernel of life, of poetry, and of the mind. Were Hyperion to return to Greece today, he would confirm all that could be confirmed in every other country in the world, in some to a greater and in others to a lesser extent. In fact, the more democracy proceeds toward its social ideal, toward justice, the more it becomes a democracy of anonymous groups and neglects the individual, the poet, the philosopher, the genuine man. This is precisely what progress demands. The poet, the philosopher, the true man must learn to live despite progress, despite the State and History. This mission will either crush the true man or make him more genuine than he has ever been, even in the classical city of Pallas Athena. Only the future, following the afflictions of at least a hundred years, or perhaps even two hundred years, will show which of the two will occur.

There are, in fact, men devoted to the spirit in the world today who have begun to live despite the State, society, and progress. And some of these men live in Greece. I cannot say whether Hyperion would have acknowledged that such intellectuals are genuine. I cannot say whether he would have acknowledged the poetry and thought of the contemporary Greek as a genuine creative process. In fact, I believe the acknowledgement would have been made with difficulty. Hyperion's criterion was absolute, superhistoric, superhuman. The mind, in its concrete life and expression, can have something of the divine in it; however, even that something, the percentage of the divine, is not superhuman, does not move outside the realm of the human soul. The great childlike state of balance as a source of creativity and the great physical harmony as a result of creative energy are impossible occurrences.

For a brief period the state of balance and physical harmony appeared strong in Hellenic antiquity; but even then, this strength was only in *appearance* and merely as a starting point. The human spirit underwent dreadful experiences from which it suffered as it was attacked and crucified. How could this spirit possibly preserve an idyllic innocence and peace? Hyperion knew at depth that one can no longer think without having suffered. In fact, did not Diotima tell him that he would not have been the "thinking man" had he not been the "suffering man"? Even though he knew this, Hyperion continued to seek the impossible.

Hyperion would find the impossible neither in contemporary

Greece nor anywhere else. Ever since the time of Plato, the Hellenic spirit has undergone intense suffering. I believe I have the right to say that the spirit has triumphed. But it triumphed only after receiving traces of all the suffering and misfortunes that it had undergone; thus it is no longer an innocent spirit. It is the suffering, guilty spirit fighting to be acquitted.

Alexander the Great honored the Hellenic spirit, but he also terrified it. Epicurus was the reaction to terror. Nonetheless, the state of balance which appeared to have been definitively secured with Pindar and Plato, was positively jolted. Along with the glory that Alexander bequeathed to Greece, he also bequeathed her with knowledge that such things as ethical self-sufficiency of the city, the state of balance within a narrow space, and harmony of the dialogue, were outmoded.

Rome caused the Hellenic spirit to accept a painful compromise. The Hellenic spirit entered the tormented body of slaves or liberated men who posed as teachers for the Romans. This affliction could not but leave its traces. As a man, Epictetus had the spiritual strength to ignore the misfortunes; however, his spirit did not remain entirely unaffected. The best product of the compromise of the Hellenic spirit with Rome was Plutarch, who gave the Romans a proud lesson when he told them that no significant Roman existed who did not resemble a significant Hellene.

Christianity brought the Hellenic spirit before the greatest and most dramatic dilemma. The spirit either had to deny itself completely and surrender passively to Christianity or else succeed in something that not only appeared impossible, but logically *was* impossible. In other words, if the Hellenic spirit was not to deny itself completely, it had to compromise inwardly by adopting Christianity, conciliating dogma and knowledge, the darkness of revelation with the light of the Attic day. In the case of the Gnostics, the affliction of the Hellenic spirit was great but equally fruitless. For the sake of the Hellenic spirit, which was just as deeply misunderstood, the Gnostics came near to destroying Christianity. But neither this nor ignoring Christianity, which contained the pale glory of the neo-Platonists, was the solution.

In the year 355 A.D. three young men met in Athens. The one, despite his Latin descent and his baptism as a Christian, considered the Latin language barbarian and called himself a true Hellene.

This was Julian, who was contemptuous of the Galileans, as he called the Christians. The other two were Basil and Gregory, who, though not yet baptized, had received the gift of Christ from the tender hands of their wonderful mothers. Which were closer to the Hellene? Today, in reading what these men wrote and knowing their steps in life, we know that the two great Christians were more Hellenes than the Emperor Julian. The miracle had been accomplished. The Hellenic spirit had been preserved within Christianity. The great path had been opened by Justin the Martyr and by Clement of Alexandria.

The path was difficult for the Hellenic spirit. In my book, *Five Athenian Dialogues*, I attempted to describe the most characteristic phases through which the Hellenic spirit passed in its attempt to find salvation in Christianity, to Hellenize Christianity, in fact, without denying the slightest element of the "revelation." The cosmo-historical integration of the two spiritual worlds, the Hellenic and the Christian, could not have occurred within the framework of logic. This was accomplished with the aid of the purest Hellenic words, that is, with the indirect and secondary aid of formal logic on the level of ethics and aesthetics as moral teaching and beautiful expression. Basil the Great combines the commands of the Gospels with the ethical proclamations of Hesiod and Theognis, with the *Phaedo* and the *Republic* of Plato. And Romanos the Melodist becomes the Pindar of the Christian world.

The thousand years of Byzantium were a thousand years of dreadful misfortunes and suffering, but they were also years of great accomplishments for the Hellenic spirit. Hyperion ignored these years. The verses of Symeon, the so-called New Theologian, which have received such fine comments from Isidora Rosenthal-Kamarinea and Demetrios Stathopoulos, gave to the Hellenic spirit an inner mystical tone which is dictated by the escape of man from a wicked reality. In fact, the desire to escape has been associated with the Hellenic spirit since the days of Empedocles, who was a spiritual brother to Hyperion. In the writings of Michael Psellus, Anna Comnena, Nicetas Chionates, Pachymeres, Nicephorus Gregoras, and John Cantacuzene, where the classical art of historiography attempts to survive, the Hellenic spirit finds life and expression as it triumphs over frightful difficulties, constantly maintains vigilance on the boundaries of two worlds, and remains firm on walls and ramparts which now and then are torn down, but which are always rebuilt to ward off the assault of the barbarian.

The great trial of the Greek mind and soul reached its peak during the fifteenth century. In my book *I Was Born in 1402* I attempted to describe the height of this trial by replanting myself into that period. Nor could I have described the inner, spiritual, as well as objective occurrences of that period, had I not forced myself to relive them. And I brought myself, as an insignificant, anonymous contemporary of that time, into direct communion with the last Emperors and their families, with Plethon and Bessarion, with George Sphratzis and Isidore, with George Scholarios and with Ducas; in fact, with all who lived, fought, and fell, defending the Greek homeland and the Greek spirit during the fifteenth century.

Hyperion wrote to Diotima that he was advancing toward Mistra after having liberated Navarin. "We are now before the fortifications of Mistra, the remnant of ancient Sparta," he wrote. It was there that he decided joyfully to cast the Turkish turban into the Euphrates and replace it with the Greek helmet.

What Hyperion did not know, however, as he attempted to liberate Mistra, was that this marvellous cliff was not the remnant of ancient Sparta, but a much newer form of the Greek spirit. Neither did he know that Plethon, equally ignoring his surroundings, the many churches and remarkable frescoes with the martyrs and angels, had attempted in that same place to reproduce ancient Hellas with a dramatic anachronism similar to that of Hyperion. Plethon was a great Hellene, but the Christian frescoes before which he stood coolly were also quite Hellenic. And a century later, the great artistic and spiritual achievements of another man, Domenicos Theotocopoulos, who called himself El Greco, were also Hellenic. Had Hyperion succeeded in capturing Mistra, I fear that he would not have understood the meaning of the frescoes of this sacred cliff, which, nonetheless, along with the frescoes at Daphni, express the Hellenic spirit and mind, just as do the Parthenon and the *Charioteer* at Delphi.

At one point Hyperion spoke about the joyful folk songs of the Greek people, which we must presume to have originated during the centuries of enslavement under the Turkish yoke. And he was justified in talking about these songs, inspired by the pure air of the mountains that had remained free even under Turkish rule, and the joy of courage. But the majority of the folk songs of those four centuries of slavery are sad songs, full of suffering, weighty and heroic. The Greek spirit of those years became humble; it sought refuge in the simple people, in the village hut, and returned to the flocks and shepherds of the Helicon.

There is a deep, invisible, secret bond between Homer, the heroic Byzantine epic *Digenis Akritas*, the great Cretan poem of the seventeenth century, *Erotokritos*, and the neo-Hellenic folk songs. Of course, the level of form falls from perfection—Homer is the unattainable unity of the epic expression—to the elliptical and and fragmentary. However, the level of the original folk wisdom, of virtue, and of spiritual alertness is almost the same.

Dionysios Solomos, the first poetic genius of modern Greece, owes his style, form of language, and to a point even his spirit, to the folk songs. This child of the Ionian Islands supported the struggle of the Greeks for their independence with the blood of his poetic soul. He wrote the *Hymn to Liberty*, which became the national anthem of Greece.

Solomos suffered to express himself. His greatest poetic achievement, *The Free Besieged*, has survived as a fragment in several drafts and variants. Solomos sought to elevate the language of the people to the sphere of a personal creative expression. He made a great beginning toward this end; but like every beginning which takes place in the middle of a historic journey, it is filled with the spasms of his spirit.

A contemporary of Solomos, and similarly a child of the Ionian Islands, Andreas Kalvos wrote his Odes with greater ease, both in language and in spirit. He ignored the language of the simple, suffering people and of the folk songs, whose assimilation was the most difficult problem, and wrote Odes in an old Greek style, though grammatically the structure of his words is not identical with that of any ancient dialect. He wrote, in other words, in a language that has never been spoken. But his general intellectual style is Pindaric. Perhaps Hyperion would have acknowledged Kalvos as a true Hellene.

Solomos was a great lawmaker; he made a great beginning, he created a school. Kalvos failed to carve a path for other men; he said and did all that he had to say and do, and stood alone on a summit cut off from the valleys of life. However, both Solomos and Kalvos stand as two respectable figures at the propylaea of free neo-Hellenic life. The one represents the suffering, weak present which leads to the future; the other, the isolated, "self-sufficient" present without a future.

During the nineteenth century the Greek spirit was invaded from the North without being prepared actively and creatively to receive this spirit. Solomos had attempted to give a Greek form to the aesthetic and moral teachings of Schiller. Hyperion condemned the spirit of the North, saying that it sought a return to itself, that is to become a "spirit of self-awareness" before learning to see what went on, before learning about Nature, before observing Nature with the divine simplicity of a child. To a certain extent Hyperion could have been right. But was not Hyperion himself a product of the North without consciously seeking to be? Hölderlin endowed Hyperion with a great many Northern feelings and thoughts that would have astounded Pindar and Plato. Thus, I think that Hölderlin knew he was making Hyperion speak a great overstatement when he repudiated the North in so categoric a manner. Hölderlin admired Schiller; in a letter he addresses him as a "great, noble man." He asked Schiller, and through his intermediary Goethe himself, to show him the way to poetic truth. He expressed the proud phrase in a letter to his friend Casimir Ulrich von Böhlendorff in December, 1802: "After the time of the Hellenes, we are once more beginning to sing in the manner of our country and naturally, in fact, originally."

The North, or more specifically, the influences of Schiller's aesthetic principles, not only failed to prevent Solomos from singing "in the manner of [his] country and naturally," but did in fact help him to embark on the simple though difficult path of neo-Hellenic poetic truth. I cannot say the same for most of those who appeared in Greece during the nineteenth century with claims of being poets or generally creative writers. With the exception of Aristotelis Valaoritis, two or three other Ionian poets who followed in the path of Solomos, Georgios Vizyenos, and Aristomenis Proveleggios, the others had no creative power within them. They were noble but somewhat narrow minds, who confused the world of the spirit with the world of knowledge, and who, considering the folk spirit and folk language to be something inferior and unworthy of attention, sought to convey knowledge and the achievements of the northern sciences or even the northern poetic techniques in a language which, though grammatically a good imitation of ancient Greek, was foreign to every living element of the Greek soul. In poetry, their failure proved absolute. It was impossible to convey Lamartine in a language that was not spoken and, removed from everyday life, was not naturally inspired by Love and Death.

In scientific writings the distance between an artificial language and daily life had not the same effect. On the contrary, important steps were made which imposed the form of language known as the *katharevousa* (purist) to the present. Adamantios Koraes, a great teacher, carved the path. Scholars, well-versed in the knowledge of law, wrote fundamental works during the nineteenth century, thereby creating a tradition in Greek jurisprudence which has been preserved to the present at the high level of the German. One group of learned men with a wide intellectual background (notably, Alexandros Rangavis, Demetrios Bernadakis, and Angelos Vlachos), created an atmosphere which inspired the respect of the Greek society for scholarship. Konstantinos Paparrigopoulos succeeded in using the *katharevousa* in a monumental work called *The History of the Greek Nation,* thus establishing this language in the sphere of historical science as well. Spyridon Lambros and Nikolaos Politis cultivated the historical folklore research with excellent results.

Hyperion would not be justified to say that these men who devoted themselves to science and research were "thinkers, but not true men," as he had said about the German scientists of his day. They were men of noble natures who exhibited an emotional and most rewarding exactness in their work. But they were not creative in the sphere of poetry and philosophy. Thus, they wrote excellent jurisprudence or historical and philological works, but not one of them wrote a single philosophical treatise. Poetry (of Solomos and Kalvos) assisted in the renascence of the Greek spirit in the nineteenth century; philosophy attempted to assist in the person of Theophilos Kaïris, but the figure of this courageous man was more or less eccentric; it was the figure of a monk who removed himself from Christianity because of an abstract piety. As Socrates, so Theophilos Kaïris died in prison. He resembled Socrates in his moral courage and in his long beard, but his sacrifices, at depth, were without meaning. If he had remained in philosophy and had not become a prophet of an inconceivable religion, he would have set his seal to the nineteenth century, and the fatal event of a rebirth of the Greek spirit *without* philosophy would not have been observed.

The nineteenth century was to arrive at its final hours before a voice, primarily poetic, succeeded in expressing indirectly, that is, through poetic expression, the agony of philosophic thought as well. The voice was that of Kostis Palamas.

Kostis Palamas, Constantine Cavafis, Angelos Sikelianos, and

Nikos Kazantzakis are the four sovereign minds in twentieth-century Greece. In saying "sovereign," I do not mean that the nation knows them, that they rule in the soul of the people, or even that they have been read by those in industry and trade or those devoted to natural sciences or to politics. How many Frenchmen have read Paul Valéry? How many Germans have read Rainer Maria Rilke or Stefan George? How many British or Americans have read T. S. Eliot?

Times have changed. Hyperion would have sought vainly in the football fields for a Pindar, from whom the people would have demanded songs praising the victors. Sovereignty of the poets is not expressed in the public squares nor in the stadium. In our days poets are kings in a kingdom without subjects. They are rulers over loneliness. If for a single moment they succeed in ruling over wider areas, the phenomenon is illusory. Those wider circles use the poet ephemerally, as an organ or symbol for political or other purposes, without even having read his works.

Thus, if I call these four "sovereign," I do so within the restricted meaning the term has taken today. Palamas, Cavafis, Sikelianos, and Kazantzakis influenced, more than any others, those Greeks who, despite modern society, remain faithful to the truth (or delusion) that poetry has not lost its value in the face of progress. The number of these Greeks is not insignificant. Only that each lives—even as the poet himself—within some great loneliness.

Kostis Palamas is the Victor Hugo of Greece. Torrential in his speech, rhetorical, prophetic, but interrupting at times the torrent of his own words to create (as did Victor Hugo) some condensed and short masterpieces, Palamas showed that the neo-Hellenic vulgate could be elevated to any intellectual activity, to the most complicated and most synthetic conceptions and to the most original junction of the sensual and spiritual world. What was agony for Solomos became an intellectual game for Palamas. Solomos labored to establish a path; Palamas walked this path with the great ease of a traveller. If the paths in the life of the mind had ends, I would venture to say that Palamas travelled successfully through the entire length of the journey.

Hyperion would find Palamas many-sided, uneven, oriented in worlds which are seemingly opposite, full of sentimentality and of verbal outbursts which are foreign to classical measure. Hyperion was created at a time when his poet Hölderlin had not yet wanted to acknowledge that "though a brother of Herakles," he was devoted to Christ. Thus, he would consider the crossing observed in the mind and poetic work of Palamas as strange. However, such crossings reveal a superior unity. Greece begins with Homer but extends everywhere. Palamas is the rich, painful *compte-rendu* of the Hellenic soul. Classical Hellas, as well as the crushed pride of the Greeks; Greek Christianity, as well as plagued Byzantium; the suffering of four centuries of enslavement; beauty and ugliness, light and darkness of the Hellenic life; these aspects are all expressed in the works of Palamas. The Italian Renaissance imagined Christ to have been beautiful and so created Him. Grünewald created Him ugly. The truth—the great truth—is found in both conceptions. Palamas faced all the forms of the Hellenic soul—of the human soul in general—with love.

Palamas is almost untranslatable. Constantine Cavafis is much easier to translate into a foreign language. And all his writings can be included in a small collection. His poems, most of them short and epigrammatic, number about one hundred and fifty, all of which have been translated into English, German, and French. Helmut von den Steinen is the German translator of Cavafis. The excellent and truly poetic interpretation of Cavafis into English has been rendered by John Mavrogordatos with an Introduction by the poet Rex Warner. During recent years two translations have appeared in French: The first, with an Introduction by André Mirabelle, is by George Papoutsakis, the Alexandrian friend of Cavafis. The second, with her own Introduction, is by the author of *Hadrian's Memoirs,* Marguerite Yournecar, assisted by Konstantinos Demaras, an esteemed historian of neo-Hellenic literature.

Palamas is the expression of all phases and forms of the Hellenic spirit. The Alexandrian Cavafis is the expression of only one phase, that of Hellenistic decadence; he lives in his spirit, with stoic patience, the mixture of races in the Middle East. But "In a Town of Osroêne" he also remembers the glorious past:

> Medes, Syrians, Greeks, Armenians, we're a mixed pack.
> Remon is that sort, too. But when shining
> We saw his countenance yesterday in the moonlight,
> Our thoughts to Plato's Charmides went back—
> (tr. J. Mavrogordatos.)

The reference of the mind to the glorious past is made with a bitter smile. Hyperion would have been enraged. However, his rage would have been unjustified. A great truth, a dark truth that that had to be enlightened by poetry, exists even in the Hellenistic decadence. In fact, the apprehension of this truth, which remains unacknowledged, is essential for every hour in history, because every hour has its darkness as well.

If Cavafis was not ashamed to belong to the decadence, Angelos Sikelianos, despite the many points of decadence which his beautiful soul possessed, set himself the task to prove with his poetic work (a work whose expression and verbal richness makes it almost impossible to render accurately into any foreign language) that the Hellenic Word is able to give new life to the old Delphic truth. However, whereas the poet of decadence, Cavafis, has an epigrammatic sobriety in his verse that is classical, Sikelianos, the high priest of Apollo and Dionysos, burdens each of his thoughts with so many words, so many images, so many ornaments, that he seems to arrive at some contradiction—an attractive contradiction— with the great Delphic ideal; to an enticing contradiction certainly, before the great ideal which he lived within himself so dynamically and which he attempted to project, or rather to impose upon the reality of today. Hyperion would say that Sikelianos resembled a Roman rather than an Hellene. And to a point he would be justified. The bright magnificence of his unforgettable, unique stature has something of the Roman, specifically of the time of Caesar and Augustus; has something of Cicero, Lucretius, and Ovid. Nonetheless, the more secret tones of Sikelianos, those heard only when our ears can isolate them from the noise of his fascinating expression, are purely Hellenic tones. They are—and this is the apparent strangeness, which is, however, characteristic of the Hellenic spirit —simultaneously Christian. In the work of Sikelianos, Dionysos unites with Christ in a deeply impressive way.

Until recently I would have maintained that the verses of Nikos Kazantzakis could not be translated with accuracy into a foreign language. Today, I cannot say this. The English translation of the greatest epic written in our century is so excellent that I am obliged to say that all true poetry can be rendered into another language when there is a translator with the intellectual strength and poetic spirit of Kimon Friar.

An epic in our day is a bold undertaking. Historic awareness excludes the epic myth. Even Virgil, writing the *Aeneid*, served a conscious aim, the founding of Rome and the Roman people on a great myth. The only genuine epics are the Homeric. Tasso, Camoëns, Milton, and Klopstock wrote excellent narrative poems in epic form, but genuine epic poetry, which could only be formed once with the awakening of the Western world, has never again been brought to life.

Even the *Odyssey* of Kazantzakis, beginning precisely where the homonymous epic of Homer closes, is not a true epic poem. We have a work before us that is simultaneously narrative, dramatic, lyrical, philosophical, and even political. The myth begins with the escape of Odysseus from Ithaca and is a metaphysical inversion of the nostalgia for homeland. Odysseus, who was nostalgic for the homeland, is transformed into a man who is metaphysically nostalgic; who, after abandoning his homeland, seeks God without ever finding him; and who, despite remaining unsatisfied in his metaphysical search, is full of life and strength and earthly certainty. In the end he surrenders "activistically" to the frozen death of the Antarctic, to the extreme cold end! This myth is not—nor could it ever be—a true myth. Nonetheless, the poetic work of Kazantzakis is great. The greatness of this immense poem is found perhaps less in its symbolism and more in its narrative technique and the inexhaustive imagination of Kazantzakis. Its philosophical—negatively metaphysical—content had already been expressed; in fact, it had been exhausted in an earlier work, *The Saviors of God* (also translated by Kimon Friar), where the diction of Nietzsche is combined and fused with the diction of the Sermon on the Mount, or even with the diction of the prophets of Israel. In some of his tragedies as well (both Sikelianos and Kazantzakis wrote tragedies of great poetic tone) the metaphysically negative and pessimistic "activism" of Kazantzakis is expressed, who, as a philosophical mind, adopted Christ without the Christian church, Buddha without Buddhism, and even Lenin without Marxism. I think I can say that the *Odyssey* owes little to the philosopher Kazantzakis and still less to his social or sexual theories. The great value of this work should be sought in the narrative intention and in the dynamic expression.

Kazantzakis's was a narrative mind with a great intellectual ability to compose. The intellectual element was stronger in him than was the purely poetic. Plot in his works is more decisive than inspiration. Nonetheless—and precisely this element determines his non-repetitive individuality—Kazantzakis managed to narrate with a surprising colorfulness and directness.

I do not believe that *The Last Temptation* will survive, even though it is excellently written. Christ cannot become the hero in a novel with a sexualistic background; the book will be forgotten. Neither does *Christ Recrucified* have much possibility of survival. The other two novels, *Captain Michalis* and *Alexis Zorba (Zorba the Greek)*, are excellent narrative works that will have much to say in generations to come. However, his one novel, *The Poor Little One of God* (Saint Francis, the *Povello*), towers over all the others because it is human in the highest sense of the word. Perhaps Hyperion would not have understood this work. But Rainer Maria Rilke, who had his eyes turned nostalgically and constantly to the "great evening star of poverty," would certainly have loved this novel.

This, then, appears most certain to me: Kazantzakis' *Odyssey* will be considered as one of the high points in our century, so long as there are men in the world who are devoted to the spirit.

Many are the Greek writers who know how to narrate. The first of these deserving our attention appeared toward the end of the nineteenth century. A most original writer, Alexandros Papadiamantis, derived his poetic rights indirectly and with the most unaffected gestures from the richness of the simple people's soul and the most innocent Byzantine piety. His short stories—masterpieces of spiritual nobility—were written in the *katharevousa* and not in the language of the people. Pavlos Kalligas (the noted lawyer who, like Friedrich Schlegel, preferred not to be reminded that he had written a novel), Demetrios Vikelas (his *Loukis Laras* is a masterpiece of pedagogic narration), and Emmanuel Roidis (his *Pope Joan* is one of the most clever and most imaginative narratives ever written), also wrote in the *katharevousa,* though in a more severe form than Papadiamantis.

With the exception of Papadiamantis, it was not an achievement that these men wrote in a language that was not spoken. Their narrative works are closer to the style of scientific treatises than to the style of literary creations. Papadiamantis, conversely, succeeded in creating genuine poetic works in this language. (George Katsimbalis has written the best study on Papadiamantis, and Michael Peranthis has made him the hero of a biographical novel.) However, the *katharevousa* of Papadiamantis follows only the grammar of this particular dialect. In style and deeper essence, it has been influenced by the language of the people. This same observation can be made for Ioannis Kondylakis in his work *Patouhas*.

At the end of the nineteenth century, Andreas Karkavitsas distinguished himself as a narrative poet. He made the language of the people, the *demotic*, victorious. Of course, Yiannis Psycharis had begun the battle for the *demotic*, but his novels are no longer read. The works of Karkavitsas, especially *The Beggar*, continue to retain their value.

Many others have followed since that time. I mention—as does Apostolos Sahinis in his well-written book *The Neo-Hellenic Novel* —Konstantinos Theotokis, Kostas Hadzopoulos, whose verses are also fine, and Gregorious Xenopoulos. Konstantinos Christomanos should also be mentioned here, even though his romantic lyricism did not permit him to give a plastic form to his images and thoughts. Nonetheless, in *The Empress Elizabeth* he immortalized the beautiful face and soul of this great friend whom he accompanied on romantic walks in Schönbrunn and in Corfu.

During the first decades of our century, poetry and literary prose blossomed in Greece. I have already spoken about Sikelianos, Cavafis, and Kazantzakis. Others who distinguished themselves in lyric poetry were Ioannis Polemis, Georgios Stratigis, Lambros Porphyras, and Georgios Drosinis, as well as a group endowed with a greater problematic sensitivity such as Ioannis Gryparis, Miltiadis Malakasis, Zacharias Papantoniou, Pavlos Nirvanas, Kostas Karthaios (the best translator of Shakespeare into Greek), K. Kariotakis, Sotiris Skipis, Napoleon Lapathiotis, Kostas Ouranis, Tellos Agras, Romos Filiras, and Maria Polydouri. I must also mention the three Cypriot Greeks Vassilis Michaelides, Demetrios Lipertis, and Nikos Nikolaidis.

Some of these poets wrote narratives as well; for instance, Papantoniou, Nirvanas, and Ouranis. Yiannis Vlachoyiannis, Antonios Travlantonis, Kostas Paroritis, and Demosthenis Voutiras, distinguished themselves in narrative prose. However, the novel, with the unity which this form demands, was cultivated by other writers, especially by Gregorios Xenopoulos and Dionysios Kokkinos. These men wrote the first novels with a "bourgeois" background in Greece. Kokkinos also distinguished himself as a scholar of neo-Hellenic history.

Xenopoulos wrote good plays as well, some of which continue to be produced on the Greek stage. But the most eminent modern Greek playwright is Spyros Melas. From his first drama *The Son of the Shadow*, produced at the beginning of our century, to the satirical comedy *The King and the Dog*, first produced in 1954, Melas has remained sovereign on the neo-Hellenic stage. He has also written many narrative works. His fictionalized biographies of the heroes of the Greek War of Independence are excellent historical studies.

Great intellectual and spiritual changes were observed in Greece, as in all countries, during the period between the two world wars. Before World War I and up to 1920 the intellectual life of Greece had the past as a source rather than the present. Some of the poets and writers became aware of their origin from classical or Byzantine Greece and reflected this awareness in their works; others reflected the tormented Greek soul of the period of enslavement or the heroic spirit of the struggles for independence. This attitude did not prevent them from using foreign authors as aesthetic measures or as more general spiritual prototypes. In fact, the invasion of the German or the French spirit, of the English, Russian, or Scandinavian, was violent. I must certainly correct my observation. Goethe or Lessing never did enter Greece with violence. However, Schopenhauer, Nietzsche, Baudelaire, Ibsen, Oscar Wilde, Tolstoy, Dostoyevsky, and d'Annunzio did enter with a great clamor.

Following World War I the main source of creative expression became the concern for the present and the primary motif was the anxiety about the future. The past was now self-evident; it had been fully conceived; it was no longer problematic. Even the fusion with the European spirit had been accomplished, that is, the relation with the intellectual life of the north had also become self-evident and no longer presented any problems. The present now was exhibiting great problems, which were within an uncertain and doubtful present and a still more doubtful future. Many of the creative minds had already taken their first youthful steps before World War I, as Cavafis, Sikelianos, and Kazantzakis. Since they had lived both periods in so individual a manner, it is difficult to say whether the change in the times also created a change in their course. A point worth observing, however, is that, if we look deeper, we will note a change, especially during their later years and following World War II. In fact, we observe this change even in the great tragedies written between the two wars. Kazantzakis and Sikelianos are perhaps the only two writers in the world who devoted an essential part of their poetic creation to tragedy during contemporary times. But some of their tragedies—such as Sikelianos' *Christ in Rome*—revert back to the past for a supporting source while exploring the meaning of the present and the future with somewhat of a political intention.

In narrative prose, even before Kazantzakis had started to give us his widely known novels, Stratis Myrivilis first dared to carve a path on the earth that had been excavated and shocked by World War I. His *Life in a Tomb* is a war novel of the highest lyrical quality. This novel and his two later ones, *The Teacher with the Golden Eyes* and *The Mermaid Madonna*, make a trilogy whose source was the war and death. But beyond the curtain of death, there is the story of man and love. Everything that Myrivilis ever wrote stands at the height of his original inspiration or even surpasses it. Myrivilis is the great master of the neo-Hellenic narrative technique in the twentieth century. Even the novelist Kazantzakis was indebted to his example.

Elias Venezis also forced his heroes to remain and to walk over a quivering earth in an uncertain present. His descriptions are very penetrating. Venezis combines a strong narrative talent with a lyrical sensitivity. His novel, *Aeolian Soil*, is a beautiful dream that loses itself in the past of childhood in order that an even more bitter and weightier present might emerge. His novels *Number 31328* and *Calm* as well as the last one, *Ocean*, are masterpieces of narrative skill. Even his short stories contain something great which at times is oppressive, but which at other times soothes and saves the soul of the reader. Venezis, who experienced the uprooting of the Greeks from Asia Minor as his own destiny, can be called the poet of the deep Greek nostalgia, which extends through 3000 years, for the lost paradise of the East.

I. M. Panayotopoulos stands apart as a lyric poet, a critic, an author of excellent travel books and of novels. He began his career before 1930 while still a young man. His novels and stories are inspired by a rich store of knowledge. In his novel *The Seven Sleepers*, with which he captivates his readers, Panayotopoulos goes back to the third (and fifth) century of Christianity for a very old legend connected with the holy city of Ephesus. The old legend becomes a good novel which attempts to enlighten our own present or, if one wishes, to enlighten every period in which, as in those old, forgotten years, the "terrorized" and not the "terrible" are those who bring terror on earth.

With the *Nea Estia*, a literary periodical, Petros Haris supported and promoted the Greek writers during the last decades. He also started to write while still very young. His collection of short stories in 1924, *The Last Night on Earth*, has made him the genuine short story writer of his generation. His contribution to the aesthetic crystallization of the neo-Hellenic short story has justifiably been praised by the historian of Greek literature Aristos Kambanis. Haris' latest collection of short stories, *Lights on the Sea*, are excellent portrayals of the Occupation period. Even his essays are narrative. Many of his essays, as those which were published under the title *When Life Becomes a Dream*, with an Introduction by Sikelianos, have narrative unity and can be characterized as an autobiography of the spirit.

George Theotokas, subordinating his material and his narrative technique to severe logical demands, elevated the psychological and the social novel, especially in the structurally unified novel *Argo*, to a high intellectual plane. Poetic personalities such as Kosmas Politis, Thanasis Petsalis-Diomidis, and Angelos Terzakis, added a precious element to the neo-Hellenic novel and more generally to neo-Hellenic intellectual life. Politis' novel, *Eroica*, at least stands at the same height as the famous work of Alain Fournier, wherein the poet of the *Great Meaulnes* brings the spirit of youth to a dramatic subject. At a most fortunate moment in his intellectual activity, while escaping the doubts of our times, Terzakis wrote the beautiful historical novel, *The Princess Izabo*, which takes us back to the period of the Frankish conquest of the Peloponnesus. This is the only novel, as far as I know, that in our century can be placed on the same level with *Liechtenstein*, written by Hauff in the nineteenth century. With the conscientiousness of a scholar, Petsalis-Diomedis takes another period in Greek history, the Turkish domination, in *Mavrolykoi*, and raises it from its darkest historic depths to the light of day.

These happy attempts of a spiritual escape from the present are also indirectly interwoven with a fear and anxiety inspired by the future. The novels written during the last decades are determined, directly or indirectly, by the burdensome present and the even weightier future.

In *The Great Pantheoi*, Tassos Athanasiadis attempted to grasp neo-Hellenic society in the historical unity of succeeding generations from the middle of the nineteenth century to the present. He also wrote a beautiful novel in which he portrayed an episode in the life of Dostoyevsky with such authenticity that we can say this novel was lived and written by Dostoyevsky himself.

Most of the novelists mentioned above belong to the generation of the thirties. Pantelis Prevelakis, the disciple and beloved friend of Nikos Kazantzakis, a proud spirit who holds himself apart from the daily present, without, however, neglecting those duties imposed on us by the heavy hours of our times, belongs to this generation also. Prevelakis was concerned with history and criticism of art. However, he found his most important mission elsewhere. In a series of excellent novels, he attempted to elevate the spirit and the painful experiences of his island, Crete, to the sphere of a mythical reality. With *The Poet and the Poetry of the Odyssey*, Prevelakis managed to repay in a most touching manner his debt to his teacher and friend, Kazantzakis. Prevelakis, as well as other novelists—Venezis, Petsalis-Diomidis, Terzakis—also wrote good plays along with Xenopoulos, Spyros Melas, Pantelis Horn, Theodoros Sinadinos, and Dionysios Romas.

Among the famous prose writers who emerged after World War I are also Thrassos Kastanakis, a realist with vivid social tendencies, and M. Karagatsis, also a realist in much wider areas of life, as well as Fotis Kontoglou and Kostis Bastias. Kontoglou, a most talented painter who carved the way toward neo-Byzantine ecclesiastical art, wrote artistically excellent pages, most of which take us to exotic times and lands or seas, as well as to the lost Greek paradise in Asia Minor, which was his homeland. Both Kontoglou and Bastias attempted to free the future of the Greek spirit from every Western or Northern influence and based it on the tradition of a most severe Byzantine tradition. *Kyriakodromos* by Bastias is a work of great moral and literary value.

Important novels were written during the last twenty years by other Greeks. Outstanding among these are Yiannis Beratis (his *Great River* is an excellent war novel connected with the Albanian front during World War II), Nikos Athanassiadis (*Beyond the Human, Crucifixion Without Resurrection*, and *The Naked Girl*), and Andonis Samarakis. Good collections of short stories have been produced by Sotiris Patatzis (*The Lost Paradise*), Petros Glezos (*The First Acquaintance*), Maria Gouma (*The Cactus Land*), and Kostas Papapanos (*People and Life*).

I cannot close this section without mentioning several women who, with their presence and contributions, have given much to neo-Hellenic literature. First and foremost stands Penelope Delta, a spiritually great Greek who belongs to a past generation. Her charming narratives—written for children and young adults, yet equally useful for mature readers—came out before World War I and have great pedagogic value. Second, I should like to mention Angeliki Hadjimichali. The works of this thoroughly industrious woman have rendered a great service to neo-Hellenic folk craft and folklore. Athena Tarsouli has brought the beautiful Greek islands closer to our hearts. Tatiana Stavrou and Lilika Nakou have succeeded in writing novels of a strong realistic content with rich and genuine sentimental motifs. Katina Papa, as Isidora Rosenthal-Kamarinea comments in her excellent *Anthology of Neo-Hellenic Prose Writers*, published in German, is a narrative poetess whose work is characterized by a "magical immediacy, originality, and tenderness." Theoni Drakopoulou, under the pseudonym Myrtiotissa, wrote verses with a musical tenderness which has remained exemplary in Greek poetry. A very good historical novel, whose plot was taken from Byzantium, was written by Loula Mavroulidou. Maria P. Ralli wrote with a resoundingly dynamic expression a kind of prose which brings to the surface some very interesting spiritual problems. And Greek women from Cyprus, like Maria Roussia, Hebe Meleagrou, and Irene Ioannidou-Adamidou, distinguished themselves in narrative prose.

The generation of the thirties continues to control the intellectual life of Greece. Those who came later—among them three women writers, Mona Mitropoulou, Galatea Saranti, and Eva Vlami, as well as Renos Apostolidis, Angelos Vlachos, Menelaos Lountemis, Rodis Skoufos, Petros Glezos, and Nestor Matsas—are attempting to cover an area whose solidity had already been secured by the hard work of the older writers. Renos Apostolidis, with a peculiar dynamism, is the great enemy of "conformism," attacking almost everything and everyone, but with a positive and creative imagination. His father, Herakles Apostolidis, wrote excellent aphorisms and essays, and devoted his life to producing the best anthologies of neo-Hellenic poetry. I must now ask the question: Didn't the generation of the thirties produce poetic minds that dedicated themselves to verse, or more accurately, to pure poetry?

Andreas Karantonis, a creative literary critic, who, contrary to what generally occurs with critics, is also a genuine poetic mind. He revealed the works and meanings of the two poets who belong to the generation of the thirties and who were and still are concerned with pure poetry: George Seferis and Odysseus Elytis. Their appearance on the scene of neo-Hellenic intellectual life had and continues to have great significance. At a time when poetry, ignoring the great examples of Sikelianos and Kazantzakis, was in danger of being severed from the eternal roots of poetic expression, of surrendering to the eccentric and nihilistic trends of our times, thereby ceasing to be poetry, came Seferis and Elytis. Without reacting negatively to the eccentric movements, which to a point they in fact assimiliated, these two poets carved new paths beyond the extremes.

The poet Seferis, who was the first to take the great step with the simplest words and verses, was certainly aided in his mission, which was to present pure poetry in the intellectual chaos of the times, by the precedence of Mallarmé, Valéry and T. S. Eliot. Nonetheless for Seferis this precedence was decisive only as an aesthetic prototype. The essence of the poetic spirit of both Seferis and Elytis is pure Greek and is determined by the earth and sky of Greece. I have the feeling that Hyperion would discover something of Greece in the works of these two poets.

Certainly, poets did emerge who ignored the example set by Seferis and Elytis, and who, posing as important men, surrendered to a literary nihilism. The only one who succeeded in emerging from these extremes as a strong poetic personality was Nikos Engonopoulos. There are other poets, however, whose verses are even less revolutionary than those of Elytis. Some, in fact, remained faithfully on the old paths. Such poets were Agis Theros and Markos Avgeris. And Georgios Athanas, whose thoughts are always youthful (as youthful as they were when his first collection of poetry, with its aroma of spring, was published fifty years ago) continues to write poetry that is characterized by the immediacy of life of the folk song without being a typical organic extension of the style and content of folk poetry, as was that of Kostas Krystallis at the end of the nineteenth century. I must mention Kostas Karavidas at this point, a courageous poet who succeeded in enclosing the whole of Olympus in a single sonnet. And I must also give special mention to a poet who, in the last forty years, has endowed neo-Hellenic poetry with words, emotions, and thoughts of singular beauty never known before. This poet is Takis Papatzonis, a noble and graceful, religious nature who finds God in the vast Creation, in beautiful nature, and in the heart of true humanity.

There are other poetic spirits who attempted to save the eternal impure poetry, even though they were more or less influenced by the current of the times. A few characteristic examples are as follows: Melissanthi (Hebe Kougia-Skandalaki) combines a soft, free religiosity in her poetry with the most tender emotions. Zoë Karelli is a poetess with a very rich emotional and intellectual world. Dialechti Zevgoli and Eleni Vakalo also have genuine poetic moments. Isidora Rosenthal-Kamarinea transfers a strong lyrical element to her verses. George Karapanos is a poet of deep feelings, and N. Proestopoulos and Theodore Xydis must be considered good disciples of Sikelianos. I. P. Koutsocheras made his verses noiseless promenades in the world of flowers and secret thoughts. I. M. Panayotopoulos and Michael Peranthis, primarily novelists, also wrote inspiring poetry. Lefteris Alexiou, Koulis Alepis, Yiannis Ritsos, and Mitsos Lygizos are genuine poetic minds. Nicephoros Vrettakos has written excellent poems which express an original, masculine tenderness. Michael Stassinopoulos is a very delicate soul, finding expression in select verses. Takis Sinopoulos and Minas Dimakis are taking original steps towards clear poetic self-awareness. Kostas Assimakopoulos, a good short story writer, has also written verses with a deep meaning. The modern satiric verse was cultivated by Paris Takopoulos, who also wrote a good satiric novel. I should mention specifically the rich poetic offering of Aris Diktaios, who seeks to build systematically and with severe consequence an entire world of ideas.

I believe Alexander Matsas belongs here with the group of poets. In genuine diction, Matsas has attempted to use the themes of the ancient tragedies—themes of great mystical symbolism—to mold his theatrical works, which have a significant lyrical and dramatic content.

It would be a grave omission not to mention the Greek Cypriot writers Glafkos Alitheris, Pavlos Liasides, Teferos Anthias, Pavlos Krinaios, Nikos Kranidiotis, Kostas Mantis, Manos Kralis, Nikos Vrahimis, Kypros Chrysanthis, Anthos Lykavgis, Yiannis P. Papadopoulos, and Petros Sophas. Some of these also wrote good short stories, as did Melis Nicolaidis, Tassos Psaropoulos, Christakis Georgiou, and Spyros Papageorgiou, who wrote mainly narrative prose.

Around 1930 another intellectual event was observed in Greece whose significance extends to this hour. The battle between idealism and materialism took place, especially in the sphere of philosophy. In the land which gave birth to philosophy, the genuine, autonomous meaning of the term "philosophizing" was virtually unknown in the nineteenth century. At the beginning of the twentieth century, several university professors with an excellent background in philosophical theories and systems taught philosophy. Among these were Theophilos Voreas, Christos Androutsos, and Constantinos Logothetis. A noted professor in the Medical School, the surgeon Constantinos Mermigas, wrote an important work concerned with epistemology. However, though these conscientious professors were experts in the field of philosophy, they were not successful in creating an awareness for true philosophic thought in the minds of the younger generation. Materialism exploited the situation. First naturalistic, then historic materialism, began to attack the consciences of the young people without finding any serious opposition. At most, and for a brief period, Ion Dragoumis opposed this materialism with his beautiful nationalistic visions that aroused transient emotion in the souls of youth, but this opposition, as well as that of a daring, aesthetic mind, Perikles Yiannopoulos, was not connected with a basic philosophic position which could convince the reader.

Historic materialism was brought to Greece by strong, demagogic minds who had the power to convince and incite. Such a mind, above all, was Demetrios Glinos, a brilliant educator and politician. Yiannis Kordatos applied the historic theory of Marx to neo-Hellenic history. Kostas Varnalis, a very talented poet, attempted to create an intellectual atmosphere wherein Marxism prevails. And Charalambos Theodoridis, next to Glinos and Kordatos, attempted the systematic philosophic projection of a historical materialism.

Opposed to materialism were Alexandros Delmouzos, an educator with a most tender humanism, and Photos Politis, an excellent essayist with a free idealistic spirit inspired by Goethe. Here I should also mention Ioannis Sikoutris, whose strong mind and pedagogic talent deeply influenced the youth between the two wars. Starting out in philology, he indirectly fought every materialistic dogma. But it was essential that a philosophic movement should oppose the dynamism of the materialistic cosmo-theory. The group to organize the greatest opposition was the circle which published the *Archives of Philosophy and Theory of the Sciences,* a quarterly which appeared from 1929 to 1940, and which greatly influenced the university students of the period.

Ioannis Theodorakopoulos assumed the initiative to organize

the circle and the periodical. He is a great thinker and a true descendant of Plato and Plotinus. A professor at the University of Athens for many years, Theodorakopoulos has written a great number of books on the thought of Plato and Plotinus. His *Phaedrus* is a gem in neo-Hellenic literature. His *System of Philosophical Ethics* is a profound study in which he not only accomplishes an original synthesis of Platonism and Aristotelianism, but even advances beyond this. The singular synthesis becomes a new axiom of freedom, the beginning of a new human conscience. A few years ago Theodorakopoulos published an interpretation of *Faust, Part I* with a very conscientious translation of Goethe's work, marking an important pedagogical and philosophical event in neo-Hellenic intellectual life.

The *Archives of Philosophy* was founded, in addition to Theodorakopoulos, by four other friends: Constantinos Tsatsos, though a specialist in the philosophy of law, is also well-known as a poet and essayist. He wrote an important philosophic interpretation of the works of Kostis Palamas and recently published a book in which his wisdom is expressed in beautifully written aphorisms. Themistocles Tsatsos is the creator of an original political theory. Michael Tsamados, a friend of philosophy, has rendered the work of Natorp, *Plato's Ideas*, into Greek. I cannot avoid mentioning myself as a member of the group.

Many people became affiliated with the circle of the *Archives*, some as members, others as collaborators, and still others as students. We all considered, as a valuable member of our circle, the philosopher professor from Harvard University, Dr. Raphael Demos, a scholar and lover of Plato. Endowed with the gentlest intellectual and spiritual capabilities, Dr. Demos has shown that he knows how to philosophize genuinely. N. I. Toole, who faced the ethical problems with a sharp metaphysical eye, also became a member of the circle. One of the most outstanding of our young students was Georgios Sarantaris. He died at an early age in 1941 while fighting as a soldier on the Albanian front. Sarantaris had an exceptional poetic mind; he confronted the problem of existentialism with surprising originality. Kostas Despotopoulos, another outstanding student of ours thirty years ago, later attempted important steps in philosophy of law and entered into the spirit of Plato through a very personal path. Panayis Papaligouras has written many philosophical essays. Later, he dedicated himself, very successfully, to politics. Vasilios Laourdas devoted himself to Plato and to Byzan-

tine thought. I am very proud of my own student, Demetrios Kapetanakis, who also became a student of Karl Jaspers. Kapetanakis
died in England at an early age, after having written some poems
of great intellectual significance, as well as excellent essays.

The *Archives* movement began as one oriented toward Kant
and toward critical idealism. Hyperion, as the poet Hölderlin
created him, would not have participated wholly in this special
orientation. However, Hölderlin, his creator, said in a letter to his
half-brother Karl Christian Friedrich Gock: "Kant is the Moses of
our country (Germany)." Thus, I believe I have the right to say
that Hölderlin would have been happy to see that we had transferred to Greece the slates of Kant's commandments, "the drastic
laws," as he calls them.

However, we did not rest on Kant. We only started with Kant
to offer the younger men a firm foundation and a measure of intellectual self-discipline for their own thinking, more so because
this took place during a time when historic materialism had caused
many people to become satisfied with very simple, thus attractive,
forms of thinking. Still, we advanced quickly beyond Kant to Plato
himself. And Plato—the true Plato who does not restrict but who
liberates the mind—permitted each of us, as well as each of those
who were influenced by us, to follow his own free intellectual path.

Others writers cultivated the study of philosophy in the last
decades independent of the *Archives* circle. Nikolaos Louvaris, to
whom Edward Spranger "gratefully" dedicated his essay, "The Unknown God," is the most important figure in the philosophy of
religion. In the gentle soul of Louvaris, the intellectually inconceivable God of the ancient mystics of Hellenic orthodoxy meets,
in friendly terms, with the somewhat free thought of Goethe on
God, as well as with the figure of God that originated from the
poetic soul of Rilke. In a most important study, the broad-minded
Evangelos Papanoutsos attempted to analyze the poetry of Palamas,
Cavafis, and Sikelianos. In his other works he combines a faultless
knowledge (I could even term it a positive knowledge) of philosophical problems with a critical eclecticism. K. Georgoulis is an
excellent authority in the history of philosophy, from the primitive
philosophic thought to the "meta-philosophy," we might term it, of
our days. B. Tatakis also knows his philosophy well. He has distinguished himself especially in the philosophic interpretation of
Byzantine thought. Christos Karousos, an outstanding archeologist,

has elevated the interpretation of ancient Greek art to a high aesthetic level. Panayotis Michelis, starting out in architecture, dedicated his philosophic and poetic spirit to the problems of aesthetics. Angelos Procopiou faced the problems of ancient and Byzantine art successfully. The poet Dimis Apostolopoulos wrote important pages belonging at the same time to philosophy and to free poetic thought. Th. Vlisidis went beyond his profession, biology, to convey his rich store of knowledge and his restless spirit in a large work called, *Man, The Universe, and God*. Yiannis Oikonomidis wrote excellent articles on philosophic epistemology. A professor of medicine, Nikolaos Spyropoulos, who died a few years ago, wrote a philosophically important verse drama called *Bellerophon*, which was translated into English, and also a treatise on Heraclitus. K. Meranaios, Basil Frangos, A. Nisiotis, and I. Skandalakis, elaborated on the philosophical problems of existentialism, or even of "personalism." Babis Klaras, in *United Thinking*, attempted to overcome every dualism, especially the classical dualism separating mind and matter. Papalexandrou wrote a good *History of Philosophy*, and Demetrios Nianias is the author of important treatises on logic.

The literary essay, made famous by Montaigne and Bacon, Emerson, Carlyle, and Herman Grimm, appeared successfully in Greece after 1920 in an excellent form. The best of the earlier essayists were Photos Politis and Kostas Ouranis. Helle Lambridi, a woman who knows philosophy well, also wrote good essays; in fact, in 1939 Lambridi was the first to look at the *Odyssey* of Kazantzakis as a great work and sought to capture its metaphysical meaning. Kleon Paraschos, Themistocles Athanasiadis, Leon Koukoulas, Georgios Phteris, Alkis Thrylos, Yiannis Hadjinis, Tassos Varikas, D. Nikolareizis, Panos Karavias, Marios Ploritis, Am. Papavassiliou, and D. Raftopoulos are distinguished critical essayists. K. Dedopoulos is the author of important philosophical essays. Kostas Tsiropoulos, a young writer, combined his essays with a very deep pedagogic mission, confronting great problems of our days with spiritual lucidity. Andreas Christophidis, a Cypriot Greek, is also an excellent essayist with a deep knowledge of literature.

The poet, George Seferis, is also an authentic essayist. The essays of Aimilios Hourmouzios are creations of great intellectual power, especially concerned with aesthetic problems. The poet and novelist I. M. Panayotopoulos gave liveliness of the spoken word to the essay. And Petros Haris, Venezis, Terzakis, and Theotokas, as well as the historians and literary critics, K. Demaras and P. S. Spandonidis, also wrote excellent essays.

It is time now to arrive at my final observations. What direction has contemporary Greek intellectual life taken today in the novel or in poetry, in philosophy or in the literary essay, in the theater or in criticism?

Fortunately, no direction has been taken. No specific direction is attempting to close the innumerable paths that are and should always remain open to the mind. This precisely is the best sign in the contemporary intellectual life of Greece. In other periods—during the Renaissance or the eighteenth century—one-sidedness was not a true one-sidedness, therefore not at all harmful. In fact, some one-sidedness was essential since it opened new roads. Today, conversely, any direction that could prevail in the intellectual life of a country would be tyrannical. We are beyond classical thought and romantic spirit, beyond naturalism and symbolism or expressionism, beyond the typical idealism and a typical materialism, beyond historiocracy and existentialism. We have undergone all these experiences, and we live them within us, either united—something rare, which leads to an intellectual pantheism—or as contradictions, of which we are very cognizant. Today, so great is the awareness of all things that a return to any of these past attitudes of the mind, especially if one attitude were to attempt to exclude all the others, is an impossibility. The future will tell if it is possible for the human spirit to survive as poetry and music, even as philosophy, after such an awareness of all things. I believe that the spirit will survive. But great struggles, painful and heroic, are demanded.

I fear that were Hyperion to return today to his beloved homeland, he would depart at once. But he would not depart from Greece alone; he would do so from any other country. The blame for this departure would lie with our times, of course. However, even Hyperion would be to blame. No matter how faulty a period in time is, it is our duty to love it, to save it through our love.

Panayotis Kanellopoulos

I. M. Panayotopoulos

(1901–

I. M. Panayotopoulos was born in Aitolikon in 1901 and was educated at the University of Athens, where he was mainly concerned with literature. From 1923 to 1938, he taught at a private institute. Since 1938 he has been founder and director of an exclusive private gymnasium, and since 1947 a professor of Modern Greek Literature at the Institute of Secondary Education. In 1920 he was one of the editors and founders of the literary periodical *Mousa,* which reflected the thought of the generation.

Panayotopoulos is a prolific writer. During the past forty years, he has contributed more than thirty volumes in all genres. Poet, novelist, literary and art critic, essayist, and traveler, he is considered one of the most important contributors to the cultural life of contemporary Greece.

His first important publication in 1921 was a critical study, *The Poetic Work of Kostis Palamas.* For the third volume of *Men and Their Works,* also devoted to Kostis Palamas, he was awarded the Palamas Prize in 1947. In 1957 he received the First National Award for the best novel of the year with *The Seven Sleepers,* a work which has been translated into several languages. Again in 1964 the National Prize for travel literature was awarded to him for *Africa Awakens.*

I. M. Panayotopoulos began his career as a poet. Neo-romanticism in *The Book of Miranda* (1924) and symbolism in *Lyrical Sketches* (1933) were his early expressions. Later, abandoning impressionism, he published *Alcyone* (1950), *Circle of the Zodiac* (1950), and *The World of the Window* (1962), in which the basic elements of his poetic contributions are a burning agony for a newer, more personal expression, and a dramatic search for escape from the specter of transiency.

Starlight (1945) is his first novel, in which he portrays the good and evil of the post-World War I generation and the literary spirit of the time. *The Captive* (1951) is a story of pre-World War II and extends into the German-Italian occupation. In 1965 came *The Seven Sleepers,* a chronicle, which, though set in the third century at a time when the Roman Empire was disintegrating, is in reality an expression of attitudes of life towards contemporary problems.

His short story collections include: *The Ring with the Fairy Tales* (1957), a story of all human suffering; *Human Thirst* (1959), a new expression of the agony of existence; and *Flamingoes* (1963), an acrid portrayal of contemporary life which leads toward decay.

An important contribution of I. M. Panayotopoulos is his travel literature. He journeys, propelled by "the nightmarish urge for escape, the thirst for the unknown day, the need to offer a more unadulterated content to his daily existence." Included are: *Aspects of the Land of Greece; Greek Horizons; The Holy Scarab: Egypt; Europe; States of the East; Cyprus: A Journey; The World of China; A Glance at Russia;* and *China Awakens.*

Collections of essays include: *Discourses of the Naked Soul* (1946); *Thought and Word* (1954); and six volumes to date of *Men and Their Works* (1943–56), the latter concerned with Greek and foreign literatures. He has also contributed to the *Great Greek Encyclopedia* and to important literary periodicals and newspapers. For the past ten years, he has served as a member of the Advisory Board of the Organization of the National Theatre and Chairman on Fine Arts. He is also a member of several international organizations.

The primary expression in all the works of I. M., Panayotopoulos is an introspective response to life. Recollections of the past, though they are a form of self-punishment, are also a means of giving depth and meaning to the present. He never looks to the future, which holds only old age and decay, but presents us with the moment, where love becomes sanctified. Though *Humble Life* (1945) is autobiographical, it is also a realistic expression of the agony of a generation. The people of a poor neighbourhood in Piraeus live with their poverty, their daily struggle for existence, their suffering, and seek only that ephemeral gleam of sunshine which makes life tolerable. The touch of irony aimed at those whose actions are irresponsible, who only add to the burden and misery of the poor, is expressed without bitterness and is overshadowed by the stronger love and compassion for human weaknesses and for the fate of the individual in a world whose joy is limited.

Humble Life

1

Many years have passed, perhaps thirty, since I returned to that neighborhood. I allowed it to remain serenely undisturbed— in memory, in tears. I sought to preserve that neighborhood untouched by time; to reflect on it at the approach of winter, beneath the lamps kindled by the lamplighter, one by one, with his magic wand.

Around the church, the wind tormented the double row of pepper trees throughout the night. They were cold in their summer finery and shook their branches thoughtfully. At times, as they bowed to one another with outstretched hands, they gave the impression of being on the verge of journeying to foreign lands. The row of trees shivered and appeared on their way down to the muddy main street which cut through the factories. After a while, the pepper trees became rooted in the same spot and stood peacefully, as though no wind had ever touched them.

Darkness was falling and the factories howled, mourned, or sang, one high-pitched, another hoarse, perhaps from the unceasing rain of autumn, while a third, far in the distance, droned in a low, cracked voice. All sounded as though the devils had come to life in their bellies and were rushing upward to override the clouds. Then the huge black doors parted in two, squeaking as they glided over their iron rollers, and spewed exhausted human beings. The streets became black; so did the shops, the houses.

Later, the loneliness. A silence full of despair, full of sorrow. The only sound came from a boat entering the harbor, or one departing. The horn of one boat blasted and went to sleep in the dock; the horn from another blasted and disappeared into the sea. My brother knew the sound of each horn and immediately identified the ship. He longed to become a seaman; he dreamed of nothing else, only about the waves, the faraway places, the strange people. His eyes flashed with pain when he confessed his longing, so much pain that even we had the urge to cry without knowing the reason; the urge to cry for no reason, as we listened to him.

He even knew the smokestacks, the markings, the colors of each ship. And sometimes we lost sight of him. He went down to the harbor, half an hour's distance away. We often found him at the docks, gazing at the boats, gazing at the sea, standing as though turned to stone, right there on the spot—so much was it on his mind to become a seaman.

At night, he sat at the table with the night lamp as sole companion and sketched. He always sketched boats and islands and harbors. He could not even find paper; he could only select a piece from the greasy scraps that came from the grocer. On this, he pressed with all his strength, dragging the pencil to create a beautiful drawing. Sometimes, he fastened his eyes to the wall, on that tiny cradle of light from the vigil lamp, and became oblivious to everything. During those moments, as well, he was thoughtful and pained; all without reason, since he was not yet of age to have made any decision about his future.

Our house contained three rooms, one leading into the other, and all facing a stone wall about three meters away; the yard was only wide enough to contain our chairs on a summer evening when we sat outside for a breath of fresh air. The front room, facing the street, was occupied by the "woman from Galaxidi." We knew her only by that name; nor did we ever address her by anything other than "kyra." We stopped at that. She was fair, very fair and very stout, as though a swelling around her body tormented her. She had a daughter, Mercedes—two women alone, one of whom remained at home throughout the day while the other went to work in the cotton factory. Mercedes would return with nostrils, mouth, and hair full of minute yellowish threads, which gave the impression that she was shrouded in spiderwebs. After washing herself, she always changed to the flowered cotton dress which she tended so carefully and sang as she prepared dinner.

Mercedes' father had been a seaman. For ten years now, he had been away in foreign lands with no thought of ever returning. He neither wrote nor sent any other kind of news; yet the woman from Galaxidi refused to believe him dead. She attempted to collect neither pension nor anything else; in fact, she even honored him on Saint George's Day—they called him Giorgis—and she invited the neighboring women to come over for treats. As she walked back and forth in that small room, she kept extolling his virtues. My family lived in the other two rooms. We even had some rusty tin cans filled with geraniums, and a broken pitcher with barbarosa.

All the forests in the world and all kinds of fragrances emanated from those geraniums and the barbarosa. The hillside rose just beyond our house. More houses, adobe houses, were scattered on that hillside, but not a single tree, not a single flower; only the gray earth with its hot breath in summer, its unbearable mud in winter. There were no streets there. Everyone built his house where he could. He appropriated a bit of land and sometimes fenced it with an ivy-like bush, sometimes with a few planks; in other words, with whatever materials were available. He built a small shack, a tiny hut, in a corner of the yard, and thus freed himself from the payment of rent—that was most significant.

Even the landlord came to our house every Saturday. Someone was forever owing him rent. Before the first month's rent had been paid, the other one fell due; thus, he always came to ask for something, hoping to receive something, poor man. We paid him fourteen drachmas for our two small rooms; the woman from Galaxidi paid eight. The landlord was a serious man, approaching sixty, perhaps more, who was constantly thinking about marriage. He was the owner of two houses; the one he rented, the other he occupied himself, living alone like a ghost. He attended to his person with great care and exhibited no signs of a breakdown. He had spent most of his years in the army. What beautiful years those had been! He had made harnesses for the cavalry—in the Wars of 1912 and 1914. After the wars, everyone had praised the durability of his harness; durability in the battles of Elassona, Sarantaporo, Yiannitsa, and a whole string of places. He had heard related by a host of people that not a single one of his harnesses had ever broken down. He received the pension of a master sergeant. Ai! It was time now that he settled down to a married life!

The landlord was short and thin, with a long gray mustache, with a number of rings on his fingers, his dead mother's rings— God rest her soul—and he carried a cane with a silver handle, of which he was extremely proud. Every so often, he sprinkled his conversation with such suggestive phrases as: "we army men . . ." or "in the War of '97 . . ." or "when I was in Taratza . . ." Sometimes, the woman from Galaxidi interrupted him. All she had ever learned about the history of the world was this: in 1897 the Turks had crushed the Greeks and forced them to retreat to Taratza. But she never even knew the location of Taratza. The landlord paid little attention, however, to such interruptions; he only fastened his crafty, beady eyes on Mercedes, as though pouring syrup over her entire body. One time, in fact, when he had drunk too much, he became sufficiently emboldened to say to the woman from Galaxidi:

"What rents and more rents are you talking about! If you were to say the word, all my possessions would become yours; my houses and my pension and my furniture. Everything."

The woman from Galaxidi flushed angrily and cast these inconsiderate words into his face: "Put such things out of your mind, Kyr-Aristomenis. I would rather bury her, do you hear? Bury her!"

On the following day, she moved in and out of her room, murmuring to herself bitterly: "Listen to that! The decrepit old man! He's yearning for the girl—"

Kyr-Aristomenis never said another word. He only gazed on Mercedes, gently grieved, and appraised her in every respect, as though he had a horse before him, which he was scrutinizing from teeth to rump to anklebones.

Even so, the landlord was never unpleasant company. And on the Saturday when we happened to have the rent money and felt no embarrassment whatsoever, none at all, we were most amused by the stories he related about his army experiences. He also carried some photographs in his wallet, which he showed us proudly. He was always remarking about his possessions; thereby spreading out his nets to catch whatever he could. And he was always freshly shaven, his suits pressed, his shoes shined, and he smelled of *manteka* and cinnamon oil a mile away, exactly a mile. He drank his coffee in long draughts, his cane supported between his legs; he twisted his mustache and smiled.

Sometimes, he stretched his gaze over the low stone wall toward the hillside. He was contemplating purchasing a piece of land somewhere up there and building something, as everyone else was doing—Who could tell? Perhaps, when Mercedes saw that he was the owner of three houses, she might soften toward him. He would make a lady of her. The girl would never again have to kill herself at the factory for a daily wage of one drachma and eighty cents. Of course, the woman from Galaxidi attached great importance to this "one-and-eighty," because the other girls received only sixty cents a day, or maybe one-and-twenty. Very few indeed had arrived at the salary scale of Mercedes. Even Savvoula, who lived next door and worked at the match factory, was able to make ends meet on eighty cents a day. And she was always well-dressed.

But people had other remarks to make about Savvoula. Every Sunday, she left the neighborhood early and returned quite late, but she never breathed a word to anyone about her whereabouts. And to say that she was a girl with any particular talents! A snip of a girl she was and nothing more. There is really no accounting for the tastes of men!

2

In the afternoon, whenever we had neither school nor studying to do, we spent our time around the church or around the pepper trees, which we enjoyed more at dusk. Or we sat on the marble steps of the church playing marbles, our favorite form of entertainment. Sometimes, when the heat was unbearable or the cold penetrating, we gathered inside the spacious church with its tall, stained windows, with its square columns extending to the sky. It was peaceful inside the church, and quiet. Only the saints gazed upon us. We had become accustomed to returning the gaze, boldly fixing our eyes upon theirs; and we dreamed. Sometimes, we even climbed high up the belfry, which had a square terrace located near the bells. From there, we could look over the entire city of Piraeus: the sea of houses and factories, the streets and harbor. All the confusion arising from the suffering and torment of men intoxicated us; stupefied us; entranced us.

Pantelis, the son of the sacristan, loved this terrace. He suffered from scrofula and always had a dirty cloth wrapped around his neck. His father feared that the boy would die early in life, and Pantelis altered in appearance from day to day, as though he were removing himself still farther from this world. Perhaps this accounted for his customary silence; his contemplation and silence. We were very fond of that boy because we knew that he would die soon. The priest and the deacon were equally fond of him, as though they already possessed him; as though they already saw him asleep in a coffin of knotty planks lined with purple paper, hands clasped, and a cheap white wreath around his weary head.

The sacristan sometimes called on us for help, especially at the approach of the great holidays. The man had no time to rest during the holidays. Night found him still at work beneath the drowsy night lamps. He could be heard breathing heavily in the empty, dimly lighted church. We polished the candle-holders with a piece of green felt, scraped off the wax from the tiles with a knife, and dusted the chairs. We were very happy indeed doing all this work.

Whenever the sacristan was absent, Pantelis led us inside the sanctuary. There, we found many objects to inspect. All those enchanted objects upon which the world gazed in wonder and fear on Sunday, we held in our hands. We held the pyx, which we found quite dusty and had to dust. We held the pincers, the lance, the cup for the boiling water used in the Eucharist—all made of silver. We even opened the cupboards and read aloud from the Book of the Lives of Saints. We put on the new scarf of the deacon and the cassock of the archmandrite, and we swept proudly over the white tiles. Then we kissed the feet of the Crucified One and prayed to be forgiven for this very small, this very harmless, amusement. It was so quiet, so exquisite, inside the Sanctuary. Something entirely different, something beyond life, a bit of paradise, let us call it. In summer, the large windows were opened and the swallows flew into the church, filling it with song. Even the pigeons, which had built their nests under the roof, flew in. The sacristan told us to feed the pigeons with corn soaked in *ouzo*. Intoxicated, they would then drop into our hands.

"A pigeon is nice and fat," he observed. "You broil it over charcoal, and then you take some red wine and say, 'Begone, poverty!'"

Little by little, we became acquainted with everything inside the church. We were at home there and accepted the church into our lives like an enchanted story. The narthex was spacious with a large window facing the front, and there in the vestibule, the priests and deacons sat after vespers on Sundays, after Mass on holidays, and at dusk on Saturdays and on evenings before holidays. The chanters came, and the sacristan with his family, and we children sat in a corner, where it was very pleasant to listen to all their conversations; but most of all, to the jokes of the deacon, who was handsome and tall and robust; a youth desired by all the women. Sometimes, he became bold under the sullen eyes of the archmandrite and changed the tune of the hymn to a *kleftic* song, one of those songs he had sung in Salona before coming to the monastery to become a monk.

They drank coffee right there, quietly, as they dunked large chunks of white consecrated bread, well-baked and spongy; bread which was never lacking from the Sanctuary, and which they carted home in baskets on All-Soul's Saturdays. They even gave us a slice on those Saturdays; sometimes half a loaf. They gave the sacristan a few loaves; the archmandrite, in fact, was extremely generous with the sacristan. The archmandrite had only recently come here from a distant community and was not acquainted with anyone in the district. He was in need of the services of the sacristan, who could recommend him when the opportunity afforded to those needing him for funerals and weddings and christenings, and even for the sanctification the very devout women held in their homes on the first of every month. Once he secured his position, he could make of these sanctifications a steady source of income, a salary, let us say. And the archmandrite counted heavily on the sanctifications.

The deacon was studying theology, but he had little ambition for study. He had become acquainted with Father and came over to our house every so often, at noontime on Sunday, to eat with us. We considered this a special honor. Whenever the woman from Galaxidi saw him open the gate, she ran to kiss his hand. But no! the deacon would not allow this, because no one ever kissed the hand of a deacon. Even Mercedes smiled at him sweetly. The deacon remained the entire afternoon at our house; in fact, he and Father often chanted hymns. The deacon attempted to teach us children some of the hymns, but we had no voice for music. We bleated like lambs.

One year, the deacon intoxicated me with joy, and this is something I will never forget. He allowed me to accompany him from house to house on the sanctification ceremony which took place on the day before Epiphany. I held the bucket with the Holy Water. He wore a scarf over his frock, carried a cluster of basil in his hand, and entered the homes chanting a hymn. I followed him, wearing a new sailor blouse and a cap trimmed in gold braid—the dream of many childhood years finally come true.

It was quite a strange, but a very warm feeling, to open the door and enter into this great variety of houses as though they belonged to us. It was so early in the morning that sometimes we found the women still in bed; then, half-naked, breasts bare, still unwashed, they would run to cover their nakedness with a scarf or a blouse, as they made the sign of the cross. They crossed themselves unceasingly. The deacon performed the sanctification and smiled; the girls—and some were very beautiful—also smiled at him. Then they tossed a coin into the bucket, whatever amount each could

spare. The nickels and dimes fell like rain. But there were those
extremely poverty-stricken people who pretended to drop a coin
into the bucket; however, since we heard no sound, we understood
that they had dropped nothing. Still others dropped in dimes from
Argentina, which were without any value whatsoever. Two or three
even dropped marbles, and Savvoula, despite the new blouse she
was wearing, a very tight one so that her breasts protruded, dropped
in a button—we recognized this immediately from the hollow sound
it made.

"That impudent one!" cried the deacon as we were leaving.
"That sinner! Did you see how she was dressed?"

I agreed with him, because, even innocent as I was, this Savvoula caused me some agitation. That night, in the deacon's home,
we counted the money. There were about sixty drachmas. The
deacon gave me five drachmas, a roll made up of dimes. An entire
fortune to me! But my feet ached; they ached unbearably. Mother
heated some water and soaked them in a basin and rubbed them.
The woman from Galaxidi came over with Mercedes; they sat on
our best chairs and drank their coffee. Both were very proud of me.

"Well, Kostakis," they said over and over again. "Well, Kostis,
you don't lack for honors and glories now. We even heard the
deacon say that he will ask Kostakis to chant the *Aspile Amolyntai*
during the Lenten services. Five days in a row—God be praised!"
And they crossed themselves mechanically.

No matter how one looks on that evening, it was enchanting;
quite enchanting. Mother rubbed the roll of dimes over her hair
and said she wished my earnings would be as numerous as the
hairs on her head—My brother was somewhat envious of me, that
is certain.

Besides the deacon, the chanter on the left side of church was
also Father's friend, and he sometimes came to our house as well.
He was short and stocky, with a pouch that interfered with his
gait. But his cracked voice had at one time given some of the most
melodious tones, in those good old days when Vitivilias had
charmed the crowds. He liked to drink the juice from boiled greens,
which he gargled in his throat before swallowing, then belched
contentedly. If, on a Saturday night, Mother happened to be boiling dandelions, he would beg her to fill a cup of the juice, squeeze
some lemon in it—then he desired neither coffee nor anything else.
His jowls were yellow, very yellow, like those of an old hen; he

breathed heavily, as though whistling. He suffered from his heart, poor man. He also worked at the post office on weekdays, but he refused to give up his church work; otherwise, he could never make ends meet. His mania was to outshine the chanter on the right side of church. Whenever Vitivilias raised his voice to a high pitch, everyone who knew of his illness feared that he would die on the spot and make orphans of a string of children. But to no avail! He considered nothing. He even joked with the deacon and threw some suggestive remarks at him, all of which we failed to understand. We only knew that the conversation concerned Pandora, who lived in a large house opposite the Sanctuary; a girl who had married very young and now carried a baby in her arms. Her husband was a seaman, away at Tunisia these past six months. Pandora had two dark eyes, so fiery that one became scorched if he looked at them; scorched, and yet there was always that desire to look into those eyes.

The right chanter took his mandolin at night and sang in back of the Sanctuary, there in front of Pandora's house. He was utterly insane, and all the neighborhood was aware of it. Kyra-Paraskevi, who had a miracle-performing icon in her home, an icon which was the mainstay of the community, and a great hulk of a man, who at one time had considered becoming a monk and so had set off for Mount Athos, only to return without having accomplished a thing —these two carried the story to the archmandrite. The archmandrite elaborated on the story and related it to the Board. The President of the Board, who owned the cotton factory which also manufactured drill cloth, reprimanded the right chanter severely. But nothing fazed the chanter. He had a beautiful and loud voice; so he was sought by all the churches. He was a cheerful man, approaching thirty, and at the height of his manly powers. And Pandora outshone Savvoula with her blouses. In fact, every afternoon, she made it a point to sit on a rock beyond the door of her house and nurse her baby, baring her breast carelessly as she did so. If someone happened to be passing by, Pandora pretended to cover her breast, but bared them ever more, so much so that she had damned the entire neighborhood, curses on her!

3

As the Holy Week of Easter approached, the woman from Galaxidi became deathly ill. Her face expanded like a woolen blanket soaked in water, and she was covered with red spots. She burned with a feverish fire. In her delirium, she kept recalling her hometown, Galaxidi, and her husband Giorgis. Her illness became one of ships and rowboats and seas. Mercedes slept little more than one or two hours during the nights and worked all day long at the factory. The doctor was called in. Shaking his head, he said that the woman would have to remain in bed for a long time. Then, pocketing his two drachmas, he left to return on the following day to repeat what he had said on the day before and to pocket another two drachmas. This went on for an entire week. Soon, the small amount of money that Mercedes had put aside, what with medicine and ice, dwindled to nothing. The girl found herself in a difficult position with this unexpected misfortune. Sometimes, she could scarcely hold back the tears, and her eyes filled, her cheeks filled—It was pathetic to look upon her.

We helped her during this difficult occasion; but how much could we do! Kyra-Katerina also came over. She owned the water-well situated on the lower street, and from that well she sold water for a nickel a pitcher. The neighbors reveled in the situation, this group of gossips. Gathered together around the mouth of the well, they talked from morning until night, exchanging every bit of gossip around the neighborhood. But Kyra-Katerina was a good woman. She said nothing; she only collected her nickels, arranged them in a roll, and deposited them in the bank. She had a horse-shoe covered with gold paper hanging over her door, on the inside, so that those who passed by might not see and covet it. How Krya-Katerina loved the woman from Galaxidi! She changed the compresses on her forehead and gave Mercedes five drachmas, an event which remained quite significant during the entire illness of the woman. Only this, the woman from Galaxidi was conscious of nothing. She continued to swell until the bed appeared not to contain her aching body, a body that resembled a hill which descended to the floor and threatened to cover that space as well.

Then the landlord began to visit here often, and he was most sympathetic. He came with blackened mustache and cinnamon oil on his hair. He sat a short distance away for hours on end, conversing with the neighbors about the illnesses he had undergone, not very serious ones, of course; only that they had cost him a devil of a lot of money.

"To get well, one must have a lot of money. Sickness is a costly thing," he kept repeating as he looked at Mercedes boldly, because now the possibility was that they would be burying the woman from Galaxidi; she would not be burying Mercedes, as she had rashly remarked that other time.

The girl pretended not to understand.

"Up to this point, we are making out all right, thanks to the neighbors," Mercedes would reply, and this would make him quite obstinate.

"The neighbors—I'm a neighbor, too—A neighbor and a landlord. I'm not a stranger."

"We thank you, Kyr-Aristomenis. We are grateful for your good intentions. It is quite enough that we owe you two months' rent—"

"Two months' rent. Two months' rent—" the landlord repeated, talking to himself. "This is no time to talk about rent." And he twisted his mustache as he passed the cane between his legs.

Kyra-Katerina tormented the landlord every time she found him in the house.

"It is time you were married and became a family man, Kyr-Aristomenis," she kept saying to him. "You carry enough years on your back; you also have money to burn. What are you waiting for?"

"First, the right person must be found—I've served my country faithfully; I have my rank, my position. I can't marry just anyone—"

"Evanthia is not just anyone, Kyr-Aristomenis. We've tried to arrange a match for you, but you've ignored her."

"Evanthia is a girl with a past," the landlord cried obstinately. "And she's more than fifty, that's for certain—"

"She isn't even forty yet. We were in grammar school together —I've told you that before."

"Oh, certainly—Since you were together in grammar school—"

"But I know, Kyr-Aristomenis. You want a girl with a future." How she made that man suffer with her thoughtless words.

The woman from Galaxidi took a turn for the worse. The doctor said they must wait for the "crisis" before knowing the outcome of her illness. Mercedes went crying to her boss. She asked him for a week's advance in pay and begged him to take it out of her wages, a little at a time. The boss gave her two days' wages; he even raised his egg-shaped eyes to heaven and confessed that these were difficult times. Business was very slow, and cotton was becoming more expensive. Easter was a black day in that house.

Mercedes might have gone hungry, had we not given her a plate of food and two Easter eggs.

She was alone when I took the food to her. Since both my hands were occupied, I could not knock on the door; so I pushed on it with my elbow and walked in. The girl, at that moment, was undressing. In fact, she had already taken off her clothing to change into another dress for the holiday. After all she had been through! And her mother in delirium, talking and talking about rowboats and about her luckless Giorgis. Something very white confused me. White and sweet, with a dark spot right there, and my hands began to tremble. Mercedes ran over to take the plates from my hands, just as she was, as though she didn't mind in the least—She only said: "You're too young yet, Kostakis. But God! How you frightened me! I almost had a heart attack!"

She wrapped herself in a robe as she wished me many happy years and thanked me for the gift.

O Mercedes! You probably never even sensed the great damage you performed to Kostakis on that bitter Easter day! Better that you were unaware of it, Mercedes; better that you were unaware.

4

Gypsy-Theodore was an important member of our group. He sat on the same bench with me in school, and I liked him exceedingly, even though he often caused me a great deal of suffering. Because he was so small, and I was no larger than he, the teacher always found sufficient room at our bench to seat another boy with us whenever we had few absences in the class. In fact, our seatmate always happened to be one of those formless, dangling creatures who also worked and only attended school occasionally, just so he would not lose contact with education entirely. Poor Gypsy-Theodore! During those times, he sat in the middle, and then the earth opened to swallow him. But never once did I hear him complain. That boy had undergone so much punishment that he had learned patience in everything. He had a round, bald head—he always shaved his head to keep the hair from growing too fast—and two frightened eyes with which he sometimes looked at the teacher, sometimes at the blackboard, as he sat breathless. That is how attentive he was in order to learn something, to become someone when he grew up.

I can recall so many things about poor Gypsy-Theodore. That short, tight coat with the faded squares, covered with numerous patches and with a fraction of sleeves. And that tattered shirt. And those trousers which fell just above his knees. And those shoes with the knotted shoelaces; shoes in so poor a condition that the shoe-repairman could salvage nothing. They were only a semblance of shoes; nothing more. Everything about Gypsy-Theodore was only a semblance; a semblance of shirt, of coat, of trousers; he even ate a semblance of food. His mother worked at the factory; his sister also worked there. Fifteen years old at the most she was, but she looked like ten. Mother and sister went to work very early in the morning, leaving him a slice of bread and a nickel. With that nickel, Gypsy-Theodore bought a sardine to eat his noon meal like a king. With that nickel and the slice of bread, he sought his education. He waited until evening, when the women returned home from work to cook something, so he could eat a better meal. Even so, he never complained. Only, he had become quite proficient in this business of the sardine. During noontime, he kept vigilant eyes on the store of Anifantis until he saw the barrel become half-empty; then he was certain to find a large, fat sardine.

Gypsy-Theodore lived on the naked side of the hill, in a small rented room which was entirely bare. A cupboard, a table with three broken chairs, and a mattress on the floor; these were their entire possessions. But they managed quite well in that room. He laid his tablets and books in a corner of the floor. In the evening, he sat on the window sill to design his exquisite letters. That boy wrote as though placing shelled peas in a row. The teacher admired his writing, because he never found a single error. But what was the good of all that? It never made Gypsy-Theodore any wealthier!

We played out in the street during recess, out in front of the school, which had formerly been a store. Now it held six classes with two teachers; the one teacher, in fact, was tall and stout and wore a long mustache. On his chin, the hair grew sparsely, which gave him a terrible appearance. He always carried a stick in his hand and screamed at us and flogged us. Those of us who were whipped screamed as well; then the entire neighborhood was in an uproar. There was a great commotion, in fact, at our school. This stout teacher had a son who worked in the butcher shop at the market place. He had barely completed the sixth grade before his father sent him to work. Sometimes, the boy came home with a bloodied apron and brought some chops or livers wrapped in paper.

The teacher immediately gave these to his landlady to cook. Since his house adjoined the school, the odor of burning oil and smoke from the broiler pervaded our room. All of us suffered terribly. We felt nauseated, but attempted to ignore all this. Gypsy-Theodore would stretch his nostrils wide, but not a single word came from him.

The teacher would then interrupt the lesson and absent himself for a time. When he returned, wiping his mustache with the back of his hand, he smelled of wine, and his eyes had a ferocity about them. At such times, he flogged and flogged. You would have thought that everyone in that school flogged the pupils, even though it was only this stout teacher who carried out the task. However, during recess, when the pupils opened their bags to take out some herring or cheese and a large piece of bread to eat, this teacher managed to mingle with the pupils, a smile on his face; all of which made one wonder what kind of man he was. He pinched a little here and a little there, chewing like a cow. Not a father of a single pupil; not a merchant nor a grocer nor anyone else could pass by without having this particular teacher take something from him. And it was they who always thanked him, because they all trembled at the sight of him, both pupils and parents. An entire generation had passed through his hands, and everyone had been flogged. Not a single person, man or woman, could be found to say that he had not been treated in this manner. His hands had now become quite accustomed to flogging. He also lost his temper at the slightest provocation. At such times, he was capable of flogging even the archmandrite, so to speak, and not a peep would come from the archmandrite.

While we are on the subject, we must say something about the great misfortune that befell us when they assassinated the King at Thessaloniki. The order came that all the pupils must wear black armbands. That was something to behold! Some pupils forgot their armbands; others paid little attention and wore the band on the right arm; still others failed to wear it high enough. Some of the boys were unable to find a black cloth; so they used faded purple, or brown, or even gray. The teacher took the order from his bosom and read it to us, over and over again; then he felt each armband. Very few of us escaped his notice; very few. There was always something not quite right. Did the blessed man never tire of flogging! Forty days this evil lasted; so much so that, before leaving for school in the morning, we rubbed salt over our hands and legs.

That was to make the floggings less painful. O how we cried for the
dead King; how we cried! Even Gypsy-Theodore received a sound
thrashing. We marveled once again at this boy who said nothing;
only his eyes filled with tears, and he turned to look at the teacher
with such courage that we thought the teacher coughed a little to
clear the lump lodged in his throat.

5

The illness of the woman from Galaxidi became quite mysterious. It was evident that the doctor was treating her for typhoid,
but the crisis failed to materialize. Instead of becoming thinner, the
woman grew even larger, and the fever refused to subside. Mercedes was exhausted. Only half of her weight remained. She neither
ate nor slept. In fact, the foreman, Kyr-Agisilaos, talked to the
doctor and hold him that it was wrong to continue insisting on
typhoid. The girl had spent all her money. Kyr-Agisilaos was an
educated man and also a good family man. Because he had a
position, the doctor respected him greatly. Thus, it was decided
that the poor woman from Galaxidi should be removed to the hospital. Only, the neighbors all said, this would be expensive, because the hospital was an hour and a half away. She must be
transported there by carriage, which could not be accomplished for
less than ten drachmas.

Mercedes was at a loss about a course of action. She spent the
entire afternoon watching the neighborhood. Whenever she saw
someone to whom she could talk freely, she confessed her troubles
and sought his help. She came to us, as well, and we gave her
fifty cents, which was all we had. She went to Savvoula, whose
room smelled of cinnamon oil; she was ironing one of those un-
mentionable articles of clothing; she was ironing it on the table,
very carefully, so as not to crumple the lace. What does one say!
Something else was surely going on inside that house! Even so,
Savvoula gave Mercedes two drachmas, and her eyes filled with
tears when she heard that the woman from Galaxidi was being
taken to the hospital.

Until nightfall, Mercedes had collected only four drachmas.
Then she made her great decision. Walking down to Stenimachou
Street, she knocked on the door of the landlord. He was sitting
quietly in his dining room, reading *The Evening News,* in which
he was following the serialized novel, *The White Lady,* and the

section of "Personalities," which made him dream of the wealthy homes distributed by the newspaper. Mercedes was struck speechless as she entered that house, so beautifully arranged, so meticulously clean, with so many pictures on the walls, with the hanging clock swinging to and fro, endlessly marking time; with the soft sofa covered in green velvet, and the embroidered pillows; with the console and the mirror, which frightened Mercedes when she saw the reflection of her own sunken cheeks and eyes. Ah, he was a man of means, the landlord! He was so astonished to see Mercedes that he was struck speechless. After seating her on the sofa, he went into the other room to return with a cup of sweets, bitter oranges they were, and a glass of water. He sat in a chair across from hers, waiting to hear what the girl had to say. He glanced at her from top to toe, as though fondling her body with that gaze and breathing its fragrance through his bristled mustache. Then he said:

"Do you know you have become thinner, Mercedes? You're much thinner. You're going to kill yourself, my dear, with the mind you have!"

She had no answer to this; she only said that it was essential they transport her mother to the hospital the next day, and that they had no money to pay for the carriage.

Kyr-Aristomenis raised his eyes to look at the ceiling as though thinking of something remote and quite involved.

"Will twenty drachmas do?" he asked after a while.

Mercedes became truly alarmed. So much money? Six drachmas were all she had come to borrow. She had already collected four from the neighbors.

"Six drachmas? And what will six drachmas do? That's enough for the carriage, yes. But you're nearly dead—You need some proper food, you know. Ai! Kyr-Aristomenis, of whom the la—" (He almost said "late," but bit his lips and didn't say it.) "Of whom your mother made fun. Now, he will prove to you that he was not lying; he meant it when he said that he would make you queen of everything in this house. Can I help it if they've poisoned your mind, those foul witches! Anyway, you'll come to understand someday what is to your advantage. You think life is to be confronted with the sweet words expressed by those lazy louts who come near you and who can't even find a place in the sun. Ai! that's not how things are! With my money, as the saying goes—and you should know it—"

"I didn't come here for such words, Kyr-Aristomenis," Mercedes murmured in alarm. "My mother is dying. Can't you see the condition I am in?"

"We're all going to die someday. But while we're alive—That is most difficult. Who will bring you something to eat, a beautiful dress to wear, new shoes, the thousand things that man needs? Who will help you to emerge from your cocoon when you're burying your youth, Mercedes? Do you hear? I hear, you should answer. Nor will you be saved by any clodhopper who hangs around the *taverna* day and night, nor will you be saved—All of you have only learned to say that Kyr-Aristomenis is an old man—And you refuse to give him an opportunity to show you that he is worth more than all those handsome louts who have become diseased by the prostitutes—"

Mercedes arose to leave.

"Shame on such things, Kyr-Aristomenis. And for you to be saying them to a girl!"

"Come, come. We'll talk about this another time. Here, now, take the twenty drachmas."

"No, no. I don't want anything. Forgive me. I thought—"

"What do you mean you thought and thought—Haven't I already told you whenever you need something to come to me without hesitation? Kyr-Aristomenis is a man of honor and esteem. You are not to worry about a thing."

The landlord insisted, insisted. He stopped complaining; he was almost in tears. At that moment, Mercedes felt compassion for him; she took the money. Relieved now, she bade him goodnight, as though, at last, she was no longer quite so frightened of him. Twenty drachmas! She clasped them in her hand, unbelieving—If she had asked for a hundred, she would have received that much.

A light shone in Savvoula's room, and a song drifted out to the street. Mercedes stopped as though entranced; stopped right there in the middle of the street, in the night. A drunk man had been hanging onto the lamppost and was retching like a cat. The entire area smelled of wine. He was wearing a heavy overcoat and a cap —Without doubt, dry land had failed to agree with him. From the harbor came the sounds of the horns, husky, sleepy; the boats and the sea, all kinds of people, freedom. Mercedes thought of Savvoula; she thought of her sick mother, of the landlord; she thought of her own sad plight. And her heart became tearful.

She returned home and began to assemble a few things, some

long nightgowns, some boxes belonging to the woman from Galaxidi, some other articles. The distance of an hour and a half away! And after that? Would her mother emerge from the hospital dead or alive? Once Mercedes had gone to the hospital to see a neighbor, and she had almost fainted. May God keep everyone away from a hospital, had been her thought at that time. The heavy hospital odor had remained with her for an entire week, and her soul had filled with something thick and flaming, like burning mud—That was what illness in a hospital was like on those iron beds with their torn mattresses; in those long halls, all tile and footsteps; with those instruments that tore and tormented the human flesh.

So it was that Mercedes remained all alone at home. Her work over at the factory, she went to the hospital, riding on the train for a distance, then walking the remainder of the way. This cost two dimes a day. At that, she always had to spend something more. She returned late at night, heart fluttering, so afraid was she that she would be unable to avert some disastrous encounter. We waited for her around the table. We saved a plate of food for her. At last, she became so accustomed to this she stopped declining; only that she cried for her mother and swallowed her food without chewing on it. She was so innocent and confused during this difficult period.

Sometimes, Kyr-Aristomenis remained late at our house, passing the time with one thing or another, waiting for Mercedes to return. He never revealed his purpose; so careful was he of Father, who was most strict about such matters, and he attributed these visits to the compassion which the landlord expressed for a neighbor. Certainly, such was the soul of the landlord. It was impossible that he do otherwise; he must bring some food; he must perform a small kindness for Mercedes. The neighbors, on the other hand, looked with disfavor on all this. One day, Kyr-Katerina could contain herself no longer, and she said to Mercedes:

"All the world knows, and you're trying to conceal it."

"What are you talking about?" the girl asked, alarmed.

"Don't pretend not to understand, Mercedes! Of course, of course; anyone who has money—Evanthia saw you with her own eyes entering his house at night. Not once or twice—Ever since you've made the decision, you've thrown caution to the winds, you poor thing—"

Mercedes was totally dumbfounded.

"I—At night? Where? It was dusk when I went once to ask Kyr-

Aristomenis for a loan of six drachmas for the carriage. That was all. May I never find joy in my mother!"

"You know the saying: be afraid of still water—"

A lump rose to Mercedes' throat and almost choked her. She could remain silent no longer.

"Had you helped me, Kyra-Katerina, I would never have gone to Kyr-Aristomenis, and gossips would not now be saying such things about me. Did I not come to beg you; did I not complain to you? What could I do with the fifty cents you gave me. Remember, you told me that was all the money you had. The money in the bank was there for a specified length of time, you said, and you would never touch any of that."

"I told you the truth, my child. Or do you think that I work at my water-well for others? When I get old, no one will look after me, I know that."

"Ah, Kyra-Katerina, we're human. God will look after all of us."

At precisely that moment, the landlord appeared with a small packet in his hand.

"What did I tell you," Kyra-Katerina barely had time to utter. "It's about time you said that I saw nothing of this with my own eyes."

And she left, as though someone had murdered the children she did not possess. The earth opened to swallow Mercedes. But she was patient. She feared the neighbors. Because Kyra-Katerina expressed her love to everyone, they all considered her a wise and serious woman. One word from her at this time and Mercedes was lost. Utterly lost.

As though this were not enough, one night, as she was returning late from the hospital, that fellow Pardalos (so the neighbors called him because he was always pinching the girls) was sufficiently emboldened to corner her and whisper a few poisonous remarks in her ears.

"Silent wife of a priest! Why don't you look around! Don't give everything to the old man—Youth has its claims, too."

With difficulty, Mercedes eluded his grasp. But she felt as though she were dropping, dropping into a hole, all mud and filth.

The woman from Galaxidi had no intention of getting well. She was no longer swelling, but contracting, as though her body had become an accordion. Her skin was dehydrating, her arms and legs were shrinking, her fever was subsiding; she was conscious now. The doctors, however, refused to decide that she was improving, whenever Mercedes asked them about her condition. There was also a young man there, always in a white, freshly-ironed blouse, an interne, who looked at Mercedes sorrowfully and sympathet- ically. One day, Mercedes overheard him talking to the accountant.

"See what a lovely face she has! It is these poor girls who are bought and sold for practically nothing. Let her acquire some decent nourishment and you'll see how she blossoms!"

Mercedes turned to look at the two men. Their eyes were glued on her, as though searching her body, as though undressing her. They were not even embarrassed by their words. They only smiled at her; the doctor patted her on the back and spoke in a friendly voice:

"We will keep your mother for a long time yet."

"Is she that bad?" the girl asked.

"She is bad, of course, but she is not going to die. We just want to keep you coming here; we like to see you. That is all."

Not a word came from Mercedes. She only opened the door and ran out. From that time on, she was extremely careful when entering the hospital to avoid running into the doctor alone.

Her heart was heavy. As she was returning home, she saw Savvoula sitting beside the half-opened shutters, waiting. It was a beautiful night; the moon sailed across a very blue sky and all nature swam in a silver sea. Savvoula called to Mercedes to come closer.

"Come inside," she said. "I've saved you a plate of meat from lunch."

"No, no; it is late now. I must rest a bit."

"You're not going to bed without something to eat! Don't be foolish! I've also put aside two drachmas for you."

Savvoula left the window and appeared at the door.

"How many days did you work this week? Four? And last week? Another four? Certainly, you're sick; you're killing yourself. Very soon now, you won't be able to drag your feet."

And Savvoula pulled her forcibly inside the house. Savvoula had eaten dinner earlier. Now, she quickly prepared something for Mercedes. Everything was peaceful and clean and beautifully at- tended in that room. Mercedes related about her mother's condition. She told Savvoula what the young doctor had said, and how this daily excursion had completely exhausted her.

"What can I do!" Savvoula replied. "God gave you beauty, but He gave you no brains; that let me tell you."

Mercedes turned to look at her. She gazed around the room and at Savvoula's face. Her eyes were lined with blue underneath, but her lips were fresh. She had some sweet dimples on her cheeks —She was no snip, this girl—

"If I were you, I would marry the old man," Savvoula continued. "I would take what I could for a couple of years, you can be certain of that. And later—Ah, later, with the money I would have, all the young men in the world would fall at my feet. Life is difficult, Mercedes. We are becoming barren; we are becoming old—The way we live now, we will never see a bright day."

"What are you telling me?" asked Mercedes. "I would rather die—"

"Well, you do not die once; you die daily. It might be all right, if your mother lives. But if she dies? We're human. What will become of you alone? Or are you going to sit listening to the stupid words of this man and that, and act the saintly Mary—I do not deny it; you are beautiful. Perhaps some penniless man will eventually ask you to marry him. But that kind—Oh, the world is full of that kind; someone to support as well!"

How wise was this Savvoula. And no one gave her any credit, either.

6

Kyra-Paraskevi, protectress of the community, quite often conducted all-night vigils in her home, in the room where she kept the miracle-performing icon. All the women of the neighborhood gathered together early in the evening for those vigils; the archmandrite came, sometimes the deacon as well, and everything was warm in that room and full of suffering, because each member had something for which to pray, something about which to cry to Her Grace. Pandora came, bundled in her blue shawl, and she genuflected many times for the sake of her husband, far off in Tunis, who had no thought of returning home. We children sat there for two or three hours in the evening; then we returned home just before daybreak. The small room was stifling hot with so many people in it, with the burning incense and candles. The old women slept in the corners of the room, and only the lively ones, like Pandora, or the God-fearing ones, like Kyra-Paraskevi, refused to become drowsy, but sat listening to that monk, Christos, who, as we have said before, had gone to Mount Athos for a time, and who wore the cap of a monk with a red cross embroidered right in the center of his forehead—They sat listening to him as he chanted in his deep, droning voice coming between yawns.

Kyra-Paraskevi loved this boy exceedingly; she consulted him on numerous occasions, because Christos had not entirely alienated himself from the "fathers." He had brought her some scented incense from Mount Athos, some hand-carved crosses, and a few papers. Christos watched over the miracle-performing icon and lived beside it in prayer and fasting. We were the only ones who disliked him because he acted with such superiority, commanding us to live on bread and water during the Holy Week, and on three glasses of water on Good Friday, one in the morning, one at noontime, and one at night, just before the *epitaphios,* and nothing more. When he ran into us on the streets, he compelled us to open our mouths wide; then he thrust his nose in there and sniffed deeply to see if we had eaten any oil and had thus sinned. We would become nauseated, so badly did his own breath smell. But we never expressed revulsion because he had hung a picture on the wall of Kyra-Paraskevi's house, a large picture showing the flames and tortures of hell and the legions of devils who prodded the sinners with their forked tongs as they pushed them into the tubs of burning tar. From time to time, we dreamed about this picture, and a cold perspiration sheathed us. Thus, we never had a reply for Christos; we only wondered how the man could endure such submission and so many hardships.

Pantelis confessed to us that, one day when he had gone to the priest's house, he had found the priest, his wife, and children eating beans with an abundance of oil over them, and an onion, which he had crushed with his fist, and he was drinking wine. But when we told this to Christos, he raised his eyes, black as ripe plums, to heaven and cried as though bedevilled: "Woe unto you, scribes and Pharisees; hypocrites!" Thus, we became frightened beyond all question and never again opened our mouths.

One night, the right chanter announced that he would be attending the vigil. Although Kyra-Paraskevi disliked the man, she considered his visit a great honor and boasted about it proudly to her neighbors. Only Christos became angry. He said that some business was taking him out of town, but that he would return early enough to attend the vigil. He returned the following afternoon. The right chanter opened his mouth and caused the entire house to vibrate. The old women were startled; they wept and crossed themselves—So much did they enjoy his hymn. He had riveted his eyes on the door, but Pandora was nowhere to be seen that night, a fact which greatly disturbed the chanter. In spite of this, however, he raised his voice as loud as he could so that it echoed far out into the street. Pandora lived a short distance away; she would certainly learn, if she did not already know, that the chanter was spending a sleepless night for her sake. She would throw her shawl over her lovely shoulders and come over. But the hours advanced, advanced.

At midnight, they all stopped chanting. The chanter went out-side to walk around, all the while keeping his eyes on Pandora's house. He saw nothing there. The night was very dark and starless, moonless, with a heavy cloud covering the entire city. The chanter smoked two or three cigarettes, one after another; then he coughed, cleared his throat, and returned to his place inside the house. At half-past twelve, he took out his watch to look at the time. He looked at it again at a quarter to one. And again at five to one. A bleariness rose from his heart to his eyes. He stopped the hymn in the middle and saw that most of those gathered there were asleep. He yawned then and told Kyra-Paraskevi that he felt ill and should be in bed asleep. Before the woman could make any kind of reply, he grabbed his hat and left the house. What should she do now? Kyra-Paraskevi took the book in hand—she did not know how to read—and continued chanting until daybreak. Of course, she could never confess these events to Christos. But he learned about them nonetheless, and his heart was gratified at the affectations of these anti-Christs who defiled the Houses of God.

The following day Pandora's husband sat at the coffee shop and bragged about all he had seen and not seen in Tunis. He had landed the evening before and had climbed at once, as the saying goes, to his house with bated breath. He brought two large, canary-yellow sponges and placed them on the console, and some flower-like sea-urchins, as well, and a honeycomb shaped like a horn, all twisted, and a piece of cherry-red silk and a shawl and a great many other things—all for his wife. He was a courser, tall, stout and heavy, with tanned skin, with thick, hairy chest and thorny eyebrows, and he had a thick, drawling voice. For a long time, he sat looking at the child, which was crying loudly in his muscular arms. Then he carried it before the mirror and thoughtfully cast a glance at his own reflection, then at the child's. Finally, he appeared convinced and his forehead cleared; he embraced his wife and kissed her. He had also brought some foodstuffs and a cluster of yellow bananas, which Pandora was seeing for the first time in her life. He opened a bottle of dark wine, and together, they sat and ate and drank heartily.

Toward morning the baby cried, but Pandora was in a state of lethargy. So much had the sea rover, with his insatiable desire, made love to her that night. And again at noontime. Finally, he decided it was time to go down to the coffee shop to find his old friends and smoke his narghile with the tobacco he had brought from Tunis. He also had his own draw pipe, all knots and mysterious gadgets. As he held it between his fingers, he brought it to his dark lips proudly. Such was the husband of Pandora. This was the reason, also, that the right chanter, during those days, forgot all about his mandolin; nor did he go down to the coffee shop. Well, one never knew!

We children gazed on the sea rover with such pride. Especially my brother, who stood listening nearby as he looked at him with dazzled eyes. The words of the courser fell from his lips as though they were pieces of meat being torn at that moment, labored and with great effort. He had an amusing manner of relating the achievements of the Arabs down there—something like disdain— and we enjoyed this immensely, because it showed us that, no matter where a Greek man finds himself, he always succeeds in climbing to the top. So cunning is he. How could those Frenchmen get ahead with their soft effeminacy. They never knew what to do, just like women, at the first sign of danger. That is how Pandora's husband described them to us. We were astonished and had nothing to say to all this.

In the meantime, Pantelis was making progress at the mill. He was two years older than I, and his father found it was time he went to work for himself.

"That child is always running around," his father said. "At the mill, he might find a bit of encouragement. Maybe he'll even get well. That's what an old woman was telling my wife the other day. And she has seen many such things in her lifetime."

He would go, every so often, to beg Kyr-Agisilaos, the foreman, to break in the boy gently so he would not become frightened

right at the beginning and refuse to do anything after that. Then
came the night when Kyr-Agisilaos notified the sacristan that he
would hire the boy—He had begged the owners because, thin as
Pantelis was and with his scrofula, he would have been more
trouble at the factory than he was worth. Sixty cents was all he was
paid for his daily wage. But as he grew up, and if he turned out
satisfactorily, he could possibly receive more, even two and a half
drachmas, or even three. How many people had started on nothing
and had ended up to be great men. Of course, Kyr-Agisilaos was
not earning a wage; he was on *salary* of two hundred drachmas a
month. He had a diploma from the "small Polytechnic," from the
Polytechnic, he always said, omitting the "small." He was some-
body. There it was now. Pantelis could leave off playing. He might
even buy a blue suit in time and acquire honor and respect.

Pantelis came joyfully to relate everything in detail. He said
that he would take the handkerchief off his neck; only two or three
scars still remained. Better that way, rather than to appear with the
handkerchief and frighten everyone. We were walking around the
pepper trees and listening to him, each of us thinking of the direction Pantelis was taking. Our teacher passed by, holding his switch
in hand. As soon as we saw him approaching, we hid behind the
trees and stood breathless. But it was dark now; a transparent darkness of starlight had poured over the church. The teacher advanced, murmuring, "Hm!— Hm!—" to himself and spitting loudly
on the ground. He also walked heavily, which gave the impression
that a cow was passing by. How good Pantelis was that evening!
Better than at any other time. No, he had no intention of remaining
at the mill forever. Just long enough to earn some money so he
could open a small shop down by the harbor where he could sell
tarred rope and tools. That was his dream. Let others talk as they
pleased! He remembered whenever he passed the harbor, how
much he liked the smell of tarred rope, that smell which brought
balsam to his heart, as though it had been sent in by the winds of
the sea. He would sit on his doorstep and look at the smokestacks
on the ships while stevedores loaded all kinds of things on those
ships. He would be his own master, behind the round window,
taking in the money with a scoop. There! This was what Pantelis
meant to become! And if he was successful within a short period
of time, no one would ever attempt to remember that he was the
son of the sacristan. He would even be able to approach the priest
with a clear brow and say to him: "Blessed Father, I used to be a

poor boy, a semblance of a man. But I have worked honorably, spent sleepless nights, suffered, and finally earned a bit of money. Now I am a worthy man. So, put aside your hymn books and come, give me your Pinio, whom I have loved for so many years!" And what could the blessed Father reply to this? What else could he do? He would have to give his daughter to Pantelis.

Total darkness overtook us. The wind shook the pepper trees, plucking their leaves, and Pantelis had no intention of stopping. So happy was he, that boy, to be going to work at the mill.

It was almost summer now. My brother was becoming increasingly restless. He formed a friendship with the son of the owner of the coffee house and spent his afternoons in that shop, utterly delighted to be listening to the conversations going on among the sailors, and, most of all, listening to Pandora's courser, whose eyes had seen so much and who was forever contemplating another voyage. He said this somewhat as a threat, but he continued to stay on. A thing of insignificance was my brother, a semblance of a man; yet he succeeded in drawing near the courser, and in going to his house to do odd chores for Pandora. It was pointless for Father to go in search of him; pointless for Mother to go in search of him. He was always to be found in the small house in back of the church, examining the large sponges and shells, breathing the fragrance of the sea, because everything in that house was reminiscent of the sea. One day, however, we were unable to locate him anywhere. Terror and lamentation extended throughout our house. Some children from a distant neighborhood told us they had met him down by the harbor. But it was nightfall now, and my brother had not returned. We sat waiting for him; and, in our imagination, we could hear a knock on the door or we could hear the door opening. Tears fell from our eyes. Mercedes was with us, and she wept for my brother and for her mother, who was not long for this world. Father was out, hurrying from house to house, inquiring after him. Twice, Father went down to the harbor; he searched everywhere. But to no avail.

At daybreak, we were still gathered around the table. Mercedes had not gone to bed that night; she had slept a little sitting there in the chair; cat-napped, that is—and, poor girl, she was so fatigued. Noontime came. At last, Father decided that it was time to go to the police. Perhaps they had located a dead boy somewhere, killed by a bale of cotton as it was being unloaded, or even criminally assaulted by hoodlums—starry-eyed as my brother was. Suddenly, he came in very quietly, as though he had done nothing wrong. He found Mother pulling her hair and Father shouting frantically. There can be no doubt; he was whipped soundly before he could utter a sound. And had Kyra-Katerina not come in to inquire about him; had she not happened to be there, without doubt, he would not have survived the beating—That is how much bitterness this boy had caused us! Later, we learned the details. That abominable servant of the owner of the coffee shop had been to blame; lazy clout that he was with large ears and nose, a veritable scarecrow, who had turned the boy's head and plotted with an old sailor. They even lied to my brother, telling him that we had been informed at home. The old sailor took the boy and set sail on a wretched little steamer, which left at noontime for Aigina to return the following morning. My brother thoroughly enjoyed his life on a steamer—the night at sea and the companionship of the crew. He also saw Aigina for the first time, and he thought it was the island of the fairy tale, distant and magical; a strange world beyond the boundaries of this earth.

From then on, we became quite resigned to the fact that this would be the manner in which we would ultimately lose my brother, so enamored was he by the sea. Father felt obliged to promise that he could go to a naval school to study, but my brother would listen to nothing, more so because he cared little for an education. He had only a single desire: to leave land as soon as possible; to leave those dirty factories behind, those dirty streets, and the heat of summer, which was now spread over us like a sheet of flaming mud.

So it was that my brother once more began to spend his nights, sometimes until early dawn, at the coffee house and at Pandora's house, where Pandora treated him as her adopted child and sent him on errands while she refreshed him with all kinds of goodies. He was a very young boy, totally inexperienced, and Pandora, without embarrassment or shame, undressed before him as she admired herself. We learned about this from the innocent words my brother spoke, at which, with extreme cleverness and cunning, we boys induced him to tell us more.

The chanter surveyed the situation from a distance. He was certainly emboldened after a while, and he, as well, began to spend time at the coffee house. In fact, he was greatly amused by the courser. Nonetheless, he discountinued playing his mandolin. Nor did he ever again attend Kyra-Paraskevi's vigils. Nor did he ever again pass by Pandora's house. He suffered, poor man, and he had no one to whom he could talk about his troubles. He also saw how pleasant Pandora's husband was, and how generous and fun-loving, which made him take paper in hand to send Pandora a letter. For days, he fluttered around my brother, smiling at him with all sweetness. He even bought the boy a Turkish delight at the coffee house; just like that, without any apparent reason; just for fun, let us say—As though a Turkish delight cost nothing. And one evening, as my brother was returning from an errand on which he had gone for Pandora, and as the courser was smoking his narghile peacefully, Pandora received the letter. Right there before the light of the lamp, she deciphered it, syllable by syllable, aided by my brother, who could read even less than she. Great confusion seized Pandora, and her olive cheeks became overspread with roses; her breasts rose and fell quickly, and her feet tingled from top to bottom. Silently, she gazed at herself in the mirror. She remained thus speechless for a long time. Then she took my brother by the hand and led him to the door where she spoke without hesitation.

"Give this back to the one who gave it to you and tell him that Pandora refuses to bring dishonor to her wedding wreath, and that he should leave her alone. That's what you tell him. Pandora refuses to bring dishonor to her wedding wreath!"

Then, as though another thought occurred to her, she stopped my brother and fell into deep silence.

"No, no, better that you tell him he should have considered my husband; *considered* him; that's what you tell him."

She pushed my brother toward the door, but drew him back again.

"Listen, Vaso, the best thing we can do is to refrain from answering. Virtuous women never even take notice of such non-sense."

She gave Vaso some bread and cheese to eat while she took the letter and wedged it behind the mirror over her console, gazing at herself in the mirror as she did so. Her hair was like a dark summer cloud around her flushed face.

The chanter was not at all disheartened. In fact, he became somewhat calmer, and he even bought my brother another Turkish delight. My brother sat and confessed to him, in detail, all that Pandora had told him and the way she had acted. The chanter also happened to see her in church on the following Sunday, all decked out in her finery, standing opposite his music stand, so that he began to sing the cherubic hymn on so high a note he came near to choking, so much did the veins in his neck swell before he was able to complete the hymn. When service was over, he discerned Pandora among the group of women, walking like a dove, her flowered dress shimmering as though it was also charmed by the fragrance of her body. As Pandora reached the narthex, she stopped shortly and cast a glance around the church as though looking for something. Her face was so radiant that, immediately, the chanter felt a desire to begin the doxology all over again, there within the golden light filled with dark-complexioned angels. At that moment, the archmandrite emerged from the left door of the Sanctuary, and he saw the chanter; then he saw Pandora at the door of the narthex. He went "Hm!—hum!—" as he moved on. Well, he was free to think whatever he pleased!

From that day, the chanter picked up his mandolin again. And his tiny house echoed with suffering and love—So much that his neighbor across the street, Garoufalia, the cross-eyed lace-maker, began to bathe more often, and, wearing her new blouse, she would go to the window without any reason. The neighborhood was quiet around there; not a single store in sight, not anything. The passersby slackened their gait; then, taking the song with them, they walked on.

Finally, the moment came when the sea rover said "Farewell!" He signed up to sail on a freighter bound for Gibraltar. The line worked the route from Piraeus, Marseilles, Gibraltar, Casablanca, and even further around to Cape Town, and only God knew where else! He planned to disembark at Gibraltar to await the "Arandora," which was coming from Bengazi to head for the North. Pandora's husband had a friend on the "Arandora," a Spaniard, who was the second engineer and who had promised to take him on as helper for a large salary; thus he could, at last, leave those coal transports to live like a human being. Pandora was very tearful when she saw him off. She cried so much his heart ached; he came near not sailing on that long voyage.

The coffee house became peaceful again; only the flies, which had grown abundant now that the heat had become unbearable, carried on their meetings in that coffee house without consideration for anyone. The cook dozed with the coffee pot in hand, and the perspiration flowed like a river from his portly flesh. The waiter also dozed, standing on his feet, his finger in his nose. That waiter always picked at something, even when he was asleep; that was a habit he had never outgrown. Even the lithographs on the walls were asleep, the "Innocent Genovefa," the "Beauty of Caucasus," and "Othello Strangling Desdemona." Even the newspapers on their wooden racks, Simon's *Fatherland,* Kalapothakis' *Forward,* and Chairopoulos' *Time,* as well as the *Skrip;* all had gone to sleep. Only as evening fell did the waiter emerge from the coffee house, sprinkler in hand, to wet down the earth around the store and to straighten out the iron tables. He also placed two large pots of basil on the window ledges and waited for the factory workers to end their shifts so the usual customers could drop by for a cup of coffee. The archmandrite also came by at that hour because he was attempting to become acquainted with the neighborhood. He sat at a table near the outskirts so the old women and the young girls could stop to kiss his hand. He sat there, but his eyes were focused on the church, on the door of the narthex. And if he happened to see the men taking the baptismal font from the church, or the sacristan leaving with the holy relics and the priest's books tied in a blue handkerchief under his arm, the archmandrite's face clouded with inexpressible suffering. He would leave the coffee house then to pass by Anifantis' grocery store and buy his famous goat cheese wrapped in grape leaves—at forty cents an oka. He also bought a cantaloupe, or a watermelon, from the stack Anifantis set out daily on a bench beside the sidewalk; then the archmandrite would take his way home, walking thoughtfully.

The sea rover embarked, and the chanter again took his mandolin in hand. He sat in back of the Sanctuary and sang as he had never sung before—so much so that all the neighbors noticed him and the archmandrite threatened to send a letter of complaint to the metropolitan—The scandal was enlarged all out of proportion now. But, as before, the chanter paid no attention to all this; so great was his infatuation. And Pandora appeared not to be on the point of submitting. In fact, Pandora locked herself in the house and cried bitterly because that dog of a sailor had enchained her with a wedding wreath and a child before this lovable, this handsome youth, had come out of the fields. In the end, she became fatigued by the singing, fatigued by all the disturbance. Suddenly, the singing ceased and the mandolin with the red hook took its place on a rustry nail in the chanter's house. The ears of the neighborhood suffered no longer. It was now time for their eyes to suffer— That was all!

7

"Whether she had anything to offer or not, she certainly managed to entice that rascal," Kyra-Katerina was observing.

It was afternoon and the late sun was falling on the red geraniums and the bushy barbarosa.

"She's a young woman, in the prime of life. Her husband abandons her for months on end while he goes off," the landlord was responding.

Mercedes was at the hospital. As the landlord waited for her return, he chatted quietly, as though, in fact, he paid little attention to what was being said. He was wearing his new vest, a white one with purple and yellow designs; a regular beauty! Savvoula also came over to ask Mother if she could borrow the iron because hers was broken. Her hair was disheveled, her slippers crushed at the heels, and her dress dragged behind like a broom.

"Oh, whatever has happened to people!" Kyra-Katerina said again. "God will scorch us to death!"

"God has other work to do," the landlord remarked philosophically. "Or do you imagine that He sits guard at the doors of Pandora and Savvoula?"

Kyra-Katerina gazed around her in alarm, but Savvoula had already departed.

"Yes, and look at her, too!" Kyra-Katerina resumed somewhat calmer. "The devil has carried her away. She has exhausted herself with all that walking she does, attempting to cast ashes into our eyes. But such things never remain silent, Kyr-Aristomenis; everything becomes known in time. The other day, they saw her at the Hydraika; imagine that, at the Hydraika, being fondled by a sailor. Then she pretends to be such an excellent housekeeper. A dark, crippled serpent has consumed her!"

"And to say that she has something to offer!" the landlord mused philosophically again.

"As for that, don't you worry. To each his own. Only you haven't found your own, Kyr-Aristomenis. And so—with all good health to us—you will die and still continue to search for that right one."

"Shift from your place!" Mother cried. "Kyr-Aristomenis is still a young man."

"A young man; that's what you think!" Kyra-Katerina remarked, "Can't you see that he hasn't a single solid tooth left?"

"Too much sugar is to blame for that," dogmatized the landlord. "Even young people often lose their teeth. That's what the doctor told me one day when I asked him."

"The doctor doesn't know what he's doing. He's always alert for a two-franc piece. Do you know what the archmandrite said? That the doctor writes out more death certificates than he does prescriptions. There, that's what he said. That man, my dear, carries death in his pocket."

The three became silent as they watched the sunset covering the yard. Saturday evening. The landlord kept shifting his position as though he was sitting on a broken chair so his eyes would be on the door.

"That door will cause you to waste away!" Kyra-Katerina whistled poisonously. "I have seen many things in my lifetime, but such persistence, my boy, I have never seen before."

"Wicked-tongued one! Poison-nosed one!" murmured the landlord.

"Well, aren't you going to marry Evanthia? The girl is weary of waiting for you. The other day she confessed to me, 'I like serious men, like Kyr-Aristomenis, for example.' Once you've lost her from your fingers, you'll come crying. But you have come hunting after young partridge. What's to be done? Someday you'll wish that afterknowledge had been foreknowledge."

Savvoula returned the iron. Her lips were now a bright red; dark circles lined her eyes. She had powdered her cheeks, on which she had painted a red spot in the center.

"Say flour!" murmured Kyra-Katerina. "Waiting is the sail-our!"

The landlord breathed in short gasps; he blinked his eyes as though a piece of straw had become lodged there.

"Are you getting ready to go out?" Kyra-Katerina asked Savvoula.

"Oh, I am so exhausted! Troubles, troubles! See now, night-time and I must go to the Kritika to take care of my sick aunt—"

"To the Hydraika you mean, Savvoula. Unless, of course, your aunt has moved for a change of climate."

"You're in the mood for joking, Kyra-Katerina. Well, what's to be done. If I owned your well, you would see."

"As for that—"

Savvoula became provoked. She tossed us a confused "good-night" as she left, slamming the door behind her.

"You talk too much," the landlord stated categorically. "You talk too much—One of these days someone will smash you and make eight hundred okas of pulp out of you."

"Just let anyone try to touch me."

Mercedes returned at that moment. She was dead from fatigue. Mother rose from her chair to prepare some coffee.

"And how are we getting along?" Kyra-Katerina asked.

"How should we be getting along? From bad to worse. She has dropsy now. Her whole body is being converted into water. They extract gallons each time."

"Come, Christ and Holy Mary! Well, if such is the case, then better that God should relieve her of such misery. That is what you should pray for, Mercedes."

The girl spread out her handkerchief and filled it with tears. The landlord was greatly agitated by all this; he also pulled out his handkerchief. Since he had no tears to wipe away, he carried the handkerchief to his nose and blew on it like a dogfish.

"Patience," Kyra-Katerina said. "Patience. What does God give that man, poor soul, does not endure. One must have a large stomach to take in all this poison."

Mother brought the coffee; she also brought a piece of bread. The evening was warm. Kyra-Katerina remembered her water-well. She had, of course, left her adopted son to attend it, but he was so shiftless and lazy—worse luck on him!—that she finally decided to go down there herself to collect the money. Kyr-Aristomenis experienced relief.

"She's a sore wound, that woman is. I'll make pulp out of that body of hers. Even patience has its limits."

"Don't pay any attention to her, Kyr-Aristomenis," Mother said. "A widowed woman she is—not quite right in her head."

"Better she should blind herself then, rather than running from door to door as she does, passing along all that rubbish about everyone. Look now. She's gossiping about Pandora, about Savvoula, about everyone. They're justified, those girls. Why does Pandora's husband have to leave so young a woman all alone while he goes roaming here and there. Gibraltar, he says, and green horses! There isn't a carcass those louts leave unstripped; then they return and preach respect and honor. And Savvoula—Well, what is the girl to do? She's becoming a consumptive in that match factory;

her lungs are filling with sulphur—Now, look at this stubborn one here, this Mercedes. You'll see what kind of life she'll lead someday, and you'll feel sorry for her. Mark my words."

"God forbid! What kind of words are those you utter, Kyr-Aristomenis!"

"The truth is the truth. Not that she'll deliberately do something wrong. Some penniless man will take her in; then the devil and the spotted goat will mock her. That's what I say. Here now, serious family men worry about making ends meet, but not those idlers and louts—"

He was playing with the chain on the watch he held in his hands. A tiny red pig hung from that chain. He played this, as well, fondling it as though it was a living being. Mercedes uttered not a sound.

"So, one and one make two," continued the landlord. "Your mother is dying; there is no doubt of that. That is bad, very bad. But you are not going to die. You will be left all alone. You will work like a dog and find no peace. Who is to care for you? Those who have no money? And what if you should become ill? We are only human. We have no contract with death."

Mercedes continued to remain silent. She had lowered her gaze while tears dampened her pale cheeks.

"Leave her alone, Kyr-Aristomenis," Mother said. "Leave her alone. She has a sick mother. It isn't right."

"I've had my say," added the landlord. "I have no sins. Whoever has ears, let him hear. I am begging her. Let her sit down and figure this out well."

He put on his black hat and said goodnight somewhat stubbornly.

"My, but he's most determined!" Mother said.

Again Mercedes failed to reply.

8

The summer evenings were so lovely. A golden moon came out to travel over the church, to travel over the pepper trees, while we collected around the marble steps of the church and rolled our marbles for hours. The fact is, we rolled marbles for such a long time that our brains rattled, and we fell over one another utterly exhausted. The laughter and noise we made were like the undulations of the sea, more so when the girls happened to come over to join us; Anifantis' daughter, Smaragdo, the priest's daughter, Pinio, and Kroustallenia, the daughter of the foreman, Kyr-Agisilaos. These three were inseparable. They had on blue dresses with white collars and red bows in their hair—a true aristocracy in the midst of our disorderly crowd. Pantelis completed his shift at the factory at six, after which he ran home to wash carefully, eat his supper, then come gaily to join us.

We were fond of teasing Pantelis. "Be careful when you come home all covered with flour. Your mother might make a mistake and fry you." That joke had every appearance of being successful because even the girls, the wife of the sacristan, and the archmandrite—all laughed when they heard it. That's how great a success that joke appeared to be.

What magical nights those were! Though the hours advanced far into the night, we had no desire to move from that place. The blame, without question, lay more on our game of marbles than on the girls, who returned to their homes early. Or, it could have been the rows of trees around the church which enchanted us as they collected people beneath their branches, factory workers and sailors, mostly youths, who came out for a breath of fresh air with the girls they loved. Sometimes, we happened to run into a boy and a girl embracing and kissing under a dark pepper tree or around a corner of the church. Then, Pantelis would murmur excitedly: "Those two are sweethearts. That's what they are called. Sweethearts!" He repeated the word over and over again, as though performing some sinful act, a repetition which caused our spines to shiver from top to bottom, and we never knew the reason for this.

The chanter waited until dark. Then, following closely along the wall, he went to the church to stand outside the Sanctuary and wait for the crowd of people to thin before he sneaked into Pandora's house. As he waited, we—just for fun—passed in front of him, shouting "good evening" at the top of our voices. What else could he do but acknowledge our greeting. Pandora, on the other hand, was nowhere to be seen now; neither in church, nor anywhere else in the neighborhood. She confined herself to her house and took pleasure in her love. Father scolded my brother and prohibited him from running errands for her. Because my brother enjoyed examining the sponges and shells, he cried when he was forbidden to go over to her house. He also cried because Pandora had promised to reward him with a large, canary-yellow sponge with tiny holes in it when her husband returned. Later, Pandora's mother came to live with her. All this time she had been living at Saint Lefteri, in the Kaminia district, with her other daughter who was married to a worker at the tile factory, a man who spent his days and nights at the *taverna*. He barely earned four days' wages a week. Our neighborhood gossiped quite freely about Pandora's mother coming to live with her.

"Do you call this slut a mother!" some of the neighbors remarked.

For Pandora, however, the situation was perfect. She had someone to care for her child and someone to run errands for her. Pandora was in the process of acquiring some respect now, because, regardless of how one looked on the situation, the woman *was* her mother. Now, the chanter became more venturesome and entered the house as though he was a friend come on a visit. Even so, Kyra-Paraskevi went to see the archmandrite again and told him a great many things. Yes, that is how matters stood. The archmandrite ought to read a penance in church for Pandora, just so those other deluded ones, who lately had taken enough rope with which to hang themselves, might profit from her example. The archmandrite gave Kyra-Paraskevi no positive reply, except to say that God had said we should forgive "seventy times seven, and await the sinner until the twelfth hour." And he began to chant, "The harlot tearfully cried, 'Be merciful.'" Kyra-Paraskevi understood nothing of all this; she only crossed herself repeatedly as she spat into her bosom, saying, "Get thee behind me, Satan!"

Although this was the only reply the archmandrite made, he did not end the matter there. Darkness was falling as we were again gathered before the church, rolling our marbles, when, the teacher, whip in hand, stood before us. Unquestionably, it was God who prevented us from falling dead on the spot.

"Is this how you study, you rascals!" the teacher boomed angrily. "Didn't I tell you to spend the summer reviewing your lessons?"

One of the boys attempted to reply, but he came up with an alien voice as he said: "We are—We are—"

"I'll show you, you are—you are—"

He raised his whip, and right there on the spot, he lashed us so hard that the narthex, the church, and everything around the neighborhood resounded with our wailings and confusion. Pantelis was walking toward us at that moment. He stopped a short distance away to laugh at our plight. Pantelis was through with school now;

he was even working at the flour mill. What did he care about the teacher! But the poor boy was unable to withstand such treatment, and he joined us, crying at the top of his voice, as though he was being operated on for his scrofula. The teacher saw him and called out: "Come here, you! Come here so you can cry better!"

He then walked into the church. He was a member of the Council, as we learned later. All those who had been whipped at some time, to a man, voted for him during the elections which had taken place a few days earlier. There went the marble games and the summer days and the golden moonlights and the church and the consecrated bread. There went everything! A lump, lodged in our throats, refused to budge.

As the teacher entered the church, he ordered the sacristan to arrange several chairs around the counter, and a table between them, and the pen with several sheets of paper. Later, the archmandrite and the owner of the cotton factory and two other men and the priest came in. They sat quietly in their chairs, talking. Only the teacher had raised his voice; the church filled with his voice. He even frightened the pigeons passing by the high round windows, and he shook his stick as though an archangel had become dislodged from the door of the Sanctuary and had taken off the teacher's face to threaten the world with it.

"We must compose the report and brand him, evil man! We must chase the leper from our midst!"

But the others, even the archmandrite, failed to agree. No, better that they took him aside and pointed out that their patience had become exhausted. And they decided to take him aside. On the following day, the chanter was nowhere to be found. Nor on the day after. On the third day, it became known that he was auditioning at another church. There, he chanted and chanted until the walls vibrated from their very foundations; the marble columns as well. Even the saints trembled within their shrines. So excellent a voice had he. Thus it came about that, on the following Sunday, the right chanter was missing. His place was temporarily filled by Vitivilias, while a pock-marked novice, one of those who sometimes recite the Credo and the Lord's Prayer, became the left chanter. The entire neighborhood was thrown into an uproar over this calamity; into such an uproar that Kyra-Paraskevi had cause to regret her actions. Once more she set out for the archmandrite's to let him know that the chanter had not done anything so terribly wrong. After all, he *was* a bachelor. The blame should be directed at Pandora. Some of the chanter's "fans" started out early on Sunday to go to the distant neighborhood just to hear him chant the cherubic hymn—then they could die happily! Everyone said that the devil had wedged his tail into this situation, that thrice-accursed devil who is the cause of all dissipation in men, a dissipation which causes them to lose their minds. Pandora was a beautiful woman, of course; but not so beautiful that the right chanter had to be sacrificed. Why had he not looked elsewhere? So many girls desired him. He could have had a dowry, as well as a trousseau, and some furniture with which to set up housekeeping, instead of losing himself from the upper world for the sake of an utterly worthless woman!

9

The landlord lost his mind completely. In sleep, in wakefulness, he thought of nothing other than that accursed Mercedes. "I will marry her, let come what may!" That was love, all right, and no laughing matter it was. Early in the morning, he pretended to go out shopping so he could stand waiting at the corner until time for Mercedes to pass by on her way to the factory. From a distance, he sent her a heart-rending "Good morning." Then, as evening fell, he sat at the coffee house, talking with the saintly archmandrite, with whom he had become friends. Coincidentally, Mercedes always passed by at that particular hour, her eyes lowered. She never cast a glance in the direction of the landlord. But he was there with his "Good evening," all sweetness and mystery. Of course, he never ceased going to the house on Saturday evening. He had decided now to conduct himself quite properly, like a gentleman who knew the world; only in thought and glance did he express his suffering. Mercedes was also human; she had a heart. Perhaps someday she would give him and his possessions some consideration.

And it so happened at this time that Chrysoula was married. Ah, the years have passed. Try as I might, I cannot remember, I cannot recall her face. Only her name has remained, and something black and blue-green, like a phosphorescent light in the dark. What has also remained is a body, tender and frolicsome, one of those which awaken a slumbering sensation and cause it, momentarily, to rave and to believe that a treasure, a paradise, is being lost, should one fail to touch that body. Chrysoula also worked at

the same factory with Mercedes. They had lived an entire lifetime
together there before one of those iron spools, breathing the same
air within that unassembled web, within that cloud which covered
their eyes completely, which constricted their throats. But, for
Chrysoula, Fate was now carrying another path. A bookkeeper, a
young man of excellent qualities and soft-spoken voice, came near
to perishing for longing of her. All day long, bent over a ledger, he
worked in the office of the company. He found, however, all kinds
of excuses to walk among the women workers, yellow pencil behind
his ear, in order to cast a single glance at Chrysoula; a timid,
frightened glance, because he was not one of those young men who
liked the rude teasings, the indecent words, which were nauseous.
Later, he waited for several days in a row at the curbstone, only
that he might admire her as she passed by, swaying her hips lightly
in a manner that she alone possessed—as though she performed this
swaying unconsciously. Chrysoula immediately became aware that
the bookkeeper had been caught in the pincers of love, and she
lowered her eyes even more. She always kept her gaze low, tormenting him thus without compassion, until, finally, the young
man, beside himself, sent his mother to ask for Chrysoula's hand
in marriage, because "if he failed to make her his own, he would
tie a knot around his throat, and the black earth would feed on his
youth." The girl, certainly, was not of his station in life; however,
as these accursed matters stood, no one could change a thing. The
wedding was therefore decided upon without delay. The bookkeeper was in such a hurry to entwine his arms around Chrysoula's
waist; around those swaying hips, which made all the men sick
and caused them to bleat inwardly like frenzied rams.

Chrysoula came to invite Mercedes to the wedding. It was to
take place on Saturday night, two days away, at the home of the
bridegroom. The guests were all important people. Invited also
were Kyr-Agisilaos, the forman, and Kyr-Aristomenis, the landlord.
But Mercedes would not decide to attend. "Good fortune attend
you, Chrysoula dear, and may you find all you desire. But I have
a sick mother. I've become lost from this world." She had little
desire to attend the wedding; furthermore, she had no dress to get
ready for the occasion. Chrysoula coaxed and begged her. With
such insistence, she was finally able to persuade Mercedes to attend
the wedding, "unless something unexpected occurred, Heaven forbid," for the sake of the tormented Mercedes.

Kyra-Katerina now talked about no one but Chrysoula.

"Listen to that, the little snot (they were all snotty girls to her), the bandy-legged! What miracles she performed. Ah, I know all those prickly-virgins! Who knows what potions were given to the young man to drink by that mother of hers, that fat potato, that worthless creature who is so filthy from head to toe!"

Kyra-Katerina was stung at heart by this marriage, and she talked about it for hours on end with the landlord. And he, in turn, said that girls who knew what was most advantageous to them did their utmost to rise above their stations, to become related to those who were their superiors, and thus find peace and rest.

"What has Chrysoula to worry about now," cried the landlord loudly so that Mercedes, who was in her room, could overhear. "Where good Fortune smiles, one should follow after. Chrysoula will enter that strange house now and make it her own, like a mistress, not a servant. Her husband will keep her on a pedestal, because he knows the world; he has seen something of the world. He always negotiates business with important people there in his office. His mind is not a dark blank."

"Only hope that he turns out to be a good man," Mother said. "No one should envy wealth."

But Kyr-Aristomenis had a contrary viewpoint.

"We're all human; we do become ill," he said. "But look at the manner in which a poor man becomes ill and the manner a wealthy one does. Is it the same to be the owner of your own home, where you have no need to worry about the rent from month to month? And besides, you can always pick up a little extra money from your renters to cover daily expenses, as the saying goes. Is all this the same as struggling to amass, not dimes, but drachmas, so you won't find yourself out in the streets someday?"

Inside the house, Mercedes listened to all this, but she made no sound. She thought only of that day when she had caught Kyr-Aristomenis pulling up his stockings—his garters had come undone. As her eyes glimpsed his thin, yellowed legs, full of blue-black swollen veins, she felt chilled. The devil take him! Let him hang himself, the old goat! Better that she should die in poverty; better that they should pick her up off the streets like a sick dog, rather than that she should sleep with that ghost, all mustache and conceit. Other people had very large houses down by the harbor, and factories, and boats of their own, and railroads, and a fleet of automobiles, but they made no exhibition of all their wealth. And here was this man, who was almost insane over his two small houses and his three rooms, in all, which he rented out; who made a pretense at being a landlord; who always bragged about his possessions, a moth-eaten console and those flowered pillows on his sofa. Yes, indeed, she would live behind God's back, like Savvoula and so many others. Sometimes, they were more successful; one saw these girls pass by like great ladies, sitting in their carriages as they paraded through the streets. Let everything go to the devil! If she had to be bought with Kyr-Aristomenis' money and his three tiny rooms, well then, she might as well sell her body to a higher bidder. For the first time in her life, Mercedes found herself very angry, so angry that she pricked her finger with the needle she was using to patch her best dress. Right there, on that piece of cloth, the blood blossomed like a poppy in the field. She sensed such great pain that she felt like screaming and cursing him, that unbearable man! Always the same story over and over again. She was so tired of it all! In a little while, she expected him to come there beside her window to start singing like a young boy. To such a miserable plight had that old man descended, with all his stripes— the man who had once been greeted by the King, as he always said. Believe it or not!

Saturday night came, the night of Chrysoula's wedding. Mercedes was missing all day long from the factory. After straightening up her house, she went early to the hospital. Finding her mother considerably improved, she sat and they talked together quietly, as they had often done in the past. Later, at home, she pressed her best dress and her shawl; she borrowed some shoe polish from us to shine her shoes with the laces knotted all the way up to the top. Those shoes were as wrinkled as a hundred-year-old woman's face. What did that matter anyway? She combed her hair, making two plaits of it, which she wreathed around her head. She took her purse in hand; and, as she went down the street to the house of the bridegroom, down a narrow lane near Lefka, her face began to glow.

The boys and girls of the neighborhood were already gathered there before the door and beside the open windows, which were draped to the floor with lace curtains, little figures running through them, some open-mouthed lions and princesses so lovely you could drink them from a glass. Well, what could be said? These people certainly did have the money. The narrow lane was cluttered with the barefoot crowd, screaming and yelling and fighting among themselves. Mercedes suddenly found herself in the midst of much confusion, and she lost what little presence of mind she had. She knocked on the gate; it was still early and the gate was closed. At once, she fell into a crowd of girls, swarming like bees in the courtyard. She told them her name because she knew no one there except the bookkeeper, whom she saw running back and forth in the inner room where Chrysoula was, his yellow pencil still behind his ear. The earth was fragrant around her, as though the musk trees were all in blossom around there. Chrysoula was sitting on a chair before the large wardrobe mirror. A tall, thin girl, her face full of pimples, was curling Chrysoula's hair with a kind of heated iron, which Mercedes was seeing before her eyes for the first time. Other girls were preparing the favors. They cut small pieces of tulle, shaped them into bags and placed five or six candied almonds inside, simultaneously sneaking one or two into their mouths; then, they tied the favors with a narrow blue ribbon. The wedding dress waited, spread out on the table. It was made of white satin and carried a long train; it had a plunging neckline and a very tight bodice. The girls said that the dress had been cut on a bias so it would show off the lines of Chrysoula's body. There was also a hand-painted vase, shaped like a pitcher, filled with flowers. The mother-in-law sat to one side and her eyes shifted from one thing to another; sometimes she compressed her mouth tightly: oh, those shiftless ones were overdoing matters; there wouldn't be a single candied almond left! The mother-in-law was a true noblewoman. She was wearing her best dress, beaded all over, and an embroidered neckerchief, which came down to her waist. Her skin was so desirably fair, a dark mole dotted her right cheek, and a bit of hair covered her upper lip. The plumpness spilled over the low-cut pumps she was wearing; two new pumps with black silk bows. Yes, unquestionably, one could admire the mother-in-law and be embarrassed to say a word in front of her. Perhaps this was the reason that Chrysoula's mother, the fat potato, dared not venture from the kitchen where she was preparing all the hors d'oeuvres and the macaroni dinner. They had also procured a young veal which made you want to lick your fingers; a rosy, fat veal. The father-in-law was sitting in the other room with the men. The bridegroom was also in there, and they all teased him as they sniffed to see if the food was ready so they could drink a glass of *ouzo,* just for the sake of good luck. The bookkeeper was a very shy young man who appeared to be always in deep thought; his eyes were of a dreamy quality, so that you thought they were on the verge of tears, even though they smiled—The bookkeeper must have known something that made his eyes smile!

Even before the priest and the archmandrite arrived, the house was quite crowded with people. There wasn't a room, there wasn't a spot in the yard, where you could drop a needle, as the saying goes. The relatives of the bridegroom were quite numerous, as were his friends, and the countless factory girls who had come to admire Chrysoula, and all the neighbors, and a whole flock of other people, all pressed against one another so that they appeared to be one thick mass, inseparable and indistinguishable, breathing deeply and perspiring freely and smelling of cheap powder and cinnamon oil. Kyr-Aristomenis came, and everyone admired his strutting airs and his grandeur, because Kyr-Aristomenis had considered long on this matter and had decided at last to wear his army uniform with the three canary-yellow stripes. He had also twisted his mustache so that it appeared to be reaching for the sky. He seemed ten years younger, maybe more. Everyone paid great attention to him, perhaps because of his uniform. You heard nothing but "Captain" here and "Captain" there. He was also wearing his sword straps, and you felt that he carried great authority. If he raised a finger, surely he would destroy a man right on the spot.

Mercedes stood beside the bride, and, on the other side of the table stood the landlord. A young man who worked at the tile factory ("tiles of the Marseilles type"), and who kept his eyes on Mercedes, looking at her with great desire and passion, stood beside the landlord. Kyr-Aristomenis gave Mercedes such a knowing glance that the girl became confused. She lowered her gaze and kept looking at the tray with the candied almonds and the wedding wreaths. Everything was so warm in that room, so very festive, that one became faint. Outside, the children made so much noise— And they were not about to become quiet either. The factory girls and the bridegroom's relatives were murmuring and gossiping about one thing or another, which made the archmandrite raise his voice to bellow "Quiet! Quiet!" as he wiped the perspiration from his forehead with a yard-long handkerchief. Much laughter went on and many jokes were cracked as they all drank wine to the health of the bookkeeper and Chrysoula. The best man, a fat individual, a grocer on Theodorou Retsina Street, down by the bridge, also drank a glass of wine. Someone gave Mercedes a glass of wine to drink. The landlord, unable to contain himself any longer, cried out: "And to your wedding, Mercedes! To your wedding!" The young man at his side glanced at him and smiled as he thought, "What kind of man is this idiot!" They danced the dance of Isaiah, stepping all over one another until some of the girls protested. A stout woman had her dress ripped in back, from top to bottom. At this, some of the more impudent fellows burst out laughing, which caused the woman to cry in a very screeching voice, so high it made you think her body was an inflated balloon, narrow at the mouth, thus leaving room only for the slightest passage of air. Later, the newly married couple sat on the faded velvet sofa, and the archmandrite made them a brief, a very brief speech about the new life on which they were embarking and about the responsibilities they were incurring in this new life. The girls passed around the candied almond favors. Everyone drank a vanilla-flavored drink from tall-stemmed glasses and ate the sweets prepared by the mother-in-law. Then the father-in-law stood beside the window and threw out handful after handful of nickels and dimes. That good-for-nothing rowdy bunch trampled over the crowd of children to be the first to gather the money. The entire narrow lane near Lefka echoed with such curses and screams that made you think a murder was being committed. The landlord's great moment came precisely then. He went out into the courtyard, took from the back pocket of his trousers a small, hoarse pistol, and "Tsaf! tsaf!" he fired two or three times in the air, just for good luck. Everyone cried, "Bravo, Captain!" And he was so glorified in that hour, as his own heart told him, that no one else could compete for honors.

It was almost dark and the rooms of the house began to clear. The young man who worked at the tile factory walked over to Mercedes and asked: "Are you perhaps a cousin of Panayotis?"

"What cousin? Which Panayotis?" the girl replied as her cheeks flushed. She was already excited by the large crowd and by the heat generated by so many people packed so closely together.

"Oh, so you aren't. You certainly resemble him. Don't you work at the cotton factory? He has often spoken to me about his cousin."

The young man stood wide-eyed, as though he wanted to continue this conversation forever.

"I also work at the cotton factory," said Mercedes, "but I have no cousin Panayotis." She made a movement to leave, even though the young man was not at all repulsive; he appeared so full of kindness.

"We've met before somewhere. I know you from somewhere," the youth said again, and his eyes filled with reminiscence as he stared seductively toward the corner of the room.

Mercedes was beginning to find this conversation rather difficult. Just at that moment, Kyr-Aristomenis, still carrying his small pistol, entered the room. He fixed his eyes on the young man, then at Mercedes. A lump rose to his throat, and he coughed dryly. Several girls were extending the table, spreading a snowy-white cloth over it, and arranging the chairs. Only the immediate relatives remained. The landlord had also been invited to remain. No one would even consider allowing so gallant a captain to leave. Mercedes, as well, had been invited to remain.

"Go help the girls!" the landlord cried out to Mercedes in a commanding tone, as though he had a company of soldiers there before him, to say the least.

"Is the girl related to you?" the young man found courage to ask.

"Certainly she is related to me, if that is any of your business!"

Mercedes became confused. This was no time, nor place, to have a murder committed! The youth raised his shoulder as though to say, "What can I do here? I have respect for this strange house; otherwise, I would show you!" Then he left without saying a word.

"What did I tell you?" the landlord said to Mercedes. "You have only been to a single wedding, and already a swarm of these loafers have attacked you!"

The girl did not reply. After all, Kyr-Aristomenis was a property owner, and he had regained his youth that evening. How could she scold him? What could she say now that the month was almost at an end and she owed him four months rent, while he kept saying, "Don't worry!" and "Don't worry!"

They sat at the table and ate and drank—What a beautiful night this was! The girls giggled, and everyone teased Chrysoula; "Make it a son! Make it a son!" they said to her. Later, they sang, and Popi, a stout girl from the Maniatika, brought out her mandolin and broke two pens on the string; so great and uncontrollable was her joy. And always, they kept repeating to the older men, "To your wedding! To your wedding!" They also said, "To your wedding!" to the landlord. He was simply elated with this wish, but he looked at Mercedes grieved. "Better late than never!" a poisonous

cat threw out her words from the other end of the table. The
father-in-law quickly sought to cover the remark by saying, "What
are you talking about? The Captain is still a young man!" He
clinked glasses with the landlord. With one event and another, the
evening passed. Kyr-Aristomenis wanted to escort Mercedes home,
but Chrysoula whispered something to her father-in-law. Two other
girls lived in the same neighborhood with Mercedes; thus, they all
went off together, the landlord and the father-in-law. "Three girls
are too many for you, Captain," the bookkeeper called out to the
landlord. The bookkeeper could never hold his wine very well, and
now, at the height of the party, his voice was thick. What a beautiful night this was!

10

Mercedes opened the gate and entered into the courtyard of
our house. Only five or six stars had remained in the sky to gaze
down on her. It was almost daybreak. She felt chilled; her head
was heavy, her knees exhausted. As she was lighting the lamp,
Mother heard her from our side of the house, and she left her bed.
Although Mother had lain down, she was not asleep. Neither was
I asleep at that hour. Only Father and my brother were snoring in
the next room. Mother called Mercedes to come over, and Mercedes
opened the door quietly and stood still under the light of the first
signs of dawn. She was so beautiful; God, but she was beautiful
at that moment! I was thinking, "How is she going to tell her? How
is Mother going to tell her?" That was what I continued to think. I
was so engrossed in this thought that I was not aware when Mother
did tell Mercedes. I only saw Mercedes as though in a dream, as
though in the dim vision of a dream, fall to the floor and beat herself. Mother was beside her, also crying, so that I, as well, came in
tears down to the room. Father awakened and called out, "Did
Mercedes come in? Well, what's to be done? That's the way of the
world. Each of us in his own time. Better that she has found rest,
poor tormented soul." My brother awakened, and he also began to
cry. All together we mourned bitterly for the poor woman from
Galaxidi, the sainted woman.

Later, the crying became a soft sobbing. Mother was now able
to tell Mercedes that a messenger had come from the hospital, very
late that night, to inform them that the woman from Galaxidi had
departed from this world, and they should send someone at once

to take her from the hospital. There was no longer any reason for
the dead woman to occupy the hospital bed; so many other people
waited to take her place. She had also begun to smell foully, "on
account of her dropsy," said the man. What is to be done? Worries
and illnesses belong to this life! Mother also explained to Mercedes
that she had become quite confused by this message from the hospital. You see, the wedding was in progress, and it was considered
a bad omen to carry a message of death over there. All the guests
would have become offended; they might even have cursed the girl.
Mercedes was unable to contain herself on hearing these words.
She began to cry loudly and to beat herself. Savvoula across the way
heard her and, opening her window, stood there beside it. Her
chest was bare, and so were her hands and arms. She gazed out into
the street where the last silvery rays of the fading moon prom-
enaded; then she tossed a shawl over her shivering back and she,
as well, began to cry and beat herself, as though the woman from
Galaxidi had been a relative of hers, "Mother!" and "Mother! Did
I have need of a gay time and the wedding, I, wicked girl, while
you lay dying, sweet Mother!" All the neighbors ran over. We
dressed quickly and opened our house, but where could we ac-
comodate so many people? It was as though we were having a
party at our house!

Nothing ever occurred that the landlord failed to smell out.
He put on a most heart-rending mourning attitude and came beside
Mercedes, anxious to spend money, to run errands, to suffer with
her. At that moment, Mercedes held nothing against him; she considered him her savior. They hired a taxi and went to the hospital,
the landlord, Mother, Savvoula, and Kyra-Katerina. They forced
Mercedes to remain at home; this calamity was not for her eyes. So
it came about that, two hours before noon, the woman from Galaxidi
returned to her small room horizontally, lying on a board from a
door, which the landlord had borrowed from some friend of his;
she was covered from head to toe with a sheet. Later, they brought
the coffin; they put on her best skirt, the black one, and an old,
worn-out blouse. They arranged many flowers around her. Even so,
there was a faint, nauseating odor from that extended corpse. And
it was this faint stench, intermingled with the fragrance of the
flowers and the cologne that Savvoula, in all sympathy, had
brought over, something resembling to a cloud, which filled the
nostrils, the eyes, the lips, which penetrated the skin and brought
on a giddiness, a tendency toward heaving; something resembling

a slow, but certain death. Father was of the opinion that the woman from Galaxidi should be buried that same afternoon; her corpse would not hold up much longer than this. But Mercedes refused to have it so; she must have a wake for her mother. She would listen to no one; so determined was she on having that wake. Evening came and night fell, a chilly night, and the window remained open, the door, as well, and the stench from the woman from Galaxidi seeped out into the street. It was as though a sepulcher breathed. Mercedes sat there beside the head of the dead woman, her head covered with a black handkerchief, and she mourned uncontrollably. The neighbors sat in chairs around the room. The large candles dripped wax; Savvoula held the bottle of cologne in her hand, spraying Mercedes from it at times, and smelling from the bottle herself at other times.

The men remained in the yard. A few came into our small rooms to sit there talking, talking. Mother made coffee after coffee until she was utterly exhausted. Kyr-Aristomenis ran from place to place; he had no thought of resting. Sometimes, he was beside the dead woman; sometimes, he was over at our house; then again, he was out in the yard, so worried was the man. Father said it would be a good idea if everyone were to make a small contribution toward the funeral expenses. But the landlord would listen to no such thing.

"She has been living in my house for so many years now. I will pay the funeral expenses," he said.

He fondled the tiny, pudgy pig dangling from the chain of his watch, and his eyes took on a kind of sad pride.

Kyra-Katerina was furious with the landlord. "Just listen to that, the old knave!" she kept murmuring under her breath. "He imagines that, with two hundred drachmas, he has already bought the girl."

Another neighbor, blind in one eye, observed: "Two women worked all their lives and never saw their destiny under the sun. There wasn't even a decent blouse to bury her in, the unfortunate woman. Misery, my child; incurable misery!"

Two or three women from the factory stood sorrowfully beside Mercedes. Anifantis also came as soon as he had closed his shop, sometime around midnight. As he bent over to kiss the icon which had been placed in the dead woman's hands, his nostrils wiggled painfully.

The men were engaged in a philosophical discussion out there in the courtyard: "That's how it goes! We live today and die to-morrow. Poor man is nothing."

"We will all pay this tax, each in his turn," the landlord ob-served. "Whatever is written is not to be erased."

Father concluded: "Comes the hour, and here it is—"

"She's gone to rest; she's through with suffering," said someone else who was sitting near the edge of the group on a chair which squeaked, and which, one thought, would surely break at any moment. It was the portly neighbor, and his bulk spilled over the squeaking chair. "We are lamenting her at this moment, while she is probably very happy in that other world with her Giorgios."

"Do you think so?"

"Of course I think so!"

Kyra-Katerina became very skeptical about all this.

"Truly, if we could only know what is to happen to us—But, nonsense! It's what we eat and what we drink—Heaven and hell are right here!"

Father coughed dryly. He looked unfavorably upon such sacrilegious words. Later he said: "We know you of old, Kyra-Katerina. We don't expect to become acquainted with you now."

She remained silent.

Half of those present in the room of the dead woman had gone to sleep. Only the women from the factory and Savvoula fought sleep and held their eyes open. But those eyes were so tired, and the women breathed so heavily! The woman from Galaxidi, out-spread before them, had a strange look on her face. They all stared at that face, as though seeking to fathom its meaning. "How man changes!" Every so often, Mercedes burst into tears and lamenta-tion. She would become quiet for a time, then burst again into tears and lamenting. Two or three times, she attempted to sing a dirge, one of those from her native homeland, but none of the other women accompanied her; thus, becoming discouraged, she no longer made any attempt. It was almost daybreak. Everyone in that room had changed in appearance; they were all like yellow litho-graphs. And as the morning was chilly, everyone trembled bodily. Other people had started to collect in the house. The owner of the factory where Mercedes worked sent over his foreman with fifty drachmas. The other women from the factory found this rather strange because they knew the owner; knew him quite well indeed.

"Kostakis," Mother said to me, "you will carry the Cross. She loved you very much. May God forgive her—"

The Cross was as tall as I was and so heavy that, as I anchored it against my body, I was in great pain. And the route appeared endless. But the woman from Galaxidi had always been so good to me. We buried that unfortunate woman and then returned home where we mourned her all over again. Everyone drank another cup of coffee and ate a biscuit; afterwards, everyone sneaked away quietly, as though seeking a breath of air; as though seeking to determine if they were alive or if they had not died as well. The landlord remained quite late at night and comforted Mercedes with very beautiful words. Where did he ever find such exquisite words! How did he remember all those words!

So ended this story. We took Mercedes over to our house where we forced her to eat a bit of food. We spread a heavy blanket on the floor because she would not consider sleeping on any of our beds, and all night long we heard her crying softly. Many times during that week, Father talked in whispers to Mother. And always, the two glanced at Mercedes with great sympathy. I caught a few words, here and there, and it was not so long before I understood that the subject of their conversation was the landlord.

11

The event of the death of the woman from Galaxidi scarred me for life. This was my first encounter with death at such proximity, and I was unable to stop thinking about it. Awakening at night, I stared at the ceiling and became afraid, so afraid—My brother alone was unconcerned about the event. In his eyes there was only the sea, an indication that he would be deserting us one of these days. He would depart for the islands, those distant islands where men never die. Undoubtedly, he would encounter a nymph on those faraway islands from whose golden cup he would partake of the immortal water. Then the years would roll off his back like birds gliding over the sea.

Winter came in with a roar. The bare hillside opposite our house, overlooking the north, pulled the snow down over our faces. Our cheeks and lips became blue with the cold; our hands ached as though they had been struck with very thin branches; they ached so much that our eyes filled with tears. Father was having difficulty making ends meet. This was obvious from the way he was forever talking to himself; sometimes, he even sighed. He went to bed quite late at night, and, as we heard him rolling from side to side, we sensed that something was tormenting him. But what could we do? How could we be of any assistance? We were so inexperienced and of no use whatever, both my brother and I. For all that, the one most to be pitied was Gypsy-Theodore. His entire possessions consisted of that summer coat and those patched trousers which barely covered his knees. He walked as though he were a rolling ball, shrunken, humped over, hands in pockets, whistling in the wind, in the snow, books and tablets under his arms. Everything was cold, so cold in that classroom: our desks, the teacher's desk, the blackboard. We attempted to write, but were unable to hang on to the pencil. For hours on end, we blew on our hands before we could flex our fingers. Even under such conditions, the teacher continued to be merciless.

"Whoever wants to warm himself, let him come near!" he shouted, walking among us like a savage beast.

He was wearing the heavy overcoat with the frayed buttonholes and his knitted gloves; around his neck, he had a woolen scarf. Many were the times he deserted us to go to the house next door with the supervisor. When he returned later, he came in chewing and acting very gay.

"The cold penetrates to the bones," he would remark.

As for that, perhaps the man was correct. Mother managed to light the brazier on the coldest days. On other days, we crowded together in the kitchen. A large table was there, around which we sat studying, and occasionally eating fry-cakes; those fry-cakes we enjoyed so thoroughly, especially when they were sprinkled with sugar. Mother asked us to bring Gypsy-Theodore home after school, and it was a delight to watch that boy. How his cheeks blossomed, his eyes sparkled, as he sat facing the flames. How attentively and quietly he sat. You were unaware of anyone in that room, so innocent was that Gypsy-Theodore! We admired the beautiful round letters he wrote and his neatness in everything.

Father would come home early; he had a great fondness for discussing and counseling us on how to make our lives successful; like his own, no doubt. So be it! Those winter evenings never lacked for charm. It perhaps seems so because they are over now and so far in the past, in the depth of time. Or maybe because the years of childhood, of youth, never return.

As Christmas approached, it even snowed. The hillside turned white; so did the streets and the neighborhoods, the harbor and the decks of the boats. The stout smokestacks and the black city changed in appearance. Over the mounds of coal, a white foam fell and everything around was given a rebirth and became purified. It was as though hardships, fever, and all struggling for existence had ceased. The sea was like a sick child, and the boats glided drowsily over her back. We went down to the harbor to watch the caïques returning from the islands with their loads of oranges, besprinkled with snow. My brother's thoughts were constantly on the northern seas; he always talked about the icebergs blocking the ocean routes, and about the destructiveness and blackness of the sea wolves in the cold, dense fog. My brother knew all these things in detail and felt no fear of winter. He had been born to struggle!

One day, Gypsy-Theodore came with us on this pointless promenade, but the snows had begun to melt now and were becoming mud and slush; only a few tufts of snow remained on the rooftops and along the sides of the streets, banked against the wet walls. The cold was intense; the north wind, descending from the heights, was like the sea rover, lashing at us with a heavy whip. We walked briskly, but were unable to escape the north wind, which followed us along the streets of the city. We were exhausted when we returned home. Our shoes were muddy; our clothing was spattered with mud. We were disheveled, red-faced, and our feet ached. Father pulled on our ears. It was wrong to be running around in such weather; we might contract pneumonia and so become lost forever. But Mother interfered; she even made us drink some hot sage tea, which revived us. Winter was really not so bad as all that!

And so it happened that on one of those nasty winter nights, Chrysoula, bundled in her cherry-red shawl, came to see Mercedes. She sat for hours talking with her in a low voice. Mother had need of something and ran over to knock on Mercedes' door. Inside that room, she found the two girls crying. Chrysoula's tears were so uncontrollable that Mother became alarmed. She thought it terribly extravagant that two such young girls should be in tears over the woman from Galaxidi; the one, in fact, still a young bride, and so fortunate. Later, it became known that Chrysoula was suffering over her own problems. Barely two months had elapsed since her wedding day; yet that charmingly furnished house at Lefkas, with the gaping lions in the curtains, had become a veritable hell for the poor girl.

"It is not the same *talking* about conditions as *living* them,

Mercedes," she said. "To have that seal of a mother-in-law over your head day and night; to have her scolding you every time a flea jumps; and then to keep harping on the fact that you were not worthy of their son—So many girls were anxious to marry him —And, ever since you entered their house, a curse had descended with you—"

"Patience," Mercedes counseled. "That is how mothers-in-law are. Eventually, she will talk herself out. Only, be careful not to talk back to her. And stay on the best of terms with your husband. We are girls of poverty; we have little to say. Always think of how you have become freed of that accursed factory; think of how you have a wonderful young man beside you; think of how we all look proudly on both of you."

"If you only knew this young man well," Chrysoula interrupted, but without haste to complete her sentence.

"What do you mean?" Mercedes asked, opening her eyes wide.

"What can I say? What can I say? His love endured for a single week only. You don't know men, Mercedes. They're solicitous until you've become their property; they bite off their sleeves with gnashing teeth, as the saying goes. Then they begin to lose their appetites; they become weary; they become exhausted. There is too much work at the office, and all that. And to say that he opens his mouth once to put his mother straight; to defend me—My dear, he's a housecat. He drags along after his mother's dress. Tss! says the seal, and he hides his tail between his legs like a whipped puppy, without a sound."

Words failed Mercedes. She had so envied Chrysoula, and now Chrysoula's words were revealing an entirely different world. That Chrysoula should be unhappy—Ah, without doubt, that was too much for Mercedes to bear.

"My advice to you," continued Chrysoula, "is to stay far away from in-laws. Better to marry the poorest man than to always have such a nuisance over your head. Not to mention, of course, that they threw my mother out of their house. 'She's such a common woman,' and 'She doesn't know how to conduct herself,' and 'She embarrasses the family,' and so many such things. Listen to that! Embarrasses the family indeed! Let me not open my mouth to speak! My father-in-law is a better man, you see, though he steals from the customs house! Every evening, he returns home with a package under his arms. 'Ai! sometimes we also get tips!' And if you want to know what the neighbors are saying about that witch, it is something frightful!"

Always fresh tears spouted from Chrysoula's dark eyes. A two-month-old bride and the poor girl had already begun to fade. Across the way, Savvoula warbled. As the street separating the two houses was narrow, her throaty song spilled melancholy and sweet. A blackbird in winter.

"She wears her hat at a devil-may-care angle," Chrysoula said. "Poverty, stay away from my door!" And Chrysoula smiled bitterly through a shower of warm tears.

On Christmas Eve we were again around the church. The winds had ceased blowing, and the weather had become quite mild in the middle of winter. The church was brightly lighted, and the people passed back and forth as though they had laid aside all exhaustion and thought only of the two-day holiday. We found Pantelis there, rattling a pocketful of nickels and dimes. He continually threw open his patched overcoat to show us the new jacket he wore underneath, at the same time telling us what a lot of money the jacket cost. At any rate, now that he was earning so much, he could afford to spend money on something which pleased him. That boy was looking ever so much better. Even the pallor of his face had almost vanished, and his cheeks were fuller. The scrofula no longer worried him. That wise old woman, the practical nurse, had spoken the truth to his father; Pantelis would regain his youth once he went to work.

As we were standing outside the church with our hands in our pockets and listening to the chanting, as from the distance of a dream, Pantelis decided to make his greatest gesture. He took us down to the chestnut vendor, who had set up his flaming fire under the pepper trees, and he treated us to many chestnuts. We were extremely embarrassed to be taking all those chestnuts, but Pantelis stood there rattling nickels and dimes in his pocket to make us aware that he possessed money. We greatly honored Pantelis that evening, not for his material wealth, but for his kindness of heart. He made us think that an education was unnecessary after all. Better to go to the mill and attempt to become masters in a short while.

Pandora sauntered by, bundled to her ankles in a new brown coat, her face red as a carnation. Pantelis winked at us in such a manner that we recognized, unmistakably, how this boy had matured.

"Just let her husband return from abroad and we'll see! We'll all have a merry time. Just remember that!"

"Why? On account of the chanter?"

"If it was only the chanter!"

We were greatly impressed by Pantelis' words.

"Whatever do you mean?" I asked.

"Kostakis, are you pretending not to understand?" Pantelis replied with some severity. "She has a whole collection of sweethearts—It would have been better if she had not taken that first step."

We entered the church and found Pandora standing beside the benches, her cheeks flushed as though she had become quite warm, wrapped in that beautiful coat of hers. Seized by an inexplicable passion, at that moment, to scrutinize this Pandora at closer range, I quietly edged my way across from her. I kept my eyes on her as though bewitched. I felt a sweet warmth enveloping me and blue angels sang within the range of those gay lights. Pandora was also wearing a coral necklace around her rosy throat. As she opened her coat, I saw the necklace burning a pale light right on that spot. My eyes traveled down to where her coat began to close again and her other treasures were no longer visible. I was so completely enthralled that I felt I was traveling on a sea of night during some starlit summer. Savvoula passed in front of me just then, but I failed to see her. Only when she was lighting her candle did I catch my first glimpse of her. She genuflected over and over, there before the icons, and murmured some incomprehensible words as though talking with the saints, who, in turn, rolled their circular eyes around the church, looking with annoyance now at Pandora and now at Savvoula—these two who were robbing paradise and carrying it to earth. When Savvoula ceased her genuflections, she turned to leave the church. She happened to catch a glimpse of me right there and smiled so sweetly that, immediately, I forgot about Pandora, so elated was I with that smile.

The next day, we took Mercedes over to our house to celebrate Christmas with us. Celebrate, in a manner of speaking, because the ghost of the unfortunate woman from Galaxidi stood in the doorway as though she had become a vampire and had returned from the lower world to join in the celebration, come what may. The landlord came in the afternoon, wearing a new gray suit. He told

Mercedes that he would see she received her pension from the
Veterans' Fund; it was pointless to wait any longer for the return
of that missing Giorgios. Father agreed that this matter should be
settled without delay; whereupon, the landlord announced that he
had a friend in this particular office, who would expedite the
matter.

"We soldiers have friends everywhere," he added. "So many
people pass through our hands."

Mercedes was quite pleased that she would be acquiring some
kind of support—so deeply in debt was she to Kyr-Aristomenis, even
though he never mentioned a word, except to make some pointless
remark like: "We'll even the score once and for all." The landlord
brought Mercedes a small package with two pairs of stockings and
a black knitted scarf. Of late, he had become quite bold, and the
girl did not know what to do about him. Savvoula kept after her,
saying that she should arrive at some decision soon. However, the
thought alone was enough to drive Mercedes insane.

"Let the mourning period pass and then we'll talk about this
matter," Mother said to her one day.

Mercedes shuddered. Suppose Mother, as well, were to advise
her to marry the old man?

"But is it necessary to talk over such matters?" she asked.

"All matters need discussing. In the final analysis, we can give
him a negative reply and find some peace."

"We gave him such a reply and also showed him several times
that he is not wanted, but he persists in becoming worse!"

"Then you must move to another house," Mother said. "And
you must try to find someone very soon to set up housekeeping of
your own."

Mercedes shuddered.

"Where am I to go, a girl alone? I've lived in this neighborhood for so many years now; I've become accustomed to it. Everyone here respects me, as I respect everyone. Furthermore, do you
think that thrice-accursed man would fail to find me wherever I
went?"

Such were the words that passed between Mother and Mercedes at the time. But today was a holiday, and Kyr-Aristomenis
was in high spirits. He related so many funny stories that we all
laughed, even Mercedes. We lost all remembrance of the woman
from Galaxidi. This man was most entertaining. As for kindness,
he had a heart of gold. As soon as it became dark, he sent my

brother to buy two okas of wine in a bottle which had been lying on our dusty shelf for ages. Mother fried some eggs and brought out the left-over meat from the noon meal. We even convinced Mercedes to wet her lips with wine. After that, the entire house smelled sweetly of Christmas so that Savvoula became aware of the celebration and came over, coincidentally, to extend her wishes. Of course, she remained with us. We admired the way she drank her wine in a single swallow. This was a woman who knew how to live—That is how the landlord put it, talking in a very serious tone. Father coughed dryly a couple of times, as though displeased with the company, but the wine bottle refused to become empty. The landlord was in the kind of mood where he could have treated us to a whole barrel of wine, but we had no appetite for it. We children, unaccustomed as we were to such celebrations, considered this so very formal an affair, so very gay, that we could scarcely believe it was taking place. That is how festive everything was. Under the influence of such unexpected gaiety, we even forgot to remember the woman from Galaxidi. "We will also die! Why bother!" We forced Mercedes to take a second and a third glass of wine; whereupon she began to laugh and cry simultaneously. All at once, she became an entirely different person. It was Savvoula, that devil, who knew the manner in which to manipulate and increase the merrymaking. Everything went well, and more than well, so that the landlord was quite satisfied, and we were all elated over the success of the celebration. After all, this roguish life was not to be taken too seriously! Savvoula left us for a few minutes to return with a bowl of walnuts and almonds and raisins. We children grabbed at these goodies with eyes wide open as a shrimp's. How many wonderful things this Savvoula had, anyway! Finally, Mother was obliged to tell us that it was time to go to bed. The table and floor were littered with nutshells. One cannot encourage children too much. They begin to make such a mess around!

12

With one thing and another the days went by and life brightened at times to again become gloomy and benumb our footsteps. Even so, you were under the impression that nothing would ever really change; everything would continue as before. We were so accustomed to conditions as they were that we had no real thoughts of change. The boats whistled and sent up black smoke; the fac-

tories whistled and sent up black smoke, as well; the streets were
covered with a thick, black mud, full of coal dust. Then came the
January nights with their large moon and their dry, biting, north
winds. We had become tired of blowing on our fingers; worries and
poverty tormented us unceasingly. Father sometimes earned our
bread, sometimes he did not. Mercedes was again working steadily
at the factory. Savvoula went to work at the match factory for a
day and laid off for two days to go traveling down to the distant
neighborhoods. The landlord enjoyed living. He had decided to
regain his youth; there was no other solution, if he was to salvage
his particular situation.

Pandora alone had lost her mind completely. That chanter must
have been a magician. But, in pointing out the way to the discovery of her true self, he had, within a short time, lost Pandora
from his grasp. The fault, certainly, lay in that he lived so far away
in a distant neighborhood and was probably ashamed to keep
coming back and forth to his old haunts. The neighbors happened
to overhear him talking very roughly to Pandora. When her mother
attempted to intervene, he came near to beating both women, so
irascible was he, and he considered that women should always
remain subjected. Kyra-Paraskevi brought the news to the others
that the cause of the entire trouble was another woman, a young
girl, fresh as cool water. Pandora had seen the chanter sitting with
this girl at a coffee house at Pasalimani. She had passed before him,
cursed him to his face, and then walked on, swinging her hips to
let him know that she was most unconcerned about him. Of course,
he paid slight attention to such things. Within a week, he had returned to the small house as though not the slightest disturbance
had taken place. Pandora told him off; the mother told him off; the
baby happened to cry at that moment—and all hell broke loose in
that house. Relating about the commotion is not quite the same as
witnessing it. At the height of all these angry retorts, Pandora's
face became red as a rose and her eyes sparkled like fires lighted
at night in the forest by the rangers. Then the chanter spoke sweet
words to her, and, at once, the situation between them became as
before. They spent a very lovely night together, all kisses and love.

In the meantime, a letter arrived from Tunis in a long envelope, loaded with seals and stamps. The sea rover had not done
so well down there. He was writing the letter from jail where he
would be spending the next two months before he could be released
from those iron bars. He was detailing the events to his wife; how

he had a fight one night in a tavern where he and a Portuguese
sailor had become involved quite seriously. (When it came to
fighting, not a fly could alight on the sea rover's knife but that he
would fly off the handle!) The Portuguese sailor had cut the sea
rover so badly on the right cheek that he would now be scarred
for life. But, in return, the sea rover had beaten the Portuguese
sailor to within an inch of his life, there outside the tavern, at the
corner where he could keep his eyes on both streets. In the end,
however, the police had arrested them both, and they were still in
the jailhouse. The sea rover failed to give the reasons for this fight;
thus, Pandora explained the situation as it best suited her: "That's
the kind of man he is! Well, I'll show him from what kind of family
I come." And she began to see less and less of the chanter, but it
was as though he, too, desired the same. Leaving the child with her
mother, she began to go visiting, two or three times a week, down
at the Kaminia where her sister lived. The tile-maker, her sister's
husband, spent all his time in the tavern; there Pandora made new
acquaintances. Her sister knew ever so many people. Let the sea
wolf remain quietly where he was in his cell. He was free to remain
there as long as his heart desired.

Pantelis conveyed to us odds and ends of all these events. We
were mystified by the manner in which this boy discovered all
these facts, and by the concern he showed over what one person
or another from the neighborhood was doing. He related everything with a kindness of heart, whispering and laughing, as though
he actually believed the world was like this. Every man went his
own way; there was neither good nor evil. Only, there, each man
was created by nature to behave in one manner or another; nothing
was altered, no matter how hard the archmandrite and the teacher
with his whip attempted to bring about alterations. Pantelis even
told us he would take us through the flour mill some afternoon. He
had become thoroughly acquainted with everything in there by
this time; thus he was allowed to circulate and observe the mounds
of wax-colored wheat falling into the huge belly of the machine.
The machine regurgitated this wheat, transformed into a sea of
thin, shining white flour. That was enough to make a person lose
his mind! That was how quickly and how flawlessly work was
being carried on at the flour mill. Anything fed into the machine
was transformed at once into flour. And all this, amid such heavy
noises that some time was required before one became accustomed
to them. Pantelis even knew the different kinds of wheat by name

and from which locality each came; he knew many things. We were convinced he would become a foreman one day, so acclimated had he become to the work that he was unconcerned about everything now.

Around four o'clock one afternoon, on a dark, foggy day that seemed about to bring rain, but no rain came, we heard one of the factories screeching strangely, painfully, in a way to freeze a man's soul with that lamentation which seemed to emerge with difficulty out of the depths of suffering bowels. Mother ran outside; she knew that screeching sound. Savvoula from across the way ran outside; so did the other women from the neighborhood. They echoed one another in that thick fog, as they wondered which luckless man had paid a heavy price for his bride. Eagerly, they sought to learn details. But no one from the factory happened to pass by. They must wait until later to learn the news.

We had just finished school for the day. We had taken Gypsy-Theodore with us; and, as we were walking along playfully, we saw people running toward the mill where Pantelis worked. We thought only of those usual tidings; tidings which caused families to become orphans. It never occurred to us that this screeching of the factory might possibly be for Pantelis. The crowd of people before the gate was unbearable, but no one had learned a thing. Only, everyone kept asking. The police came, and very seriously they cleared a path among the crowd. They posted one man at the gate, who told us after a while that we should disperse. Nothing so very bad had occurred. Only a boy who worked at the mill had been caught by a strap and had been thrown into a large funnel. The machine had almost brought him forth as sifted flour.

"It's a good thing they caught him in time, partly inside the machine, partly outside, and stopped it," the man of authority said.

"And what happened to the boy?" asked an old lady in black.

"What do you imagine happened, my good woman," he answered. "From the waist down, he's a man; from the waist up, he's hamburger. Come now, disperse. Disperse."

At that moment our hearts went cold; our hands and lips trembled. Gypsy-Theodore alone was able to ask if the name of the dead boy was Pantelis. As the man of authority nodded his head, we felt we were dreaming and all creation around us was unreal. Later, the foreman came out to post a black board over the gate. A large white paper was secured on it with thumb tacks, detailing how the accident had occurred and how the company bore "no responsibility whatsoever." You should have seen the sacristan at that moment! He had been at a christening when he heard the news of the great calamity that had befallen him. How he beat himself and screamed! Pantelis' mother also came. We were convinced the woman would lose her mind. They took away the boy in a gunny sack, from which the blood dripped. Which boy? It was a batch of crushed bones and a mangled body they carried away.

This was the end of Pantelis. There went the proud accomplishments; the stores down by the harbor where he was going to sell iron hardware and tarred ropes. There went Pinio, the daughter of the priest. Only the pepper trees around the church remained where we could continue our lonely walks and remember the boy who had been killed; remember him jingling the dimes and nickels in his pockets as he filled our hands with hot chestnuts. We felt we had been crippled; we felt like orphans. We could never pass that mill without fear of finding Pantelis as we re-created him in our imaginations, half-dead, half-alive, two legs moving, walking, dragging over an empty chaos. Father took my brother aside to explain that this was what happened to boys who performed according to their own inclinations. We scarcely understood the reason for Father's saying such things, because we knew how happy the sacristan had been when Pantelis had gone to work at the mill. In fact, it had been the sacristan who had begged Kyr-Agisilaos, the foreman, to find a place for the boy. By this time, the woman from Galaxidi was completely out of our minds. Mother said:

"Better that he had died of scrofula than to have met such a horrible death."

But Savvoula was of a different opinion.

"Do you think he felt anything? Better this way than to rot in bed and be tormented like a dog."

And Kyra-Katerina supplemented: "What's the use! One way or another—"

Such were the words that were said for Pantelis. Later, other events intervened. Life went on without waiting. Finally, Pantelis was also forgotten, as are all events and people.

The deacon was a nice young man, and now he came more often to our house to sit and talk with Father for hours. The landlord also came over quite often, at which time we children heard most important discussions—all about great men—so agreeably did the landlord and the deacon manage the conversation. Father was not to be outdone. Only that he sipped on his coffee loudly, and every so often, he twisted the conversation back to the same topic of suffering and poverty. The deacon argued about this.

"God gave us brains so we can overcome our difficulties," he said one evening. "Nothing comes of talking about something. We should look at the bright side of life as we struggle; we should create our own destiny. You should have been with me fifteen years ago when I said farewell to my family before going off to the monastery. 'Are you going to become a monk?' my oldest brother cried out. And my mother cried for the misfortune that had befallen our house. My sisters also cried. 'What am I to do here?' I kept asking them. 'This is a narrow piece of land; it's not large enough to feed so many mouths. It would have been preferable to have gone away to foreign places to work and accumulate wealth. But I wasn't able to manage that. The monastery has grazing lands, vineyards, olive groves. Since my uncle is an abbot there, I will beg him to take me under his protection. He won't let me become lost. Thus, you'll have one less mouth to feed.' Such ideas did I have in my head. I worked at the monastery and attended school. Later, I became a soldier. After leaving the army, I put on the frock once more. It won't be long now before I receive my diploma, and then I'll become an archmandrite. Well, God has not done so badly with me."

And he sighed as though something distressing stirred within him and burned him like a red flame. The landlord, on the other hand, always talked about the army and about the wonderful old days when his mother had been alive. He had no care in the world around his house. His mother managed everything so long as he gave her money on the first of every month. So much for all that. But what was to be done now that he had been left all alone in the world, now that age, no matter how one looked on the matter, was creeping up on him. One way or another, he would have to make the great decision to put his life on the right path.

Those January evenings were delightful, with a round moon in a cloudless sky and a dry north wind spread like a watchdog over the benumbed city. Mother kept going in and out of the kitchen, happily preparing something for us; the deacon stroked his beard quietly, sometimes humming a hymn and at other times a song. It was as though a holiness shrouded him. His frock smelled of candle and incense, which pleased us because we felt we were in church. And that is not to remark on our enjoyment at being with such important personages. After all, Father may have become poor, but he could still select his friends. He always managed to separate the wheat from the chaff, that's for certain.

"In poverty were we born; in poverty we will die," Father said again.

As Mother passed his chair, she shook her head as though finding fault of some kind in Father which she dared not admit even to herself. Sometimes, the landlord brought the newspaper with him. At such times, Father would put on his glasses and read one thing or another out loud. The deacon listened with mouth wide open—that was how pleasantly Father read. Imagine how much better he would have managed had he not dropped out of school in junior high. We would become sleepy quite early when they talked about the contents of the newspaper, unless it happened to be about a murder or something similar. Then we were wide awake, thinking how utterly impossible it would be for us to kill someone. What dark souls those men had who dared to perform such deeds. The truth was that we were quite innocent and timid; we had become accustomed to being patient. We knew that some kind of evil existed in the world; but, in the final analysis, evil could be defeated only with kindness. Perhaps, at times, we could have wished to see the teacher with the whip dead; to see those indefatigable hands stiffened. But it was far from our thoughts to murder him. Such a thing never entered our minds at all. And this wasn't the only thing in those newspapers. A great many other things were printed there, miracles and miracles, which we could never imagine. How large and beautiful, O Lord, is thy world! The landlord always contrived, in his own manner of putting things, to interject a few words which would show how knowledgeable he was and how widely traveled. Over in the neighboring room, we sometimes heard Mercedes straightening around and sighing, as though she appeared to be panting softly. The face of the landlord, during those moments, would become sullen, and he would remark that the deacon was right: man did make his own destiny, so shortsighted and unprogressive was he. The landlord was anxious that Mercedes join us, but she always found excuses. Only when she found it impossible to give an excuse did she decide to come over to sit beside Mother. She always kept her eyes lowered as she tortured herself over some piece of knitting or mending, as though she had much homework to complete and so little time to work on it.

Chrysoula now visited Mercedes in her room quite regularly. She always came over with a mouthful of words and eyes swollen from crying. That was how it was! Marriage was only an idea; better to call it an enslavement. You left one prison to enter into another.

One evening, the sacristan came over to ask the deacon a question. He sat with us, drinking his coffee, sipping on it loudly, and we recalled Pantelis with a tenseness around our hearts. How to believe that we would never see that boy again. We always sensed him alive beside us, suffering with the scrofula on his neck and with a passion in his eyes. The sacristan had no other children. What did he want with life now. Night after night, he lay sleepless. He and his wife sat like two ghosts in the dark as they mourned for Pantelis. The deacon said some strange words to him: "He who has patience will be saved in the end," and some other such words. But the sacristan understood nothing. He was an illiterate man, and the only thing he knew was that the accursed machine had robbed him of his child at the moment when he had hoped to find comfort and rest.

Such were the evenings of January. Long and slow-moving, with the moon and the dry north wind, and with everything unveiling like a fairy tale before us; like a strange story which we felt we had never lived. Those times have passed. Everything has faded in the long path of life. Now, there are other men, other homes, other moons. Some days we sensed a little enjoyment in this unmanageable life. But, whatever one says, we did love this old legend and have often yearned for it; perhaps we did not know at the time how numerous were the wounds man must endure, if he is to withstand time and destiny.

13

A dense gloom had settled of late over Pandora's small house, such a heavy gloom that even her mother became aware how much her impending downfall was going to be a great and slippery one, full of dangers and pitfalls. There in the neighborhood of Kaminia which Pandora frequented, the good-for-nothing girl had become a master at her craft. She was always hanging around with new crowds that never became old crowds, because they were forever being replaced; just as her blouses and dresses and shawls and coats were always being replaced by new ones. A whole rack of clothes lined the closets of her small house. It was incomprehensible to her mother what Pandora would do with all those clothes, and how she would justify their ownership to that roving sailor, her husband, who sent her so little money; he who had recently been released from jail and was now roaming over Tunis like a doomed soul.

"One of these days he'll sneak in here unexpectedly," her mother would cry. "And then a great calamity will overtake us."

But Pandora only giggled heedlessly. "So let him come! Or do you suppose that I'm going to fall at his feet? Those days are over. So many men begging me—And to say that they are my inferiors! No, my dear; each of them amounts to something!"

"That first lover of yours who gave you such ideas is to blame! It's true what they say about this business—the first boy friend should never enter the house, because, once he's entered, all is lost. There's no restraining a woman after that."

"He's not behaving any better where he is."

"No, my child; for a man it's a different story. He's a single man there in foreign places—"

"And I'm a single woman. I will not waste my youth, I'll have you know! Let him return to his home, let him become a family man again, then you'll see how I'll honor my wedding wreath."

Such were the words with which Pandora rebuked her mother. Abandoning her child in her mother's care from night until morning, and again from morning until night, she sat before the mirrored cabinet, daubing all kinds of makeup on her face and saturating the rooms with heavy perfumes as she sang, always sang, misty-eyed, as though she had given herself entirely to the devil, to a sweet, invincible devil who was master of her body and soul. Then there were times when she returned home late, when the clock in the living room struck midnight, or two, four, or five o'clock, or dawn was about to break, and she would tumble into bed, exhausted, aching, her inflamed eyes lined with shadows, gasping like a madwoman, as though her joints had become unhinged. As she undressed in the dim lamplight, she examined her body closely, as though it still burned with the surviving marks of caresses and kisses. The neighbors already considered her lost. A girdle of shame was carved invisibly around the small house, as though a piece of dry earth, a small island in a turbulent sea, lay on that spot. Pandora, however, was unconcerned, both about the neighbors and about the rest of the world. She never raised her eyes to look at a soul, but slithered downhill like a hunted animal until she reached Lefka where she would stop for a moment, draw a deep breath, and continue on her way with a new stride, as though she were a crawling flame of hell lapping the mud on the street.

In the yard of the small house stood an almond tree, planted in ancient times; an aged tree with a thick trunk, with branches like naked hands outstretched. There, her mother hung the tiny clothes of the child, and then the hands dripped with bluing water as though shedding tears over their own calamity. January came, and the small hands blossomed, the tiny yard brightened; so did the house. All at once, Pandora found herself like an errant woman in the midst of all those snowy blossoms, so incongruous was the white almond tree against her bleeding lips and her inflamed cheeks.

As February came, the weather changed. The days became longer now, and the afternoons were warmer, like small children asleep on their sick beds. The sea rover sent a message, composed of some half-uttered phrases, from Gibraltar. At Casablanca, he chanced to meet several old friends who had weighed anchor from Piraeus, blessing the waters, and who smiled at him in a strange manner—Yes sir, he was one of those men who would never accept any kind of nonsense!

The sea rover did not conceal the fact that he knew more than he was expressing. He was no kind of letter-writer to be able to express himself in detail. The mother sensed a shivering fear when she heard all this. Pandora's spine shivered, as well, as though she stood naked under a shower of cold water. She began to be more attentive to the child. She never went out nights now, but sat for hours on end, thinking, watching the street and the church and the sun, which poured its sparkling gold over everything. As always, the sea rover would fall unexpectedly into their small house. Try to explain everything to him after that!

"Mother, I am leaving," Pandora said one evening.

She said this on the spur of the moment. As yet, she had arrived at no decision. Who around there could advise her, anyway, during these troubled times?

"Christ and Mother Mary, my child!" cried the old woman.

"You have a husband and a child and me, whose fate is heavy. It is your duty to stay here to look after your belongings and your home."

"Mother, I am afraid," Pandora spoke again. And her eyes filled with shadows and tears.

"Don't be afraid of anything, daughter," the old woman replied. "All the world falls into error. You are not the first, nor the last. That vagabond should have kept his eyes open, then none of this would have happened to him. Don't worry! We will be good to him when he returns; and if he knows anything, we will deny it. Do you hear? 'That is all gossip and nothing more,' we will tell him. Besides, he will be returning blinded with lust for a woman. You haven't learned what villains men are!"

The sister became very concerned when a whole week went by and Pandora failed to appear. She made her way to the Kaminia, to the small house, where she read the courser's letter. Shrugging her shoulders, she said, "Don't worry! Pandora has no need of that incompetent man!"

"Not so incompetent," the mother replied. "He is good and capable, and he fills his house with all kinds of goodies each time he returns from foreign lands!"

The mother was now on the side of her son-in-law. Like a storm, this, too, would soon pass away. The sea wolf would be departing again, and until his next return, God would take charge. Later, Pandora and her sister went into the bedroom to talk matters over. They also talked about a certain man who was crazy about Pandora and kept asking for her. He had three houses, a bachelor he was, who would make all kinds of sacrifices for Pandora. In the final analysis, Pandora had no right to kick away her destiny. Furthermore, it wasn't certain that the sea rover would be returning. Gibraltar was so far away. He might even be going over the routes of Africa where the Arabs would take care of him and thus free Pandora once and for always. Such were the words the sister uttered. She made a packet of some of Pandora's extra dresses—just in case—and then took them home with her so that the sea rover would find Pandora with the same blouse and shawl she was wearing when he left home; a lonely and deprived Pandora at the same time that he was entertaining himself at the tavern in Tunis and being beaten up in the streets. A bit of peace appeared to be falling over Pandora's soul. Then, after a few days, she decided to go down to the Kaminia. There was that "certain person" with the

immense wealth! And she had been worried these last few days—
Well, she could die only once; she would not remain at home to
wither for the sake of one man or another!

The pre-Lenten season had opened. But then, February, as
well, suddenly remembering its peculiar habits, sprinkled snow
over the streets and houses, the second snowfall for that year, and
later, regretting, cast a golden sunlight until everything was right
again, as though nothing had happened—so faithful and such a
cajoler was this February! In the afternoons, we children gathered
in front of the church and had fun with the acrobats who gave
daily performances. There were five or six gawky fellows with long
mustaches—one had even lost his right eye—and they spread a
tattered blanket on the ground near the pepper trees, took off their
coats under which they wore red and blue tricot garments from
their necks down to their ankles, and performed all kinds of somersaults and acrobatics, which amused us exceedingly. It is one thing
to hear all this described and quite another to actually witness it.
Every so often, they interrupted their performance so that the
powdered clown who traveled with the troupe, wearing a false
nose two feet long and eyeglasses without lenses, circulated through
the crowd and collected dimes and nickels in a tin can. Say what
you will, these acrobats were something to behold. Sometimes,
they even brought a musician with them, who wore a black greasy
suit, baggy trousers that narrowed toward the cuffs and fell in folds
over his patched shoes, and a tiny gray hat, without any creases,
which sat high on his head. The musician, seated in a chair, played
on a large harmonica, and those others with the tricots gamboled
about, shouting and clapping their hands, so that we could not
take our eyes off their crazy capers.

Afterward, the camel passed by, and sometimes the urchins
under the heavy shabby cloth representing the animal's hide became involved in a fight and abandoned the camel, a bundle of
cloth and ceiling boards, there on the ground, and chased one
another around with such cursing as we had never heard before.
The bear-keepers also passed by with their heavy chains, their
clanging tambourines, and their unkempt, sulking bears, which
stood on their haunches. It was frightful to see all these, both the
dark, pock-marked faces of the keepers and the slow-moving
bears. Finally, they would set up the *gaitanaki* in the church
square. A group of clowns danced around this thick pole set in
the middle, holding the colored streamers suspended from its tip

like a bright, variegated wave. The clowns danced on and on, without even stopping for breath—so swift and competent were they. Some even wore skirts, pretending to be soubrettes. But it didn't take much, when you looked at them, to recognize that they were nothing more than a group scraped together down at the harbor, some unprosperous lovers of dance who, in one way or another, sometimes filled their bellies. And you ran into Pierrots and Harlequins and other foolish characters in this variegated *gaitanaki* which constantly stirred, like the frothy sea, with all kinds of twisting and turning and staggering and nudging—and the organ, somewhat apart, drowsily set the rhythm until it made you think: doesn't that blessed fellow cranking the handle ever get tired! It was enough to make you feel sorry for him.

For three entire weeks we had a gay time, sometimes doing one thing, sometimes another. We walked from street to street, following the camel and that shack, swinging back and forth, with the dolls, the marionettes, which some loafer set up from corner to corner, sounding his bell and collecting together swarms of children. Afterward, shouting loud, fat words, he opened the small curtain and stood behind it, unseen by anyone, and manipulated the marionettes and changed his husky voice in a thousand different ways, pretending to be like the *karagiozi* players. He performed wonder after wonder. On those days, we missed Pantelis; we missed him exceedingly. Every so often, especially in the spacious church-yard where most of the commotion was taking place, we imagined that he would suddenly appear from somewhere and meet with us in that manner of his which had been so lovable and so dreadfully pained. Such a hell of a life, really—not to find your friend at precisely the moment when the cockles of your heart desire him most!

Then came the last Sunday before Lent. Then came the afternoon, and the sunshine was sweet with a north wind blowing so softly you barely felt it, so submissive was it. People began to collect in the open space; the pepper trees, ready to drop, as though exhausted in the sweetness of the hour, made you think: "This is the beginning of the fairy tale. Good evening!" So warmly, so eternally did you desire to live. The coffee house brought out its tables; Anifantis, as well, filled his sidewalk with tables and chairs; and Uncle Demos' tavern across the street (which we haven't had occasion to mention before), also put on its festive attire, and shortly the crowd was so thick you could not insert a needle through

it. Boys and girls and middle-aged folks, even old men, abandoned
their homes, and the women, too, for they had all eaten and drunk
well. What did it matter that the weekly salary was all spent? There
is only one life to be lived, and you had the impression that hearts
blossomed and a madness blew, as softly as the northern breeze,
through all minds. Even Mother—we'll see this later—put on her
best dress and Father his new gray felt hat, an unmistakable sign
that this was a festive day, and they went down toward the coffee
house where we, too, sat for a time and ate our Turkish delight
and licked our fingers unabashedly—so sweet and rose-flavored it
was! Father sipped his coffee loudly, after first blowing on it, and
raised his eyes high as though looking at God, and Mother sat there
almost ashamed before all those people—so unsophisticated and inexperienced was the poor thing. The two organ-grinders came; one
stood under the pepper trees, the other in front of Uncle Demos'
tavern, and those blessed fellows began to play the same old songs,
over and over again:

> After all you've done to me,
> I don't want you anymore—

and

> Sea, devourer of our youth,
> Sea, poisoner of our men,
> You, who force our little isle,
> Black to wear—eternally—

and

> Mountain anemone, growing on a cliff,
> Bending over slightly, for the world to view—

and

> A hunter hunting in the woods one day,
> Chanced to meet a lovely nun—

Then they would start all over from the beginning. Later, the
gaitanaki and the acrobats and the camels came until the crowd
became so unbearable there was no room to walk or stop. The
boys told risqué jokes to the girls who smelled of powders and
colognes, and the girls nearly died with laughter as they called out
to the boys: "Now don't get fresh!" And then the boys became
bolder and barked at the girls: "Whoof! Whoof!" Yes, that is what
they said, and it was enough to make you lose your mind. It was
already becoming dark and the shopkeepers carried out more

tables—strange where they found all those tables, as though they had been vomited from their bellies—and set them up under the pepper trees, clearing a path with shouts, and shoving through the excited crowd. The lamp-lighter lit the gas lamps; the stars, too, came out, and it was truly like a fairy tale, except that the princesses were missing. At that moment, Savvoula came out for a breath of fresh air, and she was like a wax doll, smelling of a sweet, intoxicating perfume. Immediately, she was surrounded by all kinds of acquaintances, and she laughed, a throaty laugh, cheeks flushed, eyes sparkling, flexible waist swaying in a manner that made you think the devil patronized her elastic body. A sailor from the next neighborhood flung himself at her at once. With an "I've met you somewhere," and an "I've known you before," he made friends with her. Taking another couple with them, they sat under the pepper trees, and the waiter had difficulty keeping up with their orders. When they became high-spirited, they walked across the street to Uncle Demos' tavern. It was quite apparent by now that they had decided to have a gay time that night.

It was dark now; the pigeons had crawled into their holes, and the door of the church was still open. The priest was taking his walk around the narthex; the schoolteacher was with him, carrying his whipping stick. Both shook their heads sadly at all this debauchery—"People aren't the same any more; that's why God has cursed us!"—when, at that moment, Pandora came out of her small house, accompanied by a middle-aged man, the "important person," no doubt, from the Kaminia. It had been a long time since we had seen Pandora mingling so brazenly with the neighbors, and we admired her for her indifferent air and for a lot of other attributes. Pandora was beautiful that night, more beautiful than at any other time! Her body seemed to have become more mature, more firm and radiant, her flaming gaze more profound, her hair more raven and more glowing, her feet more gliding, and her hands, accustomed to fondling and kissing, more loving. Wherever she stopped, you thought the sea raged around her, a sirocco, as though there wasn't a single man who wouldn't have been unfaithful for her sake. The middle-aged man walking beside her was serious and contended. What did it matter to him? Let Pandora enjoy herself, just as he was enjoying himself! Pandora introduced him again and again as her uncle who had recently arrived from America and had brought her a thousand lovely things. And truly, you could have taken him for an American if you looked at him closely, so stocky and prosperous-looking and well-groomed was he! Uncle Demos, the tavern-keeper, brought out a table for them, setting it at the very edge of the sidewalk, and the middle-aged man gave order after order as the nearby merrymakers started to sing between gasps and sighs and jokes until, before long, they were all intoxicated and had set off for distant shores.

The landlord wore his best suit and the figured vest and coat with the fluffy nap, and he came over, early in the afternoon, to extend his best wishes. Even from the doorway, his strong breath overpowered us; it was evident that the man had taken a few too many drinks, holiday that it was. He also called Mercedes to come over, but the girl replied that she had best not stir from her room; she should remain there to think about her mother. However, the landlord insisted, insisted. Mother added her words also, and finally Mercedes decided to come over to our house to find a little relief for her tired spirits. How pleasant; what a jester; how loving Kyr-Aristomenis proved himself at that moment! So much, in fact, that we even thought he was not too terribly old, poor man—There, that was something one could never help thinking when he saw Kyr-Aristomenis in such high spirits.

"Well, I say you should all get ready at once, and we'll go down to the shops to have a wonderful time—"

Mother looked at Mercedes, but she failed to reply. She remembered again the woman from Galaxidi, and her eyes filled with tears.

"The living with the living, and the dead with the dead," the landlord said again, and he raised his voice in a manner that expressed he would bear no contradiction.

Mother would have liked to take Mercedes with us, but she was also considering that a year had not elapsed since her mother's death. It would be considered improper, most improper, to take the girl out so soon.

"Come, come. Why are you sitting there—?" the landlord cried, and his cheeks became inflated rosy-red and his nostrils opened and closed as though on fire.

Father intervened at that moment and said that it was improper. Kyr-Aristomenis should go ahead with his party—the others would remain at home to keep Mercedes company. Perhaps later, they would also walk down toward the shops for a short time, just for the sake of the children, nothing more.

A hushed silence fell at these words. The landlord tumbled heavily into his chair and lowered his head down to his suffering chest. When he raised it again, we saw his cheeks and mustache and eyes were wet with tears. The cockles of his heart trembled as though he was a green youth—foolish man! And then we all understood that the landlord was a very lonely man, and a very patient one. As though sympathizing with the poor man, Mercedes opened her mouth and said to him: "For goodness sake, Kyr-Aristomenis. When spring comes, we'll all go for a walk, someday, wherever you like. It's not such an important matter now that you should take it to heart!" We were all astonished at these words. Father looked at Mother as though making some sign to her, and Mercedes, alarmed at what she had just uttered, suddenly remembered there was something she must get from her room. We heard nothing from her until the landlord had departed, slamming the door behind him happily.

This is how it came about that the landlord was feeling so rejuvenated when he arrived at the spacious churchyard with its heavy growth of trees. He carried a bit of hope with him, faint perhaps, but what else could he do? If hope were missing, the world would be a dark, gloomy hell indeed! Mother called Mercedes to come over again, and she asked if she had given careful consideration to what she had just said about going for a walk someday with Kyr-Aristomenis. The man would be expecting this now, and the neighborhood would be scandalized for certain to see such an event.

"And do I ever think about anything else?" Mercedes replied, surprised by Mother's words. "Can't you see my loneliness and my plight?"

"Poverty is a bad counselor," Father said as he passed the ready-made necktie around his neck; an ancient one, which he was attempting to hook in back.

"And haven't I seen Chrysoula's improved condition?" Mercedes spoke again. "What am I to do? It must come naturally to become like Savvoula."

"You are a virtuous girl," Father said. "Such words are unbecoming to you—"

"Because I am virtuous, everyone has deserted me. 'The wildcat,' that's what the workers call me at the factory. What is the difference?"

"We'll look around to find you a nice young man," Mother

said, "so you can set up your own housekeeping and raise your own family. You should never have to care for that old man—"

"The nice young men demand that one have a bit of money saved up. They ask for many things; they don't become enslaved for nothing."

"As for that, Mercedes is quite right," added Father, who had, by this time, succeeded in hooking his necktie and was standing with a stiff neck.

Mother quickly put on her best skirt with the long train which swept the streets when it happened to slip through her fingers as she held it. She put on her jacket, buttoned from top to bottom; she carried a black, beaded purse in her hand—And we all went down together, leaving Mercedes with the care of her house and with her thoughts.

When we finished our Turkish delight, our eyes caught sight of Gypsy-Theodore, enjoying himself in the midst of a group of children playing a game of marbles. We left Father talking to Mother about this sudden decision of Mercedes, and we ran to join our friends to talk over our own problems, as though those chairs at the coffee house were too narrow to hold us, now that we had nothing more to do sitting in them. And then we saw Kyr-Aristomenis walking toward the church and entering into the narthex where he engaged in conversation with the holy archmandrite. He may have had nothing to say; only to show how contented he was. Later, he came out of the church and caught us at our game of marbles. He called out to us, "Bravo, you scamps! You know how to find entertainment over there!" We were greatly amazed, and we said, without doubt, it was because of Mercedes that the landlord was so cheerful. He told us some other jokes at that moment, but we heard nothing because of the great noise going on around us. He stood right there as though nothing was going on around him; as though he walked in another world. Finally, he walked over to Uncle Demos' tavern. We saw him later, drinking his wine very quietly among a group of married men, until Pandora made her appearance with her uncle. Then, the party became gay and reached festive heights. The landlord now began to drink glass after glass inconsiderately. The married men, too, began shouting with joy along with the landlord. Pandora was very beautiful. Well, there is only one life. Why repeat this over and over again! Night fell and the stars came out to ask what was going on in that place. Uncle Demos brought out the second acetylene lamp and fastened it on the tree beside Pandora's table. Her eyes sparkled again, and her hair sparkled; her laughter was heard clashing like the wave which shatters frothily against the aged rock—that's how Pandora's laughter also shattered and fell like silver dust in the open square. Then the landlord, Kyr-Aristomenis, no longer able to resist, ordered Uncle Demos to treat the group at his expense, pointing at the "Amerikanos" and Pandora. They were delighted and drank the wine to his health. After that, the "Amerikanos" treated the "gentlemen" and the "gentlemen" returned the treat and brought their chairs nearer so the group was enlarged, and all were men of some prominence, forty-year-olds or over. No one could possibly think anything wrong, even though the organ was now gasping from exhaustion. A clown with powdered face and purple nose came to bow before them, and they overflowed him, as well, with wine and threw plenty of silver drachmas into his cup; everything was beautiful and good, and Pandora now broke into song and the nostalgia increased, greatly increased, becoming one with the night and the stars, as though it had emptied from the flaming bowels of creation—

14

From this point on, events become quite involved. No matter how I attempt to arrange them in order, something in my memory always remains hazy and unaccountable—and, of course, the blame falls on me, who, feeling my knees weakened from all the running around and the sliding down the chute, took my brother and returned home, leaving many people still in the square, the festivity blazing, and the singing unfolding like a large, red rose. Afterward, the neighbors brought us the news; Savvoula first and foremost, and Kyra-Katerina. Later, a great number of other people told us as well. Did any of us close his eyes throughout that dreadful night?

They were having such a wonderful time right there that no one thought of leaving; that's how much they enjoyed gazing into the eyes of Pandora and sampling her jests and her laughter, for they all sensed irretrievable youth fluttering in their introspective hearts. The hour was far advanced, and the north wind, becoming stronger, whipped the benighted pepper trees with frozen wings, when Pandora's husband, that roving sailor, broke loose from the shadow of the church with heavy stride, a portion of shadow himself. He always returned from his foreign travels in this unexpected fashion, always weighted down with lovely things and manly vigor, uncontrollable and quarrelsome about everything, as though he were about to die and therefore sought to consummate everything but consummated nothing. He had knocked on the closed door of the small house with his thick fist, entered, and found, in the dimness of the vigil lamp, only the old woman lying beside the child. He called to Pandora, but the only reply came from the old woman, who rose startled from her tattered mattress and eyed him from head to toe as though groveling at his feet, her eyes bewildered, her hands, her entire body trembling, and her voice broken as though an unbearable hoarseness choked her. All at once, the sea rover found the house empty, empty and cold. Frostily cold. The memories collected in his heart—those scathing words, slippery and thick and full of mystery, that someone or other, a friend or a neighbor, had flung at him in foreign ports where they met, in the distant, unfriendly cities. The sea rover carried a scar on his cheek from that night in Tunis, and his gaze was heavy and dim, his lips dark-skinned, bloodless, with an oppression lodged over him like mist. The old woman lighted the lamp that was on the center table, threw a coat over her shoulders, wore her down-at-heel slippers, and it was as though she sensed him facing her like a judge; she mumbled her words so that he could not unravel a thing except that, wherever she was, Pandora would be returning, for she had gone to a sick, a very sick neighbor, and of course must have been delayed there. But such words failed to placate the sea rover's heart. He set his bags in a corner, cast off his mackintosh and his cap, and hatless as he was, hair ruffled, with his boots, his heavy blousy jacket, his nostrils sniffing the air, he appeared at the square to ask, to learn. And over there, under the yellow acetylene lamp, he saw his wife in the midst of an unknown crowd, all laughter and song, so that his stormy mind became even more stunned, as he paused for a moment, as though undecided which course to take, until finally a deep groan burst from his hairy chest. The merrymakers who still remained in the square came to their senses, and the songs ceased as a frightful chill disembodied their souls. Pandora also saw him and attempted to rise, crying, "Mother!" That was all she had time to cry before she was sprawling on the ground —the sea rover spitting a string of blasphemies from his mouth while the "Amerikanos" moved out of sight, and no one ever saw him again, as though the darkness of night had swallowed him. Everyone else scattered until the place around became deserted and was left cold and empty like a well-swept threshing floor. Only Pandora remained lying on the sidewalk motionless—she could have fainted; and Kyr-Aristomenis stood erect, even though encumbered with wine, an assistant and protector—he certainly hadn't served his country faithfully for so many years to lose courage now like a child at sight of the first insolent brute. In fact, he even cried out to the sea rover:

"Don't move or I'll let you have it!" He made a motion to draw his small pistol from his back pocket *(tsaf! tsaf!)*, only to find that he had forgotten it at home.

I won't swear to it that events took place as I am going to relate them. But the most obvious fact is that the sailor would listen to nothing; nor that anyone, except the landlord, came forward to stop him. Drawing his long knife from the sheath hidden beneath his wide belt, he fell on Pandora. The landlord became fierce and, at that moment, deserved admiration. He attempted to grab the sailor's hand, but the man was strong-armed, very strong-armed, and slipped through the landlord's fingers. Kyr-Aristomenis grabbed him a second time, by the leg now, and the sailor, transformed into a savage, slashed here and there, not caring what he struck, and knifed Kyr-Aristomenis and also struck Pandora one or two blows, the first one superficially under the right breast, and the second on her leg, near the ankle, but without much harm to her. In the meantime, the women and children in the square had begun to screech and yell; the sacristan mounted the belfry of the church and rang the bell violently, as though the very devil lived in the bell's frozen clapper. Several husky fellows rushed after the sea rover and began to beat him with their fists, striking left and right without considering where their blows fell, until his body became black and blue and his head swelled. Then, with perfect timing, the authorities came to handcuff the sea rover and take him away.

Kyr-Aristomenis remained where he was, drowned in his own black blood and wine, rolled into a ball, without human shape, as though his entire body had become a frightful grimace. The soft north wind blew over him bitingly, and everything had become very quiet in a frightful peace, there beneath the shadow of the church, beneath the intoxicated stars. A clown sat on the sidewalk before Anifantis' tavern across the street, beating his body and crying, because he loved Kyr-Aristomenis, that harmless man who had always been so very kind to him.

Until dawn, the crowd murmured and lamented in the square. Everyone mourned for the landlord, whose one thin leg, black now, protruded through his ripped trousers. They all cursed Pandora, lying shrunk against the wall, without even the strength to pull her dress around her body, but who still appeared warm and sweet in her painful nakedness. Only after the morning star had set did the authorities return to load the landlord on a cart. They covered him with a blanket, as though it were not fitting that the unfortunate man should be cold in the first light of dawn, and sent Pandora to the hospital to have her wounds attended. Uncle Demos and a waiter, the one with the big ears, began to pour buckets of water on the sidewalk to wash away the blood. The first Monday of Lent was dawning, and it was improper that any sign of carnival should remain.

"It serves her right, the slut; it serves her right—" Kyra-Katerina was remarking from door to door. "A knife wound and salt on that wound; that is what the likes of her deserve—Only, why should that poor man have had to pay for all this! What is one to say? Such was his destiny. Everything is fated in this miserable world—"

15

Mercedes mourned for the landlord as though for a relative. It was as though her final support had been removed from her, and she sensed her orphaned condition doubly, trebly. The first Monday of Lent, in the afternoon, the neighbors took him off the table at the funeral home. There was also a distant relative there, a strange man, tall and lanky, and wearing a stiff collar. He had a large nose and large eyeglasses and continually scratched at his chin as though countless lice were biting him. He kept raising his shoulder, then suddenly lowering it and again raising it—so much that one became nauseated and dizzy watching him. They placed the landlord in the center room of his house on Stenemachou Street, his coffin closed, and on it a small icon and a small bouquet of flowers. Evanthia came over, wearing a black kerchief over her head as though she was the widow, and everyone found comfort in repeating over and over that the landlord had always been such a brave man and that he had died like a brave man. That evening, they buried him. The north wind was blowing again, and people were celebrating the first day of Lent out in the streets and in the yards of their houses. The merrymakers were scarcely able to stand on their feet to silently design with their fingers the shape of the cross as the corpse passed by. The archmandrite and Vitivilias exhaustedly dragged along out in front, chanting softly through their noses, and a string of people followed the landlord as they saw him off to his final, his third, home, which he had acquired so unexpectedly.

That evening, we sat with Mercedes and the deacon, talking about the events that had transpired. Father ate his lettuce and fresh onion, drank his wine, and raised his eyes to the ceiling of the room as he commented on all this.

"What He has written, He does not erase. That is final!"

And he wiped his mustache with the back of his hand.

"Between us, the fault was his own," said the deacon. "The devil pushed him into becoming involved in someone else's affair. Why didn't he leave them alone to tear each other's eyes out?"

"No, no," interrupted Father. "Everyone pays for his weaknesses. You are still young, holy deacon; you haven't seen what my eyes have seen. The deceased, as we all know, was eternally chasing after skirts—" Father cast a sidelong glance at us children as though it was improper that we should be listening to such things. "So, no matter what he did, no matter how he guarded himself, it was inevitable that he should die in this manner."

Mercedes lowered her gaze in embarrassment, and a lump rose in her throat.

"That is not correct," said the deacon. "God gave a mind to man so he would know what to do."

Father was in the mood for conversation; so he said that it was time the children were in bed. But my bed was in the same room, and I was unable to sleep. The deacon took out a package of tobacco and rolled a cigarette, pinching it with his teeth at either end and wetting the sides under his thick mustache. He gave the makings to Father so he could also roll a cigarette. Then Mother brought out a lighted coal from the kitchen, and the two sat there smoking away and sipping on their wine and talking contentedly.

"So," Father began again. "Do you hear, holy deacon? I hear, you should say. God gave a mind to man for evil purposes, not for good. And you educated men can say what you please."

"Christ and Mother Mary!" Mother exclaimed in surprise. "What kind of talk is that!"

"You keep out of this, Wife," Father replied. And he looked at her with a severe glance.

"These are grave matters," said the deacon. "Let those who know more than we solve them."

"Who? Those who write the books? Why, holy deacon, my book is better—"

Mercedes glanced at Father in amazement. This was the first time she was hearing the man talk in this manner.

"Come! Viva! And a good Lent to us," said the deacon, raising his glass.

"Amen. God willing!" replied Father.

And he continued—there was no way of stopping him now: "You all think that books make life. But it is life which makes the the books. Here now, Kyr-Aristomenis was taken away quietly. And how should he have been taken away? Rowdyism and skirts killed him. Did he ever have anything else on his mind? Do you know what was said to me once by an old man who had learned 'through fire and iron,' as the saying goes? A man's vice is his destiny. When I first heard this, I did not believe it. No, this could not be right. But, on closer examination, I saw that the old man was right; very right. One man has this vice; another had some other vice. And each man is tormented and destroyed by his own particular vice. You say, this thing is crooked; so you straighten it out. That thing is upside-down; so you right it. In time, and with a great deal of trouble, we set things right. But a vice, you see, is deeply ingrained in the soul; you cannot uproot it. May Easter find us well, holy deacon."

And he emptied his glass again. At this moment, Savvoula came over, also worried. She sat between the deacon and Mercedes, at the end of the table. I was lying in bed, and my eyes fell on her legs. Certainly, I didn't care at what I was looking, but that's how things were! As Savvoula sat comfortably in her chair, her dress rose to her knees, and I saw her fresh body shining in that dim light. I began to snore quietly as I heard Mother say, "Kostakis is already asleep." I opened my eyelids narrowly and looked and looked again in the same spot, and I became satisfied without knowing the reason. Savvoula drank her wine without refusing another glass, and the deacon ate his lettuce, leaf by leaf, and his teeth went "kritch, kratch," like a lamb's. They rolled more cigarettes until the room became so thick with smoke that our eyes burned. Mother said with a smile, "You blessed men are pouring incense over us with those chimneys of yours," and she went to open the door for a breath of fresh air. So thick was that smoke!

"We haven't heard what finally became of Pandora," said Savvoula. "Wonder is that knife didn't go through her heart to kill her outright."

"Such carcasses don't consider things like that," replied Mercedes.

"That is the truth," added Mother and closed the door again. The cold north wind was no joking matter.

"So be it! Now she will become a different person," said the deacon. "It's only that she has destroyed two men; the one she has sent behind bars; the other to his grave."

"Must we say the same thing over again," Father said. "It's only until the trouble blows over, then—'What have you, Johnny? What I've always had!'"

He looked at Savvoula in a strange manner. But she failed to comprehend his meaning; her mind was elsewhere. And Mother thought: at the home of the hanged man, one doesn't talk about a rope. Tactfully, she changed the subject. Thus, they returned to talking about God, and the deacon started to chant a hymn as Father accompanied him with a smile. Savvoula looked at the deacon as he dragged the words of the hymn softly and sweetly, and her eyes had a provocative light in them; better to call it a provocative flame. Finally, they decided to break up the party. The deacon bundled himself well in his warm overcoat. They drank a last glass of wine. Savvoula also left, and I dreamed that someone was chasing me with a knife to kill me. It seems that I cried out in my sleep, because Mother came and lifted me in bed. "Christ be with you, child!" she said, caressing me. Then I saw that the room was empty, the lamp had gone out, and the vigil light flickered on high. I sensed an unutterable sorrow because Savvoula was missing.

Pandora remained in the hospital for a week. In the meantime, a whole group of policemen and examiners tormented her. Her mother took the child and went to the Kaminia to her other daughter. The small house remained closed, and the neighbors stared at it with cold fear, as though it was haunted; as though the devils had sprinkled it with red and black human blood. The deserted almond tree swayed its branches and let fall its last flowers in the frozen yard. One night only, Kyra-Paraskevi said a man came, bundled in a heavy overcoat, his collar raised and his hat pulled low over his ears. He stood looking at the house for a long time;

then he left and with a sigh was lost in the darkness. Everyone thought this could be none other than the right chanter, who was suffering there in the distant neighborhood where he lived.

Pandora, nonetheless, had a good time in the hospital, Caressing, wheedling, sweet-talking with the internes, the male nurses, the servants. Not a male was left who had not failed to bend curiously over her face and who had not read the destiny of man in her eyes. The attorney of the sea rover arrived and talked with her for a long time. It wasn't enough to have the policemen and the examiners; this one had to come as well to complete her troubles. Things could have gone badly for Pandora, if her mind had not suddenly become clear. Finally, she left the hospital with two scars on her leg; two small scars, as though she had carelessly scratched herself. That was how superficial the wounds had been. She hastened at once to the Kaminia where she embraced her sister and her mother passionately. She took her baby in her arms and kissed it insatiably; that is how much she had yearned for it. Later, the attorney returned and related one thing and another in detail. He was a young man, blond and blue-eyed, all necktie and politeness. Pandora felt great sympathy for him and enjoyed conversing with him. The sea dog had not yet calmed down. He was still biting away at his iron bars with his teeth and cursing gods and demons.

The attorney made many trips back and forth without asking for a nickel. He was just beginning his career and was attempting to prove himself with such a trial. He liked Pandora; that much was obvious. He would take her aside and make her confess to him. Pandora, as well, enjoyed relating everything in detail. His eyes sparkled, his lips became dry, and his hands trembled. No one knew exactly why his hands should tremble. It wasn't long before the "Amerikanos" made his appearance. Pandora became wild with anger when she first saw him, but, in the end, she knew that the man was not to blame for anything. They had all been drinking their wine and singing quietly in the tavern. That good-for-nothing had no reason to think evil thoughts.

"The one in jail has need of many things," the "Amerikanos" said. "Trials cost a fortune, you know. And you, a young mother, with the unfortunate old woman, as well, to care for. So, don't you worry about a thing." He threw his wallet on the table as though saying he had no need of being bought with a dowry. Pandora's sister opened her eyes wide as she thought, "What wonderful men are in this world!"

From that day on he began to walk down to the Kaminia every other day. He was very punctual, the "Amerikanos," and he had no need to say a word to anyone.

In the end, Pandora decided to go to the jailhouse to meet with the sea dog. She neither adorned herself nor painted her face on that day—so much did her heart ache for him. She was sad and humble, an unhappy woman, who was to blame for nothing in the least—if the men had only not chased after her! The jail-keeper who asked her whom she wanted to see, eyed her breasts and then murmured, "She's certainly worth it!" That is what the jail-keeper said as he made her stand outside the bars to await the sea rover. He came through the door like a raging, wounded animal and stood opposite her. You thought that, had the bars not separated them, he would have killed that unfaithful woman right there on the spot. But Pandora did not raise her eyes to look at him. She fell to her knees on the cold stone floor of the jail, there before him, as though facing a just judge, and she shed a river of tears. Her sobs caused her breasts to rise and fall like a sail, and she said nothing other than, "My master, my husband." So patient and humble had she become. The sea rover was unable to control himself any longer. He pushed his hairy hand through the iron bars and stroked her hair. Then she grabbed his hand and filled it with tears as she kissed it. She kissed it with her flaming tongue. Peace and suffering spread throughout that unlighted jailroom as though suddenly a white flower had blossomed.

Later, the sea rover said to her: "You owe your grace to the devil that I didn't succeed in killing you."

And he smiled, a cold but painful smile.

16

Summer returned. Gypsy-Theodore and I finished school. At last, we were through with that teacher and his whipping stick. Gypsy-Theodore was a deserving person, and he found work as a helper to the barber, who had a beautiful shop with two large chairs and new mirrors and many lights. The barber's shop was situated between the coffee house and the grocery store of Anifantis, opposite the tavern of Uncle Demos. There, that poor boy would finally find peace and rest. And I was proud of him on Saturday nights when I saw him doubled over, shaking out the towels, carrying in the water for shaving, and dusting off the customers. He took the money he made and dropped it into his bank. "It won't be long now before Gypsy-Theodore is able to buy himself a suit of clothes," I thought. I went there in the afternoons when everyone was away, and I felt an inexpressible joy reclining on the straw couch down there as I read the newspaper like an employer. We were following a novel in the newspaper. Gypsy-Theodore and I said to one another, "These men who succeed in learning whatever happens in the world in all its details and then write about these things so beautifully are very mysterious people!"

This sudden nobility of Gypsy-Theodore became a great temptation to me. And one night, as we were talking about it with Father and were happily planning which road I was to take, I could control myself no longer, and told him that I had had enough of education. It was time now that I found a job somewhere, preferably in a store rather than the factory, so that I would no longer be a financial burden on my family. Father looked at me from head to toe as though disparaging my weight and my height; then he burst out laughing in a way that even Mercedes in the next room heard. That's how it came about that my suggestion was left without a reply, and we allowed matters to take their own course.

The sea rover was sentenced, but the attorney went to considerable trouble to prove that the murder was committed "in the heat of passion." Eventually, the sea rover was released from jail. He took Pandora and their child, and together they went down to the harbor to live in a distant neighborhood. Later, we learned that he had set off again for foreign places. Their old house was rented by an old, God-fearing, couple who were proud to be living so near the church. They became friends with the holy woman, Kyra-Paraskevi; they donated a hanging lamp to the grace of Mother Mary and many people came to love those two innocent and kindly people. The old woman, who knew the sacristan and who had counseled him to send poor Pantelis to the factory, came one day to worship at the church. She told us that Pandora was living her usual life down in the new neighborhood. After that, we heard nothing more about her. The days began to shorten and the nights to become cool. Father told us that, as soon as fall came, we would have to change houses. He was always thinking about going to work elsewhere. "The boy, too, will be going to high school now," he said, meaning me. Mercedes became very upset whenever she heard these words. She was expecting to become an orphan again.

Fall came and everything happened as God had planned. We

called over the relative of the landlord, who had inherited his houses, and told him that he was free to rent our rooms. We loaded every one of our possessions on a cart; we climbed on it and took the road toward new surroundings. Mercedes saw us off as far as the church square. She shaded her eyes against the sunlight and continued to wave her wet handkerchief. Gypsy-Theodore, poor boy, stood in the doorway of the barber shop, and he, as well, was crying as though someone had killed his mother or his sister. At length, the road became wider and longer. Gypsy-Theodore could no longer be seen in the distance; the handkerchief and sweet face of Mercedes could no longer be seen; the square of the church and the pepper trees could no longer be seen. A new world and a new life became our concern and our problem. How I suffered at that moment. How I suffered!

Now, nothing remains but the memory. A faint, painful memory. And many years have passed, perhaps thirty, from the time I last returned to that old neighborhood.

Emmanuel Roidis

(1836–1904)

Born in 1836 on the island of Syra to an aristocratic family, Emmanuel Roidis was taken to Genoa at the age of five. He spent the next eight years learning Italian and amassing impressions which he was to use later. One experience, the bombardment of Genoa in 1849, was to become the genesis of the only novel he wrote, *Pope Joan* (1860; translated into English by Lawrence Durrell). Following the bombardment, his parents decided to send him back to Syra to complete his education at a private gymnasium there.

The Syra Roidis found on his return from Genoa was a cosmopolitan island. It was also a haven for the expatriate Italians, to whom Roidis was endeared because they recalled memories of Genoa. One group of short stories presents these memories. But his most important stories, as the one included here, are satires on the morals and manners of the new types of islanders.

A slight deafness at the age of nineteen resulted in a trip to Berlin to seek medical aid and also to continue his education at the university. The deafness was not corrected, and, in fact, it became progressively worse, resulting in almost total deafness in later life. This deafness was, for Roidis, a personal tragedy, compounded by the loss of his personal fortune when he became a victim of swindlers. The one loss excluded him from the companionship so necessary to him, and the other from the bright life the dapper young aristocrat had always enjoyed. Even during his school years, Roidis was naturally inclined toward satire, but he withdrew more and more into his private world during his middle years. He pierced sensitivities and contemporary writers, as well as the emerging women writers, with such critical acumen that he became a target for numerous controversial attacks.

Roidis first appeared in Greek letters with a translation of Chateaubriand's *On Travelling*, with excerpts from *Spirit of Christianity, Martyrs,* and *The End of the Hapsburgs*. Most of his original work is polemical in nature. In 1875 he founded the periodical *Amsodaios* as an outlet for his satire, chiefly against politics and politicians. When a change to a more favorable government occurred a year later, he suspended publication of the magazine because it had served its purpose. His next attack was against the literary criticism and poetry of the day. With publication of *Secondary Works* (1885) *and Idols* (1893) until 1890, he concentrated on the battle begun by Ioannis Gryparis, and which to this day has not been completely resolved, on the use of the spoken language as the written one. Roidis believed that the spoken language, as analytical and periphrastic, gave concrete words and phrases which "portrayed things and not called attention to themselves."

Roidis spent the last years of his life as Director of the National Library, translating Macauley's *History of England* and Taine's *History of English Literature*, which was never completed.

Among his significant works are: *Concerning Contemporary Poetry* (1877); *Concerning Criticism in Greece* (1877); *Let There Be Light* (1878); *Aristotelis Valaorites* ((1879); *Aristotle* (1880); *"The Voyage" by Psycharis* (1888); and *Idols* (1893).

Psychology of a Husband
from the Island of Syra

I was embarrassed to admit it. Eight months have passed since our marriage, and I continue to be in love with my wife, even though the primary reason for having married her was precisely because I detested the state of a lover. I was convinced that there was no other illness quite so tormenting. I had no appetite, no sleep, no desire for work or entertainment. Except for Christina, I found everything else to be insipid, saltless, tasteless, and vexing. I remember one day how I made everyone in the restaurant laugh when I complained that the mackerel lacked salt. My relatives objected to this marriage because Christina had no dowry, and I had practically nothing: only my ancestral home, an income of three thousand drachmas from two warehouses, and a position which paid me one hundred and sixty drachmas. How could we live on that, especially since the young girl, though lacking a dowry, was an only child accustomed to the very best and loved the best society, entertainment, jewelry, and dancing? Everything that I had been cautioned about, I now found to be true! I cannot even excuse myself on the grounds that passion blinded me, nor is there, I believe, a more positive individual than I. Other lovers imagine the enjoyment of their beloved happiness to be so great that they have no fear of being deceived, but purchase this pleasure at whatever cost. But I was not romantic. I had no unusual dreams, other than to have situations return to their normal condition as they were before I fell in love. I recalled this blessed condition with the same passionate longing that a sick man recalls the time he enjoyed his health. I wanted Christina only to delight in her, to become satiated with this delight, to become weary of her, and then to begin, as before, to eat, to sleep, to go for a walk, and to play cards at the clubhouse. Even so, I never would have decided to marry her, if my uncle, whom we all considered penniless because he dressed like Diogenes and ate like a hermit, had not by chance passed away during these days owing to privation and hardships. Some time before he had asked me for a hundred drachmas to pay the doctor and drug bills, because he suffered from a chest ailment. However, instead of using the money for such purposes, he had preferred to add it to his other fifty thousand drachmas concealed inside the straw mattress on which he was found dead one morning. His misfortune caused me to think how foolish it would be to continue suffering from lack of appetite and sleep, as long as I had the means of curing myself. I married Christina as someone takes quinine to relieve a fever.

Though I was impatient, I was obliged, out of common superstition and by our bishop Lycurgus, to wait until the end of May before marrying her. Immediately following the wedding, we went to the island of Kea for a honeymoon. I can say that those were happy days. The island was green, our summer cottage comfortable, the food excellent, the weather enchanting, and even more enchanting was Christina. What had made me prefer her to all the other girls was that Christina alone had none of the customary faults of chastity, for which young maidens generally disgusted me. Not too thin, nor anemic, nor shy, nor very young. In fact, I believe she was slightly older than I. Twenty-six or twenty-eight years old, dark complexion, tall, broad shoulders, full breast, an animated glance, and an elegant foot. So that this collection of attributes might not appear unbelievable, let it suffice for me to add that she was from Smyrna.

We remained on the island of Kea throughout the summer, and my recovery made remarkable progress. I believe that I discovered the truth of "Blessed are they who possess" long before Bismarck. The romantics consider such a possession to be an imperfection, especially in marriage, which is the tomb of love. But I could never complain, precisely because I had married to bury love, desiring peace of mind, not marvelous enjoyment. And each day I succeeded in becoming more peaceful. In the morning we bathed in the sea; in the afternoon we took long walks or a boat excursion. I returned thoroughly fatigued; I ate like a wolf, and after uttering to Christina all I had to declare, I slept without once awakening until morning. I no longer dreamed, except once, a dream which I could attribute as a symptom to my total recovery.

The evening was warm, and we had gone out on the porch after dinner for a breath of fresh air. I cannot recall a brighter full moon, nor such a scintillating sea, nor such fragrant exhalations from the forest and gardens. Christina was equally charming in her white, waistless dress, or *pegnoir*, as it was called, over which her long, loose hair spilled to her knees as the deluge of a black river.

She looked at the sea, humming a song which was popular at the time: "Ernani, Ernani, won't you abduct me!" when suddenly she stopped modestly, extending her ear to the song of the nightingale which resounded from the neighboring garden.

All these circumstances were certainly very poetic, but at dinner I had eaten too much mackerel, which I had washed down, considering mackerel too heavy for the stomach, with two or three glasses of the sweet wine of Kea. I was overcome with sleep and I dreamed—not of the song of the nightingale, nor of the black braids of Christina, nor of the glittering moonlight, but that I was on the island of Syra, at the clubhouse, and that I had won three hands in a row from Aloisius Katzaitis, an expert at cards. It was futile, after such a dream, to doubt that I had not been thoroughly cured.

The following week we returned to Syra, after a three-month vacation at Kea, and I had regained my former peace of mind, all my simplicity, and two okas in weight, as I ascertained upon weighing myself on the scales at the customs offices when we disembarked from the boat.

I would certainly have laughed loudly had someone told me at the time that within a few days I would be more in love and more miserable than before my marriage. The first cause of my relapse was a dance given by the mayor in honor of the visiting Minister of the Navy, to whom he was extending hospitality. This dance was planned prematurely and unexpectedly, which left very little time for the women of Syra to make their preparations. They were all thrown into a state of confusion. For three days Christina ran out to the department stores, and on the fourth day, our entire house was converted into a garment factory. There were pieces of fabric everywhere, linings, accessories, brassieres, and shoes waiting to be fitted. I no longer found a place to sit down. In the evenings, I had to wait until nine o'clock, or later, before the seamstress cleared the dinner table so we could eat a salad or some fried smelts. Our single, and indeed knowledgeable, servant had also been pressed into service as a seamstress, and she had no time to cook. It would have been futile for me to complain about this, since the evil was generalized. It is customary in Syra that, aside from Christmas, Easter, and all the major holidays, we fast on the eve of the important dances. The most annoying thing of all was the endless preoccupation of Christina and the various scraps of paper in which she wrapped her hair at night. From the day we received that accursed invitation, it was as though I had no wife.

Great as my abhorrence was for all these preparations, I must admit that Christina's adornment was most successful. Her dress, with a long train, was a deep, cherry-red silk, and on her head she wore the last relic of her mother's box of heirlooms, a kind of antique diadem of rubies, whose red flames matched perfectly against the jet-black color of her hair. Adorned thus, she reminded me of Semiramis, Phaedra, Cleopatra, Theodora, and all the other heroines who had disturbed my sleep while I was still in school.

The house of the mayor was large, but even greater was his fear of forgetting even the most insignificant supporter to his party, even though he was a candy-maker, a skipper, a tanner, or some other businessman. The crowd, as a consequence, was immense, and, as always happens in Syra, the male dancers outnumbered the women by three to one. The men awaited the women outside the door with a dance pad in hand and followed them up the steps begging for a dance. When we entered the room, at least fifteen men dashed toward Christina, whose courage and promptness at disbursing a glance and a smile to each claimant as though she was distributing sanctified bread, I admired during this attack. This distribution continued without intermission for the duration of the party. For me alone she had nothing left, though the adventures of the dance did bring her near me once or twice. Having no desire to dance and burdened with my annoying thoughts, I sought some friendly face among the crowd, when I perceived, clinging to the wall like a tapestry, Kleareti Galaxidis, a forty-year-old spinster, of whom I was extremely fond, certainly not because of her mature beauty, but because of her kindness, her courtesy, her simplicity of manner and dress, and her apparent lack of every claim to conquest and coquetry. She danced exceedingly well, whenever she chanced to find a partner. With this old maid, I was on very intimate terms, as those of a good friend rather than of a lover. She also appeared pleased to be conversing with me, counseling me on my health or on the economies of a household. Sometimes, she sent me anise cookies so I could appreciate her excellent art of baking. My surprise, in view of this, is understandable when, instead of extending her hand to me as always, she replied to my greeting with a cold, almost hostile, glance.

"Aren't you dancing tonight?" I asked without thinking, forgetting that this was independent of her desire.

"No, *Kyrie*."

"Why, since you are the best dancer here? This is strange."

"Other things are stranger."

"Won't you tell me what they are?"

"There are some men who, having assured a young woman for years that it would be impossible to love any but a woman who is sensible, quiet, modest, a good housekeeper, now go out and marry a profligate, a coquette, a scatterbrain who has made love to all the world and who continues to do so even after her marriage."

From this, I was forced to conclude that Kleareti was not so good as she had appeared to be, nor her attentions, her counsel, and her gift of cookies without ulterior motive, as I had thought. This unexpected revelation of marital claims by the old maid, who could have been my mother had she married early, was, of course, comical. But on that evening I was upset and, instead of laughing, I was capable of taking vengeance by answering: "I don't remember ever having said these things to a *young* woman!"

Kleareti bit her lips and turned her back on me. But her remark, "She had made love to all the world and continues to do so even after her marriage," did not stop echoing through my ears like the hissing of a serpent. It is true that Christina was carrying matters too far. As I continued to spy on her, I noticed that her glances and smiles were not as impartial and casual as I had first imagined them to be. She paid greater attention to an elegant blond man, who, having danced two dances with her, remained behind her while she danced with someone else, then continued to carry on an incessant conversation with her during the intermission of the quadrilles. The strangeness was that this young man was a total stranger to me, even though the inhabitants of the microscopic Hermoupolis are all acquainted with one another like monks living in the same monastery.

I was greatly perplexed when my old friend, Evangelos Haldoupis, came to sit beside me. Evangelos was the most intelligent, but also the most evil, of all the inhabitants of Syra, impudent as an ape and more cynical than Diogenes. To avoid derision from everyone, he had discovered a way to laugh louder than anyone else over the numerous blatant infidelities of his now-deceased wife. On the walls of his office he had hung pictures of Hephaistos,

Agamemnon, Menelaus, Belissarius, Henry IV, and his own along-side those of his "illustrious brothers." During the entire five years of his marriage, not once did a complaint fall from his lips, not a reprimand, not a reproach, not a remark of any kind, but only irony, mockery, and smiles so bitter that it was questionable whether his wife died of cancer or of the sharpness of these re-marks. At any rate, immediately after the period of mourning, he again became an eligible bachelor. However, out of fear, as he said, that his spirit might become exhausted should he have to use it as before to defend his honor, he already set the following three requirements for the future Mrs. Haldoupis: that she be ugly, dumb, and wealthy. This sought-for triad of attributes he had found attached to the person of Miss Panayota Tourlotis, a kind of young hippopotamus, whose great bulk frightened away all the other fortune-hunters.

After observing me for some time with an annoying persistence, this strange man asked: "What is the matter? Your face is as down-cast as the mountains of Gourna."

"Nothing," I replied. "I have a slight headache."

"And it aches all the more because you paid no attention to me when I told you that Christina was not for you, that she has too much blood running through her veins, and that she somewhat resembles my deceased wife. I see her old friend, Karolos Vitouris, is beside her," he added, pointing to the young blond man who con-tinued talking with Christina. "It seems they have much to talk about."

"Her old friend?" I asked. "How is it that I don't know him? This is the first time I have seen him."

"Because he only returned from abroad the day before yester-day. Five years ago, before you came to settle in Syra, he was in-sanely in love with Christina. But her parents would not let her marry him, because he had no means of supporting her. He was so despondent that he wanted to commit suicide. And he would have, too, if my wife had not taken it upon herself to console him. He was, I believe, her first lover. I caught them red-handed in the garden of Koimos, one day when I had gone there to visit Anika. My wife tired of him very shortly, because he was extremely romantic. Also, it appears that he continued to think of your wife. Then they sent him to France to forget both women and to study pharmacy to succeed his father. But it looks as though he was un-successful in finding the herb of forgetfulness. Observe how his eyes

are swallowing Christina. I advise you to watch him, and don't
bring your wife to the dances so often."

"I will follow your advice."

"Don't forget. If you appear jealous, if you distress her and
seek to confine her, it is almost certain that you will make a fool of
yourself."

"Then what should I do?"

"I don't know. Since you paid no attention to my advice in the
first place, the best advice I can give you now is to imitate my
example and, no matter what happens, don't take it to heart. Think
that the event in itself is nothing. Go hang on your walls, as well,
the pictures of Agamemnon, Hephaistus, Menelaus—"

I stood up suddenly, fearful that I would not be able to withstand Satan and so spit in the face of this wicked man. At that
moment, a *cotillon* started, which seemed endless to me. Thank
God, it was finally over, and people moved to depart. I went to get
my wife's fur coat. I bundled her in it, and we walked toward the
door, when three dancers blocked our exit, contending that the
galopo finale was yet to be danced, and that my wife had promised
this dance to all three. She did not remember this. The simplest
and most usual manner of settling these demands would have been
for her to say that she was tired and thus dance with none of them.
Instead, she suggested that they choose to see who would get the
knotted handkerchief. Fate, or maybe a bit of cheating, favored
Vitouris, and my martyrdom was extended for another hour. I must
admit, however, that the music of this dance, composed by the
director of the orchestra, the violinist Patsifikos, was charming and
the rhythm so lively that wings sprouted even on the mayor's feet
and on other equally honored citizens of Syra. The tray of warm
wine which was passed around heightened the general liveliness,
and I alone stood vexed in a corner, watching Christina as she
whirled around in the arms of Karolos. Haldoupis attempted to
come near me again to pour his poison into my wound, but the
glance I gave him, I suppose, was so savage that he considered it
wiser to show me his back. We were almost the last to leave the
dance; and as we entered our bedroom, the clock struck five.

It was strange indeed—or rather it appeared strange to me,
though it was only something natural—that everything I had
suffered at that accursed dance from the slanderous remarks of
Haldoupis and the conduct of Christina, instead of making me cold
had made me love her, or at least desire her, even more than on

the day I had decided to marry her in order to cease desiring her. Aside from jealousy and the ten-day abstinence during the fasting period, what contributed to the excitement of my passion was also the remarkable luxury of her inner adornments, her silk brassiere, her embroidered petticoats, her silk shoes, and the intoxicating fragrance of iris and the aromatic oil of tropical plants. The fortunate inhabitants of large cities could obtain all these whenever they desired them with one or two twenty-five franc pieces, but for the unfortunate inhabitants of Syra, they were unusual and were only enjoyed when an important dance was being held. It was like sampling sweets, or champagne and stuffed turkey on Christmas and Easter. Thus, when I approached Christina, I must surmise that my eyes were "eloquent," as our literary authors of light reading succeed in writing, and whom I was wrong, it seems, to mock for this. In fact, before I opened my mouth, Christina hastened to reply to my glance.

"I am worn out, dear; utterly exhausted. Please leave me alone tonight."

I said goodnight with heavy heart and withdrew to my own room. I must, however, say that she was not to blame for that separate bedroom. I had suggested the idea upon our return because it was more aristocratic, and furthermore, because I had become quite satiated at Kea. Aside from other attributes, lovers have this additionally: they are unable to comprehend that they can become hungry even when satiated, nor that they can become satiated when hungry.

On the following morning, she was still asleep when I left for my office at about eleven o'clock. On returning home, I found her at the piano, good humored and animated.

"Listen," she said. "How beautiful this gallop is! I, who am unable to play anything without notes, heard this only once, but I remember it all."

With these words, she began to play the thrice-accursed gallop of last night's dance, which tune recalled my vexation.

"I am slightly dizzy," I said abruptly, "and that music annoys me. Please play it another time."

She glanced at me in surprise, closed the piano, and went to lean against the window. A bit later, I saw her waving to someone with great charm and friendliness.

"Whom are you greeting?" I asked with as much indifference as I could muster.

"The dancing teacher, old-man Kouertzis," she said.
I hastened to the window in the adjoining room and indeed
saw the old man, Kouertzis, passing by, only he was supporting
himself on the arm of Karolos Vitouris. Why had she only mentioned
Kouertzis, while, in all probability, the leonine portion of her greeting must have been intended for his companion?

That year was an exceptionally happy one for the people of
Syra who, no sooner were their accounts balanced, became dance
fiends out of joy. During the period of a single month, eleven large
and small dances were held. Christina did nothing but prepare herself all day long, exhaust herself in the evening, and rest during the
following day. And I did nothing more than to accompany her, to
remain awake until late, to be envious, to spy, and to dream about
Hephaistus, Menelaus, and Vitouris, who continued to pass under
our windows. Fortunately, the customs of the island did not permit
visits, except on New Year and on the Feast Day of the master of
the house. The visit of a gentleman to a lady on a weekday and
during workhours would have been scandalous in Syra, no less a
breach than the violation of a harem. There remained, however,
the dances and the daily meetings on the boats and the square.
Aside from these, I happened, two or three times, to see my wife
coming out of the pharmacy of Vitouris. I could not, however, consider this reprehensible, nor even mistrustful, since all the women
of high society procured their makeup and perfumes from this
place. Of course, this knowledge did not prevent me from becoming
anxious. What tormented me and worried me even more was that
I was seldom able to see Christina alone and at peace. Not even a
general on the eve of a decisive battle could have been so pre-
occupied. The excursions back and forth to the department stores
were succeeded by conferences with her friends. Now she was
provoked with the seamstress, who had not kept her promise; and
now with the only hairdresser in Syra, Anastasis, because he had
been late in appearing, or he had presumed, worthless man, to
propose combing her hair in the afternoon, because he had no
time in the evening. After all this came the exhaustion of the dance,
the somnolence immediately upon the return home, the deep sleep
until noontime, and my own tormenting wakefulness—I was not
only unable to sleep, but I could not even remain quietly in bed.
As the mirage of fountains, rivers, and green meadows tortures the
traveler in the desert, so was I tortured by the memory of the

delightful days on Kea, the solitude, the peacefulness, and Christina stretched out on the Turkish divan in a white housedress, book in hand. And what I recalled with a greater burning passion, were not the pleasures of the honeymoon, but the peace and harmony of mind and senses which succeeded these pleasures, and which allowed me to find delight in all the other pleasures of life. Now, on the contrary, I was concentrating my passions, because of envy and abstinence, on one thing alone, and this had transformed *me*, the sensible man from Syra, into a kind of Oedipus or Erotokritos, reciting plaintive monologues.

One night, unable to endure any longer, I opened the door which separated our rooms noiselessly and advanced a few steps toward her bed. The room was lighted, as usual, by a blue vigil lamp burning before the icon box. That blue light, imparting the color of a dream to reality, had also been my invention during the happy days in Kea. Her fatigue and drowsiness upon our return that evening had been so great that she had scattered her garments everywhere. Her dress was on one end of the sofa, her petticoats on the floor, her brassiere on a corner of the bed, her garland on the bust of Koraes; and strewn on all the chairs were the fan, the corsage, the gloves, and her ornaments of the *cotillon*. Her favorite cat slept on the white *burnoose*, and the stones of her bracelets and necklace sparkled on the marble hearth. The room resembled a temple to the goddess Untidiness. It was impossible that this room, which had all the constituents of beauty, should be so joyless. To the other attributes of Christina, I must add that she was accustomed to sleeping with one knee bent and her hand behind her head as the ancient statue of Hermaphroditus. At that moment, she was perhaps dreaming of her triumphs at the Club, as I surmised from the slightly parted lips forming a smile, similar to the kind she had distributed to her dancing partners. I advanced another step. But suddenly, my feet were nailed to the floor by the thought that, should I awaken her, that sweet smile would be succeeded by a grimace of displeasure, a yawn, an "Ouf!" and she would turn her back on me. Nor would such a reception be at all unjustified, since she had gone to bed only an hour before and even now, through a crack at her window, the dim light of a winter dawn was visible. I withdrew on tiptoe, closed the door, and began walking around, talking to myself. As I thought how easy it would be for that woman to make me the happiest of men, if only she loved dancing and flirting somewhat less, I had the desire to choke her.

There was no such danger for her. I believe no man exists with a softer heart than mine. Had it been essential for me to kill the chicken I must eat, I believe I would have chosen to feast on bran, as they did.

I beg those who might tend, from the above, to think me a simpleton, to consider how difficult is the position of the man who is unable, as a lover, to beg without becoming ridiculous, or, as a husband, to demand without becoming hateful. I feared both of these condemnations so that, if Christina happened to ask why I was not eating, or why I was indisposed, I replied, sometimes slandering my stomach, or my head, or my teeth, and at other times my nerves, but always attempting to conceal my true suffering, as though it were a crime. I knew very well indeed, that a woman can forgive everything, even infidelities, insults, beatings, and everything else, except for one thing alone. She cannot forgive that someone should love her more than she deserves. To the man who commits the folly of admitting to a woman the extent of his suffering on her account, there is nothing left but to part from her at once and to fall into the sea with a rock tied around his neck.

Two days following this painful wakefulness, upon returning from the office earlier than usual, I saw Christina's face change as she rushed to conceal a piece of paper she was holding behind the mirror. My thoughts immediately went to Vitouris, and my suspicion that this was a letter from him was confirmed by the increasing uneasiness and embarrassment of my wife. Nor was it possible in this case to apply my system of silent toleration out of fear of something worse, since, in all probability, the proof that nothing worse remained about which I had to fear was enclosed in that envelope.

The impending eruption was averted by the sudden opening of the door, the diffusion of perfume, and the impetuous entrance into the room of the vivacious wife of our mayor, coming over to show my wife her new coat with the feather trimmings. Christina was obliged, willy-nilly, to receive her, while I, on the pretext that I wanted to leave the women to talk over their own secrets, removed myself to the adjoining room after I had overtly taken the envelope from behind the mirror. My hands trembled as I opened it. However, instead of a letter from the romantic Karolos, I found three invoices from Poulos, Yiannopoulos, and Yeralipoulos, for silks, hats, veils, ribbons, and other items whose total came to two thousand seven hundred drachmas. The sum, of course, was a large one, but the relief I experienced at proof that I had unjustly considered myself a colleague of Haldoupis was even greater. My joy was comparable to that of a condemned man whose death sentence has suddenly been commuted to a simple fine. I was under the influence of this feeling when, following the departure of the visitor, Christina entered the room timidly, under the impression that she must explain and attempt to appease me. Instead of remarks or complaints, I hastened to embrace her wholeheartedly, saying: "Don't you fret."

She was greatly amazed. It was difficult, in fact, for her to guess how I could consider her extravagant squandering of six months' income within a period of a few days meritorious of civility and kisses.

After a while she went to prepare herself for our evening walk. But the sky unexpectedly became overcast. Lightning flashed, and it began to rain violently. I was sitting by the window of our small sitting room, looking at the yellow cataract which fell from the heights of Upper Syra, the muddy stream conveying orange peelings, broken bottles, cast-off shoes, and bodies of chickens and rats, when, suddenly, the panorama was supplanted by a deep darkness which covered both my eyes. This blindness had been brought about by the hands of Christina, who, despairing of going out, had returned noiselessly to the room and, seeing me absorbed, decided to amuse herself by blinding me. This recalled our past joyful days. Thanks to that violent storm, we at last found ourselves peacefully alone for the first time since our return from Kea. When Christina removed her hands, the expression in my eyes was, supposedly, again so expressive as to bring a slight blush to her cheeks. Then she smiled, turned, and passing by the door, went to sit down on the sofa and motioned me to come sit beside her. At precisely that moment, while I was being submerged in a sea of sensuality, the raging storm was at its peak. The rain had become a deluge; the wind ripped through the tiles of the rooftops; and repeated claps of thunder reverberated everywhere. Whether I had any inclination or not, my fate ordained that I should be romantic. The burning passions and monologues in the night were succeeded by a locking of the door and an extending on the divan under the hissing of the storm. It appeared futile then to resist what was preordained, and it was preferable that I comply with conditions as they were. I must also confess that my antipathy toward romanticism had decreased by far during this last hour. In fact, comparing the quiet pleasures at Kea with the sensual shudder which possessed me, when, after my two-week exile, Christina motioned me a short time before to go beside her, I arrived at the conclusion that the amount of blessedness a man can feel beside a woman is precisely analogous to the restlessness, envy, abstinence, and all other torments preceding it. Only the man who has undergone such purgatory can later be privileged to enter the sanctuary of the highest degree of sensuality. The doors of the sanctuary cannot be opened to us by a modest maiden, nor by an affectionate husband, nor by a beloved mistress, but only by a flirtatious, capricious woman who misbehaves during the daytime.

The dances continued, but not Christina's special favors to Vitouris, which had disturbed my sleep. Christina already appeared to prefer the sighs and blond locks of the romantic youth with the black mustache and broad shoulders, those of our pugnacious Commander of the Garrison. After a few days, however, she found him uncouth when comparing his Greek manners with the excellent nobility, the charm, and wit of the newly appointed consul from France. But neither was his reign to be of long duration. The elegance of his Paris evening suit was shortly eclipsed by the sparkling uniform and decorations of the Commander of the British division. Then came the turn of the Italian improviser, Regaldi, who toured the East to collect laurels and dollars, without deeming below his dignity those of the island of Syra. It amused Christina to keep this old swain in Syra for an entire month, and she made him appear so foolish that he was not content with what bits of poetry he wrote in her journal, but recited from the stage a hymn "To the Siren of the Aegean," which more than scandalized the people of Syra, and particularly those who understood no Italian. But I was already more than calm as I watched the favorites succeeding one another as phantoms of a mythical lamp. It would indeed have been difficult for one who desired to conquer all the world to find time to love anyone. I gradually became accustomed to this boundless coquetry of my wife, considering it a security against the greater calamity. It served as a kind of lightning rod, or, as Haldoupis might have said, "a lightning horn." The only thing that continued to worry me was that only such a little time remained for me. I had despaired of seeing her in a state of calm before the long-awaited Lenten season, when the death of the old man, Monsieur Lionis Legamenos, related to all the dancing circles of the island, suddenly disrupted the festivities. I believe that not even his millions of nephews who were his heirs attended the funeral of the old man who had deigned to die with greater gratitude than mine.

As with misfortune, so with good fortune; they rarely come alone. A few days after my deliverance from the nightmare of the dances, while checking over the five tickets of Hamburg, which I had inherited from my deceased uncle, in the *News of Sweepstake Winners,* the number 14517 blurred my eyesight. It was the third winner, and I had won 55,000 florins, or slightly more than 3000 drachmas of Syra. I ran breathlessly to announce the good news to Christina, who, fortunately, was away visiting friends. I say fortunately because her absence gave me time to think that she would feel gratitude toward me and would give me greater reward if, instead of considering me a wealthy man, she considered my eagerness to please her in spite of my limited resources. Thus, without saying a word to anyone, I left three days later for Vienna on the pretext that I was going there to consult a specialist for the nonexistent annoyance of my stomach, which I had used as an excuse for two months now to conceal my psychic torments. From Vienna, I hurried to Hamburg and, after collecting my winnings and converting these into negotiable securities, I returned three weeks later, carrying back to Christina twice the number of ornaments she had asked me to bring her. As I observed her surprise and happiness while opening the box, I thought, congratulating myself on my hyprocrisy, how much cheaper my gifts would have appeared to her had she known of the unexpected generosity of fortune. An essential term of a harmonious cohabitation with a flirtatious woman is to conceal carefully these two things: nine tenths of your love and at least one half of your possessions.

I felt no inclination to dazzle the people of Syra. I decided in favor of a quiet display of everything and an almost secret rise in standard of living. I resigned from my position, suggesting that I could earn more by working for myself. Then, under the pretext that two of the ceilings of the house leaked whenever it rained, I remodeled our entire home. The interior decorations I entrusted to an Italian refugee who was called Orsati, former set designer at the theater, La Scala. He was especially successful in decorating Christina's bedroom, which he transformed into a veritable Oriental chamber, in imitation of the bedroom of Zaires from the opera of Bellini of the same name. The resemblance was completed by heavy drapery from Proussa, a divan covered with fabric embroidered in gold, which had originally come from an old uniform of a bishop, a Persian brazier, benches with mother-of-pearl inlay, and a silver-plated Byzantine fond, transformed into a magnificent stately flower vase. All these things had been procured cheaply by the interior decorator on one of his excursions to the island of Naxos, where considerable remains could still be found from the luxuries of the Franko-Turkish days. He succeeded in adapting these, one to the other, with such taste and precise knowledge of the rules of contrasting colors and the diffusion of light, that they enchanted rather than dazzled the eye. This same precious man helped me to grab through outbidding, or as the people from Syra say, to *zevgatiso*, the Milanese cook of the bishop from Upper Syra, whose ravioli, shrimp soup, and Lenten capon were renowned throughout the islands of the Cyclades. The sadness and indignation of this high prelate were such that he considered it his duty to accuse me to his superior for proselytism.

The adornment of her nest somewhat restricted Christina's eternal preoccupation with herself. I was attempting to encourage this interest in housework, offering her everything I thought would entertain her, plants of camelias, a stamp collection, a grand piano, a stereoscope, a tutor of vocal lessons, and an Angora cat. She accepted these gifts with immense gratitude and appeared, for some time, to be enthusiastic. But one day, after asking to know the price of the silver tea set which I had offered her on her birthday, she cried somewhat plaintively:

"It is a pity to give so much money. With those six hundred drachmas, I could have ordered a velvet dress."

"Order the dress," I replied.

She jumped for joy, kissed me on both cheeks, and ran out to order the dress. Her mania for adornments appeared to be incapable of a cure, but fortunately, I was not lacking the means of pleasing her. It was right, I thought, that I should make use of her for my own pleasure. For this, I gave her a subscription to the *Chronique Elegante* and the *Vie Parisienne*, from which she was not long in learning that true luxury of daily attire did not consist in covering, as the women of the aristocracy in Syra were doing, the cotton camisoles and gingham petticoats with satin and moiré, but rather to conceal shirtwaists valued at one hundred drachmas, silk stockings, embroidered, and laces, with simpler materials. Thus adorned in her gold-decorated bedroom, where every ornament and every fold of fabric had been placed in position by an experienced technician according to its intended use while the aloe burned in a gold censer and the blue vigil lamp scattered a sapphire light, Christina resembled a statue in a temple. But neither did I concentrate for long on the blue light alone, but like Darwin, concerning the germination of plants, I also sought to examine the influence of every color of light on the imagination and senses. Rose was a soft color and most poetic was blue-green; but incomparably more stimulating than either was the light shining through the golden glass of an antique church candlelabrum.

An appropriate initiation rite before the entrance to this sacred enclosure was, of course, the pontifical dinners which the Milanese cook served us. To appreciate her pious attention to the laws and traditions of the orthodox culinary art, I need only mention that the time required for boiling eggs was fixed by the recitation of two *Ave Marias,* and was the first to teach her favorite fisherman to kill the red mullet with a prick of the needle as soon as it was taken from the net and before its spasms of a long agony had time to make the meat bitter. She boiled the gurnet with all kinds of aromatic herbs, in the juice of unripened oranges, and the turkeys, or as the people from Syra called them, the *kourneys,* she fattened on nutmeg three days before killing them. But her masterpiece was the *capron magro,* a Lenten capon, invented by Father Klimentos Ganganelli; that is, fish decorated with shellfish, mussels, shrimp, and other kinds of seafish. Even though I am from Syra, I am neither a glutton nor a heavy eater. I appreciated good food, especially for that serenity of psychic mood which follows a good dinner, one which makes us forget our troubles and causes us to see all the pleasures of life through a magnifying glass. A similar disposition of well-being, it seems, is sought by those who smoke opium or hashish. But these people have the disadvantage of being in a temporary state of cheap well-being; this unhealthy stimulation is far removed from that blessedness generated by a luxurious table which gratifies all our senses, the warmth of the hearth, the reflection of light on the silver and crystal articles, the fragrance from the flower vase, the sea aroma of the oysters, two or three glasses of old wine, and the presence of a young woman, whose face gradually flushes and whose glances sparkle.

Winter brought the dancing parties again, with all their annoyances and their restlessness. But these feelings were greatly minimized by my daily increasing confidence, not in the love or virtue of my wife, but in her coquetry and egoism, which were capable of dissuading her from every kind of dangerous foolishness. Christina did not belong, certainly, to the species of turtle-doves or doves, but rather to that of the peacocks. Her passions appeared to be confined to dazzling the other women of Syra with her extravagant clothing and with attaching to her hems an extremely large retinue of admirers. Of these, the visiting officials were, fortunately, migratory birds, somewhat moulted by age, while the sentimental phrases of the native youths resembled greatly the love couplets in which the candy-makers wrapped their caramels. Then, great as my modesty was, I was unable not to have confidence in my own excellent qualities as a husband, the condescension, the hypocrisy, the patience, the abstinence from every claim, and the willing liquidator of every bill. It is true that I suffered greatly when I saw her rubbing bare shoulders on the gold epaulets of a naval officer or withdrawing to a corner for a long time, talking secretly behind her fan, and even more, when, immediately upon our return home, she said, "Good night." But experience had taught me to consider both viewpoints. The other viewpoint was that, had she behaved better toward me, I would have loved her, certainly, much less, since only by being suspicious, envious, and restless, could passion be maintained at a high level. My earlier pedantic opinion, the one which limited happiness to the deliverance of such torments, had been converted in entirety when I came to understand how these contributed to heightening sensuality. It would have been futile, and somewhat ungraceful of me, to complain against my wife because she was doing precisely what she did to make her kisses sweeter. Had I a wife daily, I would never have had a mistress of such excellent qualities at intervals.

Thus ran my thoughts on a warm evening during Lent, as I sat on the porch after dinner, smoking and considering unjust those who proclaimed the world ugly because the roses had thorns. Instead of becoming indignant about these thorns, I considered it would have been a dark ingratitude not to bless God, reflecting that I was not yet thirty years old, that I had an income of thirty thousand drachmas, thirty firm teeth in my mouth, the stomach of an ostrich, a wife capable of incarnating the dreams of a Sybarite, and a cook for whom even Talleyrand would have envied me. I saw my life extending before me as a long procession of magnificent dinners, transparent clouds of lace, gleams of black eyes, and lamps of every color.

Alexandros Papadiamantis

(1851–1911)

Alexandros Papadiamantis was born on the island of Skiathos in 1851 and died in Athens in 1911. He studied literature at the University of Athens but failed to receive a degree. His contribution to Greek literature is mainly in the short story, which, for the most part, expresses a deep nostalgia for his island birthplace. Endowed with a unique, lyrical mood, he created hundreds of memorable characters drawn from the simple, humble life of the villages. The basic characteristics of Papadiamantis' work are a strong Christian faith, a love of nature, and a true Greek atmosphere. He attempted to penetrate the cosmic mystery surrounding man and showed the catastrophe that can result when man seeks a substitute for God. The major portion of his work was serialized in newspapers and magazines during his lifetime. After his death, several collections of his short stories and novels appeared.

Important works include: *The Gypsy Girl* (1912); *The Murderess* (1912); *The Enchantresses* (short stories, 1912); *The Dreamer* (short stories, 1912); *Christmas Short Stories* (1912); *Easter Short Stories* (1912); *New Year Short Stories* (1914); *Merchants of Nations* (1922); *The Abandoned Orphan* (1925); *Chris Milionis* (1930); and *Children's Stories* (1932).

The Dreamer

The moon, in its third day of the last quarter, appeared over the top of the mountain; and the woman, dressed in white, spoke between sighs and many passionate songs.

"If I could only climb into a boat now—I have a feeling—We could reach the other side!" And she pointed her hand to the shoreline across the harbor.

Mathios was unaware that she had shifted from the formal to the informal address at the end of her wishful expression. Spontaneously, without thinking, he replied: "I can cast the boat into the water—What do you say? Shall we attempt it?"

He had also shifted to informal address at the end of his sentence. Again without thinking, and as though desiring to test the strength of his muscles, he began pushing at the small boat.

The youth stood beside the beach, where one after the other, the onrushing waves were softly absorbed by the sands, which never became sated by the everlasting salty spatterings, just as the waters never became weary of playing their eternally monotonous game. The young woman was standing on the porch of the house which her husband, a man of fifty years, had rented so that he might receive her as his wife; a house situated near the beach, partly in and partly out of the waves, depending on the flow from the south and the ebb from the north. The boat was beached on land, stern swaying in the waves; a light, graceful boat, sleek-prowed, with a capacity for seating four or five people.

A large native schooner had put into port three days earlier to await fair weather before sailing to the end of its journey. For the third night now the skipper was enjoying the pleasures of his wife and children. The mates, all natives of the island, walked from one tavern to another to compensate, in three nights, for their temperance of weeks and months. The cabin boy, a stranger in these parts, had remained the sole guardian of the ship, the riggings, and the cargo. And the dog was the sole guardian of the cabin boy. But that evening, the tall, eighteen-year-old cabin boy, whose responsibilities were those of a sailor, except for the wages, had been delayed in a tavern a short distance away, on a side street in back of the market area around the beach. He was also consoling himself for being a stranger in a strange land. He had left the boat, partly pulled up on the beach, prow buried in the sand, stern swaying in the waves, the two oars resting on the prow; two light oars, which even a boy could manage with indescribable joy as he admired his strength, increasing in the fleeting softness of the waves, docile as the weakness of a mother for an indulgent infant who takes her wherever he desires with his whimperings and demands. Oars like two wings of a sea gull which carry the white-plumed body of a bird so long on the sea, guiding the boat in the arms and sands of the beach, as those wings guide the seagull into the cave of the sea-tormented cliff.

Mathios supported his two hands on the prow, planted his feet solidly, pushed with all his strength, and the small *felucca* yielded and fell into the sea with a clapping sound. The boat almost got away from him as it responded to his violent thrust, because he had not thought to hold the rope at the prow. Despite this, he kicked the light sandals off his feet; and before he had time to raise his trousers, he was in water up to his knees and caught the boat by its prow. He pulled it toward a small, improvised jetty.

The woman, in the meantime, had disappeared from the balcony. Within a few minutes, she reappeared from the north corner of the house, dressed in a white waistcoat which sparkled under the moonlight, and walked down to the beach. The youth saw her and sensed joy intermingled with fear. He worked unconsciously. He had not dared to hope that she would be capable of following through with her expressed desire.

The woman, not a person who expressed her innermost thoughts, said: "So be it. Let us go once around the harbor, now in the moonlight."

And after a while, she added: "I want to see how I will feel when I embark for the other side—"

She always said "on the other side" and meant her birthplace. Behind the first green mountain over which the moon had risen, another mountain, dark in the night and gray-black now under the moonlight, raised its peak as a tall, white mountain, in places covered with snow, in places barren and rocky. Here was her native land, the land of her birth. She sighed for it, as though an entire ocean separated her, while, in fact, it was only twelve miles away, and the small ridge of the green mountain was not sufficiently tall to conceal the brow of the tall white mountain in the daytime. She longed for her birthplace so much, as though she had been deprived of it for many years, while, in reality, she had been on this neighboring island only a few weeks.

Meanwhile, she laid her soft white hand carelessly on the shoulder of the youth, who shuddered at the touch; and she entered the boat. He followed after her; taking the oar in hand, he began to row awkwardly. But instead of pushing away from the pier, he pushed off toward the deep sea to the right; thus the boat tilted and struck lightly against one of the rocks on the pier.

"What are you doing? We'll break this boat, which does not belong to us—" Her words caused her to think more soberly of the matter, and she added: "Won't they be searching for the boat? Won't they be needing it? Whose is it?"

The youth replied in embarrassment: "We will only go once around the harbor and return—I don't think they will need it before we return, whosever it is."

He sat beside the oars and began to row. As she sat at the stern, the pale light of the moon fell on her face and painted those delicate beautiful features as though with silver dust. The youth looked at her timidly.

He was not a sailor, but he knew how to row as one who had been brought up beside the sea. He had come here in the middle of the year, having abandoned the high school in the capital of this state, where he had ben studying of late, because he had not been able to accept the punishment inflicted on him after an agrument with one of the instructors, who appeared to him to be more than ignorant. He was barely eighteen, but he looked nineteen or twenty with an already thick growth of brown beard and mustache.

After seating herself, the young woman cheerfully uttered this thought as an extension to her former expression of anxiety about the owner's search for the boat: "The skipper will be searching for his boat, and Uncle Monahakis for his Lialio."

The youth smiled. Uncle Monahakis was the name of her husband. She was called Lialio.

At that moment, the loud barking of a dog was heard from the deck of a boat. It was the dog of the schooner to which the *felucca* belonged. The dog had jumped on the figurehead, the rough

image of Aeolus on the prow. At the beginning, he wagged his tail
and whined, having recognized the boat. But when the boat drew
near, and he failed to recognize the cabin boy or some other
member of the crew among its two passengers, he began to bark
and howl fiercely. The youth sailed away from the schooner; but
so long as the dog could see the boat pulling away, he barked even
more fiercely.

"Why doesn't he stop?" Lialio asked perturbed.

"It seems that he has recognized the boat."

"Does the boat belong to that schooner?"

"So it seems."

The youth pronounced this conjecture with sorrow, foreseeing
that the incident would, of necessity, curtail his dream-excursion.
Strangely, however, Lialio clapped her hands like the naughty child
which has found the greatest joy in doing what others insisted on
forbidding.

"Then I'm glad," she said. "Let the dog bark for his boat, and
let those at home search for me."

The youth found courage to ask: "Where was Uncle Monahakis when you came down from the house?"

"He always spends his time at the coffee house—He never
leaves there before midnight—He always leaves me home alone—"

She seemed on the verge of tears. But with great effort, she
restrained herself and did not cry.

The youth continued to row. After a while he arrived near the
eastern mouth of the harbor. Visible now, on the opposite side,
obstructing the horizon, was the distant island with the white mountain, partly snow-covered, partly rocky. When they came near the
cliff forming the enclosing crag of the high cape of the harbor,
which was surrounded by two or three islands toward the southeast,
the young woman fastened a resolute gaze on the depth of the
horizon as though to pierce deeper and thus see more clearly what
was visible in the pale moonlight.

"Let me take a look over there, then we can return," she said.
And she sighed.

The youth became bold enough to ask: "What is that song you
sometimes sing?"

"Which song?"

"The song—which talks about the sails and helm—And about
the distant mountains," whispered the youth.

"Ah!"

Despite this, she began to sing in a tender contralto, in a athetic, whispered tone:

When will I sit at the helm, when will we fly the sail,
When will I see the distant hills, when will I cease to wail!

She repeated the couplet two or three times to an old familiar .ne.

"There, now you can see the distant mountain," said Mathios. Only instead of sails, we have oars. And we are without a helm."

The young woman sighed again.

"Is it time to return?" the youth asked. He spoke sorrowfully, ne words seeming to emerge from his mouth in a shriveled con-ition.

"Longer, a while longer," said Lialio. "The shadow from those lands won't let us look all the way into the depth. I can only see)erphi."

"Derphi is farther inward," said the youth, pointing to the land of Euboia toward the south.

"We call the large mountain of my birthplace Derphi," con-radicted Lialio, as she pointed to the east.

She repeated her song again, changing a single word.

When will I sit at the helm, when will we fly the sail,
When will I see the Derphi hills, when will I cease to wail!

The youth let out a deep breath resembling a sigh.

"A! I forgot that I am about to dislocate your shoulder with ll the rowing," said Lialio. "Truly, I'm behaving as though I've)st my mind—Your hands are not fit for rowing, Kyr-Mathios."

The youth protested. "No, no, I am not tired—The oars are uite light—Is it possible that such oars can wear me out?"

Lialio insisted on taking one of the oars. Bending forward lightly, she began to move one of the tholepins with her white ands in an attempt to shift it to a position closer to the stern. But ne youth resisted, and their two hands met in a warm touch.

"You talk about my hands being delicate," complained Mathios .iscreetly.

"Then let us fly the sail, as the song goes," the young woman .roposed playfully.

"With what?"

Unconsciously, his eyes fell on her white waistcoat. Liali laughed and leaned once more against the stern.

They had already reached the mouth of the harbor and wer between a precipitous promontory which apeared to have bee formed by an earthquake or an immersion and abruptly disrupte the fertile, harmonious line of the mountain and of the two or thre islands sealing the harbor on the southeast end. The moon con tinued to rise in the sky, obliterating the last stars, shining obscurel and timidly on the edges of the sky. The sea quivered calmly i the soft breeze, the remains of a wind which had furrowed it sinc morning. It was a warm night in May, and the soft breeze wa cooler as they approached the mouth of the harbor. Two di masses, faintly dazzling and silvery under the melancholy moo light, were outlined, one toward the east, the other toward the wes making the details of the land indistinguishable in the intermitter light and shadow. They were the two neighboring islands. Th moonlit night spread a mysterious charm. The small boat saile near one of the islands on which alternate dark and light spo were discernible; where cliffs gleamed in the moonlight and fair bushes rustled softly in the night breeze; where fierce waves bea against the caverns; where one surmised the existence of sea-bird and heard the agonized flapping of wings from the wild doves a they flew away at the sound of the advancing boat and the rowing Toward the northeast, shimmering lights were visible among th folds of the mountains, indicating the place where the small whit houses of the village high above the sea could be seen in the day time. On a small, hollow, cavernous cliff beside the island, th waves struck with a great roar, broke against the cliff, and create a disturbance in the general harmony of the moonlit sea. It wa like a self-directed orchestra, which, all alone, made more nois than anything within the enclosures, the anchorages, and th beaches on all the sea coasts and reefs struck by the waves. Instinc tively, Mathios raised the oars and laid them on the thole wher he held them for a long time. He remained silent, resembling white bird of the sea which dips playfully toward the wave, remain motionless for a few moments with one wing lowered and the othe raised before it rushes to grab the swimming fish and toss it in th air, panting with desire. Mathios sensed an unspeakable fascina tion. Lialio, as well, was experiencing an unknown attraction, an their eyes met.

"Shall we make sail?" repeated the young woman.

She had evidently not stopped thinking about this from the moment she had first uttered the words, and she repeated them now with such simplicity and naturalness in manner, as though interpreting the thoughts of both.

"Let's," replied Mathios unconsciously. And because he was unaware of what he was saying this time, he failed to ask what they would use for a sail.

But Lialio relieved him of the necessity of seeking a way to make the sail. She stood up, leaned over happily, and with dextrous gesture, took off the white pleated waistcoat and held it out to Mathios.

"You get the mast ready," she said.

Astonished, but charmed nonetheless and laughing, the youth took one oar, raised it vertically on the beam over which he sat, took the end of the rope and used it to tie the oar to the bar. Then he picked up the other oar, and untying the other end of the rope from the rung of the prow, tied this horizontally to the first oar to serve as a mast. After this he took the waistcoat of the young woman, still warm from its recent contact with her body, and attached it to the second oar as a sail.

Lialio remained in her underskirt, short to the ankles, white as the waistcoat, and in her white stockings, under which one divined the shapely ankles, even whiter. She remained with the freshness of her neck partly covered by her red silk scarf; and she sat modestly beside the stern, even shorter than she had seemed in her average, graceful height.

The breeze was stronger now. The improvised sail swelled, and the boat sailed on.

Not another word was said about returning to the harbor. To what should they return? It was obvious now that they were sailing "to the distant mountain." Mathios sat timidly, not too near her, on the other side of the stern, and gazed toward the sea to avoid keeping his eyes on his companion and thus causing her embarrassment.

At that moment the song of an Ionian poet passed through his mind, a song which had played such an important part in all the romantic loves of that period. "Awaken, my sweet love—." And he recalled another song: "Only the pale moon—," and the other couplet:

> Ravines and springs, cool waters, fare ye well,
> Soft daybreak, birds on wings, to you farewell.

He remembered these verses, but he had no desire to sing them. They seemed no longer appropriate. On the contrary, the more acceptable song of this night was the beloved song of Lialio:

> When will I sit at the helm, when will we fly the sail,
> When will I see the distant hills, when will I cease to wail!

He sat not far from her; in fact, near enough so that he was unable to glance at her comfortably, and yet, far enough not to be within the radius of the warmth of her body and breath. But he longed to look at her. Finally, looking at the waves, he became dizzy.

The youth took off his light, short overcoat and begged her to put it on to avoid catching a cold, because, with the advancing night, a cool breeze blew from the mountains. She refused to accept the garment, saying that she did not feel the cold. She was, in fact, quite warm.

Mathios did not insist, and he began to reflect on matters involving her, the portion of her fate and life with which he was acquainted. The young woman had become friendly with his family during her short sojourn on the island. Lialio was not in the first bloom of youth, although she did retain her maiden freshness almost entirely. Nor was she as newly wed in her marriage with Kyr-Monahakis. She was about twenty-five and had been married five years earlier. Kyr-Monahakis had taken her as his second wife after having buried his first wife and married off his daughter, who was a year older than Lialio. He had the impression that he was becoming twenty years younger by marrying this twenty-odd-year old girl. But as long as he remained far from his native birthplace while serving wherever the government chose to transfer him as a finance clerk, Lialio suffered little. She remained beside her parents, unable to follow Kyr-Monahakis in his gypsy wandering over Greece where he was assigned with each transfer, cast about as he said, "like an old boat, with the breeze here and the breeze there."

No breeze blew here, appropriate to her delicate youthfulness and she would wither within a month if profane hands presumed to transplant her. The flowerpot was of alabaster, the plant fragile and the flower gave forth a delicate scent, which was not for coarse ostrils. But when Kyr-Monahakis was transferred this last time, fter great effort, to the neighboring island, then he convinced his ather-in-law, who respected him more than all his peers, to send .ialio to his post that he might live with her under one roof. Tearully, Lialio took leave of her stepdaughter, toward whom she felt sisterly devotion, and who had just given birth to her child and hus relieved Lialio of all fear that her stepdaughter might bear a on, a nephew to her own child; and entering a boat, she went, or ather moved to the neighboring island.

On the day of her arrival, Kyr-Monahakis had a party for his riends; but immediately on the following day, he stopped receiving isitors at home. There was nothing strange about this, since he vas never at home. He was either at his office or at the coffee ouse. He would light his long pipe, which gave off smoke almost ncessantly down the entire length of his blue-colored pantaloons. nd he was gay, always talkative, and a loud braggart, with cheeks o red they matched the color of his tall fishing *fez*, tilted slightly n a small pleat over his right ear, the long, thick, twisted tassle anging to his shoulder.

From the second week, if Lialio happened to be awake during he midnight hours when her husband returned home, she never eased to complain and even to demand that he send her back to er native homeland. She told him how impossible she found it to ive removed from her parents. In fact, from the beginning of her strangement from her parents, her heart ached, she lost her ppetite, and her face became pale. But Uncle Monahakis very everely gave her to understand that it was improper, now that he had come, to depart so soon. He developed a long theory about ow a woman's duty was to be with her husband; otherwise the urpose of a Christian marriage was thwarted. According to the nost orthodox sources, this purpose was not the propagation of the ace, but the wisdom exercised between man and woman. Othervise, he said, in the case of childlessness, it was only natural that divorce would result. As for the propagation of the race, what ufficed, aside from the Christian marriage, was the natural marriage, which was quite different from the religious and civil marriages. He recounted passage after passage from the Old and New Testaments: "This is bone of my bone and flesh of my flesh," and "Whomsoever God hath joined, let no man put asunder," and "Man hall be the head of woman," and such-like. She buried her sobs in he palms of her hands and in her twisted braids, and she dried

the traces of her tears with the two edges of her white kerchief
The youth, as a neighbor, had been informed about all these
events, and he had secretly fallen in love with her. The graceful
movements of her lithe body were not effaced by the waistless
shift she wore. And the curls which adorned her sensual brow were
natural, not artificial. The sparkle in her deep, black eyes burned
darkly under her long lashes; red lips appeared darker in the pallor
and purity of her cheeks, which had a slight rosy tinge at the least
exertion or emotion. But the soft, peaceful fire of her eyes scorched
the heart of the youth.

In the end, he loved her. Whenever she came out on her porch,
and this she did often, she gazed at him for a moment, dreamily
and distractedly. Then she would shift her eyes from him to a
point in the horizon toward the east, toward the distant mountains.
As the moon rose this evening, with her husband absent from home,
she saw the youth standing along the beach where he had come
after dinner for a breath of sea air. Perceiving her on the porch,
Mathios greeted her. After exchanging a few words, she suddenly
and carelessly made that amazing proposal about a sea stroll, out
of which this strange journey resulted. The young woman appeared
to be living a dream life. From time to time, she would unexpectedly
awaken from her long dream and momentarily seem to regain an
awareness of the world of reality. But only momentarily. Again
she would relapse into a numbed reverie as she sank farther into
her dream.

It was already midnight. The current of the sea—or was it the
cool breeze from land—had gradually pushed the boat farther
north, because they had no rudder, until they were across the
flickering lights from the uplands village, which seemed quite near
now. They were beside the isolated northeast shore of the rocky
island, the prison yard of a few rabbits the islanders had dropped
there, and the palace of all the gulls and other sea birds. This was
White Island.

At that moment, Mathios took up the oar, because he considered it proper to dispense with the makeshift sail and return the
waistcoat to Lialio, who was feeling the cold, though she would
not admit it. He used the oar as a helm in an attempt to direct the
prow of the boat toward the right, toward the most easterly point
of the neighboring island, the one called Trahili. But he saw that
the improvised helm was not responding; the current proved to be
unfavorable. Thus, he was forced to sit beside the oars once more.

But the nymphs of the night breezes, blowing from land, or from the current of the sea, and making furrows in the passage between the two islands, seemed to be favoring Lialio. They had barely passed left of White Island, sailing beside the three islands to the southeast, when they saw a large cutter appear at the mouth of the harbor. It was sailing at top speed, prow directed toward the cliff of Trahili. Its six oars struck the water, and it raced toward the south as the runaway horse races in the field. Lialio disappeared. The youth turned to look. Automatically, he ceased rowing and remained uncertain.

"Hurry, hurry!" Lialio whispered, apprehensive that the echo of her voice would be heard. "Behind White Island. In back—"

The youth began to move quickly. They were directly in the shadow of the shoreline, which was concealed by the moon. They turned behind a protruding rock and found shelter in back of the island.

"What do you think it is?" Lialio asked impatiently.

"Unquestionably, it is searching for us," the youth replied.

"They came in pursuit of us?"

"They are following us, without doubt."

"What a large boat that is!"

"It is a cutter, which has a number of oars and sails fast."

"Trahili is to their stern. They would have overtaken us quite soon, had we gone in that direction."

"So it is well that we came in this direction."

"It was involuntarily. The current carried us here."

"The currents know what they are about," Lialio said in a tone so exquisite it resembled that of men dreaming wisely and improvising imaginary maxims. As she spoke the words, she believed that inanimate objects had a mind of their own, and that everything is subject to some divine guidance. In fact, it was to appear later that a Nereis of the sea currents or the breeze blowing from land had thoughtfully and deliberately pushed the small boat with its charming passengers into that direction.

"What are we to do now?" Mathios asked, sensing himself inwardly impotent without the assistance of a benevolent bride. Suddenly, he understood why, since the beginning of time, gynecocracy had always prevailed.

"Now," said Lialio, speaking quite correctly and with mathematical precision, as though she had anticipated this situation, "we will wait for half an hour. If they do not suspect our whereabouts

and direct their search here, we will put into port at Saint Nichola
as they proceed on down to Trahili. Do you know Saint Nicholas
From there we can walk for half an hour to Platana, the village i
the uplands. And from Platana, at God's daybreak, we can wal
again for another three hours to the large village, my village. Jus
let me set foot once more on that holy ground! But if they shoul
suspect that we are here and turn their prow in our direction, the
we will quickly head for your country, Kefala, as you call it. W
will cast the boat ashore at Kefala and return to the village on foo
'Where were you, Lialio?' 'I went for a boat ride, Kyr-Monahakis
and here I am, back again.' "

She laughed to herself as she made this remark. Later, becaus
the youth continued to be troubled, she spoke again.

"Just so they fail to overtake us," she said. "I am not concerne
about what everyone will say. I am not in the least concerned. S
long as we are innocent, then let the foolish ones accuse us!"

The youth leaned over passionately and kissed the tips of he
fingers, thinking he was certainly innocent. Many men had bee
accused unjustly, as history says, and had been condemned to di
a slow death by fire.

She added severely: "If I wanted to make love, the best wa
would have been to have remained beside Uncle Monahakis. Th
proof that this was far from my intentions is that I set out to retur
to my parents. They would never shield me if I were to love. Uncl
Monahakis, however, would shield me, and more than amply."

A sharp breeze rent the heart of the youth. He believed tha
the young woman, undoubtedly, had a lover back home. She wa
racing, then, to this lover. She was attempting this strange voyag
for his sake! And what was his own position? Under the circum
stances what was he? Was he a bridge over which two belove
beings walked toward an encounter? Death to such infernal love

O, what a flame consumed him! And at that moment, he fe
the instincts of the tragic hero who roared with inner fury! (An
how he could convert the present idyll into a drama, if only th
literary conscience of the author permitted it!) Imagine the cutter
pursuing the two escapees in their small boat; Mathios escapin
through a miraculous maneuver of the oars, only to discover, a
the last moment, that the Dreamer actually had a lover across th
way; then slitting her chest with his knife, or sinking the boat an
first drowning the woman in the waves, later himself! Finally, i
seeking the boat, they would discover the two bodies at the bottom

of the sea, under the moonlight! What a miracle of romanticism. What tears of sensibility!

With great effort, Mathios managed to control himself. Fixing his gaze on the young woman, he asked simply: "Did no one ever love you over there before you married Kyr-Monahakis?"

"Many men had loved me, let me tell you!" Lialio assured him gaily. "Only, this is how it was. No one ever loves a poor girl, except in the manner he would love a flower, taking one whiff of its scent, then allowing it to wither, or else pluck its petals apart. You see, I had no large dowry to attract the love of one who would marry me 'in pomp and circumstance,' ceremoniously, or ask me to elope with him and marry me secretly by some priest, assured that my parents, ever after, would be compelled to give my dowry whether they wanted to or not—That is why no one but Uncle Monahakis ever asked to marry me. That was better than nothing!"

A bit later, she recited the demotic song in a whispered voice:

> My parents gave me away in marriage
> Nor did they ask for my consent—

"Then why are you fleeing from Kyr-Monahakis?" asked the youth, referring to her last exclamation, the crucial point of her words.

"I'm not fleeing from him. I am simply returning to my homeland. I am going to find my parents—If Uncle Monahakis ever returns to my homeland to find me, I will be happy to see him. He knows very well I am not capable of betraying his honor. But he also knows that I cannot live in strange places."

The youth was restless. He suspected that the woman was cunning. In his imagination, he became the victim. He asked roughly: "Can it be that no one ever loved you in a manner that differed from all the others, and that you did not reciprocate to his love—before your marriage—or even afterward?"

Lialio sighed deeply and replied: "A, yes—To be honest with you—The one who did want to marry me—and the one I also wanted to marry—was drowned in the Black Sea some six years ago. The ship went down with all hands—But if you have compassion, why must you insist on cross-examining me about all this?"

Meanwhile, the cutter, for which the two escapees had not ceased being on the alert, had pushed on for some distance, its prow pointed toward the east. Suddenly, as it reached the upper

end of the third, most easterly island, it stopped for a few minutes
Mathios remarked about this to his companion.

"I know what it is," she said.

"What is it?"

"You will see in a minute."

The youth looked into her eyes.

"Be patient, and in a little while I will satisfy your curiosity
Now you will see the cutter turn its prow toward Trahili."

"How do you know? Are you a sorceress?"

"Yes, I am—a sorceress!" she said quite confidently.

Mathios sensed an invisible fear in her scintillating glance. A
that moment, the cutter turned directly toward the east and re
peated its journey at a speedier pace. An exclamation of amaze
ment escaped Mathios.

"This is the explanation," repeated Lialio. "Ninety-five chance
in a hundred Uncle Monahakis is in that cutter."

"So?"

"Those others in the boat pulling on the oars probably con
vinced Uncle Monahakis to search around the islands, hoping t
find us concealed somewhere, because they wanted to reduce thei
labor on such a long journey, and because they considered this th
wisest move. Uncle Monahakis, who knows well that I have n
business among the islands, and that I am only anxious to retur
home is certain that I headed straight for Trahili. If he finds m
before I step foot on Agnonta, the harbor of our small island, h
hopes to convince me to return to your village. That is why h
considered it a waste of time to search among the islands. Thi
would have given me time to get away from him, once I had se
foot on the other side. He has now convinced those at the oar
that they should steer straight ahead, even though they are prob
ably cursing him inwardly. What's to be done!"

"So?"

"Let them proceed for a distance, then we will cut across. Giv
me one of the oars."

The youth offered no resistance, but transferred one oar to th
stern. After a while, the cutter had proceeded so far that it wa
barely discernible in the pale horizon as a black, swaying flag an
as a dark speck on the silvery surface of the sea.

"We will start rowing now!" Lialio cried with gay charm.

Kyr-Monahakis indeed was in the cutter. The Dreamer ha
not been deceived. Half an hour after the two escapees had em

parked in the boat, he had the displeasure of learning that "his Lialio" was no longer at home. In the coffee house where he sat loudly discussing politics, his long pipe smoking everlastingly beyond his wide pantaloons, a ten-year-old boy, without shoes on his feet and wearing a striped shirt and trousers to match, entered to say: "Uncle, your wife has left you."

"She's gone? Where has she gone?" asked the good man in surprise.

"I don't know."

"You don't know? And how did you hear about it?"

"Markena's boy, Vasilis, was right there on the beach, and he saw her."

"And who is this Vasilis, son of Markena?"

Turning toward the door, the boy said: "There he is. The one standing outside the door."

Kyr-Monahakis and his companions of the moment, whose curiosity was greatly aroused, all faced the door. A second boy, about eight years old, also shoeless, hatless, one trouser leg rolled up the calf of his leg, feet wet from the sea, stood outside the door, concealing his face behind the doorpost, half his body behind the wall, staring with one eye inside the coffee house.

"You there, did you see my wife leaving?" Kyr-Monahakis called out to him.

"I saw her, Uncle," replied the child.

"And where was she going?"

"How should I know?"

Kyr-Monahakis rose anxiously. With an angry gesture, he prepared to throw his pipe to the floor. The first boy, who was standing not five steps away from him, jumped out of his way, afraid that he was about to receive a blow with the pipe. He ran to escape. Meanwhile, the boy standing outside the door vanished behind the wall.

"Do not be afraid," Kyr-Monahakis said. "If you are telling the truth, you will not get a beating. But come here—Tell me all you know—Why—"

This was the only word he uttered which disclosed his affliction, his anger, and his embarrassment.

"Here, Uncle," said the boy, assuming courage enough to stand near the doorway. "Vasilis saw the boat, and then he saw the woman get in with the son of Kalkoras. They went off toward Daskalios for a boat ride. Vasilis called me and showed me the boat

in the distance, but I did not see the people in it. We thought they
would return soon. We saw them heading in the direction of Pounta
and then they left the harbor. We waited for them to return, but
they didn't."

"How long ago did you see them?"

"Well, it is now about two hours or more—"

"And why didn't you come sooner to tell me!"

"Well, it hasn't been so very long ago—maybe an hour—a little
hour—or maybe less—a little while ago."

Kyr-Monahakis made an angry gesture again to throw down
his pipe. The child scampered away to escape.

In the meantime, Markena's Vasilis, who preceded the group
by about three hundred steps, ran with the eagerness of a child
who sought to be first to relay the good or bad news so that, first of
all, he would be rewarded, and secondly, he could be amused by
the confusion of the person involved. He arrived breathlessly at
the house of the skipper of the schooner. Standing on the porch
from where he could see the many lights in the room through the
open doorway, he started to call out with all the force of his lungs:

"Uncle, they have taken your boat!"

Vasilis had not dared to enter the coffee house earlier to give
the news to Kyr-Monahakis. But seeing that his companion had
carried the news without receiving a beating, and knowing that
the heavy rod of the skipper would not be able to reach him out
on the porch, he had become emboldened and sped to arrive at
the skipper's house ahead of his companion to have the pleasure
of making the announcement.

Captain Kyriakos, who was still sitting at the table, relishing,
picking at his food and drinking wine, as is customary to sailors
who have returned to spend a few days beside their own hearth,
thus extending and dissecting indefinitely this rare pleasure, rose
to his feet and went out on the porch.

"What is it, you out there?"

"Well, they have taken your boat."

"Who has?"

"Mathios, son of Malamos."

"Which Mathios, son of Malamos?"

"Well, the son of Kaliorna, or whatever her name is."

"And where is he taking the boat?"

"Out of the harbor."

"Is he alone?"

"A woman is with him."

"A woman is with him!" repeated Captain Kyriakos in amazement. "And who is this woman?"

The boy's voice was not heard again. He thought, in any case,
it would be best to seek protection under the balcony.

"And why didn't you come to bring me the news earlier?" cried
Captain Kyriakos.

But the boy had vanished behind the wall, and only his footsteps were heard scampering over the pebbles.

"That cabin boy, that son of the devil, must be drunk somewhere!" Captain Kyriakos said, talking to himself. "And he abandoned the boat to its own fate."

After this, he sent someone to hunt for the cabin boy. Searching fruitlessly through all the wayside saloons around the market-
place, they finally found him in a secluded tavern on a side road.

The skipper sent a message to two of his companions, who
were also enjoying the pleasures of their home, to lend him a boat
of some kind so he could go up to the schooner and launch the
large cutter with the six oars from the deck. He was not so much
concerned about the woman who had been kidnapped, as it seemed
to him, nor about the fortunate youth who accompanied her, as he
was for his newly acquired, sturdy, sleek boat. He also sent orders
to two or three boatmen down by the beach to act as oarsmen and
speed off in pursuit of the boat. Meanwhile, Kyr-Monahakis, having
learned to whom the boat belonged, appeared sadly before the
house of the skipper.

"Can you go along on the cutter?" asked Captain Kyriakos,
who had learned to whom the "kidnapped" wife (as everyone interpreted the incident) belonged.

Kyr-Monahakis had precisely this in mind; he wished to go
along with the cutter. He was afraid to be left behind in the small
town to wait in agony, for he felt that an active part in the pursuit
would distract him, and he would feel the pain to a lesser degree.
He had faith in Lialio, that she was not capable, as she herself had
said, of betraying his honor. But then, who can say? Can anyone
ascertain the mysteries of feminine idiosyncracy? He knew her
weak, dreamy disposition and her boundless, intense nostalgia. But
how could he make these people believe such things? Woe to the
man who falls into a pit full of water, even though the water is

pure. Someone may perhaps decide to extend a helping hand, but he will never cease to mock. He, however, was confident about his Lialio, as confident as any man can be about a woman. As a close friend of the family, he had kissed and played with Lialio on his knees at the time he was thirty years of age. To Lialio, five years old at that time, he had given sweets with no ulterior motives and not as a token of future aspirations. Ever since she had first begun to stammer and call him "Uncle Monahakis," to the day on which, becoming his wife, she continued to call him "Uncle Monahakis," he had considered her in turn, a child, a young girl, a woman. He had observed her well and knew that, more than any other woman, she conducted her life according to the dictates of her head and her nerves.

A half hour elapsed before the sailors of Captain Kyriakos could be persuaded to leave their homes. Another half hour before they found a boat to go up to the schooner to launch the cutter into the sea. Another half hour before they could recruit the sailors or fishermen from the beach to serve as oarsmen. Their boats, two-oared or four-oared, were too heavy and unsuitable for pursuit. More time elapsed before they were all in accord and ready to set sail. At length, they entered the cutter. Kyr-Monahakis, as the seventh passenger, sat at the helm; and they set out.

After rowing for a short time, they left the harbor. But where would they find the boat? The sea, chattering like a woman, is also as secretive as a woman, and never discloses what she has concealed. So it is impossible to find traces of a boat on the pale blue expanse of the sea. "Who can tell? She is a woman," Kyr-Monahakis finally thought to himself. Love is a deceiver, and youth is easily misled. Who could tell if she was not already a sinner? O! He was right in telling her that she was safe beside him, because, at that distance, an old man is a father substitute for a young woman. But she was also right in saying that she felt secure beside him, even were she tempted to sin. In this circumstance, however, everyone would accuse her, though she were a thousand times innocent. By his side, though she sinned a thousand times, she would yet remain virtuous in the eyes of the world. Alas! If justice were imposed by an arrowshot, only the delicate fingertips of her one hand would be pierced by that arrow, just as the princess in the fairy tale.

The small boat sailed on the sea, through the passageway between the two islands. The friendly Naiads of the sea raised a current under her keel to assist the boat, and the kindly breeze blowing down from the mountain sent the small blast of wind to its stern. The fresh breeze strengthened the arms and shoulders of the youth and tightened the soft muscles of the young woman. They rowed as though they were two experienced oarsmen. They sensed no fatigue from the light oars, and they were already half way across the watery path.

When the cutter, racing like an unbridled colt, approached the cliff of Trahili, then only did the sailors glimpse the small boat.

"What is that?"

"The boat!"

Kyr-Monahakis turned his head to the left.

"A! There she is!"

"Who knows? I don't believe that is the boat," said one of the sailors, who wished that this was not the boat to relieve him of an additional and quite wearisome task.

"That is the boat, without doubt," someone else said, who wished at all events that this was the boat, because he was consumed by such curiosity over this sea scene, to see if they would catch the boat carrying the woman and her lover.

"That's the boat," said Kyr-Monahakis. "Let's turn in that direction, boys. Let me sail closer to the wind—"

"Why is the boat heading in that direction?" a sailor asked.

"She is goint to Saint Nicholas. You see, they have chosen the shortest route. And all this time we have been dislocating our shoulders in vain, chasing after her."

"Let's turn around, boys!" cried Kyr-Monahakis. "I beg you. Quick, let's turn around. Move over someone so I can sail closer to the wind."

The six oarsmen had dropped their oars, and the cutter continued to proceed with its "generated speed." Kyr-Monahakis continued to shout, thinking only of the time they were wasting.

"Straighten out, boys; straighten out. Now, turn in that direction—Luff, cutter!"

But no one paid any attention to him. A council was taking place in the middle of the sea. Some were saying they should proceed straight ahead; others were saying they should proceed northward in the direction of the small boat. In the end, the opinion of the majority, who were electrified with anticipation of an enjoyable scene, prevailed.

They turned the prow toward the left and picked up the oars

with renewed strength, the kind of strength of an unknown chase
But the cutter was far from the mooring toward which it was
directed, about three times farther away than the small boat. And
though the cutter had triple the oar power, it also had five times
the weight and three times the submersion level.

Mathios was in time to see the abrupt about-turn of the cutter
and pointed this out to his companion.

"Look!" he cried. "They are pursuing us."

"Let them catch us now!" Lialio cried in delight. "It seems to
me they are farther away than we are."

"O, certainly. Much farther away. But they have more oars."

"And we have greater strength!" She doubled her eagerness
in rowing.

For an hour or more, along the length of that shore, while the
pale moon descended peacefully toward the west and the voice of
the rooster was heard dispatching its second call around the grain
at the slopes and farms of the valleys, a game was played between
that dreadful monster octopus pursuing the small fish, and the play-
ful, diving dolphin hunting roe. The cutter raced ahead with a
rhythmic sound of her oars in their iron tholes, with the strength
of a sinister shark, pompous and monotonous. The small boat glided
over the waves like a cock, with the soft sound of a kiss, parting
the water with its toylike oars, which caressed the sea and ran
along, accompanying it like an honorary escort, proceeding before
and after a royal carriage. One had the impression that visible
Tritons kept the boat on the surface of the waves so it would
maintain speed with its immersed keel.

It was quite evident now, however, that the cutter was gaining
rapidly over the small boat. The boat raced still harder and faster
but the cutter continued to gain ground, coming closer, until the
distance separating the small boat from the shoreline was already
negligible. Despite the speed of the racing cutter, Mathios had
time to cast the small boat forcefully in the shallow waters of the
sandy beach.

"Let there be a good voyage always!" Lialio cried gaily.

She stood up; and as she caught a glimpse of the white wall
of the small church of Saint Nicholas, shining in the moonlight
she crossed herself and was the first to jump on the sands of the
beach, wetting her toes in the water. Mathios jumped after her and
endeavored to drag the boat. The cutter was about twenty yards
from the mooring. The youth did his best to pull the boat on the

sand, in a hurry to accompany Lialio to the village. He suspected that the men in the cutter would pursue them even on land; and without quite understanding the reason, he felt quite elated about this. Lialio's last confession about the loved one who had drowned in the Euxine had no effect in calming his fears, and temptation inspired the thought that a woman who could have forgotten that unfortunate youth to marry the old man was indeed capable of abandoning the old man for some third man who lived in her native village. But if those in the cutter pursued the two on land; if she entrusted herself to his care, and they set off together for her village—O, then his love would be sanctified both on land and on sea.

Suddenly, the voice of Kyr-Monahakis, who could be distinguished under the moonlight, standing against the stern of the cutter, was heard in the silence of the night.

"Lialio! E, Lialio!"

Lialio stood pensive. Bowing her head before speaking, she said: "What it is, Uncle Monahakis!"

"Do you want to go to your parents, my love? It is well that you should go. Wait for me, and I will accompany you there to see that you do not fall into misfortune traveling all alone, my love."

"You're welcome to come, Uncle Monahakis!" Lialio replied without hesitation.

The youth stood beside her in embarrassment, gazing at her, fearfully and uncomprehendingly.

"Return in health to the cutter, Mathios, my love," Lialio said in a tone of genuine emotion. "It is a pity that I am older than you. Had Uncle Monahakis died, I would have married you."

Konstantinos Theotokis

(1872–1923)

Konstantinos Theotokis was born on the island of Zante in 1872. Both his parents came from a long line of literary figures, thus it was only natural that their son should have become interested in literature. After completing the gymnasium, he went to Paris to study but made no attempt to obtain a degree, pursuing only those courses which were of interest to him.

He traveled widely throughout Europe, stopping in one place long enough to attend particular classes at some University. At the age of nineteen, he married the Baroness Ernestine von Mallowitz and took her to live at the family castle in Zante. There he devoted himself entirely to writing, translating classical and foreign authors into modern Greek and working on his own stories, which were published in the *Noumas* and *Art*.

Theotokis returned to Germany in 1907, and in the winter of 1908 enrolled at the University of Munich. There he met Konstantinos Hadzopoulos, who had already embraced socialism. Theotokis was so deeply influenced by this new ideology that when he returned home, he organized the Socialist Party of Zante. His writings of the period reflected this ideology. With the outbreak of World War I, however, Theotokis abandoned socialism to devote his entire energies to national defense.

Two opposing currents of thought appear in the writing of Theotokis. In the short story, "The Passion" (1899), he imitated Nietzsche; in "Honor and Money" (1914), he was a socialist. The stories written between these years were inspired either by historical events and legends or by life in the villages. As a realist, Theotokis presented an environment shaped by the inflexible customs and morals of the provincials, and they become characters with natures so hardened they can never enjoy life. Deceit, petty jealousies, and hatreds ultimately lead to their destruction and to that of others.

Besides the collections of short stories, Theotokis also wrote several novels. Best known are: *The Convict* (1919); *Life and Death of Karavelas* (1920); and *Slaves and Their Bonds* (1922), the first social novel in Greece.

Village Life

That afternoon, Petros Kladis, a landowner from the village of Xaherades, waited impatiently at home. He often glanced out the window down the road leading into the village, scrutinizing each of the rare travelers as he waited for a particular man to appear. He sighed with pleasure when he distinguished the figure of Spyros Stratis, an old man from the same village, walking up and entering through the doorway. Petros greeted the old man with a smile.

"Welcome, matchmaker!" he said quickly. "You've earned the pair of shoes. They have undoubtedly accepted!"

The new arrival wrinkled his brow, remained thoughtful for a moment, then replied sadly: "What could I do, Petros? I said everything I could, but I wasn't able to bring it about. Half the embarrassment is yours; half is mine."

"A, you want to tease me," the other man said, flushing. "Which family in the village would refuse to give a daughter to my only son. Everyone knows the boy comes from a good family. He's young in years and handsome."

"In truth, they rejected him. Believe it, if you want! In fact, the charming Margarita herself told me that your son resembled a monkey. She refuses to have him."

The insult struck Petros full at heart, and he became furious. "How's that!" he cried. "My son a monkey? He's a hundred times better than she is. She isn't even worthy of the worst part of him."

"As soon as you sent me there yesterday, I went to Handrinos' house. I told him what I was after. Today, I returned for my answer. The father was enthusiastic. He had been eager even yesterday. The mother was even more eager. But that utterly spoiled girl doesn't want to see or to hear of your son. They talked to her, but it was useless. She remained adamant in her obstinacy, like the Jew in his faith."

"So, she doesn't even want to see my son, eh? And what harm has she ever experienced from him?" Petros asked, adding sarcastically, "A! She doesn't want to be married properly, with all honor and glory. She wants to exchange kisses first with the bridegroom,

then she'll consent to marry him. She'll find what she's after, don't
you fret. That's how these modern girls are. But there are other
women. I will marry my son to some other girl, even better than
she."

"Positively. Send me wherever you wish. Even to the country."

Petros failed to reply. He was thoughtful for a moment before
speaking. "It isn't your fault, Spyros, that they didn't accept us.
You performed your duty. Take the shoes, since I've already bought
them. Only, remember this: the Handrinos family will repay me for
this insult."

The old man took the gift gratefully, bade farewell, and went
out with a sad face. The other man, alone now, became thoughtful
as he paced up and down the room, the only room in the house, a
large room, whitewashed with asbestos. It was without a couch
and window panes. Nor did it contain any furniture, other than a
large bed and two carved chests placed against the wall.

"This kind of treatment was quite unexpected," he thought to
himself. "That crafty Handrinos family. This I didn't expect from
Margaro. And here I thought I had accomplished another great
service for my house. This marriage was indeed suitable for my son.
The girl has both property and a house. An heiress of great means.
And she is pretty. But she gave the impression of being so humble,
so kind, so honest. By the saint, I no longer understand the world.
Why should she reject us? Now, where will I find another girl like
her? And I simply must get my son married off as soon as possible,
because I fear he intends to set out for foreign places. Youth seeks
to travel and easily forgets the village. I will do what I can, but
later on—If the matchmaker is telling the truth—and I see no reason
why he should be trifling with me—it is Miss Margarita who will
not condescend. Her parents must have desired the match. Where
could they find someone better? God be praised! With my hard
work and my cunning, with my maneuvering, and with my business
ability, I have managed to accumulate something in this world. I
won't be leaving my son only with what my father left me. I have
cultivated the fields; I have developed and made them productive.
I will never be lacking a piece of bread; neither will my son. The
Handrinos family know this. Besides, I have never harmed them.
It's the girl, then, who won't consent. It is she, without doubt; that
spoiled girl, that depraved one of the world! But why? Is it possible
that she, a grown girl, has no desire to be married? Something else
is wrong here. Someone has been much smarter. He has persuaded

the girl, rather than her parents. If I only knew who the man was. If I knew that the affair was an innocent one, and that her honor has not been violated, I could somehow remedy the situation and still bring her into this house. But it is better that I don't bring her here. What good will it do me to bring home one of these devils who cast loving eyes at one man and another. Woe to women who dare to raise their eyes. For my part, I have no desire for this kind of woman. On the other hand, how can I overlook such an insult. O, no. If the Handrinos family ever fall into my hands, I will know how to torture them. Margaro will repay me for everything. If her father owed me any money, I would force him to sweat in court. For the time being, I must have patience."

Darkness had fallen. More and more people were now appearing on the road. Group by group, men were returning to the village from the fields; older women and young girls were exchanging laughter as they prodded their animals. The clamor of people and animals floated through Petros' window.

Petros leaned out the window to see if his family was returning. He rested his elbows on the marble to wait. Before long, he sighted his wife and two daughters, who were also walking slowly toward the village. They escorted the team, two well-fed black, shiny oxen, bellowing now and then, or fiercely turning their heads to chase the flies with their curled horns; the sheep, the one goat, and a pack animal, burdened with the plow. Other strange animals accompanied those belonging to Petros, but his animals cut loose when they came in sight of the house and recognized it. The women opened the doors of the huts. The animals passed through the threshold unconcernedly, first the larger ones, moving lazily, then the smaller ones, jostling one another until they disappeared into the darkness. The women laid aside their bundles. They unloaded the plow, which they carried into the hut to secure it in place. In loud voices, they gave one another directions and, before long, emerged from the hut, closing the door behind them. The girls went to the cellar of the house to start a fire while their mother made her way upstairs. She was a middle-aged peasant woman, tall and heavy, somewhat ugly. But on that evening, her face brightened with a kindly smile. She greeted her husband humbly and sat on one of the chests, wiping her face. Petros returned her greeting with a nod of his head, looking at her in humiliation. She became suspicious. She gave him an useasy glance as she asked: "Did the matchmaker bring an answer?"

"Your son resembles a monkey," Petros answered sharply. "So the Handrinos family say. Margarita doesn't want him."

"She actually refused?" the woman asked in surprise. "She and all her property can get lost!" After a moment's thought, she continued, "But the worst part is that, for three days now, our daughters and I have been talking about our son's marriage. The entire village knows we wanted him to marry Margarita. Now everyone will laugh at us."

"We'll put things in order," Petros replied thoughtfully. "Tell everyone that I was against the marriage because I didn't want to assume the burden of her father's debts. He who laughs last laughs best. But let's drop this conversation. Tell me, is there anything new from down below?"

"Nothing," she replied sadly. "The men worked in the fields. We had the animals out to pasture near the hut of Handrinos. In fact, the girls spoke with Margarita, but they didn't tell me anything. Demetris Lazos passed by a couple of times and stopped to look at Margarita as she planted vegetables. Do you think she is involved with him?"

"No, no," came a high-pitched voice which belonged to one of the daughters, a peasant girl, fifteen years of age, small in stature and dirty. She had just come upstairs. "She doesn't love Demetris. He is the one who keeps annoying her. I think she wants Markos Saittas. They've known each other for some time now. She told me so herself."

"Markos Saittas," Petros repeated, smiling. "She will never marry him."

It was Shrove Sunday. The churches of the village had summoned an early Mass because, as every year, everyone would be attending the dance in the afternoon.

That is how it came about that, following the short service, the villagers, men on one side, women on the other, all gathered around the dance square. Everyone, on that day, was satiated with a good dinner; everyone had drunk wine; everyone was happy and had forgotten the bitterness of life, the cares, the sterile labors, in order to feast. The women, wearing their best apparel and jewels—those who had jewels—were clean and well-groomed. Laughingly, they conversed in low tones. With their glitter and their happy faces, they gave a festive appearance to the dance, as though not a single person present had ever known misfortune. The violinists and the tambourine player stood in the center of the dance square. Directly across from the women stood many men, though not all the men of the village, of course. Some walked around, here and there, while others entered the taverns for a drink. A number of men amused themselves by singing.

The bells of the churches were ringing now, and the laughter and gaiety continued to increase. The tambourine beat a rhythmical invitation to those who desired to dance. The women took their places, eager to be chosen by the male dancer to lead the dance with him. Everyone waited with great anticipation for the public entertainment to begin. The violinists began to play the unvaried tune of the *syrto*, simultaneously swaying backward or forward as they kept in step with the dance. Everyone watched, but no one moved, afraid to presume to lead the dance without an invitation. Several minutes passed in this manner. Then a middle-aged man, tall and handsome, wearing a new pair of wide pantaloons, came forward. It was the mayor of the village. The musicians stopped playing. The women unconsciously touched the kerchiefs over their heads to see if they were securely tied; they straightened their dresses, glanced at the gold brooches pinned to their breasts, and waited. The mayor walked in their direction. Each woman held a colored handkerchief in her hand. The man chose the women of his preference, the prettiest, the most bejeweled; his own women. He took the handkerchiefs and knotted them together. Then, on one side of the dance floor, he arranged the women, some fifteen of them, side by side in a single row. The other women from the back row gave their handkerchiefs to the women in the front row. The dance was now ready to begin. The leading woman dancer made taut the line of handkerchiefs, and the other women placed their hands on this taut line. The violin again played its unvaried tune, while the tambourine beat time. The male dancer grabbed the line of handkerchiefs in the center; he led the women for two or three steps of the dance to get them started and then left the center. The women continued to step rhythmically, seriously, silently, glances lowered. They took two side steps forward and two smaller steps backward, always leading with the same foot. Together, they kept in step with the male dancer, who jumped in front of each in turn, starting at one end of the line and moving to the other. He twisted his body, crossed his feet in midair, placed his hands on his hips, and displayed all his dance skill. Now, other men joined the dance, carrying out the same movements as the leader; they had come to assist the leading male dancer. The row of dancers turned round and round the square, always unvaried; the women moved as though they were a single unit, maintaining their positions in a disciplined, orderly fashion, their glances to the ground. After a quarter of an hour, the violins and tambourine became silent. Everyone stopped dancing. The male leader of the dance took off his red *fez* and saluted the women before paying the musicians. The women returned to their former places; the men who had assisted the leader walked over to a store to dry their perspiration. The first dance was completed; the musicians tuned their violins in preparation for the second dance.

Demetris Lazos walked quickly over to the women, fearing that someone else would arrive there before he did. He asked for their handkerchiefs. He was a young man of slight build and dark complexion and had a restless glance. He selected a leading woman dancer and opened the dance, glancing around, meanwhile, to see if Margarita, daughter of Handrinos, was present. When he caught sight of her, he motioned for her handkerchief, but the girl ignored him, pretending not to have seen him as she moved a short distance away. Demetris' face became livid. For a moment, he looked wildly at her. Margarita was eighteen years of age. She had a beautiful color in her cheeks, rare facial features, and was extremely courteous. Her clothing was simple and clean. Like all the unmarried girls, she wore no jewelry. Her appearance calmed Demetris at once. He selected other women with indifference and began to dance.

Petros Kladis, who, among others, was observing the dancers, thought to himself, "O, O, she refused him. My daughters were telling the truth." He shook his head as he felt the giddiness of a dancer. After dancing a dance similar to the one of the first dancer, Demetris came to stand beside the spectators. Petros Kladis followed Demetris' movements with his eyes. Quietly, he slipped beside the young man and greeted him with indifference. The third dance was led by a young man renowned in the village for his dancing skill, while the fourth was led by Petros Kladis' son. Margarita gave her handkerchief neither to the one nor to the other. Then Markos Saittas, a handsome, graceful youth, walked over to the women. Margarita gave him her handkerchief with a smile, and Markos placed her second in line after the leading woman dancer. The musicians struck the tune, and the dance began.

With an ironic laugh, Petros Kladis whispered in Demetris'
ear: "She doesn't want you. Look how she smiles at Markos. You're
wasting your time."

Markos, meanwhile, danced gracefully, skillfully crossing his
feet as he twisted his body before each of the women and jumped
high. But it was while dancing before Margaro that he applied his
greatest skill. He was even more charming as he performed the
most difficult movements. Demetris was consumed with envy.

But that dance was finally completed. At the taverns the
people drank wine and sang; at the dancing square, the spectators
complimented or censured the costumes, jewelry, face, and dresses
of the women. After two or three more dances, it became dark.
Finally, Markos again sought the handkerchiefs of the women.

It was then that Petros Kladis whistled in Demetris' ear: "He
has taken her right from under your eyes. No one else is dancing
tonight."

His temper aroused, Demetris dashed toward the women,
grabbed the handkerchiefs Markos was tying together, and said
angrily, "I'm going to dance."

"I was here first," Markos answered resolutely.

"I'll take the handkerchiefs from you!"

The two men looked at one another in wild anger. The women
exhaled and drew back. The entire village knew there would be a
fight, but, for the moment, no one moved from his place.

"How?" Markos asked angrily. "I'm a man, too. Do you think
I must ask your permission, you scoundrel, before I can dance?"
And he pushed Demetris aside forcefully.

The women left their places immediately and withdrew. There
was general confusion. Several men approached the two men who
were arguing. A few justified the actions of Demetris; others, the
actions of Markos. The confusion increased with each moment. The
more sensible people looked on sadly, forecasting murder. Petros
Kladis, however, seeing that the situation was as he favored it, also
approached the two men. Because people generally respected
Petros, they became silent to hear what he had to say.

In a loud voice, Petros issued an order. "Let the musicians
leave. No one is going to dance."

Taking hold of Demetris, he continued in a reprimanding tone:
"You are wrong. You always confound the village with your jealousy." Then, turning to Markos, he added, "You go to her house
and do whatever you like there. Why must we be witnesses to

your exchange of signals! Margaro is to blame for everything. She almost caused a murder to be committed."

Everyone was astonished to hear this unexpected indictment. Suddenly, they all became silent. After a while, they whispered to one another, deriding the daughter of Handrinos.

As a consequence of this argument, the dance of Shrove Sunday was dissolved for that year in Xaherades village. It had become quite dark now. The women had returned to their homes. Many of the men were still at the taverns, drinking to intoxication. Some were singing at the top of their voices. Markos was nowhere to be seen, but Petros Kladis continued to remain at the dancing square beside Demetris. Finally, he said, "Let's go to my house. I want to entertain you tonight."

"As you like," the other replied.

As they walked along, cutting through the main street, bidding goodnight to the people they passed, Petros thought contentedly: "Margaro, you will never marry Markos. And you will be humiliated besides, as befits you." To Demetris, he said: "Keep an eye on those two. You will be able to make fools of them yet."

"Yes," Demetris replied.

Winter had passed. The trees began to swell now with new sap as they emerged to a rebirth under the warmth of the spring sun. In the village the laborers cultivated the fields and hopefully surrendered the ripening of the seeds to the soil. They pruned their vineyards, and, in the evening, returned home exhausted from their daily labors. At the home of Petros Kladis, they no longer spoke about the argument on the night of Shrove Sunday, nor about Margarita. Even Petros appeared to have forgotten the insult. Daily, he accompanied his laborers to the valley and worked in the fields. But Margarita lived in restlessness. Her name had been attacked on the day of the dance. The women talked about her in abusive terms. Everyone looked on her with suspicion. Although she was aware of all this, deep inside, she was being consumed by an unquenchable passion. She loved Markos with all the strength of her heart, even though he was a poor laborer; even though all the wealthy families of the village sought him for a son-in-law; and even though her own parents refused to consent to her marrying him. She saw him often, and they cried together.

One evening, around the feast of the Annunciation, she was walking up to the village with her animals. She met Markos and felt faint. As he passed her, Markos said softly, "Tonight, at your hut."

She gave him no reply, but sighed deeply as she drew her scarf closer around her face in confusion. Her eyes widened and her cheeks became inflamed to resemble the tips of the mountains which were now glistening in the setting sun. She quickened her steps, walking in a daze. On every tree, the happy birds sang their harmonious joy; they sang ever of new loves. On the ground, the grass swayed with the spring breeze which was descending from the heights of the heavenly dome, and the setting disc of the sun sprayed a red-gold light around as it prepared to dip into the golden sea. All nature had become enervated, ready to abandon herself to the tranquillity of the unknown mystery of night.

Margarita walked on. She kept asking herself about the eventual outcome of this love, which had been born involuntarily in her heart, and whose strong roots had grasped at her very being. Bitterly, she thought of those days in the past, of her lost complacence, her lost virgin purity of soul. Disturbed now by the invitation of the man who had enslaved both heart and reason, she knew fear as she passed through the dark lanes. She feared everyone, because she suspected that everyone waited to accost her with an evil purpose; that everyone, more or less, knew about her guilty passion. She feared her own discomfort; she even feared the trees and high rocks because, in her excited fancy, these things were capable of assuming speech and thus betraying her deep passion, the sweet martyrdom of her soul, which men looked upon as disgraceful. Unconsciously, she covered her ears with her hands. The small birds sang in all the trees overhead, and it seemed to her that, through the dark outlines of the branches, even they condemned her forbidden love.

That night Markos truly awaited her at the hut. It was located nor far from the village, on a fertile slope. She appeared shortly, frightened by her own action. In the dark, after she recognized him, she stood for a long time without speaking; neither did Markos have courage to speak to her. All around there was a great silence. Only the voice of the nightbirds, calling in the distance, was heard. There was no wind blowing. The lovers surrendered wholeheartedly to their love with the impulse of youth, and the dark hours of night passed quickly. Much later, they saw the half-moon rising through the cracks in the hedge surrounding the small hut, and they realized sadly that their love tryst must come to an end. Markos whispered: "My love, the night has already gone. When will we meet again?"

They both sighed, but Margarita made no response. Markos continued, "Better that we should go to my house. We'll be married at once."

"I would do that, as well, for your love," Margarita replied tearfully. "For your sake, I have cast everything aside. But not tonight. Tomorrow night, so I can at least bring some clothing with me."

The moon had risen to some height by this time, and the nightingale sang its most harmonious melody. Unconsciously, they both listened to the nightingale, deeply affected. How sweet it was! Simple at the beginning and gradually becoming shriller and more elaborate. In whistled tones, the bird sang its spring song, a hymn to the rebirth of nature, to the desire for creativity in all creatures. She trilled and gurgled and was plaintive. And the echoes in the tiny throat stirred the two young people and caused them to forget their bodies. In a little while, the other birds joined with their songs. Dawn was breaking. The lovers rose in preparation for departure.

At that moment, they heard a loud laughter from outside, a terrible, sarcastic laugh which froze the blood in their veins. Margarita became crystallized with fear. Markos whispered to her: "Let's go to my house, Margarita, if we can make it. They have discovered us." And he caught her by the hand, leading her toward the door of the hut.

Someone was pulling chunk after chunk off the hedge. A voice called beyond the hedge, yet quite near. "Well done! Well done!"

Markos recognized the voice. It belonged to Demetris. He prepared to fight in defense of Margarita. But at that same moment, through the opening at the hedge and opposite the doorway, a man appeared, holding a lamp in his hand. It was Margarita's father. He stood silent for a moment, eyes wide open, yellow as gall with shame, and wished the lovers a terrible punishment. "Accursed ones! Accursed ones!" he cried hoarsely.

His daughter let out a thin scream, but Markos had opened the door. He caught the girl around the waist, and together they started to run through the olive grove, throughout which one light after another was now appearing. The old father continued to pour curses from the hut; he wanted to give chase. And the voice of

Demetris called after them vengefully: "You have been shamed!"

By dawn, the entire village had heard in astonishment all that had taken place during the night. In every store, in every home, they gossiped about the daughter of Handrinos. Demetris carried the news at once to Petros Kladis, who, on hearing everything, looked Demetris straight in the eyes without believing, at first, that his hour of vengeance had come so soon. He stood thoughtful for a moment before smiling demoniacally. After that, he called to the women, who were preparing their animals for departure to the valley. He made Demetris relate the story from the beginning, without concealing his own joy. As Demetris finished, he added: "She got what she deserved. But she will never be able to marry him. She will always live in sin. Spyros Stratis knows, and he told me, that they have been baptized by the same godfather. And he will divulge this, because Spyros is a good Christian, and he is afraid of being excommunicated by the church."

Andreas Karkavitsas

(1866–1922)

Andreas Karkavitsas was born in Lehaina, in Peloponnesus, in 1866 and died in Athens in 1922. He studied medicine at the University of Athens, and later, as an army doctor, lived in various Greek provinces. Essentially a short story writer, he first appeared in 1885 in the magazine *Weekly* with four short stories, "Asimo," "Captain Verga," "Evytho," and "Two Skeletons." In 1905 he became a member of the National Language Society, an organization for the promotion of the vernacular as the national language. In 1908 he was among the founders of the Folklore Society, aiding considerably in the work of Nikolaos Politis in collecting folklore material. He was also one of the founders of the Educational Society (1911), whose purpose was the reorganization of Greek education.

He was a naturalist, describing life as he found it in folktales and legends of the villages, in provincial settings, and in sea voyages. A pessimist, he often expressed bitterness at the narrow social environment and the destructive powers of the close family unit with its traditional mores. Man, for Karkavitsas, was a plaything of fate.

His selected works, among which are also children's books, include: *The Beggar* (1896); *Old Loves* (1900); *The Archeologist* (1904); *Third Grade Reader* (1918); *Fourth Grade Reader* (1919); *Fifth Grade Reader* (1920); and *Stories of Our Heroes* (1922).

The Sea

My father—consecrated be the wave which entombed him—
had no intention of making me into a seaman.

"Stay away," he would say. "Stay away, my son, far from that
accursed spirit! She is not to be trusted; she feels no compassion.
Worship her as you please, honor her; yet she pursues her own
ends. Do not be deceived by her smiles, her promises of treasure.
Sooner or later, she will dig your grave or cast you on the world,
skin and bones, a broken man. Whether you mention sea or woman,
you talk about the same thing."

The man who spoke these words had spent his lifetime on a
boat; his father, grandfather, great grandfather, everyone back to
the roots of his ancestry, had expired on the cable. But he was not
alone. Even the old men of the island, now veterans of the sails,
and the younger men, whose hands were still calloused, shook their
heads whenever they sat around the coffee houses to sip their
narghile, and they would sigh as they said: "The sea is no longer
a place to earn your bread. If only I had a single grapevine on land,
I'd cast a black stone over my shoulder."

The truth was that many of these sailors could have acquired
not only a grapevine with their money, but an entire island. But
they had cast it all into the sea. They had competed with one
another to see who would build the largest boat, who would be
the first to become a captain. And I, who often heard their words
and saw how contradictory words were to their deeds, was unable
to solve the mystery. Something divine, I thought, came and
dragged all those souls and unwillingly hurled them into the open
seas as the wild north wind hurls the pebbles on the shore.

But this identical power was also driving me in the same
direction. From childhood, I had loved the sea. I had taken my
first steps, so to speak, on the water. My first plaything had been a
box of wax wicks with a small stick inserted vertically through the
center to serve as mast, with two pieces of string as cables, a piece
of paper as sails, and my inflamed imagination, which converted
this box into a three-decked barque. With beating heart, I had
gone and cast it into the sea. If you like, I had also been on that

173

barque. However, no sooner had I launched it, then it sank to the bottom. Before long, I had made a larger boat out of wood. The shipyard for this one had been the small harbor of St. Nicholas. I cast the new boat into the sea and swam after it to the mouth of the harbor from where the waves carried it off into the distance. Later, I became an expert oarsman, an expert swimmer. Only the fish scales were lacking.

"Boy, bravo! You will put us all to shame," the old sailors would say when they saw me floundering like a dolphin.

I strutted around and believed that I would fulfill their prophetic words. The books—I was attending junior high school at the time, I remember—I closed forever. I found nothing in them to accord with my passion. On the contrary, everything about me, animate or inanimate, spoke of myriad matters: the sailors with their sunburned faces and their gaudy clothing; the old men with their tales, the planks with their striking stature, the graceful maidens with their songs:

How handsome is the sea wolf, who, drenched in sea and spray,
Changes to a suit of white and takes the helm so gay.

I heard these words from the time I was in my cradle and had considered them the words of our island which lured the men to a life at sea. I longed for the day when I would become a sea wolf, to sit, sea-drenched, at the helm. I would become handsome then, truly a valiant youth. The island would look on me with pride; the girls would fall in love with me! Yes, I loved the sea! I saw her extending from the promontory far, far into the distance, until she was absorbed in the foundations of the sky like a flat, smooth and silent, sapphire slate, whose secret I was attempting to fathom. At other times, I saw the angry sea beating with foam against the promontory, overriding the precipices, clinging to the caves, dashing and reverberating, as though she sought to reach the heart of the earth in order to quench her flames. And I ran intoxicated to play with her, to make her angry, to force her into giving chase that I might feel the froth over my body, to tease her as one does the chain-manacled wild beasts. And when I saw the boat pulling up anchor, emerging from the harbor, and sailing out to sea; when I heard the shouts of the sailors turning the capstan, and the farewells of the women, my soul fluttered over that boat like a mournful bird. The ash-gray sails, billowing, the

ender riggings, the cleats which left a bright line overhead and
illed me to follow, all promised me other lands, other men, wealth,
appiness, embraces. It came to a point where, night and day, my
oul longed only to go on a journey. Even during the hour when
itter news arrived on our island and the drowning of some
lander crushed all our souls, and affliction poured mutely from
ie wrinkled brows to the soulless rocks on the shore; when I saw
ie children made orphans in the streets and the black-draped
omen, the inconsolable betrothed girls; when I heard the ship-
recked sailors recounting their ordeals, I became obstinate be-
iuse I had not been in that boat as well; obstinate and simultane-
isly chilled.

I no longer withheld. Father was away on a voyage in his
:hooner. Captain Kaligeris, my uncle, was preparing to embark
or the Black Sea. I threw my arms around his neck; my mother,
; well, begged him to take me along, fearful that I would become
l. He took me along.

"I will take you," he said, "but you will have to work. The
oat demands work. This is not a fishing boat where all you do is
it and sleep."

I had always feared my uncle. He was as fierce and mean with
ie as he was with the sailors. "Better to be a slave at Algiers, than
) be with Kaligeris," they would say to indicate his heartlessness.
ll the spoiled salted meat, the moldy codfish, the bitter flour, the
rormy hardtack, the chalky cheese, were in the storehouse of
.aligeris. And his words were always a command, a vile curse, and
n insult. Only those who were desperate ever went to work for
im. But the magnet dragging my soul caused me to forget all this.
)nly let me once set foot on deck, I would say, and I would do
·hatever work he demanded.

In truth, I fell to laboring with all my strength. I made a
ame of the rope ladder. The higher the work was, the more eager
·as I. Perhaps my uncle had intended that I should suffer right
·om the beginning so I would regret sailing. I went from scrubbing
·ecks to scraping; from mending sails to plaiting ropes; from un-
istening riggings to securing them. Now at the pump; now at the
apstan; loading, unloading, calking, painting—I was there first.
'irst? First. What did it matter to me? It sufficed me that I climbed
igh up the crossbeam of the mainmast and saw the sea below,
irrowing and receding as though submitting to me. The rest of
he world, those on land—I looked on with compassion.

"*Tse* . . . !" I said contemptuously. "Is theirs a way of life. . . .

In the midst of my exhilaration, I heard the voice of the ca▮ tain thundering beside me: "Take in sails. . . ! Furl and clew dow▮ sails. . . . !"

Startled, I ran after the sailors. They jumped to the jibbing; followed close behind. They scrambled up the yardarms; scrambled up as well. In five minutes the mast was bare. But t▮ captain continued to shout, to curse, to blaspheme. I looked at hi▮ but damned if I understood what he was saying.

"What's the trouble?" I asked the man beside me, there as v▮ were securing the main skysail.

"The twister! Can't you see? The tornado!"

"Tornado!" I shuddered. I had heard about its wonders, a▮ how it carried off whatever happened to be in its path; ripp▮ sails, toppled masts, crippled anything afloat. Now I was seeing with my own eyes. Not only one tornado, but three or four. T▮ were moving toward Batoum; two others were aproaching fro▮ the open sea. And before us the frowning Caucasus was reveali▮ jagged coastlines. The sky was covered with clouds, the sea w▮ black with a slight tremor, as though it shivered. For the first tin▮ I saw my favorite frightened.

The one tornado, lean, proud as the trunk of an elephant, clu▮ to the waters, black and motionless. The other one, stout, uprigl▮ was suddenly split in half like a column of smoke, scattered at t▮ base, and the needle-like summit remained suspended from t▮ clouds. I saw it stretch its neck from one direction to another, sha▮ its tassles like serpent tongues, as though seeking something in t▮ water, and suddenly coil and come to nestle in the darkness. T▮ third, however, ash-gray, resembling the trunk of a poplar, sw▮ lowed enough water to become bloated, then staggered and a▮ vanced directly toward us.

"Down, you! Come down!" I heard the voice from the bridg▮

I turned around. All the sailors had come down from the ma▮ Clinging to the crow's nest with all my strength, I had become cor▮ pletely absorbed in gazing at the wonder. I slid down beside t▮ captain. I saw him looking, wide-eyed, at the evil spirit. In h▮ right hand he held a black-hilted dagger, and he stood near the a▮ mast as though using it as a bulwark. Beside him, the bosun quick▮ filled the rusty blunderbuss, and all the sailors around stood pet▮ fied, looking now at the sky, now at the sea.

The tornado, however, was overtaking us on winged fee▮

wallowing water and spouting it into the sky, a black darkness and urmoil. At any moment, it seemed as though it would strip our oat or yank it into the air. Thus it came to about twelve feet from s. It sparkled all around, greenish-yellow, like smoky crystal, and its center a piston rose and fell as though attempting to extinuish a great fire in the heavens.

"Strike!" ordered the captain.

The bosun emptied his gun at the monster. Old nails, pencils, orks, were all digested in its sides. It appeared to shudder, and en it stopped. It attempted to stir again; it made a couple of ow turns in place and stopped for a second time, joining sea and ty.

"We did nothing!" the captain cried bitterly to the bosun.

"I see that, too. Purge the evil with the five-pointed star, aptain, and I will shoulder the sin."

"O Lord, I have sinned," the other murmured decisively, making ae sign of the cross.

With his dagger he carved the pentalpha on the deck and id three times: "In the beginning was the Word, and the Word as with God, and God was the Word."

And he plunged his dagger in the center of the pentalpha as iough piercing through the entrails of the wild beast.

A thunderous noise was heard as from a bursting cannon, and tremendous wave rolled over the deck. Simultaneously, a flash of ghtning and a dying roar came over the Caucasus; a hurricane roke out and the terrified sea foamed now and raged from one id to the other.

"Up sails!" the captain ordered quickly. "The topsails! The bs! Clew down fast!"

We hoisted sails, and the boat resumed its course.

Three weeks later we arrived at Constantinople with a load. here I received the first letter from my mother. The first letter, the est knife wound through my heart.

"My son, my Johnny!" my old woman wrote. "When you return the island with the help of St. Nicholas and my blessing, you ill no longer be the son of a captain. Your father is gone; his eautiful schooner is gone. Gone is all my pride and joy! The Black ea has swallowed everything. Now you have nothing left but the nall hut, your poor useless mother, and God. Blessed be your ands! Work, my son, and respect your uncle. If you can sometimes spare a little from your labors in foreign lands, send it to me to lig the vigil-lamp before the Saint, for the soul of your father."

I folded my hands and gazed at the sea with brimming eye The words in the letter appeared to be echoing the words of n father. For many years he had been master of his own boat, an now his widow was expecting some small contribution from n labors in foreign places to pay for a memorial service. As for l body, his steel sinews—who could tell what waters were beatin against them, what seagulls were tearing off his flesh, what wa was bleaching his long, slender bones!

Woe is me! We had met for the last time when he had entere Theodosia. As he saw me on high, reefing the top mainsail, I made the sign of the cross and stood speechless.

"Why do you look at him, Captain Angelis?" Kaligeris crie out to him. "I would not exchange him for your best sailor."

I prayed doubly that the sea would open to swallow me. A the time I sensed his eyes on me, I could find no peace. I dashe quickly from one end to the other, down to the bow, up the bridg crossed the staysails, grabbed the capstan, worked the pump. I understood how disconcerted I was and did not rise from his sea He only followed my movements with a plaintive glance, as thoug seeing me on my deathbed.

The following day he intercepted me as I was on my way the city. As soon as I caught sight of him, I attempted to hide; b even from a distance his gestures were so compelling that my fe froze.

"*Bre*, my child, what has happened to you?" he said. "Hav you considered well what you are doing?"

For the first time I knew tenderness in his voice. But this di not confuse me.

"Father," I said, "I've thought it all out. My decision is perha₁ not a good one, but I cannot do otherwise. I can live in no oth₁ way. The sea is calling to me. Don't try to prevent me from goin₁ Let me remain where I am; or I will go away, and you will nev₁ see me again."

"Very well, my child," he said. "Do as God enlightens you. have done my duty. I have spared neither money nor words. R₁ member this, so you will not curse me later. Go with my blessing

His last blessing, my first affliction. The sea repaid my love f₁ her during my first journey. I remained, out of necessity, a worl man for Captain Kaligeris. A workman for a piece of bread. Brea

r myself and for the Captain's wife, my mother. But, in spite of
y mother's advice, I was no longer able to respect or to work for
y uncle. If I was to continue working as a sailor, I thought, praise
e to God, there were other boats. Better to accept the insults of
stranger than those of a relative. I decided to disembark, if all
ent well, at the first port.

"May all go well, but wait and see," Captain Kaligeris said
hen he surmised my intentions.

One day I went to ask him for a bit of olive oil for my dinner.
"There is none," he said. "The olive oil is for the man who sits
the helm."

I returned a second time. The same response. I returned a
ird time. Still the same response. I waited for the day when I
as at the helm, then I took the icon of St. Nicholas, tied it to
e wheel, and left it flat. The boat started to circle recklessly in
e sea.

"*Bre*, Johnny!" shouted the captain. "Who is at the helm?"

"The one who eats the olive oil."

The sailors burst out laughing. The captain became furious.

"Go!" he cried. "Quick! Get your clothes and go!"

"I'll go! Give me my wages."

He took me to his cabin and began to figure my account in his
stomary manner.

"On this day, we came to an agreement. On this day, you
tered the boat. On the following day, you brought your clothes.
n the day after, we departed; and on the day after that, you
arted to work. Isn't that so?"

He was cheating me out of five days' wages, more or less. It
uld have been worse.

"So it is," I replied.

And I disembarked at Messina with two sovereigns.

My life as a sailor began in all respects at this time. Life and
iscipline. A true ant. An ant at work, but never at amassing wealth.
/hat was one to find; what to amass out of a daily wage, barely
ough to live on. A pair of shoes, one wage; a slicker, another
age; a bit of entertainment at Kemar-Alti, another wage. One
onth out of work, six months in debt. Try to save anything and to
pport a home at the same time. Praised be Charon who closed
at house quickly. The Captain's wife, my mother, died at the end
the year, thus releasing me from all obligations. From boat to

boat, from captain to captain, from journey to journey, ten year
I worked at sea. The words of my father resounded in my ears da
and night. But what was the good of that? Can you strike a dagg
with your fist! Had I a grapevine on land, I would have cast
black stone over my shoulder. But where was the grapevine?

I came to accept the situation. Either the waves would destro
me, or they would return me to the world all skin and bones. Ver
well, then. A gay life for me! Work and play. Was I perhaps th
only one? The entire world of sailors is thus thrashed about.
served on many boats; I also saw foreign sailors, but I sensed n
envy for their fate. The life of a sailor is everywhere identica
Curses from the captain, contempt from the stevedores, threat
from the sea, resistance from those on land. Wherever you turn
you always find yourself at odds.

One time, when I arrived at Piraeus on an English frigate,
thought of going to my village. I had never returned there sinc
my departure with Captain Kaligeris. Fate caught me in her wing
and deposited me on land like a spinning top. I went to the village
found my home in ruins, my mother's grave covered with weed:
and my old sweetheart a mature woman. I had memorial service
performed for my mother, lighted a candle to the soul of my fathe
and cast a couple of glances at my old love. With the second glanc
I shuddered.

"Who can tell?" I thought bitterly. "Who can tell? Had I listene
to the words of my father, wouldn't I perhaps have been Mario
husband today?"

Her father, Captain Pararis, was an old boat-owner, a con
temporary of my father. He had been fortunate at sea; he ha
harvested well. He had found the right opportunity, sold his boat
purchased fields, and converted them into a garden. He expresse
disdain forever for the sea.

I did not depart on the next day, as I had planned; nor on th
following day. Nor the next week. I do not know what held m
there; I had no work to do. But at every moment, a thought cam
to mind to extinguish all other thoughts: "Had I listened to th
words of my father, wouldn't I perhaps have been Mario's husban
today?"

And I strolled by her house. Every evening, at dusk, I stoo
beside the path she took to the well for water so I might catch
glimpse of her. What should I say! I fell in love with Mario. Whe
I saw her pass by with eyes lowered, proud bearing, full breast

nd wavy hair draped over her shoulders, I longed to embrace her.
.he magnet which had drawn me as an inexperienced boy to follow
he sea, now drew me toward the woman. I cast myself with equal
»assion in pursuit of the beautiful girl. At that time, Captain Kali-
;eris had acted as the matchmaker; now it was the old woman
.alomoira.

"I will not leave until I have an answer," I thought.

The matchmaker arranged everything excellently. She sweet-
ned her words and charmed both daughter and father.

"Let me tell you," Captain Pararis said, taking me aside one
vening. "Your intention is good, and honorable your behavior. I
ould ask for no better man to enter my house than the son of my
ld friend, of my comrade. Mario is yours, with one stipulation.
'ou will forsake the sea. I repeat all that your father used to tell
ou. The sea is faithless; she feels no compassion. You must forsake
he sea."

"And what will I do?" I asked. "How will I live? You know
ery well that I have learned no other trade."

"I know. But Mario has her own means."

"So I must take a wife to support me?"

"No, she will not support you. Don't be angry. I mean no in-
ult to you. You will work; both of you will work. There are the
ardens; there are the vineyards; there are the fields. They only
wait the workmen."

The truth is that I wanted nothing better. I could forsake the
ea twice over. I had become like St. Elias who had shouldered
is oar and had climbed the mountain, seeking shelter from men
vho did not even know the word for "oar." Thus I. Neither the
vord for sea, nor her color, did I want to recall. Her charms held
o secrets for me; her spell had been subverted.

"We are in agreement," I said. "You have my word."

For three years I lived with Mario on Trapi, the village of my
ather-in-law; three years of actual living. I learned how to handle
he hoe and worked beside her in the gardens, the vineyard, the
.elds. I scarcely noticed the passing of time. Labor and love.
Now we hoed the ground, now we ran under the citrus trees like
nbroken colts. I learned how to rake the ground around the
itrus trees, how to prune the vineyards, how to plow the fields.
received fifty talera a year from the citrus fruit, twenty from the
vine, and forty from the wheat, besides the cost of seed and the

expenses of operating a home. It was the first time in my life I wa
actually seeing wages in my own hands. The mute earth attempte
in a thousand ways, in colors, patterns, scents, fruit, and flowers
to say "Thank you" for cultivating it. I furrowed the earth, an
it remained furrowed, receiving my seed, concealing it from th
birds, warming and moistening it, until it could produce some
thing for my eyes that was fresh, green, golden, as though to sa
"See how I have revived the seed!" I would relieve the vine
its burden, and the vine quivered with tearful joy, opened it
eyes like a butterfly, and suddenly emerged laden with grapes.
would prune the citrus tree, and she, with graceful branches
grew proudly taller and presented me with shade for my midda
rest and fragrant sleep throughout the night. She refreshed m
entire being with her pale golden fruit. A! God blessed the eart
and gave her sensibility. Not like that heartless monster whic
you furrow, while she hastens to stamp out all traces of your tracks
You cajole her, you flatter her, you sing to her, and she pushe
you aside as though to say, "What do you want here!" and roar
on to dig your grave. Cain should have become a seaman afte
committing his crime.

At every sunset we went up to the village. Mario walked o
ahead with the capricious, bell-adorned goats. I followed behin
with the hoe over my shoulder, leading the mule loaded with fire
wood. Mario lighted the fire to prepare our supper. I lighted m
pipe, sprawled on the threshold between the pale honeysuckl
clinging to the walls, beside the basil, the mint, the marjoram
all of which required only a little hoeing and a drop of water t
bathe us gratefully in their fragrance.

"Good evening."
"Good evening to you."
"Good night."
"A good awakening to you."

I exchanged heartfelt greetings with my fellow villagers. I n
longer gazed at the sky; I no longer calculated the position of th
moon, the flickering of the stars, the direction of the wind, th
appearance of the Pleiades. And when, late, I came to anch
in the arms of my wife, what other bosom or which port coul
grant me such joy!

Thus, the second year went by, and we embarked upon th
third. One Sunday in February, my wife and I went down t
the village of St. Nicholas. Her cousin, Captain Malamos, wa

christening his brig, and he had invited us to the festivities. It was a beautiful day—the beginning of my passion. The shipyard was full of thick planks, masts, boards, filings, and shavings. The wind was saturated with salt spray from the sea, the smell of pitch, tar, and hemp. Mounds of oakum, mounds of scrap iron. And from one end of the shore to the other, there were handsomely painted boats, overturned brigs, dismantled caïques, unpainted keels, full of barnacles. Skeletons of caïques, schooners, sharpies, ketches, stoops, and yawls, some with prow's beak and crossbeam, others completed to the gunwhale, and others still unfinished. The gear of the sailor world, the simple passions and great hopes, stood on the sand, all constructed of wood. The guests were the entire village; dressed in Sunday-best they wandered about the drydock scaffolding; the children jumped in and out, the men stroked the beams admiringly and spoke a multitude of words to them. They discussed their value; they estimated the speed; they offered advice on everything to the master builder.

The brig of Captain Malamos, propped on the drydock, with sword-edged prow, with garlanded stern, with buttresses protruding to right and to left, resembled a centipede asleep on the sands. The deep blue sea glittered playfully and came up in small waves around its base, sprayed foam over it, and sang to it secretly in confidential tones:

"Come, come, I will let you slumber in my bosom. I will nurture you with one of my kisses. Why do you remain a soulless piece of wood, heavy with sleep? Aren't you tired of the drowsy forest and the useless existence? For shame! Come out to wrestle with the waves; dash forth with bare breast to tear the wind to tatters. Come and be the envy of the whale, companion of the dolphin, haven of the sea gull, song of the sailors, pride of your captain. Come, sweet one, come . . . !"

And that novice, the brig, began to creak, eager to leave her bed.

Captain Malamos, freshly shaved, laughing, in serge trousers and wide belt, his wife beside him attired in silks, were both glowing as though they were being remarried. And the violin, the lute and flageolet, spoke of happiness to the far ends.

I—What shall I say? I was not at all happy. Seated in a daze, I watched the sea pull up around my feet, and a kind of sadness knotted my heart. After many years, I was seeing my first love again, attired in blue, laughing and gay. I was under the impression that

she was gazing straight into my eyes, that she spoke sorrowfully
that she scolded me plaintively:

"Unfaithful one, deceiver, coward . . . !"

"Get thee behind me, Satan!" I said, making the sign of the
cross.

I attempted to leave, but my feet refused to move. My body
heavy as lead, was glued to the mooring rock, and my eyes, my ears
my entire soul, were abandoned to the wave, listening to the complaint:

"Unfaithful one, deceiver, coward . . . !"

I was almost in tears.

"E, my sweet, what are you thinking about?" I heard a voice
beside me saying.

I saw Mario, beautiful as ever and laughing, with her handsome
figure. I became confused, as though she had caught me in the act
of infidelity.

"Nothing," I said. "Nothing—Help me up because I feel dizzy."
And I clung to her as though afraid that the wave would carry
me off. The priest, wearing his vestments, was reading a blessing
over the new boat. The master builder began to issue commands:

"Release the aft shores!"

"Release the fore!"

"Release the keel and hull . . . !"

One by one the props were released from the hull, and the brig
started to quiver, as though numbed by inactivity, still lacking
courage to face the new life. The children who had climbed on deck
were running together, fore and aft, side to side, with a deafening
roar, resembling hoofbeats of a herd.

"Foreward!" shouted the master builder.

The guests shoved, and the boat sighed as it slipped into the
water like a duck, carrying its beardless crew.

"Happy voyages, Captain Malamos. Happy voyages! And may
the nails be gold!" the entire sailor world cried, sprinkling sea water
over the pair.

But at that moment, a child was injured and fell fainting into
the water. I lost no time, but leaped into the sea fully clothed. I
dived twice before pulling the child out of the sea. I pulled him
out, but I myself became ensnared in the nets of the sea. From that
moment, sleep and joy left my side. The dip into the sea, the cool
water which embraced my body, dragged my soul after her like a

lave. I recalled the incident and felt as though something alive was
unning kisses up and down my spine.

I no longer went to work. I attempted to go to the gardens, to
he fields, to the vineyards, but they were all depressing. All day
ong, I wandered aimlessly along the shore, dipping into the water,
reathed the salt spray, rolled in the seaweeds. I hunted for sea
rchins and crabs. I often went down to the harbor and timidly
pproached the group of seamen to hear their talk of a ship's gear,
f voyages, of storms and shipwrecks. But no one turned to look at
ne. I was a villager, you see, an old farmer. They were seamen,
avage dolphins! The younger sailors looked at me as though to say:
Well, from where did that ghost appear!"

The old sailors sometimes condescended to say: "Johnny, you've
ecured your mooring rope well. You no longer fear the wind nor
ea. You are safely anchored." Which was tantamount to telling
ne: "You are through. You are dead. You no longer live in this
vorld!"

I returned to the beach to relate my affliction to the waves. In
ne end, I began to make small boats, intricate boats with oak decks,
vith masts and sails; and with my flaming imagination, I saw them
s three-decked barques.

Mario would look at me and make the sign of the cross.

"Mother Mary, my husband has lost his mind!" she would say.
She vowed to take candles to the Virgin of Tinos; she walked
arefoot to the country shrines; she had my clothing blessed and
rayed to the saints to restore me to my senses.

"Say what you like, Mario," I said to her one day. "Neither
fferings nor saints can cure my illness. I am a child of the sea. She
alls to me, and I must go. Be it sooner or later, I must return to
ny trade."

Upon hearing this, she dressed herself in black.

"Your trade!" she cried. "Are you going to become a sailor! Will
ou end up as a sailor!"

"Yes, a sailor. I cannot help it. The sea calls to me . . . !"

But Mario did not want to understand; she did not want to
ear of it. She began to cry, to implore me. She clung to me; she
ulled me tightly against her breast, she covered me with kisses.
he cursed the sea, she abused it, she blasphemed against it. In
ain! Neither her embraces nor her kisses could secure me any
onger. Everything became stale, even going to bed with her.

One evening at sunset, as I was sitting by the promontory, I saw a frigate with full sails. She resembled an immense rock in the sea. All her riggings were clearly discernible. I saw the jibs, the mainsails, the topsails, the foresails, the cleats of her masts. I can even say that I saw her hatchways. I saw the quarters of the captain, with his icon of St. Nicholas hanging high and his vigil light sleepless. I saw the hammocks of the sailors, I heard their conversations, I smelled the woodwork. I saw the galley, the water barrels, the pump, the capstan. My soul sat on that frigate like a sorrowing bird. I heard the wind rip through the riggings and sing the song of a sailor's life. Women, blonde, brunette, dark-eyed, flower-decked, and bare-breasted—all paraded before me offering their kisses. I saw noisy harbors, smoke-filled taverns and wine glasses, sweet-voiced santouris and lutes. And then, I heard a sailor singling me out to his companions and saying:

"Here is one who denied the treasures of the sea because he was afraid!"

I jumped to my feet. Not because I was afraid, never! I ran home. Mario had gone to the stream. Slinging my bundle of clothing over my shoulder, I took our small savings from beneath the pillow and disappeared like a thief. It was dark when I arrived at St. Nicholas. I untied a rowboat and went out to the frigate.

From that time, life has been a dream. You may ask: have I no regrets? Even I do not know. But even now, should I return to the island, I would never find peace.

The sea calls to me.

Konstantinos Hadzopoulos

(1868–1920)

Konstantinos Hadzopoulos was born in Agrinion, in southern Peloponnesus, in 1869. He studied law at the University of Athens, but early abandoned his practice to devote himself exclusively to literature. In 1898 he founded the literary magazine *Art*, in which many young writers of the day, fighting for use of the vernacular as the literary language, published their works. The first translations of English, German, and Scandinavian authors also appeared in *Art*.

He wrote poetry, short stories, novels, plays, essays, and also translated Goethe and other north European authors. He first appeared in Greek literature with two collections of poetry, *Songs of Loneliness* (1898) and *Elegies and Idols* (1898). In 1900 he went to Germany where he remained for the next ten years. There he became interested in labor movements and finally turned to socialism. Two novelettes, *Love in the Village* (1910) and *The Castle of Akropotamos* (1909), are social documents describing life in the village with its moral taboos, superstitions, and poverty, all of which allow for exploitation.

In a significant collection of short stories called *Taso, In the Darkness and Other Stories* (1916), Hadzopoulos showed the influence of Zola and Flaubert. He was pessimistic about life, especially that of the villagers and criticized the social structure which forced men to act as they did. His principal themes were about life that remained unfulfilled and happiness that was never achieved. He became a great influence on the writers of the twenties.

Other important works include: *Superman* (1915); *Simple Manners* (1920); *Evening Legends* (1920); *Annio and Other Stories* (1923); and an important novel which introduced symbolism into Greek literature, *The Autumn* (1917).

Clara's Dream

No one had ever fallen in love with Clara. She refused to believe that she was so ugly, though this was precisely what she feared. But no one had ever fallen in love with Clara. When her companions chattered about their love affairs, Clara was compelled to create imaginary stories and give an account of the young men who had once loved her and of the other young men who continued to pursue her. She sometimes gave her companions accounts of romantic walks in the forest with one of these young men; or perhaps it was a boat trip on the river and the lakes with someone else. All these adventures took place on Sunday, the day Clara spent at home keeping her invalid mother company, or in the evening when she walked in some secluded spot to breathe fresh air and to weave (more appropriately out in the open) the dream she would be relating to her companions on the following day.

Her current friend was a foreigner with dark complexion and black hair and eyes. He had come from a distant land where no snow ever fell; where the fields disappeared into the horizon in a fiery haze, and the trees bowed their branches to the ground; where strange birds inhabited the forests, and the columns and rooftops of the white, silent castles are reflected on the motionless waters of the rivers. Clara's companions observed her wide-eyed when she mentioned that this friend had a castle of his own, to which he contemplated taking her to live with him.

Even Clara awaited his arrival, as she had awaited the arrival of all the others who had not come. Then, one evening, as she was returning home, she suddenly sensed that someone was following her, softly and slowly, with footsteps which kept pace with her own. She began to wonder if this might not, in reality, be the man. But immediately her blood froze; her heart beat so rapidly that she was unable to glance around. Only when she reached the door of her house and had passed through it, did she venture to turn around for a quick glance. Across from her, she saw two eyes sparkling under the lamplight. She climbed the stairway quickly and ran to the window. The man was still standing motionless beside the lamppost, his eyes fastened on her window.

Clara spent a sleepless night. The following night was also a sleepless one, because the footsteps of the stranger had followed her again as on that first evening. When she had entered the house, he continued to stand like a column, facing the window, his eyes fastened on it. On the third night, Clara could endure it no longer. She put on her hat and walked out into the street. She had come out of the house intending to go directly to the stranger. But, involuntarily, she walked straight down the street without a destination in mind. One street led into another, and that one out to a large park. Clara passed through the well-lighted section where people were gathered and entered one of the narrow, serpentine, dimly lighted lanes, which disappeared under the dark arches of the branches. Forcing her way through here, she walked on. She sensed the stranger following her, slowly, always keeping pace with her own footsteps. She walked on until she came to a small lake, half-concealed under the trees, which divided the park in two. When she stopped, the footsteps stopped close by. And when she sat on the park bench at the water's edge, the stranger was suddenly there beside her. A light, suspended among the trees, made it possible for her to glimpse his face again. His complexion was dark, his eyes black, and his long hair was also black. It was *he.*

Clara gazed at him without speaking and without moving, as though seeing a vision. Small, slender trees, bowed with twisted branches; trees with scattered leaves or long, bladelike strange leaves, glistened familiarly golden, then became alien in the rosy glare of the sunset. The expanse of fields, which disappeared in the horizon in a fiery vapor, lay outstretched before her in a blue haze. She had read in books about the inner eyes, which sometimes perceived before the outer eyes, and she gazed on at the stranger, waiting for him to speak. She dreamed and ardently desired that he speak to her about his distant homeland; about the strange birds which inhabited the forests; about the silent, yellow waters which reflected the white castles. But the stranger kept his mouth closed. He only looked at her in silence, without moving. He remained silent throughout the first evening. He remained silent like that, and motionless, throughout the other evenings, one after the other, when Clara pulled him like a magnet, and he came to sit beside her, quite close to her on the same bench, there by the edge of the water.

Now, Clara no longer spoke to her companions about this story.

She remained silent and thoughtful throughout the day, as though living in a dream, and waited only for nightfall.

At last, one silent, dark evening, as all the others had been, one evening when the lamplight fell on the stranger's face, as always before, and crawled at his feet like a serpent, and quivered on the edge of the water in a yellow reflection, Clara moved closer and caught his hand.

He did not move, but allowed her to hold his hand. He looked into her eyes and asked: "What is your name?"

Clara gave him her name.

Without taking his eyes off her face, the stranger whispered: "You are not the one."

Clara's eyes widened.

"You are not the one. You only resemble her. You resemble her in ugliness."

Clara attempted to withdraw her hand, but he clung to it.

"The same hanging lips; the same skinny, bony, protruding cheeks; the same colorless, lifeless eyes; the same deformed body. She was also the ugliest of them all. No one looked at her; no one spoke to her; no one ever loved her. Men cannot see the soul. And she had a beautiful soul. She never spoke, and she never laughed with me. She always shrank into a corner, all alone, and looked on without a sound, like a leopard in a cage, while the others laughed with me. They could not compare with her. They were no match for her; she had no equal in the world. That is why I killed her."

Clara was startled, but the stranger held fast to her hand.

"I loved her, and I killed her," he continued. "But do not be alarmed. I do not love you. You are not the one, as I had imagined when I first saw you. I thought her soul had passed on to you, that she had been resurrected in you, that she had returned to live in you. But no! You are not *she*. You are trembling. She never trembled. She unbraided her hair of her own volition and placed it in my hand. She handed me her hair, and I wound it around her throat, pulled on it, held the knot tight—and her eyes, her beady eyes, opened wide in chaos, expanded as doors leading to an abyss. Her colorless eyes sparkled white like plates of enamel; her sightless eyes sparkled like blood-red rubies. I became frightened and covered her face. I saw only her naked body, over which pale yellow and rose lights flickered; over which flashes of blue-white, green, and gold blended. You know how muted colors blend on a

sunny day in mother-of-pearl; or how the silver moon flickers in the
waters as it pierces through the leaves. That was how her naked
body sparkled before me."

Clara looked at the lake to which he was pointing. The waters
were dark; the moon was nowhere in sight. Only the lamplight
flickered yellow by the edge of the water in front of them.

"Why did I kill her while she was naked? She disrobed of her
own accord when she saw that I wanted her naked, and she
stretched out on the bed. You have no desire to disrobe. You have
no desire to unbraid your hair of your own volition."

He brought his hand to her throat as though seeking to un-
button her blouse. Clara shuddered again.

"Don't be frightened. I don't want you," the stranger said and
withdrew his hand. "She permitted me to disrobe her, and she fell
across the bed naked. I did not defile that body. I covered her
naked body because it also frightened me as it glittered. I only
kissed her hand, which was hanging down uncovered. Her hand
was so small, so soft. Your hand is ugly. I will not kiss it. Coarse,
wide, deformed—You are not the one; you only resemble her. You
have no desire to die; you have no desire to love. You cannot love.
Or can you? Tell me!"

He paused, continuing to hold her hand tightly.

Clara bowed her head. She was unable to look at him. She
dreaded meeting his eyes which sparkled, opened wide, black, cold,
under the yellow light.

Presently, she felt him withdrawing his hand. When she found
courage to lift her head, the stranger had disappeared.

The following evening, as she was returning home, she failed
to hear the footsteps following her. And when she looked out her
window, she did not see him standing across the street, waiting.
She waited, waited, but he failed to appear. Later, she went out
into the street and involuntarily made her way to the park where
she sat on the bench by the edge of the water. For hours, she remained there alone, motionless, her head bowed. The stranger
failed to appear. It was only when she stood up to leave, and just
as she entered the dark, narrow lane, that she thought she heard
a short, ruffled, loud, wild laugh, which faded behind her as though
it were near, or perhaps distant. Perhaps the laughter could only
have been within her.

Stratis Myrivilis

(1892–   )

Stratis Myrivilis, pseudonym for Stratis Stamatopoulos, was born in 1892 on the island of Mytilene. He studied literature and law at the University of Athens. For many years he was a journalist, editor of many publications, General Program Director of the Greek National Broadcasting Institute from 1936 to 1951, and for many years the director of the Greek Parliament Library. His literary productions include short stories, novels, critical essays, and poetry. He has been widely translated into French, German, and English. Most well-known is his *Life in a Tomb* (avaliable in English translation, 1931), whose international theme of war is an expression of the need to share all suffering and joy with others. The lyrical realism characterizing his work is composed of two elements: love for lyrical expression and ability for characterization. He is especially gifted in describing the erotic fragrances of nature and the wild, unspoiled vegetation as they affect (most particularly in *Pan*) the most primitive aspects of man.

His selected works include: *Red Stories* (1914); *The Teacher with the Golden Eyes* (1932); *The Green Book* (1935); *The Blue Book* (1939); *Small Flames* (1942); *Vasilis Arvanitis* (1943); and *The Mermaid Madonna* (1955).

The Cat's Eye

We hadn't seen one another for a long time. Every now and then, my friend left Athens to travel to Crete where he supervised some work going on in the harbor. From time to time, he wrote me warm, friendly letters and took no offense when I failed to reply. Perhaps he was aware that a man who had been a professional writer for a lifetime develops a dislike for the pen; and that whenever he is able to escape from such enslavement, he does so with the joy of a youngster playing truant from school. In any case, he knew that I never stopped thinking of him with love.

It was one of the most pleasant autumn days in Athens. Sunlight poured over the sloping streets of Mount Lykabettos, filling the hearts of men with joy. As I was passing along Homer Street, I knocked on his door. I stood for a moment before ringing the doorbell, simply out of habit, certain that he would still be away. I only rang the doorbell, as though to greet my absent friend, and I had already turned to leave when the door opened. He saw me, and an unexpected delight glittered in his mauve eyes. He kissed me and took me into his office, his arm about my waist.

His office, as always, was full of architectural drawings, blueprints, and charts. On his huge work table, which was almost as long as the room, his bundle of papers, tied with black ribbons, lay in a row. And in a familiar place, to the right of the inkwell, was Nella's photograph. It was a full-length photograph in a dark brown folder, without ornamentation, leaning against a very simple silver base.

She was a girl from Istanbul, only daughter of a former professor of the Great School of Nationalism. A truly beautiful girl, with hair combed straight back. Thus, her divine forehead, austerely serene, was disclosed and contrasted strangely with her eyes—a pair of large, sensitive eyes, as romantic as the eyes of all the girls from Istanbul, and full of affectionate tenderness. I suspect that such eyes now blossom only in the shadowy side streets of Phanari —eyes which perpetually retain within their gaze the hoarfrost of an unfinished dream. Most of the time, a part of the pupil is concealed by the upper eyelid, which makes the enchantment of the eyes almost irresistible.

193

He saw me admiring the beautiful photograph and said in a voice which was almost violent: "You know, I haven't seen her for two months—"

This amazed me because I knew of his deep love for this girl, whom he was even planning to marry.

"Two months?" I asked, thinking that perhaps I had heard wrong.

"Two months."

It was only then that I noticed how changed my friend was. His bronze face seemed to have become longer and wrinkled from loss of weight, and an abundance of gray hair blended with his sideburns, although he was only twenty-seven years old.

"Don't you love her any more?" I asked simply.

He looked at me somewhat amazed. This was a question which he had not had the courage to ask himself. Afterward, he looked at the picture for a short time and shrugged his shoulders. A bit later, as though to explain this gesture, he remarked: "Do I know?"

He pursed his lips as children do when they are attempting not to cry. The storm disturbing his soul passed over his sincere face. He turned to look at me. I had been watching him, a trifle bewildered. I patted his hand.

"Don't tell me anything you shouldn't," I said. "Or anything which distresses you."

"Oh, no, no," he said. "You've come at the right moment. I've thought a lot about you lately. My heart really longed for you. You know, I have really been through some difficult days. Even now. I wanted to tell you about them. They are so unusual—"

He looked at me attentively for a moment before speaking again.

"I understand from the smile that just flashed through your eyes exactly what is running through your mind. You've been thinking that all men, once they have fallen in love, at once consider their situation different, amazing, and marvelous. You've told me all this before. Every intelligent man is afraid to get into this pack of 'couples' who understand one another with the same flaming, senseless words, who live for a time under the spell of an amorous submission, which in general consists of elements subjective to each individual involved—A selfhypnotic condition, actually pitiful, climaxing in everyone in the same generative motions, which are ridiculous enough and which have been repeated without variation since the beginning of Adam and Eve. You see, I remember your theories—almost to your very words."

"Words without deeds are empty and futile."

"At any rate, you know that I am an engineer. A practical man accustomed to converting his ideas into cement blocks and looking at life with the mathematical precision of its phenomena."

"An engineer in love is only one more man in love and nothing more."

"All right—then listen to an incident. You know Nella well enough. She's a girl of culture, isn't she?"

"Extremely cultured. Well-bred and good by nature, too."

"That's right. And sensitive and courteous?"

"Unquestionably. I honestly believe that she is a type of woman rare in intelligence and rich in heart."

"Yes. Now do me the favor of listening to me carefully. It was an afternoon—two months ago. Exactly two months and three days, counting today. I had just returned from Crete and had hurried to her house. We were all alone in the small dining room. You should remember the room well. You had dinner there with us two or three times last winter. We were sitting on the sofa—the gray one. I, Nella, and Doudou, our cat. You wouldn't remember the cat, because I only gave her to Nella three months ago. She's a very beautiful cat, brown and black, with a soft, silky fur and green eyes —green as emeralds. A tame animal, affectionate, and coquettish, really adorable. Nella raved over her. I'm relating everything as it happened. It was afternoon, and the room was peaceful and full of shadows. I was lying with my head on Nella's lap, looking up at her as she bent over my face. I was intoxicated with happiness— that serene kind of happiness which is completely detached from every sensual agitation, but which is nevertheless the happiness of love. She was looking deeply and strangely into my eyes, like one who bends over to look into a well. One other time I had observed her looking deeply into my eyes in that same strange manner. Suddenly, she said to me, 'Close them! Close them!' and covered my eyelids with her hand. I sensed a hoarseness in her voice, which was almost like a cry. Doudou was beside us, rolling on the cushions of the sofa, rubbing against Nella's elbow and against my head, seeking caresses. I took Nella's hand away from my face and kissed her palm, always with my eyes closed.

" 'All right,' I said. 'My eyes are closed. But why?' "

"I heard her rapid breathing. She spoke nervously as she said: 'So—So I can kiss your eyelids. So—Keep them closed!.'

"I waited for her to kiss my eyelids, when suddenly I heard a wild meowing from the cat; a sharp, indescribable shriek.

"I leaped up, and what was I to see! Doudou was writhing on the carpet, her small face covered with blood. She was spinning like a top, tearing her hair, and howling mournfully. With the claws of her two front paws, she was struggling to remove a pin which had been thrust into her eyes. It was my pin; I recognized it instantly. A long tie-pin with a coin bearing the image of Sappho, a small, gold antique. I realized at once that it was my pin, for I remembered Nella's hand fumbling at my tie while my eyes were closed. My hair stood on end in horror. I couldn't control my wrath and my revulsion. The cat disengaged herself from the pin and staggered drunkenly out of the dining room. She kept stumbling over the chairs as though she couldn't see at all; and behind her on the polished floor, she left a trail of blood which was dripping down her face and which she streaked as she walked over it. The extracted eye dangled over her nose like a crushed grape. She continued to shriek unceasingly.

"I turned to look at Nella. She had fallen face downward on the sofa. She was crying, sobbing, her back and waist twitching convulsively.

"'What have you done?' I asked.

"I was beside myself. Bending over her, I shouted like a maniac: 'What have you done?'

"I felt horror at thought of touching her. Horror and loathing. She tried to formulate words, but was unable to do so. She stammered between tears and convulsions which shook her sides mercilessly. I got up and left—I left as though I was being pursued. I felt the need of transfusing her with my horror for what she had done and with my contempt. I left, and I called to her as I was going out the dining room: 'I loathe you. I never want to see you again!'

"I saw her arm raised in terror at these words. It raised and fell back on the sofa like a bird's wing. That was all. Since then, I haven't seen her. It is now two months and three days—"

He was silent, rubbing his forehead with the palm of his hand, obviously distressed and unhappy. Then he spoke again, wearily, more as though addressing himself: "Isn't it dreadful?"

He asked the question in a toneless, low voice, and one knew that he had asked himself the same question many times and that he expected no reply.

We were both silent for a short time. Then I asked: "And if it happened—by accident—without any intention?"

He removed his hand from his brow and looked at me calmly. He spoke in a tired voice as he said:

"No. Not for a moment did I have the slightest doubt. I'm positive that she removed my pin to thrust it into the cat's eye. I know that this was the reason she had me close my eyes. Perhaps there's a terrible Asian flaw in this creature. I sensed all the details of the crime as soon as I heard the animal shriek and saw her extracted eye. Furthermore, there's not the slightest doubt about it. Nella herself sat down and explained everything to me. I left for Crete at once—on the first boat. I only returned the day before yesterday. And yesterday, I received this letter, which is actually a document. But does it constitute an explanation and a solution? Here."

He pulled out the drawer which was in front of him and took out a big blue, thick, envelope. It had been ripped open with the fingers, without the intervention of a letter-opener. It had been torn open and ripped with impatience. Through the frayed edges I could see several pages of stationery of the same color as the envelope. He tossed the envelope to me.

"Read it," he said. "I really want you to read it. I've read it several times, and I still don't know what to think. I want you to tell me what you think—you who aren't mixed up in all this, who aren't in love, and can think coldly and impersonally—What do you think I should do? The whole thing has me whirling, and my mind is exhausted from thinking about the incident."

Here is the letter:

My darling,

Forgive me for still calling you this today, knowing how low I have fallen in your estimation since that tragic afternoon. But I can't go on any longer. Forgive me; I must come to you, even though it is only through a letter. I've never stopped for one moment, all my breathing hours, to be full of thoughts of you, to live with the remembrance of you, with the bitter agony of your memory. This feeling holds me powerless in its claws. Day and night, asleep or awake. Late yesterday, I was able to sleep for an hour or two, and suddenly, I awoke to find myself crying. You must know that I hadn't been crying when I had gone to bed; nor did I awaken because of a bad dream or a nightmare. Nevertheless, when I awoke I found my pillow soaked and my face wet with tears. So—my body had been crying all the time I was asleep. It was crying of its own accord, as we cry for a loved one, silently, so that the body won't be aware of its plight.

I haven't seen you since that afternoon. I learned that you had taken the first boat to Crete. Naturally, I understood the meaning of this sudden trip. You were going away from me; you were going away from Athens. And your flight was one of horror and pain. What can I say? You were right. More than anyone else in the world, I can understand exactly how right you were; how natural such a move was.

All this time, I have been writing letters to send you. Every night, as the silence of the house filled me with agony, I felt the need to seek refuge near you. To talk with you. I would write the letters, write the address in Crete, seal the envelope, and stamp it. When day broke, I always realized that I had neither the strength nor the right to send the letter to you. As time passed, I became accustomed to this and tossed the letters into a drawer of the bookcase. There is a crack in the bookcase where the wood does not hold together very well. I tossed the letters in there, and it seemed to me that I had dropped them into a mailbox. I tried to fool myself, to pretend that I was writing to you, that perhaps you were hearing me as I spoke to you, the way everything used to be. (Ah, I write "the way everything used to be," and with terror I see this short phrase coming between us with all the coldness of the passage of time, which converts the dearest days of our lives into distant chronological occurrences. The days which contain the essence of our lives! I wonder—can one possibly conceal human hearts that are still glowing, still flaming, with such a pallid phrase?)

By continually telephoning to your club, I learned of your arrival. The boy replied: "He's here. Out on the veranda. Hold the line a minute while I go call him." My heart started to beat abnormally. I wanted to shout, "No! No!" But I didn't have the strength to pull the receiver from my ear. Then I heard your footsteps approaching the telephone. You always bring your heels down hard. I heard those footsteps as they reverberated along the marble and approached. I heard your voice as you said nervously to someone, "One moment!" Then I recovered, and I replaced the receiver, terrified. What could I possibly say to you? I would begin to cry as soon as I attempted to speak.

But yesterday, I finally decided to write, now while you're still in Athens. I would write to tell you everything. What is "everything?" My unhappiness, my longing, and my love. So I started today, early in the morning, and I am writing you this long letter. I will certainly mail this one.

Darling, you must listen to me, no matter how much you hold me in contempt, no matter how much you "loathe" me. Listen to me, because I'm calling you from the depths of my love and desperation. You must heed me in the same way those on shore heed the voice of a drowning man who cries for help.

I simply want to explain my dreadful action to you. You have every right, as far as I'm personally concerned. But you haven't this one right: to forbid me to explain to you how "that" occurred. I beg you, allow me to explain. I have absolute need, at this moment, to do so.

The beginning of this whole evil situation started three months ago. It was evening—out on the veranda—after we had finished eating, and later. Mother and I were listening to the radio—to a selection of songs from the Vienna station. Father, buried in his armchair, was reading. I was deeply moved. "Father," I said, "aren't you listening?"

Without raising his eyes from his book, he said, "Of course I'm listening. I read and listen at the same time." I stood up, went over to him, and took his book away by force. "No," I said, "you can't do both simultaneously."

Thus, the situation was reversed. He laughed, rubbed his beard, as he is in the habit of doing, and settled down to listen to the music. I glanced at the open page by chance and began to read. It was *Oedipus Rex* in the ancient text. The last time I had read the work was in school. My glance fell on verses 1268 to 1280. Since that time, I've repeated them so often; they've tormented me to such an extent that now I can write them without stopping. These verses are horrible.

> He rips from off her dress
> The golden broaches she was wearing,
> Holds them up, and rams them home
> Right through his eyes. . . .
> Not once but many times,

> And all the while his eyeballs gushed
> In bloody dew upon his beard. No, not dew,
> No oozing drops, but a spurt of black
> Ensanguined rain like hail beat down.

At times, I read the verses mechanically. Then I reread them, once, twice, three times. And each time their horror attracted me more, their repulsiveness overpowered me like a strong, bitter drink which burns the throat and nearly chokes the drinker, but which is drunk precisely for the kind of intoxicating poison it brings. Troubled, I closed the book, and then I, too, sat in a corner and attempted to listen to the music. I struggled to listen—without success. I opened wide the windows and doors of my soul to let in the melancholy songs of Schubert and thus replenish my soul and make it tremble with a sweet tenderness. It was useless. The horror of the ancient tragedy remained in my soul, thrust there like a dagger. And the action described in verses 1268 to 1280 continued to take place before my eyes with all the savagery of its details. Finally, my head began to ache. I went to bed and felt the unbearable necessity of rereading the passage before going to sleep. I took the book, and lying flat on my back in bed, I read the passage again. I read the verses once, twice, thrice, five times. Finally, I closed my eyes and read them verse by verse in the darkness. I still saw the numbering of the verses—the numbers at every fifth verse, glittering one by one in the black void.

My misery began that night—a weird, unusual kind of misery. Ridiculous and childish at depth, but it was so persistent, so unconquerable. With passion I began to imagine the pain from a "golden brooch," if thrust directly into the pupil of the eye, exactly into its black center. What pain and horrible sensation, I said to myself, one would feel precisely at the moment the point of the pin entered the eye, that is, when the protective covering over the pupil would be pierced and shattered. That would be a double sensation. Not only the sharp pain jarring the entire body to the last extremities to which the pain would reach, but also the impression of the contact of the hand thrusting in the pin, at the moment of the thrust. And even the part that sound would play in this sensation. I imagined the sound as a small, yet dreadful particle, a "click" to be sensed rather than heard, similar to the sound of a pin thrust through a very tautly stretched piece of satin. I imagined all these reactions which such a gesture would provoke in the body;

I thought of them so vividly, so steadily, that I almost felt them on my own flesh.

I placed my fingers lightly over my closed eyelids to feel the eyeballs quivering under the tips of my fingers, a living, movable object. And simultaneously, I repeated the frightful words of the description. Not all the words—only those which gave me the keenest sensation of the act: "He rips from off her dress the golden brooches she was wearing, holds them up, and rams them home right through his eyes. And all the while his eyeballs gush. . . . A spurt of black-sanguined rain like hail beat down."

Every time I went to the mirror for my toilette, I began, against my will, to look very closely at the pupils of my eyes. I carefully examined the exact point where the golden brooch of Jocasta would have to enter, right in the center of the pupil. It was as though the little black dot existed solely for the purpose of marking the spot where I should stab with the tip of the pin. It became an obsession with me to record the execution of the ancient lines on my own eyes each time I looked into a mirror. This was true whenever I looked closely into someone else's eyes, my father's, my mother's, and yours. I went through this each time I looked intimately into the eyes while I was kissing one of you.

One day I advanced to the following state of mind. I brought my face up to the mirror, then I took a long hat-pin from an old hat, opened my eyes wide, aimed, and rammed the tip of the pin against the glass, directly at the center of the eye. I heard that fragile "click" on the surface of the mirror—a molecule of sound. On the crystal of the eye, such a sound would be even more imperceptible; perhaps only the two fingertips holding the "brooch" would be able to conceive it. This test gave me a slight shudder at the moment of striking the mirror. Afterward, as I thought about it, I cried out in fear. I was afraid of myself. From that day on I was possessed by a secret terror. Perhaps in time I would be unable to control myself; I would be unable to withstand the fearful desire for pain which would distort my body, should I actually execute those verses. I was truly in a state of panic. I held my fists over my eyes to protect them, to save them. I did the same each time I looked into your blue eyes, where the black dot is more noticeable in the dark mauve pupil. Similarly, I avoided kissing my mother, but even more my father, whose white beard I already pictured as soaked with the "red hail," with the "black rain," of the extracted eyeball. I arrived at the point of thinking of the results of this deed. I saw Father, eyes torn from their sockets, as the old Oedipus; and I, posing as Antigone, guiding him on his way, as the group appears on a German copper engraving.

One day a satanic coincidence occurred to intensify my madness. A Turkish captain, a friend from Istanbul, came from Anatolia. On his regular trips to the Anatolian harbors, he had collected a number of icons from pillaged churches and Turkish coffee houses. He thought they could become a profitable trade, and he brought them back for resale to refugees and collectors. Father went to see them and selected five or six splendid Byzantine religious paintings: two of Christ, one of the Virgin, one of St. John, and a larger icon of the Incorporeal Heavenly Host, which was a gathering of archangels. They were armed with flaming swords, and all had terrifying wings which dragged on the ground, and large, widespread eyes. Well—the pupils were missing from the eyes of all those figures in the icons. All the saints, and all the archangels, stared with empty eyelids. The Turks had removed them with knives.

The thought occurred to me that all those barbarians who had blinded saints and angels had left the same terrible obsession and the same hedonism tormenting me, and had given vent to their madness on the icons. After a while, I was even afraid to enter the library where Father had arranged the blinded icons in a row.

One evening, Father told us that we should get dressed to attend a premiere at the National Theater. *Oedipus Rex,* in Photos Politis' modern translation, was being performed. For a minute I considered telling my parents the whole story and not going. But I was ashamed before Father; I was ashamed of myself. I became obstinate. I knew very well that the whole situation was only a ridiculous eccentricity which had become fastened on my mind. I also knew that only through an extension of my will power, through a ceaseless resistance with logic, would I be able to overcome this feeling. I will go, I said; this is no more than a foolish neurosis. I must overcome it at all costs. And so I went.

Later, I realized that I had undertaken a struggle which was beyond my powers. As the play progressed, I waited with longing, my heart pounding with expectation. I heard nothing; I waited for nothing more than the moment when the verses 1268 to 1280 would begin. For me, both in the theater and in the play, nothing else existed. Finally, the terrible moment arrived, and the narrator, a young actor with excellent elocution, began the frightful narration:

He breaks the golden booches which hold
Her dress, and seizes them and thrusts
The tips into the pupils of his eyes,

. . . .

And opening his eyelids, he jabbed
Continuously, and his burning eyeballs soaked
His beard, nor did they spring forth only
Like drops of dew, but a black rain
Spurted over him, a black hail of blood.

I closed my eyes, rubbed my eyeballs with the palms of my hands, and began to cry. Oedipus—Veakis—entered the stage with extracted eyes. The echo of his lamentations filled the palace and the theater. His beard and tunic were soaked with the "black hail." I felt my knees trembling, trembling, and my cheeks twitching at the corners of my mouth. I cried, full of the painful pleasure of horror, full of the ghastly thirst for affliction. I cried, terrified.

From that evening, I removed all pins, needles, and hatpins from me and from my room. I even put away my letter-opener, and everything with a sharp point on it. Mother wondered at my sudden nervousness when I saw her pincushion on the table or in her workbasket. I took the pincushion and locked it away, or else I left the house on some pretext.

I was in this state when you came on that fateful afternoon. Everyone was away from the house; I had told you this in advance. You had your head on my lap, and you were looking up at me. Your eyes were a deep blue, and the afternoon shadows were making them purple, as the eyes of the archangels must have been before the Turks had removed them with their bayonets. I felt that I was on the brink of a deep pit. A dizziness sweetly intoxicated me. I was being pulled hypnotically by a magnetism which seemed to arise from a blue abyss. Should I abandon myself and be twisted and turned like a straw to the bottom of the chasm! Your eyes were there before me, offering themselves horizontally. They were clear, widespread. In the middle of the blue circle shone the black dot, the tiny spot ready to receive the tip of the needle. That black dot was obviously calling for the "brooch" to be pinned through the center, as though this was its fateful sheath.

I wanted to scream, to howl like a dog, to shout for you to leave, to save yourself, to save yourself! To save your eyes, your

blue eyes so beloved to me. For days I had been watching that
pin of yours with the head of Sappho on it. I had observed it on
your tie. It was of gold, long, and with agony I had tested its
sharpness against the tip of my finger. I carefully laid my bare
arm over the piece of antique and shuddered waiting to pull it out,
to thrust it—"click"—At that moment, I saw the unfortunate Doudou.
She was envious of the caresses I was giving you and had crawled
up on my lap, rubbing her whiskers against my chin. I turned to
look at her and saw her green eyes widespread before me, very
close, almost in my face. Then I closed your eyes, pulled out the
pin, and buried it in the cat's eye.

I have nothing more to say except that, after this awful
incident, my agony came to an end, as though it had been removed
with a knife. It was as though the evil had been exorcised and had
left me. Now all of this seems to me like a nightmare, as though I
had awakened and escaped strangulation. My parents know nothing
of all the torture I underwent; they don't know that you left me,
resolved never to see me again, that you hurled at me those dreadful words, "I loathe you!" Was it cowardice or hope? I still don't
know. I told them that you had suddenly been called to Crete, and
that you wouldn't be returning for a long time; that it had been
through my unforgivable negligence that Doudou had been stabbed
in the eye. How I suffer now, and how I shall always suffer as
long as I see that poor cat looking at me that way, with her single
green eye, as though she's struggling to understand the reason I
did that to her. Because I know: Doudou understood that I pulled
out the pin on purpose for that reason, to put out her eye. She
doesn't come near me any more; and whenever she sees me entering the room, she gets up and leaves very quietly. You'll never be
able to understand what a heavy judgment this is to be tried and
condemned by an innocent animal.

My darling, I have nothing more to tell you. I send you my
supplication; I send you my voice from the depth of my unhappiness, from the depth of my love. I love you till death. Determine
my life.

                                                           Nella

I finished reading the letter, folded the papers into a bundle,
and very slowly replaced them in the large envelope, deeply
affected. My friend watched me, the agony of expectation trembling
in his gaze.

"Well?"

Instead of answering him, I asked: "After this letter, what do you think of Nella and her love? Do you continue to 'loathe' her?"

He said vigorously: "I pity her. I keep remembering how her shoulders convulsed with the sobbing—And how she raised her arm when I reviled her, and then let it fall back on the sofa—"

"You love her as much as you did before—and even more. You *should* love her more now, after she has undergone such a horrible ordeal. No one but you can help her."

He spoke again, thoughtfully: "What was this thing—?"

"I believe it was a psychoneurotic crisis that Nella underwent, as one undergoes a serious illness. You have no right to humiliate her further. She's not to blame for anything. Quite the contrary, her psychic stamina is to be admired. You must go to see her today—"

I saw a flame of joy glittering in his blue eyes. I knew that I had done nothing more than to voice his own desires; at the same time, however, I saw that he wanted to ask something more but couldn't. I came to his rescue.

"Once these fixations have passed," I said, "they're gone forever. I know through experience—Look at me; I have undergone such an experience, too!"

"No!" He jumped up excitedly. "Tell me about it!"

"All right. I underwent something similar. It really does have a lot in common with what Nella has suffered. And it happened to me in the same way—after reading. It happened when I was about twenty or twenty-two years old and a student at the University. I read a vivid description somewhere about the well-known, strange, and awful method which was used to kill Odysseus Androutsos— by pounding his genitals—at night, in the tower of the Acropolis. From that moment, I was frightened to death that something similar would occur to me. Every time I saw a motorcyclist coming toward me, I squeezed my knees together, and my heart trembled in case I have the same repulsive fate as Androutsos. It reached a point where I wouldn't set foot on an athletic field, and I developed a psychosis with regard to the gymnasium. It seemed to me that, whenever the athletes kicked the ball, they were aiming straight between my legs. I squeezed my knees together and turned pale when I had to attend a football game, even when I was a spectator. I even quit horseback riding, which had been my favorite sport to that time—"

"And then?"

"Oh, and then I had to take my law examinations. I had to read all the time to prepare myself for the exams. I was isolated day and night with the Roman Law. By the time I completed my exams, the phobia of Androutsos had completely left me. It had been pushed out of my mind by the Latin legal terms—"

He continued to look at me for a short time, smiling. Suddenly he gripped my hand.

"Thank you," he said in a warm voice. "I knew it—Something kept telling me to wait for you."

When I left his office, I thought worriedly: "Had I been in his position, would I have given so lightheartedly the advice I had just given?"

Translation by Irvin Ziemann

Elias Venezis

(1904–)

Elias Venezis, pseudonym for Elias Mellos, was born in Aïvali, a town in Asia Minor. In 1923 he escaped the Asia Minor catastrophe and went to live in Athens. He has been Secretary and Advisory Director of the Greek National Theater for many years. In 1939 he was awarded the Greek National Prize for Literature. At present he works as a director of the National Bank of Greece. He is the author of some twenty books, including novels, travel impressions, and histories. Three characteristics of his work are: a depth of perception and feeling for events of everyday life, a dreamlike atmosphere, and a restricted use of the elements of technique. Earlier, he published short stories, which have been collected in *Winds* (1944), *Hour of War* (1946), and *The Defeated* (1955). His first novel, *Number 31–382*, appeared in 1931. Venezis is the second most widely translated Greek author. His best known translation, available in English, is *Beyond the Aegean* (1941, 1955).

Other works include: *Peace* (1939); *Block C* (1946); *Aeolian Land* (available in English, 1943, 1949); *Autumn in Italy* (1950); *Archbishop Damaskinos* (1952); *The Land of America* (1955); and *Ocean* (1956).

Mycenae

In faraway Anatolia, many years ago, surrounded by immortal trees, isolated from the world, Katerina Pallis, the noblewoman of the vicinity, had withdrawn with her small son and lived on the lands of her ancestors. She had been quite young when her husband had died; their son had just been born. She had undertaken alone to prepare that son for true manhood. She had taught him from childhood to love the land and sun; to revere the toil of others; and to believe that a conscience is vindicated only through the deed. As a child, she had put him to sleep with legends that spoke about distant lands; about lands constantly hammered by strong winds and tempests; about men of the sea who carried on a lifelong battle against the cold and water and the phantoms of the sky. The glance of these men can penetrate the night, and their ear can catch the echoes carried by the winds from miles away. They worship the lightning which records with flames in the darkness. Their hands are rough, and violent winds beat against their bodies and hearts. But in the hour of Judgment, this heart emerges pure and spotless because it had performed its duty in life: it has struggled hard and suffered much.

This is how young Philip was being brought up. When he reached the age where he began to understand and ask questions, Katerina Pallis spoke to him about his father. This was also like a myth, which continued for many nights. With warm voice, she attempted to restore to life the figure of that unknown father, who slowly assumed shape out of uncertainty and came to live among them, serene and divine.

And when young Philip became still older, when his mother finally considered him sufficiently prepared, she spoke to him about Greece. It was winter, the trees in the forest groaned, and the hungry jackals howled. Thick trunks of trees burned in the fireplace, the air in the room was somewhat cloudy, the heat rose in undulations toward the high ceiling, while the boy listened with widespread eyes to stories of the gods of Olympus; of the gods of the forests and seas of Greece. Strange indeed were the myths describing the gods; gods who resembled men, who sported with the joy of life, who hunted in the forests, who fell in love and suffered. There was nothing vindictive or ascetic about these gods; they governed the winds, the fire, and the lightning. Only one thing was lacking in them from the dignity of man; this was the dignity of death. They were immortal. In other words, never once, during any mystical hour, had they shuddered with a frightful tremor, which was the call of death, that which gives men the right to become helpless, exalted, and alone; the shudder of the grave.

The mythical heroes of the land of Greece lived under such gods: Agamemnon, Klytemnestra, and Iphigenia. Once, evil men from the lands of Asia had come to make off with Helen, Queen of Sparta. Then the young warriors of the land became angry indeed.

They said: "We can't allow it! We must retrieve our Queen!"

And all the women said to their husbands: "Don't desert our Queen alone to the barbarians! She is a woman and helpless as a reed—!"

The warriors armed themselves with "sea oars" to set out on an expedition to the distant land of Troy. But the spirits of the winds were unfriendly; the sails refused to swell; and the ships remained motionless on the shores of Greece. The soothsayer consulted the spirits, and they replied that they desired the sacrifice of a young maiden. Iphigenia, the maid with the raven hair and black eyes, the first maiden of the land, heard this and said: "This fate is for me!"

She went of her own accord and offered the youth of her sixteen years to the spirits of the winds. Afterward, the wind blew favorably, the sails swelled, and the ships were on their way.

In this manner Katerina Pallis related the story of Mycenae to her son. The boy became thoughtful as he listened to this astonishing myth, and attempted on his own to grasp the meaning of the sacrifice, the incentive of the brave deeds, the power of serenity. Outside, the night was black and starless; the jackals howled; the land of Anatolia, unexpended and virgin, nourished the worms and the seeds.

"A, when will spring be here!" prayed the boy. "Will we go to Greece in the springtime?" he asked, and his voice trembled because all the myths and dreams, the adoration of gods and men, the divine land, lived within the voyage his mother promised for the springtime.

"Let spring come!" the mother assured him. "Then we will go to Greece."

Spring arrived. Katerina Pallis took her son and went to Greece. It was late afternoon when they arrived at Mycenae. On foot, they were climbing the hilly road leading to the Acropolis of Mycenae when they were overcome with fatigue. They gazed around. Nothing was to be observed. Only the arid land and Sarra, the austere mountain covering the land of the tombs.

"Is it much farther?" the boy asked his mother.

"I don't believe it is," answered Katerina Pallis. "If you want, we can sit here."

At that moment they saw a herd of goats, escorted by a young goatherd, descending around the bend in the deserted road.

"Let us ask the little goatherd," said the mother.

When the young goatherd was near enough, she asked: "Is it far to Mycenae?"

The young boy was perplexed. "Mycenae—?" he asked. "I don't know any Mycenae close by."

"And this place around here, what is it called?" Katerina Pallis asked again.

"A, here—? These are the grazing lands of my grandfather Kakavas!"

The boy from Anatolia laughed mirthfully.

"See, Mother!" he said. "And we are looking for the tombs of our ancient kings—!"

Katerina Pallis, however, became even more serious and hastened her footsteps. At that moment, a man appeared at the top of the road. The old man was descending laboriously, tall and serene. His white whiskers enclosed his face in tight ringlets. He had thrown his cape over his shoulders; he wore a white, billowy *foustanella* skirt made of wool, and his sun-baked face was like bronze.

A soft wind blew his hair around, but it was his steady gait which gave the ultimate serenity to his entire appearance. He was the animated presence of the ancient figures of the area, as portrayed in books and statues.

"Look! Look, Philip!" the mother said to her son. "See how Greece continues to live—"

"Really, Mother! Really—" he said with emotion. "How strange it is—"

In the simplest manner, with a goatherd who appeared to record his aspect across the evening landscape of Mycenae, the myths of Olympus began to assume a vivid form—the expedition to Troy, Agamemnon, and the raven-haired Iphigenia—

The old man approached. He waved his staff in the air, then lowered and supported it on the ground. But he did not bend his head like the peasants and shepherds of Anatolia. He looked directly at them, his body straight as a tree.

He said: "Welcome to our land! You must be strangers."

Katerina Pallis no longer asked if this was Mycenae. She only said: "We are strangers, old man! Where are the tombs of our ancient kings?"

The old man made a slow gesture, pointing behind him.

"On the other side of Mount Sarra," he said. "That's where you'll find Mycenae."

There, as night fell and the sea of Argos had finally disappeared from view, they found the tombs. First they saw the large, vaulted, royal tomb of Agamemnon, into which they entered. For preservation these thousands of years, the earth had collected around it, had become a hill; grass and trees had grown, the earth had blossomed. Then the hour came when the tomb should be revealed to the adoration of men. Darkness and a deep serenity were within the tomb. On a small altar, where the sanctuary might have been, or the place for votive offerings, Katerina Pallis found a few dry twigs. They set fire to them so they could see. Nothing. How desolate everything was! Except that, now and again, a few drops of water trickled down the vaulted roof. The earth collected the water, preserved it in her bosom, sanctified it, and later allowed it to seep under the hard rocks of the vaulted roof to impart an echo to the serenity of the tomb, a message from the world and from eternity.

"How lonely the great king is in here—" the boy murmured.

Katerina Pallis pulled him away, and they went outside. They passed by the other humble tomb of Klytemnestra. The boy said that they should enter there also, but the mother had no desire to do so. What could she possibly relate to him about Klytemnestra and about her horrible deed? What should she tell him? No, she had no desire to enter.

"Let us go to the Acropolis," she said, and led the way up the hilly footpath.

When they reached the Gate of Lions, a fear clutched at the heart of the boy. He caught his mother's hand.

"Are you afraid?" Katerina Pallis asked. "For thousands of years now the citadel has been empty. The dead don't talk."

She only said this, despite knowing well that truly the dead here in Greece do talk—

This was a happier place, simpler. There were no vaulted tombs. Only a bit below the surface of the ground were the graves. Wildflowers, yellow and red, grew here and there.

The boy stooped to pick a flower. Later, when they descended from the Acropolis, he asked to re-enter the tomb of Agamemnon. And there, on the ashes at the altar, the ashes from the burned twigs, he placed the flower with love, a message of the joy of the external world, so that Agamemnon would not be so lonely.

How much time has passed since then! How many years!

Katerina Pallis is journeying again, this time alone, all alone, climbing the road to Mycenae. Now it is not springtime, as it had been that other time. Heavy clouds hang over the Acropolis of the tombs. And she is dressed in black. Mourning seals her pale face, and her hair is gray. Nothing remains of what she had lived for and had reared. Everything was left behind at the scene of destruction in Anatolia. Dead also is the young man she had prepared for true manhood, who would revere the dignity of man, and who was to believe that a conscience is vindicated only through the deed. What is the meaning now to the myths she had related to him about the far-away places, about the lands which are hammered by strong winds and stormy seas, about the men with pure hearts who struggled throughout their lives against the cold and water and the spirits of heaven. What is the meaning now to all that?

Katerina Pallis entered the tomb of Agamemnon. The same serenity, identical with that of years ago. The same desolation and the silence of death. There are no longer any ashes on the altar; nor are there any dry twigs as there had been that other time. Only water from the earth slowly trickles down the vaulted roof; slowly, at uneven intervals.

"My son—" the mother says softly. "My boy—" she repeats, and she remembers the humble flower he had carried from outside to place on the altar so that Agamemnon would not be lonely.

"So Agamemnon won't be lonely—" she murmurs. "And you, my child, where are you now—?"

With her white head bowed, with slow, tired footsteps, she went outside. She gazed around. Her glance fell on the other humble tomb where Klytemnestra rests. Her eyes remain fixed there. And then, only then, does she see, *truly* see, that grave for the first time. Humbly, her footsteps carry her to this tomb. She enters. What silence in here as well, the silence of death! Slowly, the light disappears, time disappears; only shadows stir in the air. And from the depth of the shadows, the forms slowly emerge and become clearly discernible. Once there lived a brutal king. He was called Agamemnon. The people in his kingdom were oppressed by his tyranny and spilled rivers of perspiration so he could accumulate countless treasures for his citadel. His power and tyranny spread as far as eye could see, throughout the valley of Argos. Once, travelers who had lost their way, happened to come to these places. From them, Agamemnon learned that, in a wealthy land at the other end of the sea, toward Anatolia, lived Priam, and that he had mythical treasures concealed in his palaces; gold and much copper, herds of livestock, and women whose color was that of wheat and whose eyes sparkled.

Agamemnon's thoughts became inflamed. Immediately, he sent messages to the neighboring kings of Arcadia, and at once they decided on the expedition to Troy. The entire army gathered at the beach of Aulis to set sail. But a favorable wind refused to blow. For days they waited; for weeks. Finally, the soothsayer consulted the stars. And the stars replied that Agamemnon must sacrifice his daughter Iphigenia, the maiden with the raven hair and black eyes, if the angry gods were to be appeased. For a moment, the king hesitated, but only for a moment. Then he thought of the livestock, the gold and copper, and the slaves of this distant land at the other end of the sea. His thoughts were hazy, but he no longer hesitated. He sent a message to his wife to bring the maiden. And there, beside the waveless sea, he surrendered with his own hands the maiden with the raven hair, Iphigenia, to the executioner. Then the wind blew. He took the fast-moving ships, he took the laments of Klytemnestra; and the land was filled with her broken-hearted cries and her curses.

For years Klytemnestra waited for Agamemnon to return from that strange land, and for years she contemplated her terrible vengeance. Her slave watched daily, from dawn to dusk, for sight of the greatly traveled ships. Then one day, the slave came running out of breath and fell at her feet, bringing the great message.

"He is returning! Agamemnon is returning!"

Klytemnestra withdrew to her quarters and remained alone

for a long time, praying to the gods. She was not crying. She was only beseeching the gods to come and stand beside her during the divine hour when a mother must perform her most sacred duty. Afterward, she emerged peacefully to the Gate of Lions, while in her eyes a determination sparkled. She sent for Aegisthus to stand beside her, should her hand become feeble at the final moment.

Agamemnon returned, dragging behind herds of slaves and animals, spoils from Troy. Beside him followed the barefoot Cassandra, daughter of Priam. Klytemnestra led him to the bath. She gave him scented oils to rub over his body, and as soon as he had bathed, she threw a large sheet over his face. While he was drying himself, Klytemnestra raised an ax and split his head. Afterward, she sent her slaves for Cassandra. And she murdered her with her own hands there beside the bleeding body of Agamemnon, as he had butchered their child Iphigenia beside her—

It is growing dark as Katerina Pallis emerges from the tomb of Klytemnestra.

The weather is heavy; black clouds beat against one another in the sky. They touch the tip of the naked Mount Sarra and race back, as though fearful that the mountain might cling to them. Mount Sarra's bulk rises vaguely, a dark divinity which is waiting.

Katerina Pallis gazes around her. After a time, her embittered glance falls to the ground with serene resignation—the refuge of men who have suffered greatly.

Then she saw it at her feet. It was a poor yellow, lonely flower of the earth—How could it have endured there in the dreadful loneliness? How could it have endured?

Bending over, she plucked it. Afterward, slowly, performing the same action her son had performed many years ago, before they had taken him from her hands—but now in an entirely different spirit—she went in to lay the desolate flower on the tomb of Klytemnestra, so that a mother, the mother of Iphigenia, would not be lonely.

Kosmas Politis

(1893–   )

Kosmas Politis, pseudonym for Paris Tadeloudis, was born in Athens in 1893. He spent several years in Smyrna and upon his return to Greece in 1910, he became Director of the Ionia Bank of Greece. He first appeared in literature in 1928 with the novel *Lemon Grove,* "a story of a life," as he calls it. Though it was based on an older, more sentimental tradition, full of reminiscences of incidents and even quotations from Shakespeare, it became very popular because of its excellent descriptions, beautiful dialogue, and psychological insights into characters. Among the best known of the works that followed are: *Hecate* (1933); *Eroica* (1938), which became a landmark in modern Greek prose; *Three Women* (1943), a collection of short stories; *Plum Tree and Other Stories* (1946); and *Constantine the Great* (a play, 1957).

Politis is considered one of the important writers of Greece today. An attractive feature of his work is a strong lyrical expression. Sentimentality in the older tradition dominates his early works, which can also be considered novels of manners of the Athenian aristocracy. In his later novels and short stories, he shows himself to be a realist. He is the first writer to express concern over the problems of the adolescent, and more precisely at a critical time of life, as the story "Plum Tree" clearly shows. Younger writers were deeply influenced by Politis' work.

A Double

"Eh, how are you?" he asked, stopping me in the shade, on the marble pavement.

"Eh! How are you?" I also asked.

"It's been a long time since we've met, two or three years, perhaps more—"

"That long for me, too," I replied.

He hesitated for a moment, scrutinizing me.

"Will you let me buy you an *ouzo?*" And he nodded toward the bar a few steps away.

Something caused me to hesitate, something stopped the effusion which would have been so natural, especially since I hadn't seen my old classmate for so many years. The fault, of course, was mine. True, there were bags under his eyes; his cheeks above his chin were baggy, too. And his glance had a sidelong expression, sometimes spiritless and tired, sometimes gleaming with a crafty sparkle—Unless this was merely restlessness. But, without question, it was such affectations, or a superficial crisis, which hindered me from grasping his hand. The fault was mine—Nonetheless, even during our years at the gymnasium, a similar feeling, indefinable, had always restrained me. It could have been his carefree attitude, or perhaps his manner of speaking about the girls we both knew, and somewhat of an arrogance—not really arrogance, but a familiarity which he assumed with everyone, even though he might not have been granted that familiarity—at least I had not—It was as though he imposed his arrogance on me, or as though he infringed upon my approval.

At any rate, he was always eager to perform a favor in order to appear pleasant. Yet, even his eagerness was an example of the ease with which he moved through life. But perhaps it was the fault of my own character.

The truth is that later there had been a rumor about him—I mean to say during the Occupation. An affair which does not belong to the present, and which perhaps I ought never to relate. It would reveal the morality of our times, something I don't intend, because, as some of those with whom I converse say, the foundations of our society have decayed, and Europe has her eye upon us. Even America.

"What do you say to an *ouzo* on the rocks?

It was a very hot day, even here in the shade, on the marble pavement. And something more. During these days of economic rehabilitation of our country, one needed about four hundred drachmas for a drink or two, if the appetizers were to be somewhat appropriate, and if one hadn't been clever, as some said, during the days of the Occupation. What is past is to be forgotten; the time is up, as the newspapers wrote a few days ago.

"An *ouzo*? With pleasure," I now said heartily. "It has been so long since we've met!"

"They will take good care of us here. I am a steady customer."

Inside the bar, the revolving fan reigned supreme, fanning the small room from one corner to the other.

"Like a machine gun," I said as the fan blew on our faces from right and left.

I looked intently at the bright stars on his epaulets. Even so, not one of the three stars was ripped off by the blowing fan.

"Let's go sit in the back," he said.

"Are you cold?"

"I'm perspiring," he replied, using a handkerchief to dry his forehead under the khaki beret with the national emblem on it.

We were sitting across from one another and drinking our *ouzo*. I again noticed his glance. It was a bit restless, and even more, it was a suffering glance—Or did it appear so to me? I made an involuntary motion, as though I wanted to withdraw my earlier reservations—something like a spiritual gesture which gave him remission of his sins. I even forced myself to speak freely to him, to remind him our youth, of some innocent games at a time when I was sending flowers, each with its own secret interpretation, to a girl I loved, and he would mock me. My flowers were an expression of an entire confession—"the language of flowers"—I wanted to tell him much more, but my throat constricted.

"Will you have a second *ouzo*?" he asked me.

"Have you already finished yours! I intend to enjoy mine at leisure."

He motioned to the waiter.

"An *ouzo* for the Captain!" the waiter called, turning to the bar.

"Why worry!" he said. "We have only one life to live: all one can eat, all one can drink, and all—I have an idea of my own—entirely my own!" he repeated, striking his fist on the marble table-top.

"Has he already been affected by the first *ouzo*?" I thought.

"Is that so?" I said. "My congratulations—" And I pointed to the stars on his epaulets. "I knew you as a reserve officer. Where were you during the Occupation? In the mountains?"

"But—I was here. Working on contracts. Don't I have an engineering degree? Air ports—concrete—Now I cooperate with the British as a liaison officer, as they call it in English."

"Oh!" I said with admiration. "I understand."

"Yes—Will you have a second *ouzo*?"

"Two drinks for the Captain!" the waiter called out.

It was as though he had evil intentions. Then again, it could have been a habit he had acquired in the army, with the British. His glance became dull again.

I sought to entice him with a story of our days at the gymnasium, but he didn't give me an opportunity.

"Have you ever thought about electricity?" he asked. "Look at the way it turns the fan or lights the bulb. Have a cigarette—Because of this, I tell you that life is nothing more than an electric current which passes through us in the same way as it passes through a lightbulb. When our times comes—when the lightbulb breaks or burns out—everything comes to an end, everything. The electric current will go elsewhere. Nothing will remain of us. When they talk about a soul, an afterlife, I listen to them *gratis*. There is no future life, neither down here, nor anywhere else. You never thought of me as a man who could think seriously. And yet, this is my idea, entirely my own!"

"Why do you say that I never took you seriously?" I objected vehemently. "Nothing but that!"

"I know what I'm saying. Waiter!"

"No, I won't have another *ouzo*. My budget doesn't allow for more than two drinks."

"But I'm treating."

"I know. I meant my stomach's budget."

The waited looked at us indecisively. Finally, I motioned that I wouldn't have another *ouzo*.

"One *ouzo* for the Captain!"

"And so, everything comes to an end down here. Future life? Let me laugh, ha—ha—ha!"

"For certain," I thought, "he is drinking more than he should. The *ouzo* has affected him."

"Isn't my idea right? Have a cigarette—Or are you perhaps one of the foolish who expect to have life continue in the other world?"

"I don't know," I answered. "I'm an agnostic."

His fingers trembled. "What do you mean?" he asked.

"I only mean that imagination replaces reason in such things, so long as we lack proof of what is destined for us—lack scientific proof."

"So you don't concur with my idea?" he asked, wide-eyed.

"I mean to say that, since that's how matters stand, only the present life has any meaning."

"A, so you do concur with me—? Waiter!"

"One *ouzo* for the Captain!"

"Listen!" I said to him. "You are drinking too much. Don't you think you're drinking too much?"

He looked at me squarely, eyes wide, bloodshot, and waited for my reply as though it was a divination, and as though his future, his freedom from care, depended on my judgment.

"Listen," I said again. "I know nothing of all this, nor do I live in anticipation of a reward in this or in the other world. I would hope that everyone would concern himself with man's happiness in life, the one we know for certain, since we live it; that equality, freedom, and justice would prevail; that poverty would no longer exist—"

"What!" he exclaimed, interrupting me.

He looked at me suspiciously, half-closing his eyes.

"Tell me, are you a Communist?"

The people at the nearby tables turned around to look at me. But he laughed loudly.

"Ha! ha! ha! I only said that to aggravate you. Only the wretched become Communists."

Then he continued, "I must explain to you—"

But suddenly he furrowed his eyebrows, and his eyes sparkled as he glanced over my shoulder.

"Hello!"

I turned to see whom he was greeting. A British officer was approaching our table.

"Hello!" he repeated and added a few words in English.

From his gesture I surmised that he was inviting the officer to sit with us. The Englishman shook his head negatively, patted him lightly on the back in a friendly gesture, and thus, smiling with a kind of austere expression, slightly embittered, he spoke a few words in English. He turned his back on us and went to lean his elbows on the bar, engaging in conversation with the barman.

It was hot. I began to feel uncomfortable. I had to hold out my right hand to cool it off as the rapid whirling of the blade of the fan passed over it. The Englishman was drinking something as he stood before the bar. I saw his sharp, tanned features in profile. At the corner of his eyes wrinkles fanned to spread now and then to the edge of his gray hairline.

"I'm afraid that I'm the cause of his not sitting with us," I said to my companion.

"Let him go to the devil! Waiter!"

"One *ouzo* for the Captain!"

"Where did you meet him?"

"They're all hypocrites and Pharisees. Nonsense and emotion. How much difference is there between a man and a child? To understand how their minds work—No, you must hear me. You will justify me in this matter as you did in the other. Or am I in error? Isn't that what you said, that you concur with my idea? Everything comes to an end here—He and I were together in a tank—"

"In 1941? During the German attack?"

"No! I'm talking about the civil war in December in the Psyrri Square—Have a cigarette—A ragamuffin, a bastard, who must have been fourteen or fifteen, was behind the roadblock with his machine gun. It was raining. 'What is he doing there?' the Englishman asked. 'Can't you see! He's shooting at us!' I said. But without result. We were inside our tank; the shells flattened against the armoured plate as though they were made of wadding. 'Yes,' he said, 'but why does he move his hand up and down before firing? There, look, he is on his feet again!' Do you understand? The bastard was standing upright behind the roadblock, making the sign of the Cross quickly, and then firing a shot. After that, he squatted down again. 'He's making the sign of the Cross so he can get a successful shot,' I said to the Englishman. 'But he won't rise many more times.' I caught hold of my machine gun, the heavies, the 20's.

" 'Don't!' the Englishman cried. Do you know English? No? 'Don't!' he said. 'Don't shoot him. He's a child!' 'It's such bastards that you should fear,' I told him. 'No,' he said. 'You will do an evil deed! (Hear! hear!) You will deprive your country of a good soldier and a good Christian.' 'But he is a Communist,' I said. 'Perhaps,' he replied, 'but he is fighting for freedom.' 'Aren't you an Englishman?' I asked to provoke him. He was from Newfoundland, from the New World. He said, 'I volunteered to fight for freedom against the Nazis and Fascists.' (Hear! hear!) 'And the King?' I asked. 'For whom did you come here? Didn't Mr. Churchill send you to Greece in the name of the King?' He shook his head thoughtfully. What could he reply to matters that were evident and well-documented?

"They first sent us out for slaughter, and then they pretended to be saints—But I kept my eyes on the spot where that bastard was, there behind the roadblock. On the armor of the tank the shells went *platz! platz!* We felt nothing inside; four inches of steel the tank was. I was beside the machine gun. As I saw him come up again and start to make the sign of the Cross, I fired a shot, a second, a third, a whole round of shots, to right, to left, and up and down. He wanted a Cross, eh! Well, here was the Cross! The bastard fell forward on the wheel of the cart and remained there with hands suspended. It was raining. From his head the blood flowed to mingle with the rain. 'Eh!' I said to the Englishman. 'What do you think of that?' And what do you think he replied? 'You performed an evil deed! You killed a good patriot and a good Christian'—Have a cigarette—A little while ago when he stopped here, he repeated the same words—Do you want another *ouzo*? Why are you preparing to leave? I'll come with you. No, I'll remain here. What, because he's here? Let him—(And he used a word which I had written, but then I remembered that I was a gentleman and erased it.) I'll remain. We are agreed, though, on my idea, eh? Every thing comes to an end down here."

His fingers were shaking as he raised his hand to signal the waiter.

"Yes," I assured him. "All accounts are squared one day—"

As I was leaving the blade of the fan caught my cheek.

I heard the voice of the waiter saying, "A double for the Captain!"

Petros Haris

(1902–   )

Petros Haris, pseudonym for Yiannis Marmariadis, was born in Athens in 1902. He studied law at the University of Athens, but early turned to writing as a career. Essentially a short story writer, he has also written many critical essays on Greek literature and on individual authors. Since 1933 he has been editor of the literary magazine *Nea Estia,* and for a number of years he has held various positions with Greek and International Theatre associations.

His first collection of short stories, *The Last Night On Earth,* appeared in 1924. They were warm lyrical impressions of life and reminiscences of the past. A distinctive feature of his writing is the probing of the inner world of his characters for that single moment of painful discovery. He has also written many children's books.

His works include: *Children's Dialogues* (1924); *Dialogues and Poems* (co-author I. M. Panayotopoulos, 1926); *K. G. Kariotakis* (1943); *Distant World* (1944); *Critical Hour* (1944); *When Life Becomes a Dream* (1945, 1947); *Free Intellectual Men* (1947); *Greek Prose Writers* (1953); *Cities and Seas* (First National Award, 1955); *Lights on the Sea* (1958); *Post-war World* (1962); and *Life and Art* (1963).

Lights on the Sea

The tiny island lived on, forgotten both by men and God. Even the foreign soldiers had slighted its existence. They had sailed into the small harbor during the first days of the Occupation and posted only two well-armed guards. Later, they had removed even the guards, deserting the tiny island and abandoning it to float between sea and sky, yet ever to remain in place.

But then, even when the years had been good, this island had always been neglected.

"You see, we're on a barren course," they said, explaining the desertion of their harbor.

They had no desire to think about another thing. What else should they think about anyway? Had men ever come to the island to be seen, to become acquainted, to be loved or hated by the islanders? Two hundred and fifty, possibly three hundred souls in all, lived here on the island, together with a prefect who was the supreme authority, and a telegraph operator who talked with the winds and the clouds, and then, like a magician or a prophet, recounted all that was occurring throughout the rest of the world.

During the peaceful years their two small caïques had sailed around to the other islands to sell a few things. Occasionally, they had even ventured as far as the port of Piraeus, from where they had brought certain things back to the island. Now, the boats were tied to the pier. Sometimes, though very rarely, the boats went on short fishing excursions from which they returned speedily to the harbor. The sea was deserted, so deserted it was frightening. Neither smoke, nor sail, nor feather. This was the ancient, the very ancient sea, the sea that had preceded man. Alone, endless, and unenslaved during the daytime. And at night, sea and moon, or maybe sea and darkness, in a discourse that resembled those carried on in the first hours of creation by spirits and strange powers of the world, discourses never heard by human ear, but for whose meaning the mind of man is constantly searching.

Very soon, the islanders concluded that they were to undergo the entire period of the war with only the possessions they had on hand and with whatever produce their earth would yield. If they

223

could only learn what was occurring in other parts of Greece, they would be content. Times would be difficult, without doubt. But no one on the island would die of hunger, even though something would always be lacking. Only illness frightened the islanders. Still, even in peacetime, when someone became ill, he was rarely saved from danger because somehow the ship was always delayed in passing, the caïque slow in starting. The expense involved was too great, the deliberation too long. And finally, when the sick one was transported to the big city, it was often too late to save him.

Thus, they remained alone in the sea, far from the war and men. They, and the telegraph operator, who sometimes told them how man was being converted into a wild beast in the West or in the East, at the large or small battlefronts, and how God protected them and relieved His weary eyes on their quiet life. The prefect no longer possessed authority. Had he sought to raise his voice, he couldn't have; he no longer had any power. He ate the small piece of bread the island had to offer and stopped wasting his breath on shouts and threats. Something happened to his equipment, so he closed his office and stopped being the magician and the prophet. The sole cord joining the island with the rest of the world had been severed. Then came the nights abounding in strange dreams, and the days when the older islanders interpreted these dreams as messages relating to the war, to the famine, to the disaster that had befallen the world.

After many months the foreign soldiers reappeared on the island. They didn't remain long and had little to say—that is, one of the islander's own men who knew the language of the foreign soldiers and was accompanying them said all there was to say. They left a single order.

"No lights at night! Not even a lighted cigarette!"

The foreign soldiers arrived at daybreak; they departed at dusk. The small craft carrying them quickly disappeared in the darkness.

The islanders questioned the prefect, who had exchanged a few words with them. They learned nothing. They questioned the priest, who had been greeted by them. Still they learned nothing. They asked the community secretary, who had come out to tell the soldiers, "The president is sick in bed." Not a word. Tight-lipped the soldiers had arrived; tight-lipped they had departed. Nonetheless, they had spoken. The war was still in progress on their homeland. Indeed, the war continued in other parts of the world as well —wherever there was land or sea, wherever there were men.

The nights were again filled with dreams. During the daytime the dreams brought hope or even panic, and the tiny island waited, always waited. It became accustomed to waiting and even ceased to question the sea, which must have heard much, must have known much. But the sea was equally tight-lipped; her secrets were not appearing in her huge eyes, neither when they were serenely blue, nor when they became playfully green. Not even when they darkened in anger.

The winter days rolled by swiftly, but the nights were endless. Even with dreams, they were endless. It was impossible to fill all those hours, those slow hours of the December and January nights. The small houses clustered around the harbor resembled a group of people prepared at every hour to face any difficulty. And the harbor was deserted. A few boats beached on the sand, the two caïques tied to the pier, and the wind, sometimes wild, in discourse or in battle with the sea and the masts.

The hour must have been ten, a very late hour for the island; consequently, when the great commotion came, it found everyone in deep sleep. The church bell awakened them, tolling wildly in a way that cried, "Get up! Run! Run fast!"

The islanders ran, some dressed, others half-dressed, only to find a youth, high up in the belfry, causing the uncontrollable alarm.

"Oh, the crazy fool!" they all cried.

The youth was Vangelis, the island idiot, who had no home and scarcely any clothing, and who slept sometimes at one place and sometimes at another with someone always to give him a piece of bread to eat. Those who arrived first rushed to yank him from the belfry and teach him how to sleep at night. But the priest, who had run out with the others before he had time to put on his frock and hat, held them back.

Looking up at the belfry, he ordered, "Come down, Vangelis!"

The youth looked at the angry crowd waiting below, the crowd which was fast increasing. He hesitated, but finally came down.

"What happened to you, Vangelis?"

"A ship, Father; a ship! I saw it with my own eyes. I saw it plain and rang the bell so the others could see it, too."

The crowd waited to hear no more. They forgot Vangelis and ran to the harbor. Many others, awakened by the bell, joined the first group, trembling in expectation. Last to follow were Vangelis and the priest.

The crowd at the harbor increased. Soon it included everyone in the village. And it consisted of eyes, island eyes that knew how to search the night, especially the night of the sea.

Not a single breath was heard. Even the sea was quiet, barely moving, as though she, too, had been awakened by the wild tolling of the bell. The darkness was deep, so deep that a single speck of of light could be discerned, had that light been there. But they saw nothing. They couldn't make out that speck of light, let alone see an entire ship, a whole lighted ship, at that. They looked at one another, verifying that they weren't mistaken, and they became angry again. But Vangelis was not alone. The priest, who knew that he was dealing with an idiot, was also at the harbor.

"Where do you see the ship?" he asked severely, concealing his anger.

"I don't see it any more, Father," Vangelis said, shaking his head.

"And where was it when you saw it?"

"There, Father. Over there."

And the youth pointed to the left, far in the horizon, out toward the path coursed by ships that used to pass the island once in a great while.

They all looked in the direction the youth pointed; they all attempted to discern something. But still they saw nothing. And the priest, aware that evil can occur in the night, especially before so many angry people, attempted to vindicate Vangelis.

"Did you see the ship plainly, or did you imagine it? Were you awake or asleep?" he asked patiently.

"I saw it, Father. I saw it, I tell you."

"Where were you when you saw it?"

"At the big window of the warehouse," the youth replied slowly. He would rather have said, "I saw it from the window of the dilapidated shack that has been my home this winter."

"And how did you see it? Weren't you asleep at such an hour?"

"I wasn't asleep, Father." And he added softly, "My stomach ached. I haven't eaten since the day before yesterday."

Vangelis no longer needed the protection of the priest. Two by two, three by three, the islanders turned their backs to the sea and departed. They returned home to dream about the ship they hadn't seen by the edge of the sea.

A week had scarcely passed when the night was again shattered by the tolling of the bell. Not everyone left his bed this time. Those who did get up, however, did so with the intention of finding Vangelis to tie him up. When they reached the church, they saw something they couldn't believe; they heard something they couldn't understand.

"I saw it!" Christos called down from the belfry.

Christos was a healthy young man, one of the best workers in the village. And he never had much to say.

Christos was not a village idiot. However, when he followed all those who had come to the harbor at the tolling of the bell and saw nothing, not even a single ray of light, he almost went out of his mind.

"It must have been the sea nymphs passing at a distance," an old man concluded. "Come now. Let's go to sleep."

But Christos refused to budge. He didn't take his eyes off the sea and the darkness. And if it hadn't been for his friends, who after a while gently led him away, he would have remained there in the deep darkness until morning. He had seen the big ship. He could swear to that. He could place his hand in fire. When the others were present, the ship disappeared; he couldn't see a thing. Now, he couldn't even point to the direction where he had seen the ship.

The next morning Christos felt the eyes of the entire village staring at him strangely. It was all very well for Vangelis. He had imagined seeing the ship and so had mounted the belfry to toll the bell. But for him, Christos, to have mounted the belfry, for him to have tolled the bell! He wouldn't be able to endure this for long.

Before ten days had passed, Avgoustis saved Vangelis. Avgoustis, too, mounted the belfry and tolled the bell in the wild hour of midnight. Again everyone awoke, but very few ventured outside this time. And Avgoustis, who was a very obstinate man, remained beside the harbor until morning. That ship he had seen had not been passing at a distance. It had been heading straight for the island, straight for their harbor.

They had no other idiot on the island except Vangelis. They had no ghosts, no sea nymphs. The ship was the first ghost to disturb the sleep of the islanders. Someone suggested that they should exorcise the spirit, that they should pour consecrated water into their harbor to send the spirit far, very far away, to other seas. That's what they said, but they thought it over and hesitated. What was that ship? Why were they so afraid of it?

"On a ship, on one of our own ships, which will have all its lights shining, if it is nighttime—Isn't that how freedom will come to us?"

The priest said this. The prefect agreed. The islanders were content with this explanation. The nights remained quiet, even when the bell tolled. And these nights when the bell tolled were not a few. After Avgoustis, another eighteen people mounted the belfry, both young and old of the village, people who weren't idiots, people who had all their wits about them. They all saw the ship clearly, very clearly. And they could even tell the number of lights it had, and the course it was traveling.

The months of slavery passed slowly, the years rolled on. The island remained forgotten by the foreign soldiers, forgotten even by other men. And the bell never ceased tolling. On winter nights, on summer nights, even on spring and autumn nights, the bell tolled. One by one, each man saw the ship for himself; but when they were all gathered together at the harbor, the ship disappeared. But they were all convinced that some day or some night they would all see the ship together. And they waited—

Takis Doxas

(1913–   )

Takis Doxas, novelist, short story writer, poet, and critic, was born in 1913 in Pyrgos, Elias, where he resides permanently and is Director of the Pyrgos Public Library.

The prose writings of Doxas are inspired by life in the Greek provinces. His characters are the oppressed peasants and provincials for whom life holds little or no hope, aspirations, and ambitions, and who become symbols of the spiritually agonized man of today.

He began writing at a very early age and has published the following volumes: *Stories Re-told* (1932); *Apology of the Hunchback and Other Stories* (1936); *Maria Polydouri* (1937); *White Streets* (1938); *Esoteric Art* (1940); *The Sonnet of the Shadows* (1949); *Bitter Times* (1950); *Journeys Without Sun* (1953); *Shipwrecked* (1955); *Rodostamia* (1957, for which he received the First Prize for Literature of the Peloponessus); *Light of Olympia* (1960, 1964); *History of Elian Literature* (1963); *George Seferis* (1964); and *The Chronicle of Pyrgos* (1965).

The Traffic Officer of Phigalia

The intersection was certainly dangerous, but neither the Commune nor the Police Department had ever tackled the problem. Furthermore, the village had no great traffic, despite the fact that the road led to Linistaina and Zourtsa, and even extended to the Epicurean Apollo, where people of all kinds from almost every part of the earth traveled to view the Sun King, seated roundly in the depth of the temple. But Argyris was incapable of abandoning all those people to their destiny. He would never have endured the sight, if some day a collision had occurred among the automobiles passing through Phigalia, racing like lightning to overtake time and the landscape. So he took matters into his own hands.

The fact is, he built a well-proportioned stand by nailing together some old boards he gathered from one place and another. The stand, furthermore, assisted him in encompassing the street from one end to the other, in checking and forestalling traffic jams. He was a very small man, because he had stopped growing after an old illness which had dulled his mind. He was unable to grasp the full meaning of his life. He had no power to make any distinction between himself and the rocks which caused his naked feet to bleed. Yet, he sincerely believed that he was destined to become "a great man!"

At all events, Argyris was extremely punctual in his work. Winter and summer he went to work at seven in the morning, taking a short break at noontime for something to eat, and returning to remain at his post until late in the evening when darkness blocked all the streets of the village and confined men in the coffee houses or their homes. Standing on his feet all day long on that dilapidated stand, he regarded every movement. He watched for buses and automobiles, wagons and horses, pedestrians, and even dogs and chickens, which ran around in disarray, searching quickly through the earth and grass for their daily sustenance.

The traffic officer had been to Athens once, and his straying thoughts had come to a standstill at the sight of the first traffic officer, who wore a uniform, sparkling in the sun-bathed April afternoon. It was as though this was the most amazing thing he had ever seen in his entire lifetime! He was impressed neither by the immensity of the houses, nor by the display windows full of mannequins, nor by the twinkling lights which brightened the night and cast that vast city into a variegated ocean, intoxicating it—From the moment he confronted the traffic officer, he never moved an inch from his side! During all the time he remained in Athens, he spent his days and nights there in that same spot at the Hafteia, observing the traffic officer as he went through his signals with such simplicity, such self-assurance, such magnificence, now upward, now downward, on University Street; then to left and to right, indicating Patisia Street. He learned all the lessons and returned to Phigalia to enforce them.

Argyris, in fact, performed more than the traffic officer in Athens. He even talked. Signaling with his hands in a magical fashion, indicating the four points of the horizon with his disabled palms, he shouted: "This way to Phigalia! This way to Linistaina and Zourtsa! And that way to the Epicurean Apollo! Attention, please—"

In time, the inhabitants of Phigalia became accustomed to him; the strangers, on the other hand, stopped to stare at his affectations. At the beginning, of course, everyone mocked him and imitated his actions. And when evening came, they pulled him over to the coffee house and made him repeat signals of a traffic officer to alleviate their boredom. They gave him a cigarette, a lemonade; sometimes, they even slapped him playfully across the back. Then all together, they broke into roaring laughter that caused the coffee house to vibrate. Argyris, however, failed to understand that they were mocking him. He was only interested in seeing that no one was involved in an accident, not even in the coffee house. He wanted each signal to go like clockwork; he wanted the automobiles to cross without incident. He even wanted the pedestrians to avoid a collision. Not even a baby chick must trip out of line, one of those baby chicks from the swarms the mother hens hatched and then abandoned to the mercy of God while they went around unencumbered to peck at the seeds of the earth.

In the coffee houses, someone made the noises of a tram—to give the proper atmosphere. Argyris believed all this to be authentic. He took his position at a hypothetical intersection; and moving his hands with tragic ease, he loudly directed the four-wheeled vehicles and the four-legged creatures to Phigalia, and to the Epicurean Apollo.

The smoke from the cigars, which were asphyxiating in that

small enclosure, and the noises did not annoy Argyris; they failed to diminish his zeal for his work. Within the strangeness of his mind, he enlarged that space into a wide expanse, and filled it with a stifling transportation problem as he pretended to be at the Hafteia in Athens. He perspired over and over again in order to remain irreproachable in his work and made great effort, in the persuasiveness of his imagination, to see that everything proceeded in an orderly manner so even the slightest accident should be avoided—God, so that no one should be killed!

And if he happened to have an ill-tempered pedestrian, especially one of those reluctant donkeys which had been loaded by its master with two cumbersome baskets and then allowed to proceed down the road without guidance, or perhaps a baby chick which paid no attention, either to the mother hen or to the traffic officer, Argyris never became angry. He stepped down from his stand, took the donkey by the reins and changed its course. He bent over, picked up the baby chick in the palms of his hands, fondled it tenderly, and replaced it in the swarm of its brothers. He caught the stubborn pedestrian tenderly by the shoulders and begged him to understand what was most advantageous for his life.

"As long as I am giving you the signal to proceed right, why do you proceed left?"

"That's how I like to go! This is my village, and I'll walk any way I please."

"Certainly. But the doctor's automobile is coming from the left, and it will run over you without any reason. Why do you want to die like a dog in the vineyards?"

"What do I care—"

"But what am I doing here? Do you want me to get into trouble without any reason, just for your sake?"

The pedestrian would grumble. He would even be sarcastic: "And who will make trouble for you, Argyris? Someone at headquarters?"

"Of course! Someone at the Department of Traffic Regulations."

And he actually believed this.

He always said that he had been appointed by the Department of Traffic Regulations, that he had attended classes in traffic school in Athens, and that he was punished for every violation and mistake he made. For that reason, he was punctual, accurate in his signals and the traffic rules he remembered from Athens. For that reason, he was always at his place, even in the rain. Only, when it rained, he would put on a long, deplorable-looking coat and an old leather cap, made threadbare through time. The rain from God fell inconsiderately and uncompassionately over him, but Argyris never even felt it. He had only one concern during the rain: that the landscape before him became hazy and he could not project his eyesight far enough in the distance to perform his duty faithfully.

Aside from his traffic duties, the people of Phigalia also mocked him for one other obsession. They saw him wearing his borrowed coats and trousers, they observed the cap as it became threadbare on his head, and they teased him:

"What kind of a Department of Traffic Regulations is that, Argyris, which hasn't even sent you a uniform yet?"

For years now, Argyris gave the same stereotyped reply: "Eh It is on the way—"

"Do you think you'll have it by Sunday?"

"Without question! You'll see me on Sunday and be proud of me. I'll be a traffic officer in all respects—"

Then he would describe his uniform as he remembered it in detail, exactly as he had seen it at the Hafteia in Athens. A gray-green uniform, full of hope, with a white band looped from the left shoulder across the chest, and a wide ornament with a gold buckle encircling his waist. On his hands he would wear a pair of long, white gloves, which would beautify his palms; on his head he would wear a helmet of pure silver, which would cause the sun to lower its eyes enviously.

The uniform was coming by way of light and wind, through hollow words, and Argyris appeared to be wearing it already! He pretended to straighten out the creases in the coat and trousers; he pulled on the gloves; he fastened the helmet on his head. And he became taller. That small man, to whom an injustice had been done, rose from the ground, puffed his anemic chest, and swaggered proudly. The sickly wrinkles disappeared from his face; his eyes sparkled. It was as though he was no longer called Argyris—the foundling Argyris, as the inhabitants of Phigalia and of the neighboring villages knew him. Because that was how it was. That was how Argyris had come into existence. An unfortunate being, who could tell from what poor origin, which had been abandoned in swaddling clothes on a wintry night in front of one of the houses of the village; and he had not even known how to wail! By chance, an old woman came out to go to the outhouse; she saw the baby's skinny hands searching in the darkness for the heartless breast of its mother; and the old woman took the baby in. She brought it up by begging; and when she died, she abandoned it, twice an orphan.

With the imaginary uniform of the traffic officer, Argyris gained an identity. He had a new name and surname; he had the name of a father and mother, the year of birth, and an occupation! The Sunday, of course, on which he expected to receive the uniform, came once a week for years on end, but each Sunday came and went without bringing the uniform. Even though he prepared himself every Saturday night to receive the uniform, to try it on once to see if it had been made to his measurements, and to see how he looked in it, he always awakened the next morning to the same patched clothing. And he went to work, anticipating the end of the new week, only to find that Sunday came again with the same empty, heartless hands—

"So, Argyris!" an urchin teased him. "What's happening to that uniform from the Department of Traffic Regulations?"

"Didn't we say that it would be here on Sunday? For certain, it will arrive in Phigalia on Sunday."

"Is it yellow?"

"Certainly not. It is green. All green—"

Nonetheless, he made certain attempts of his own to obtain the uniform. Must he depend on the Department of Traffic Regulations alone to obtain a uniform? Whenever a stranger passed by and expressed astonishment at the work he was doing, Argyris stopped him and confessed his great heartache. It was only a single dream, the only dream of his life. He enumerated to the stranger the things he wanted. He counted them on the fingers of his hand —one, two, five—And as he made an error in his arithmetic, skipping numbers with the disorderly wings of his mind, he would begin again: "Three, one, two, six—"

The strangers smiled sadly. They took a coin from their pockets and slipped it into Argyris' palms to stop his counting. And, in the end, they would promise, as soon as they returned to Athens, to make it their first consideration to purchase and send him a uniform.

Argyris was easily deceived out of hope, and he followed after these strangers, coming near to being dragged under the wheels of the automobiles as they rolled away, having already forgotten his existence. He stretched his small face forward and called after them; but, naturally, only he heard the words:

"And the helmet, Sirs; and the helmet! Don't forgot the helmet and the gloves. The gloves must be white and the helmet silver!"

The wheels of the automobiles drowned his words and crunched at his dreams. Still Argyris persisted.

"Do you hear? In the name of God, do not make a mistake! The helmet must be white and the gloves silver—"

When the rural postman brought the package, it was already dark. He, therefore, made the delivery to the offices of the Commune. It was on a Saturday, in heavy midwinter, and the postman almost sank in the mud under the burden of the bundle of happiness he carried on his back.

Only the Vice-President and the Secretary were at the office of the Commune. But this particular news was of such interest to the entire village, which experienced a boredom in all that loneliness, that in no time at all a multitude of people flocked in to see the package.

"Who is sending it?" the most impatient member of the group inquired. "Is it the Department of Traffic Regulations from Athens?"

"No," replied the Secretary, putting on his glasses. "The name of the sender is here on the front—"

He smoothed the creases on the paper with his sleeve, and, in the silent agony of the others, he read: "Sender: Anna Street, A-tens."

"What does that mean?" someone asked in surprise.

The Secretary was quick to reply: "It appears to be an American lady who lives in A-tens—"

"It that A-tens far away?" a local geographer asked.

The name "Anna Street" circulated from one mouth to another throughout the village. Everyone searched through his memory, until finally they pieced together the identity of Anna Street. It was truly an American lady who had passed through Phigalia one day. She had stopped at the intersection to exchange a few words with Argyris, half in Greek and half in her native language. She spoke with two or three other villagers in the same conglomeration of languages.

"Was it that blonde woman?" some of the people asked.

The blonde, the thin woman who was wearing shorts. A tall woman with a melancholy aspect, whose eyes exhibited the memory of her son. The boy had been studying archeology; and, after having visited Delphi, Mycenae, Olympia, and the Epicurean Apollo, he had vanished—At that time, the newspapers had carried the story that the mother was coming from Chicago to search for her son over every bit of land and sea in Greece. The son had been traveling in a tiny blue automobile, and his name was William Street.

When the American woman asked Argyris for information about the tiny blue automobile and her son, he had answered eagerly. He remembered having seen the automobile drive through that same street. In fact, he had given the signal for the direction the driver was to take.

"Was it William?" the mother asked anxiously.

"William!" replied Argyris.

The eyes of the woman filled with tears. And when she offered him a gift, Argyris casually mentioned the uniform. "Traffic officer!" he said loudly, accompanying the words with gestures. The American woman wrote in her notebook: "Traffic officer!" And the uniform she sent him was that of a traffic officer.

The villagers took the things out of the package, one by one. Everything was quite new, of the finest quality, and neatly pressed. The coat, the trousers, the band, the gloves, the helmet, and the belt. And something else was added: a pair of shoes and a pair of sunglasses—blue glasses, the color of William's tiny car.

The Vice-President of the Commune decided that it would be more appropriate to give the package to Argyris on the following day, on Sunday, the day on which he had been expecting its arrival for years now. The others agreed. All at once, the entire group gathered there in the office shuddered with emotion. Not a single man presumed to utter a sound of mockery! Argyris' story had returned from the past to unfold itself before their eyes with the snow and his tattered clothing, and everyone sensed a genuine bitterness.

Later, they sat down to plan their actions for the following day. They would take the traffic officer's uniform to Argyris at the intersection, at the place where morning always found him and where the sun bade him farewell each evening. The presentation would have a formal, let us say, tone. Each member of the Advisory Board would carry one article of the uniform. They would form a single file and walk to the intersection. Freshly shaven and smiling, wearing a gay flower in the buttonhole of their best Sunday suits— Should they even have the church bells ring? They should even do that! Someone suggested that they throw cherrybombs, the kind lighted around the Sepulcher of Christ during the Resurrection services and made the urchins wild with joy.

The Vice-President, an old-time teacher of the village, offered to make a speech. He would take the opportunity to tell Argyris that they had entered his name in the registry of the Commune.

He would also announce Argyris' surname. And his profession, of course: Traffic Officer of Phigalia.

Later, when they dispersed for the night, each man had an easy conscience for the first time. And within that conscience floated the same happy, smiling semblance of a man: Argyris.

At eight o'clock the next morning, when they all got under way to walk to the intersection, Argyris, of course, was already at work. Without suspecting a thing, he stood on his rotting stand in the drizzling February rain and went through the signals with his hands despite clouds that were overcast in the south, and the wind dragging them by the mane as it prepared to cast them to earth.

The procession was indeed a magnificent one. Were not eight men, each carrying one article of the uniform, sufficient to carry so much happiness!

They had set off from a distance; thus Argyris had not seen them. Furthermore, on that particular Sunday a large excursion of foreign tourists was under way, and his entire attention was absorbed by the movements of the pullman buses heading for the Epicurean Apollo. He even called out directions, though the rain drowned his voice.

"This way to Phigalia! That way to Linistaina and to Zour—"

Suddenly and quite unexpectedly, he was unable to complete "Zourtsa." After the first syllable of the word, a small bus skidded on the wet street and knocked him from his throne, and threw him two metres away. The bus, of course, disappeared like a bullet to follow the large pullman. But Argyris, pitched on his back, had already soiled his clothing with a profusion of blood, flowing from several wounds on his body. He attempted to rise to his feet to resume his place on the stand, but he was so badly mangled he could not move. He was in frightful pain. All he could continue doing as he lay stretched on the ground was to move his hands to direct traffic, feebly and desperately.

Everyone around there rushed to lift him. The village doctor happened to be among the group. He tore Argyris' tattered clothing to uncover his chest and examine him.

"He has lost much blood," the doctor said. The rain, heavier now, carried the blood away, adulterating it.

The doctor ordered the others to lift Argyris and carry him to his house. Argyris had injured the back of his head, his spine,

and his pelvis. His left leg was broken. Meanwhile, he had re
covered somewhat and asked in agony: "Did the tourist buses get
through all right?"

"Yes," they told him. "They went toward the Epicurean Apollo."

"There was no accident? Tell me! Was any passenger injured?"

"No, Argyris. No one was injured. Be quiet now."

Argyris was relieved. Later, he looked around more attentively
He saw the men from Phigalia who had gathered around him, each
holding in his hands an article of the greatly treasured gray-green
uniform, and this revived him. His eyes, heavy and blurred with
pain, shifted from the helmet to the blue glasses, then returned
to wander again over each item.

"Did the uniform come?" he asked in a weak voice.

"Yes, Mr. Traffic Officer," someone replied in an official tone.
"The blonde American lady sent it; the lady who came to look for
her son, the one who was driving the tiny blue car. You remember
her son William."

An ardent desire for the uniform warmed Argyris' blood and
revived him, as though his injuries were not so serious. When two
or three men from Phigalia lifted Argyris to carry him to the
doctor's house, he stretched his trembling hands, pleading for the
uniform.

"I am cold," he complained, shivering. "By the time you get
me to the doctor's house, I could freeze and die. Have you no com
passion for me?"

"We will run to save you!" they cried.

"Don't you understand, I am cold! You should dress me. Put
on the new uniform. Since it came today, isn't it right that I should
wear it at once?"

The men looked at one another and smiled bitterly. They un
dressed him quickly, there in the rain, and put on the uniform of
the traffic officer, the entire uniform, and the area became green
with hope—They started with the shoes and finished with the hel
met. Nor did they forget the gloves. Two long white gloves in which
he buried his hands up to his elbows for a bit of ease. Those hands
felt relief and security.

It was true that they rubbed his body well, and the rain
washed it with love and care. But the blood flowed with such force
and passion, that before long, his uniform was wet, painted with
strange figures, especially the gloves.

The doctor's house was at the other end of the village. Many
people from Phigalia accompanied Argyris there. Two men held

him by the shoulders and two by the legs, as tenderly as they could. The bells, of course, did not ring, neither out of joy nor out of sorrow; nor did the urchins throw their cherrybombs. On the contrary, everyone was burdened by the same anxiety and prayed a thousand times for Argyris' life.

Argyris, stretched across their hands, had already forgotten the death which threatened him. He was not even concerned about his wounds, which were spotting the road in huge drops. He was proud in his uniform, and he smiled. And every so often, he raised his gloved hands and signaled to direct the traffic on the street.

Yiannis Manglis

(1909–   )

Yiannis Manglis was born on Kalymnos in 1909 and lived there until he settled in Athens during the 1930's. For many years he worked with the sponge fishermen of Kalymnos and came to know the hazardous, almost inhuman life which he recreated in his first collection of short stories, *The Damned of the Sea* (1940). He is a realist concerned with the lives of actual people and the environment which shapes them. Fortunately, his characters are men of action and adventure, but one always discovers in his work a rich vein of Greek life carefully revealing contemporary social and economic problems. In 1956 he received the Second National Short Story Prize for his collection *There Are No Sinners,* and in 1958 the First National Prize for *My Brothers, the People,* which deals with the German Occupation of Greece and the Resistance.

Other works include: *The Barbarians* (1944); *Samuel* (a play, 1948); *In the Bog* (1949); *Contrabandists of the Aegean* (1953); *The Human Passion* (1961); and the autobiographical novel, *The Sun Hasn't Set Yet* (1962).

The Wedding

Thodoris and Panagos had been "working" together for three years now. That they were working is to make an understatement. But work is what they called it. They traveled to Anatolia, seized the animals, and carried them back to the islands where they sold them. They traveled to Greece, carried away gunpowder and guns, and a load of salt, which they sold to the natives down in Barbaria, in Syria, in Lebanon—anywhere they could. From there they received tobacco for narghile smoking, matches, pressed grapes, cognac—and brought them back to Greece. All contraband. Even so, they called this work.

Thodoris was nearing fifty and Panagos, exactly on the Day of the Assumption, great be Her Grace, would be going on twenty-eight. They were both handsome men. Tall the one, with dark complexion and large savage eyes, with a narrow chin split down the middle. A trifle shorter the other, chestnut-colored, thick-haired, with a wide jaw and eyes dark as roasted coffee—full of murder.

Thodoris loved to engage in conversation; the other did not. Nor did he even want to listen. The first one laughed at times, called the children to him, and gave them gifts. The second man never laughed. There was also a third member in the small sailboat, a very young boy who had not begun to shave yet, Onouphrios. He was either from Fournous or from Leipsous—or he could have come from Arkious. He had been on two trips with them, and now they were on their way to the Greek islands.

In the green sailboat with its beautiful frame, a well-traveled boat with large sails, sat Aglaoniki, mistress of Thodoris. She was a tall, corpulent, brawny woman, with wavy, raven hair and large eyes, as black as prunes. Her thick lips were as red as a sun-burst pomegranate.

She came from the island of the Aegean, from Spetsas or Hydra. She longed for adventure, she longed for a trenchant love, and she said to Thodoris the contrabandist: "Will you take me with you on a trip?" And he, who found delight in the vigor of her body, said, "I will take you with me on one journey."

A proud sun resembling an archangel fell on the sea and covered it with its golden hair. There was a great calm, and the

241

three men pulled oars with all their strength to reach port that much sooner, there to drink a glass of wine to relax, to bring equilibrium to their blood.

Close to noontime, they arrived at the pier. They cast anchor, secured the cable. The harbor was small and was open to the sea from the south. It wasn't really a harbor. It was a pier shielded from the northern waves with an extended chasm, rather a hole; with a gaping mouth.

There were no sailors there. As for fishermen, only a few—The inhabitants lived off the land and the animals. Those who could, retired to the mainland of Greece, or to America, or wherever they could go. In years past, when the islands had been under Turkish domination, well, then everyone had plenty of room. They sailed far to Anatolia and carried on trading. Later, the Italians came, and the people remained on the island to struggle with their poverty, rather with their hunger.

They cast anchor, secured the cable to the mole, set out the plank, and stepped on land. One after the other, they crossed the empty narrow wharf, entered the town. The heat was unbearable. The air was thick and brown like honey. Perspiration rolled from their faces and bodies. Breathing was difficult. They came to the small square and sat down under the mulberry tree at the tavern of Mastrovasilis.

"Bring us food to eat and something to drink—Bring everything—" Thodoris called out.

"It's fasting time, Captain. For the fifteenth of August, the Day of the Assumption," the tavern keeper said alarmed. "I have egg plants, olives, onions; all good things."

"Fool!" angrily cried Panagos.

"Have you any eggs?" Thodoris asked.

"I have."

"Since you have eggs, you must have chickens. Make some eggs and be quick about killing a couple of chickens. Do you understand?"

"I understand, Captain," the small man replied hesitantly.

Beside the mulberry tree, under its shade, ran water from a fountain which had been built during the time of the Turks. There on the marble around it some sayings from the Koran were carved. "Justice is happiness," "Peace is prosperity," "Cool water is happiness." Aglaoniki approached, ran the water through her hands, wet her head, cackled with laughter, and the entire land became beautiful like a song. Captain Thodoris stood up, put his palms under the water, filled them, and poured the water down his face and head. He had a handsome head, round, with a high forehead, and thin curly hair.

"The water is warm, but it refreshes," he said. "Come, Panagos, wash up!"

Panagos neither spoke, nor did he rise. He was rolling a cigarette. He had a pouch of tobacco and a cigarette case before him. Taking some tobacco, he placed it on the cigarette paper, whirled it over backward, straightened it out, and the tobacco was swaddled within that thin paper, isometrically. With his tongue, he licked the edge of the cigarette paper and glued it down. Smooth, thick as his small finger, the cigarette went into the case.

Onouphrios' soul longed to play with the water. But he was afraid of this sullen, harsh man. He glanced at him sidewise without moving.

The eggs were brought, the olives, the onion.

"Have you any cheese?"

"Cheese in a goatskin."

"Curses on you, billygoat!" bellowed Panagos. "Bring the cheese wrapped in goatskin."

They drank their wine; they ate their appetizers.

"Bring your glass and sit down," said Thodoris. "What's new on the island?"

"Nothing," the tavern-keeper said and looked at them frightened.

"There must be something. Tell us—"

"What news should there be, Masters. These are difficult years, jobs are few, the inhabitants struggle against poverty with their axes, with their animals. Ever since they closed the great mainland of Anatolia, the people have been suffering."

"We know all that," said Thodoris. "Tell us something different."

"Like what?"

"How many carabinieri have you on the island?"

"Five and one brigadier."

"And are these enough to get all your women pregnant?"

"Our women are not what you think they are, Captain Thodoris."

"Shut up!"

"I accept that, Captain."

"To your health!"

"To your health, Captains!"

"Have an appetizer."

"Many happy days, Captain, but forgive me—I am fasting."

"Stuff yourself!" said Panagos.

"I'll stuff myself, Captain," the tavern-keeper replied feigning joy, but very much afraid.

"Is it very long since smugglers came to the island?"

"Captain Zaphiris was here during the last moon."

"Did he get his leg? I heard that he went to Athens to have a new one put on."

"No, Captain. He's still running around with the wooden leg. If he had two legs, he would take over all of Turkey."

"Nonsense!" bellowed Panagos, and swore foully.

"Nonsense," echoed Mastrovasilis, the tavern-keeper, and he repeated the foul curse.

"To your health!" said Thodoris. Then he added, "Turkey isn't taken over by smugglers. The smuggler goes on land, enjoys a Turkish woman, knifes a Turk in passing, puts the animals on the boat, and weighs anchor. It's only what Greece is able to do."

"You're right a thousand times, Captain. It's only what Greece is able to do."

"I said."

"You said, Captain."

"To your health, then," said Captain Thodoris.

"To your health, then," repeated Mastrovasilis the tavern-keeper.

"And what was it the crippled man brought?"

"The usual things—spirits with mastic, mash, matches, tobacco."

"What did the carabinieri do?"

"They weren't aware of a thing. The smugglers unloaded at the cape."

"The carabinieri were playing with your women. Do you agree?"

"I agree."

"To your health, Captain."

"What other news?"

"Like what other news. Yes, Socrates Bafas returned from America."

"Who is he?"

"You knew his father, Captain."

"Describe his features."

"He had a grocery store down the lane. He was short, stout. You drank wine together. He liked you because you were generous

and a truly straightforward man. Many times we said good words
about you, Captain. He liked you very much—as I do."

"Is he dead now?"

"He is dead, Captain. He liked you very much—like I do,"
Mastrovasilis repeated softly.

"To his soul."

"To his soul, Captain."

"And so Socrates returned?"

"He returned, and he is looking for a bridegroom to marry his
sister."

"Which sister?"

"The daughter of his father."

"What is she called?"

"Marigo."

"She has her years, around thirty-fivish."

"Did he bring any money?"

"He did. They say he has plenty of dollars."

"To your health!"

"To your health, Captain."

"Go see about the chickens."

"My wife is cooking them, Captain."

"Go see for yourself."

"I am going." And Mastrovasilis rose to his feet.

"Did you hear, Panagos? Socrates has returned, and he wants
to marry off Marigo."

"I heard."

"And he has dollars."

"I heard."

"Have you nothing to say?"

"Like what?"

"I believe you would do for a bridegroom."

"Me?"

"You. Who else? Don't you think so?"

"Depends."

"Then, listen—" Thodoris scratched his head for some time and
smoked. "To your health!"

"To your health."

"Listen, my boy. We'll eat and drink, and we'll fill our pockets
with money."

"Say on."

Thodoris smoked thoughtfully and said nothing, remaining
thus for some time. Suddenly, he said, "I have a thought."

"Wait," said Aglaoniki. "I, too, have a thought."

"You shut up. What kind of thought have you, idiot. You're serving another purpose."

"I thought of something. What will you give me?"

"Confound you. Shut up. You made me forget. To your health, Panagos."

"To your health."

"Listen. I am adopting you. Do you understand?"

"No."

"Here, I am adopting you. And you have been to school! A pity the beatings you received—I make you my son. From today, I am making you my son. You will call me father."

"I wouldn't condescend. My father was an honest man, a worker, a brave man—There was a halo over his head."

"Yes, but he had no breeding. I have breeding. Do you know it? My father was a schoolteacher; my uncle a storekeeper and a holy chanter; the father of my first wife was a doctor; her uncle was a priest! You see—"

No one spoke.

"You will call me father, for a while at least, until the business has been completed. Do you agree?"

"Go on."

"To your health!"

"To your health."

"You are to call me father. You will pay attention to what I say. What kind of work do we do? We're merchants. Honest men, generous; and we have a reputable name. It will be an honor for them to come into our family, to be related with us through marriage. Do you understand?"

"I understand."

"I can't tolerate those Americans. Rubbish. They've earned five dollars and act like roosters. They've become weighted down with gold teeth, gold chains, pencils—and they don't even know how to write. Let them go to the devil's mother, to America; I don't care. Let them go. But when they return here and pretend to be important, with all their watch-chains, then I'm offended. I can't tolerate them. Can you tolerate them, Panagos, my son?"

"E, they've never done anything to me. Perhaps I can tolerate them."

"We said that we would agree. Can you tolerate them?"

"I can't tolerate them."

"To your health!"

"To your health," they all repeated.

"Mastrovasilis, bring some wines and come here beside us. And, curses to you, bring those chickens."

"They're coming, Captain. In ten minutes they'll be here."

"Bring them at once. As they are. I have spoken—"

The food came and the new wines. Thodoris caught the chickens in his large hands and tore them apart.

"Eat! Have a piece, Mastrovasilis."

"Begging your sympathy, Captain. I am fasting."

"Still? It's very well. I also fast at home. My deceased mother was God-fearing. Signs of the cross, fasting, priests. A saintly woman, I tell you. An angel. To the soul of my mother!"

"To her soul, Captain."

"And my wife Aglaoniki also. She observes fasting all the time. But as the Bible tells us: 'The traveler and the sick have no sins.' Isn't that right?"

"Right, Captain."

"Listen, then—I will confide a secret to you, Mastrovasilis. You knew my first wife? Well, it doesn't matter. She was a doctor's daughter. Plenty of money, an education measured by the pound. Do you know why I divorced her? Well, for this. The shameless hussy had no respect for religion. She wouldn't kiss the priest's hand; she wouldn't fast. Nonsense, the slut would say. Religion, she would say, is for the illiterate. Fasting is for imbeciles. She quarreled with my deceased old woman. My son, my old mother would say, you have brought Satan into our house. She will damn us all. We have been brought up differently; we are God-fearing people. I endured her as long as I could, then I dismissed her. Now at home, I want you to know, Aglaoniki observes fasting. Chick peas, kidney beans, and all that. Can I have a drop of oil, wife? No, she says. We will not contaminate our mouths. Very well, I say, don't yell. I'll do as you like. Not as I like, she says, but as Christ and Mother Mary like. Do you agree, Mastrovasilis?"

"I agree, Captain."

"To your health!"

"To your health, Captain."

"Listen and I will confide something else to you. We're getting old, Mastrovasilis, and don't argue about it. One of these days we'll shake our bottoms and deliver up our souls. It is our duty, then, to become good, serious men and good Christians. This is what I keep repeating to my son Panagos. I tell him to marry and settle down; to become sensible; to drop all strange women."

"Pardon me, Captain. Did you say—to your son Panagos?"

"Don't you know?" Thodoris said, affecting surprise. "Ever

since his mother Ephtychia, my sister, died, I adopted him. I made him my son. God gave me no children. The doctors in Athens told me, 'Thodoris, you can't have a child, and you should know it.' So I said, 'Very well, it doesn't matter—It's the will of God. When my sister dies—she suffered from her heart, you see—I'll make Panagos my son.' That's what I said, and that's what I did. Isn't that so, Panagos?"

"It is so, Father."

"To your health!"

"What do you say about Marigo, Mastrovasilis? From all you've said about her I have her in my heart. Do you think they can get along as husband and wife?"

"They'll get along, Captain. She's a wonderful girl. No one has ever gossiped about her. And she is good. Sit down, her brother tells her—and she sits down. Get up, her brother tells her—and she gets up. A real treasure."

"Do you think they'll consent to the marriage? You see, we are people of breeding. You know—"

"I know. Do I know, he asks! And the boy is a vigorous, handsome youth. Now that you have adopted him, he also has a worthy name. If it was in the good old days, Captain, when Anatolia was accessible to us, when Russia was accessible, and we built two- and three-story houses with the dollars that came in, and the breasts of the girls were filled with gold crowns, and the rugs and blankets and sheets were piled as high as the ceiling—E, Captain, things were different then; different, quite different—But now, you see, all the young men are gone; they've left for foreign places. They either get married over there or else come back as useless old men. So, Captain, when we tell them about Panagos, they'll even turn somersaults."

"To the health of the bridegroom."

"To the health of the bridegroom," they all repeated.

"Speak, Mastrovasilis, my brother. I am listening."

"Captain, let me handle the affair. When the day cools off, Socrates will wander down here, and we will talk it over then."

"Very well. Take the food and drinks. Bring the coffee. Large cups of coffee, made just right, so we can lubricate our brains to make them work—"

"Now, respected and loving husband, what percentage will be my share?"

"Just let me stretch out my hand, and I'll smash you full against the face!"

"Try it. I enjoy it when you beat me. My entire body aches and rejoices."

"Witch. Unsated mare."

"I am a witch, and I am an unsated mare, and I like it when you beat me!"

"Vile creature!"

"I am also a vile creature. I am everything."

Thodoris moved his dark glance over the table, but there was no wine to drink. He took some tobacco, put it on the cigarette paper, and set to rolling it, murmuring softly, "Curse you, idiot. Consider yourself lucky that this business is intervening."

It was six days later, under the mulberry tree, beside the fountain, at the eating place of Mastrovasilis. The company was the same, with the exception of Onouphris, who, at the captain's orders, had returned to the boat. Socrates Bafas was with them.

They had already discussed the affair. At the beginning Mastrovasilis and Socrates had discussed it; afterward all the company went to the bride's house to wish her happiness and to drink a glass of wine.

Naturally, Marigo was not thirty-five. Had she been a nanny-goat for slaughter, she would have to be fattened for two or three days. And had she been cooked for another two or three days, she might have been fit to eat. She was stout, with large flabby breasts that came down to the belt around her waist. But her face was calm, and her eyes were large and sweet, overshadowed by a smile of suffering.

Now it was a calm, balmy evening. The sun had set. Having completed the day's work, the sun had set. In the distance, the flames continued to caress the horizon, and up higher, drifted a cloud of heat, coral red. Directly before the harbor, on a wide expanse, the sea was rosy—a reflection from the illuminated cloud. Beneath the mulberry tree, and even around it, the golden honey was suspended in the warm air. All the area had assumed the color of the honey.

They had agreed to hold the wedding on the Day of the Assumption. A double feast day: of the Blessed Virgin, exalted be Her Grace, and of Panagos, the bridegroom, who was Her namesake.

The last three days had been extremely hot. A fiery wind blew heavily as though discharged through the mouth of a flaming furnace. People's nerves had become paralyzed. The housekeepers closed the shutters of their windows and doors to keep out the intense heat. The water would not keep cool in the pitchers. Throats became thoroughly parched. They wet their throats with water from the long-necked pitchers to quench their thirst, but before the water could roll down, the throat was dry again, forcing the cry, "I am thirsty!"

"Relative-in-law, you said that you were taking the children to America. Do as you like. You should know that my wife Aglaoniki and I will be miserable at losing the boy. But so long as it is for his own good, it will not matter. We'll steel our hearts."

"Well, I'll take the children. Panagos will be my brother from now on, and I'll make him a partner in my business. I have a good business, a restaurant and beer parlor, and I need someone of my own, someone I can trust. I need an honest man who works hard, who doesn't play cards and drink much liquor, who is courteous."

"Panagos has all those qualities. If the boy isn't talking now, it it out of respect for you. He respects his father, you see. We taught him early to be respectful. If he is now drinking a glass more than he should, it is because he is deeply affected. The occasion calls for it; he is a bridegroom, relative-in-law. The boy is scared. He's young, generous; he's confused. That's how I was when I was being married to the doctor's daughter. You understand, relative-in-law?"

"Well, I understand. As I said, relative-in-law, I'll take them to America. Except for Marigo, I have no one in the world. I'm father and brother to her. I'm old now, and tired, and I can't live alone any longer; I can't take care of my property. And when, with the help of God, they have a child, I will also be a grandfather. Everything will belong to them when I die."

"To your health, relative-in-law. To your health!"

"To your health."

"You have made me happy, relative-in-law. I'm on the verge of tears. If my deceased mother were living, she would also be crying for joy. My son, she used to say to me, when you marry, choose a girl from our island. If she's not your equal in station, find one from the neighboring islands. I didn't listen to her, relative-in-law, and I've regretted it. My son Panagos has now heeded the voice of my old woman. I told him: you will marry a woman from our islands. The boy said, 'As you think best, Father.' Is that right, Panagos?"

"Right."

"Relative-in-law, I have never been as moved nor as happy as I am at this minute. I want to say something. Pay attention. I am giving a gift of fifty thousand drachmas to my son Panagos. This is what I had to say."

"*Well*, and I am increasing the dowry of one hundred and fifty thousand drachmas to two hundred thousand."

Thodoris bit his lips. "E, how stupid I am!" he thought. "Would it have cost me anything to donate a hundred thousand, especially since it was gratuitously!" He laughed stupidly.

"Relative-in-law, it is a custom on our island—it must be the same on yours—to withold a portion of the boy's dowry to help the other children, the girls and boys who have not yet come of age."

"But you haven't any other children, neither girl, nor boy."

Thodoris had not expected this reply, and he was thrown into confusion for a moment.

"No, I haven't. But where there are no children, it is the custom that the parents withhold the money. They worked, they spent money, they suffered to bring up the children—"

"*Well*, keep your fifty thousand."

"A, you insult me, relative-in-law. Mine are a gift to the boy. I will take them out of the dowry."

"If that is the custom."

"It is. I give you my word of honor. You, Mastrovasilis, come here."

The tavern keeper approached, and Captain Thodoris explained the situation, twisting his mustache and looking savagely at him.

"Is it or is it not the custom?"

"It is, Captain."

"Two days after the wedding, the father of the bride gives the dowry to the father of the bridegroom so that he and his family can support themselves throughout the festivities. Mastrovasilis, is what I say true or not?"

"It is, Captain."

"If that is the custom, I will conform to it. I was a child when I left, and I don't remember. But I am fond of the island customs; so I will respect them."

"Well," said the Captain. "To our health!"

"To our health," they all cried, and the tavern-keeper ran to bring a glass for himself.

"And what does the mother receive?" Aglaoniki asked, disturbed.

"Shut up!" Captain Thodoris retorted angrily. Then he remembered and immediately became mild and laughed. "The husband takes care of everything."

On the Sunday of the Assumption of the Virgin, praised be Her Grace, the bells rang from early morning. The evening before, most of the islanders had taken the road toward the southwest, to the chapel of the Virgin. They had been celebrating all night long with drink, song, and dance. Now, at dawn, they were returning thoroughly exhausted, sleepless, and half-intoxicated. In the afternoon, the children began ringing the bells of Saint George the Knight, and around five o'clock the group set out for the wedding.

Men, women, and children; no one was missing. All the island had gathered together. The old men had gone early to enthrone themselves on the church pews. They were observing through small, round, lashless eyes, which moved slowly, as they engaged in small talk. A few were catnapping until the priests, the chanters, and the wedding party entered the church and awakened them.

"Marigo still looks good," an old man remarked.

"So, so," another man said. "When her mother was giving birth to her, my wife was giving birth to Mihelio. The midwife left our house to go to hers."

"And when was Mihelio born?"

"In '82."

"Which is to say that it was some time ago. Eighty-two to nineteen hundred is eighteen, and thirty more is forty eight."

"That's right."

"E, not so loud. The strangers might hear us," one of Socrates' relatives said.

"Now, my son, whether they hear us or not, the bridegroom is in the bag."

The usual things pertaining to a wedding went on in the house: people, noise, folk music—violins, lutes, and the ever-present santouri. Food and drink. Much to drink.

Poor Marigo had been an old maid. Quite unexpectedly, both bridegroom and happiness had entered the house and had taken her by the hand; they had brought her to the middle of the room, to the middle of the island, where she became an object of curiosity.

The house was cleared around two in the morning. The dishes on the table were partly empty; so were the glasses. The guests could eat no more. It had been years since the villagers had had so much to eat and drink.

"Eat, friends; drink. Everything is yours," Socrates Bafas cried, half-drunk. "I have only one sister, and I am marrying her to a man of station."

The villagers ate and drank and beat their gums like hammers pounding on ammonium salt, and they loosened their belts. But the moment arrived when it was impossible to eat more. "Stop," they said. "We can't hold any more." Then they stood up, two or three at a time, and departed.

The relatives remained a while longer. Afterward, they also departed. Then the shrew, Aglaoniki, took Marigo by the hand, and drunk as they both were, they climbed the ten steps slowly, gingerly, to reach the upper floor. There were three rooms on this floor; on the right the bride's room, in the back, the brother's bedroom, and on the left, that of the relatives-in-law. Aglaoniki began to undress the bride and to talk with her.

"Pretend to resist, and don't be a sitting hen. Man loves to be resisted; that's how he's made. But don't continue resisting for long. Only for a short time. And well, you're no longer in your prime; you carry years on your back. You must have heard, and all these years probably someone has grabbed you in the dark. Don't betray all you know. Be patient. Man is jealous. No matter how many lies you string for him, he believes them. He wants to believe them because he's flattered. Tell me, are you a virgin? Confess to me. I must know so I can control the course of action we're to take."

"Yes," whispered Marigo breathlessly.

"Well, you poor woman. And how have you restrained yourself all these years? How have you endured?"

"E, this way—with hope—" Marigo again said softly.

"E, you poor wretch. You've wasted your youth. Are you afraid? But why am I asking; you're trembling. Don't be scared. It is nothing. It only lasts for half a minute. And later, you will see. It is more wonderful than sweets. You must have a little happiness, poor thing, even in your old age. You must know—I'm speaking to you as a woman. I feel sorry for you, and I suffer for you—I feel sorry for you—"

The bride put on her silk nightgown and went to bed. Her heart was fluttering. She sighed, and a blast of wine rose from within her being intermingled with fear.

Aglaoniki lowered the lamp, leaned over, kissed her on the forehead, closed the door, and went into her own room. She was drunk. She attempted to unfasten her dress with heavy hands, gave up finally, and half-naked as she was, she dropped on the bed. Immediately, sleep descended, sat down and covered her.

"To your health, relative-in-law," said Captain Thodoris.

"*Well,* to your health, relative-in-law."

"You know, relative-in-law, all this territory in Anatolia once belonged to us; lands, animals, the Greek people, let me tell you."

"I know, relative-in-law. I had lived those times—"

"I—that is, me that you see here—don't tell lies. I don't like lies, brother. That's my prerogative. Man will surrender a soul. Word of honor, relative-in-law; we will surrender a soul. Where, you will ask me. To God, or to the devil; it doesn't matter—Do you agree, relative-in-law?"

"*Well,* I agree."

"To your health, relative-in-law!"

"To your health, relative-in-law.

Thodoris turned to Panagos. "Don't drink so much," he said. "Bridegrooms don't drink."

But Panagos was already drunk, and he discounted the advice. He refilled his glass and drank. Then he took some tobacco, placed it on cigarette paper, and rolled it for a long time; but he was unable to smooth it out. He became angry and crushed the cigarette between his fingers. Afterward, he took some cigarette paper, two or three sheets, and crumpled them.

"You see, relative-in-law, I don't know America. When you return there, in all good health, send me the ticket and some dollars so I can find you. People I love, I want to see quite often. Do they carry on smuggling down there?" he asked suddenly.

"They do."

"Liquor. There are large gangs which smuggle liquor. They bring it from France and Scotland, and they sell it as contraband."

"Bravo America! I didn't know this. I always thought that smuggling was carried on in our parts of the world only."

"It is also carried on in America, I tell you. Millions of dollars."

"To the health of America, relative-in-law!"

"To her health."

"And don't forget, relative-in-law, to send me the ticket. Our country here has become poor—He says millions of dollars, and I didn't know it—I spit on my mustache."

"There is a leader of the smugglers in America, an Al Capone, who is very rich. He has villas, palaces, millions of dollars in the bank."

"And the police?"

"They are paid, and they close their eyes."

"Bravo! What is his name again, this brave man's, relative-in-law?"

"Al Capone."

"To your health, relative-in-law. To the health of the man in question!"

"To your health."

"Do you know him, relative-in-law?"

"No, I don't know him. I have no busines with him."

"That's bad, relative-in-law. You ought to become acquainted with such men."

"I have no business with them."

"You should start having business with them."

"They made a movie of him, and people trampled over one another to see him."

"Bravo to them! Such men make the world beautiful. To the health of America!"

"To her health, with pleasure."

All three were drunk. The bridegroom, sullen, wordless, drank and smoke incessantly. Socrates was still sitting in his chair, sometimes resting his head on his left shoulder, at other times on his right.

Thodoris was able to drink considerably more. He was ecstatic over everything. Over the fifty thousand he carried in his bosom from his "relative-in-law" and over the smugglers of America. He would somehow manage to get over there, and he would carry on a good business. He would buy villas; he would loan dollars. They would make a movie of him, and people would flock to admire him.

"Let us drink one last glass of wine, relative-in-law, to the health of the bridegroom, who has a double holiday today. Then he must go to find the bride. Poor woman must be dead tired waiting all this time."

So saying, he filled the glasses to the brim. With glass in hand, he toasted: "My son Panagos, I wish you every happiness. You're a good boy, an honest one, a good worker—you will succeed. Your brother Socrates, or let us say your father, will take you to America. He will also take me there, he said. 'On my word of honor, I will take you.' Everything is fine. To your health!"

Socrates attempted to speak, but he could only say *"Well"* two or three times. He began to cry. Tears rolled from his eyes, and he said *"Well."* They drained their glasses, and Panagos rose to his feet.

"Let me kiss you, brother and son," said Socrates.

"Let me kiss you, too, my good son," Thodoris also said.

Panagos belched. He stood for a while, churlish, looking at them. The two relatives-in-law were deeply moved.

"My son Panagos, I give you another fifty thousand drachmas," Thodoris said tearfully. He dug into his bosom and covered the money with the palm of his hand.

"And I give you another fifty thousand," said Socrates.

Thodoris refilled the glasses.

"When will you give them, relative-in-law?" he asked.

"I will deposit them in the bank in the name of the bridegroom."

"It is better that you give them in cash. I don't trust the banks. They steal. To your health, relative-in-law."

"To your health."

"Bend over, you, so your brother and father can kiss you," Thodoris said to Panagos.

"Tomorrow," Panagos replied as he moved toward the stairway.

Time passed. Thodoris and Socrates continued to drink. Socrates fell asleep; Thodoris talked on, making plans. Every so often, he nudged Socrates. "Relative-in-law," he said, "to your health!" Socrates, with eyes half-closed, gripped the glass Thodoris offered him and murmured, "To your health," then drank a little.

Thodoris became tired of talking and drinking alone. It must have been four o'clock. "Better go to sleep," he thought. "God has more for tomorrow. The wine won't run out."

He shouted to Socrates; he nudged him softly, then roughly. Nothing. "Let him go to the devil and to his America, these lost souls. They get drunk on the first glass."

He lighted a cigarette, reached out his hand to refill his glass with wine, and gulped it down. This was the last one. He climbed the stairs, went to the door on the left, opened it. The lamp was quite low, so he wasn't sure he was in the right room. He walked over to the bed and was about to take off his jacket.

"What the devil!" he murmured. "Is this one Aglaoniki or two?" He closed his eyes and opened them again. He saw two. Now wait, which was the real Aglaoniki? "Wretch, Aglaoniki, which is the real you?"

He bent over, feeling with his hands. It was not Aglaoniki, but his "son" Panagos, who had embraced Aglaoniki, fully dressed as they both were. He let out savage cries; everything that came to his throat.

"Infamous ones!" he howled. "You bastard, Panagos, smuggler, thief, murderer! You whore! I picked you out of the gutter, and you are cuckolding me before my very eyes!"

He fell to beating both of them. They awakened. Aglaoniki jumped out of bed. She sobered at once. She attempted to defend herself, to say that she wasn't aware of anything—that she knew nothing. But Thodoris' fist and blows caught her full in the face. Quickly, she opened the door and ran toward the stairs. Thodoris caught her at the head of the stairs and kicked her buttocks. She almost fell, but quickly managed to run down four steps, wavered for a moment, then lost her balance completely, and fell headlong down the steps. She was hurt and began to shout and cry. Howling and crying, she reached Socrates, who was sleeping with his head on the table. She shook him several times, but was unsuccessful in awakening him. She embraced him; and between sobs, she began to describe what kind of men these were.

"Criminals, relative-in-law, murderers. They hatched this plot of the wedding to fleece you of your money."

But Socrates was sleeping and heard nothing. She continued to embrace him; she spoke to him; she cried that she was in pain—once it was her back, then her leg, then the back of her head. She was in great pain.

Panagos nailed himself upright in the middle of the room. His face was hard as granite, aggressive, flaming red from anger. His glance was dim, full of murder. He attempted to speak, to explain how he had made the mistake. Instead of taking the door to the right, he had taken the one to the left. For what—? To deflower the virgin! And not to mention that he was drunk—But he condescended to say none of these things.

Thodoris looked at the hard, determined face of Panagos and regained his equanimity.

"The way we've managed everything, come, let's go!" he said and led the way. Panagos followed him. They reached the sailboat, unfastened the cable, weighed anchor, and set out.

Inside the house, Socrates remained asleep, with Aglaoniki embracing him as she talked and cried: "Take me to America, relative-in-law. Take me, and I'll be your slave. Take me, with or without a wedding wreath—Any way you like—"

Only in the bride's bedroom, the old maid Marigo was crying softly, bitterly, very discreetly, for the virginity she had not lost.

Markos Lazaridis

(1911-   )

Markos Lazaridis was born in Smyrna in 1911. He studied litera‐
ture and later law at the University of Athens, but interrupted his
studies to emigrate to Ethiopia. Today he lives in Diri Dawa where he
is supervisor of the Greek Community School.

He first appeared in Greek literature in 1950, contributing short
stories to the literary magazine *Nea Estia,* and later to other magazines
as well. He is essentially a short story writer, and his collections include:
The Northern Cross (1953), which was awarded the Frist Short Story
Prize by the Committee of Twelve, *Tropical Vertigo* (1954), and *The
Gazelle* (1961).

Lazaridis clearly shows the influence of Knut Hamsun, but his atti‐
tude toward his characters is more humanistic and compassionate. He is
widely read because he was the first to present the enchanting, exotic
life of remote tropical lands.

Fear

Approximately two years have passed since the appearance of this strange man on the dusty streets of our small town. At first, none of the white or colored inhabitants, who resembled signs which corresponded to the flowing mosaics of the town, knew anything about him; neither his race, nor his place of origin. Furthermore, within this small Babel, burning to a slow crisp under the young sun, the new faces have considerably increased in number during these last few years; thus it was pointless to ask any questions. The hospitality of the Ethiopians is as boundless as their land.

Yet, everyone shrugged his shoulders in surprise at sight of the stout, middle-aged man passing by. He took off his grey hat with a sweeping gesture and greeted charmingly with a slight bow, even though the people he was greeting were strangers to him.

"Bonjour, Monsieur!" he would say with a strange accent, which revealed at once that he was a Frenchman.

During the early months, he was attired—holiday, workday, day and night—in a grey woolen suit, a black necktie, and black shoes. Everyone wondered how he was able to endure all the heat and dust. Many people had only to look at him to begin perspiring.

It was a long time before he became acclimated. Did he perhaps lack sufficient money to buy a cheap shirt, at least, and khaki trousers, as most people here were wearing? Or did he perhaps desire to remain segregated from the others and for this reason suffered his martyrdom? Shortly, it became apparent that the first reason was true. He must have found work somewhere and, with his first earnings, was able to purchase a khaki shirt and thus cast off the heavy coat and necktie. The following month, the trousers and shoes had their turn. He had no intention, however, of discarding the hat. It remained there, a crown upon his head.

In the evenings, and even during the nights, he was the only man circulating with a hat on, that grey hat, vastly tormented by the endless greetings. By now, everyone understood that it was inconvenient for him to do anything else; that it was essential he wear a hat in order to tip it in greeting the people.

Sometimes, he happened to be before the cinema as the picture was ending and the spectators were pouring out into the street like a thundering river. During these moments, he sought to stand by the corner, to tip his hat and bow like a coiled automaton. Simultaneously, through his mouth came a stiffled murmur like that of a drowsy monk reading evening vespers at the monastery: *"Bonjour, Monsieur—! Bonjour, Monsieur—!"* The Greek inhabitants of the town were not long in christening him "The Greeting One." Everyone now knew him by that name alone.

When the *yialesouk*, those dark urchins, saw him approaching from a distance, they lined up beside the sidewalk, took a deep bow all together, pretended with their hands to be taking off a hat, which they were not wearing, and said in chorus with comic seriousness: *"Bon Jour, Me-si-ee!"* Then, in the wink of an eye, they vanished like smoke, chuckling while their white teeth simultaneously flashed in the sunlight, glittering hard.

It did not suffice him to be greeting everyone he encountered in the streets, but he must also raise his head, his eyes, to the verandas, the porches, the windows, and even the terraces, seeking to discern a head high up there which he might greet. He gave the impression of being possessed by a secret agony, of being endlessly tormented by an inescapable fear of dreadful punishment about to be inflicted on him should he continue on his way without giving that greeting. His glance, kind but languid, and eternally alarmed, poured out of the right eye alone, because he always kept the left eye, which appeared to be injured, half-closed. His face, square and pale, with flabby cheeks, his wrinkled brow, and that short-clipped, graceless mustache over his colorless lips, revealed a tortured and prematurely-aged man. In spite of his height and robustness, he lacked vigor; his shoulders drooped, his paunch protruded, and his footsteps were sluggish and uncertain.

When he walked alone in the streets and no other pedestrian happened to be walking beside him, he had the air of one who was absent-minded. His lips moved nervously, as did his hands, giving the impression that he was conversing with an invisible companion. However, when he sensed someone approaching from the opposite direction, he ceased his silent monologue, greeted in his stereotyped manner, and once again became submerged in his own world, which he always transported with him.

Eventually, he became fatigued from his excessive walking, and he always sat at a side table in the coffee house. As he sipped his coffee slowly, he read something from a newspaper written in a foreign language: Slavic or Armenian? Now and then, he stopped reading to gaze for long into the distance at an immovable object, as though some kind of vision, which had absorbed body and soul, unfolded before him and petrified him. Was he reproducing something he had been reading in the newspaper? Or had beloved persons transported him from the newspaper and whirled him along through familiar, nostalgic places of his distant homeland? Perhaps this was it, because now and then he smiled vaguely and whispered something. At other times, he took out a handkerchief to wipe his good eye. Then he twisted a bit on his chair, reseated himself in a different position, and began to read again. But the newspaper would once more fall to his knees, and his glance would travel.

One Sunday morning he entered the Greek church. He lighted a candle, made the sign of the Cross—three fingers joined together —kissed the icon of the Holy Trinity where it stood on its worshipstand, and stood beside the tall bronze candelbrum, on which the reverence of the faithful had become a mound of golden flames resembling a blazing pine tree.

He attended to the services motionless, even though he understood nothing of what the priest was saying and what all the chanters were chanting. But when it was almost time for the priest to pass by with the Holies, the Paten and the Chalice, he began to murmur something, to make signs of the Cross, one after another; and his face assumed an agonized expression which reached a high point at the moment the priest emerged from the right door of the sanctuary, the Holies in hand. The man shook bodily; his shoulders jerked as though he was undergoing a convulsion. He rubbed one palm against the other, and squeezed his hands in a thoroughly distraught manner. His countenance, always pale, had now become sulphurous and, all at once, as if he could no longer stand on his feet, he staggered and fell kneeling, striking his knees loudly on the slabs.

The bowed congregation and the priest who was standing— without interrupting the blessings he was dispersing in a deep, peaceful voice—curiously observed this strange man attending mass, who appeared to be in great torment where he had fallen on the slabs, humbling himself before God and men. What could have caused him to suffer so, to supplicate so frantically, without heeding the numerous eyes observing him?

As soon as the priest had passed through the Holy Gate of the Sanctuary, the kneeling man stood to his feet and became somewhat calmer. Later, he underwent the same tortured motions when they began to chant, *"We praise Thee."* His glance shifted from left to right, his lips fluttered, and his hands became acutely distressed. As the services ended, he was the first to leave the church. He stood on the steps and unceasingly tipped his hat to all the people who emerged from the church. He waited for the priest who was late in changing to street clothing, because he had stopped to read blessings over some sick babies. When the priest finally appeared, he kissed his hand, saying, *"Bonjour, mon Pere."* Then, walking backward for a few steps, he departed.

At the large iron-rail fence of the churchyard, he was forced to stop because loud-mouthed, dark beggars, about ten in all, had blocked his path. Taking a handful of coins from his pocket, he distributed these. The beggars followed him to the far corner of the street, chanting, "Jesu Christus— Jesu Christus—" To rid himself of the beggars, he altered course. He took off his hat. Waving it two or three times, he bowed as he said: *"Merci, merci!"* The beggars, it seems, found this rather amusing, and they began to imitate him, shouting with laughter. However, the man paid no attention to them, because he had become pre-occupied with gazing over the high fence, which was adorned with flowers—a multitude of blue, almond-shaped eyes with canary-yellow eyeballs on the curly, dark green metope of the creeper vine—a slender-stemmed Japanese lilac, which waved its arms to the sun, full of clusters of mauve flowers in the softest pale tone. That ethereal tint of the flowers absorbed him, perhaps because the entire tall tree was in full blossom where almost no green was visible; only the flowers.

On the other hand, he could have stopped to listen to the multi-voiced symphony of a world of invisible birds sitting in the thick, flamboyant foliage which, having shaded the garden and veranda of Madame Fontené, spilled over the fence to spread its green fans out into the middle of the street. Madame Fontené was proud of these tall trees, even more than she was of the fact that her two daughters played a Chopin *Polonaise à quatre mains.* From an aperture in the fence, at that moment, and for a moment only, the plump head of the woman passed by, her face grey with an abundance of powder, her orange hair cut like a man's. She dyed her hair the color of henna, as the old Arab men did their whiskers; and because of this the Frenchmen, playing on words, called her, *"La mère rouge—"*

The man was standing out on the street, admiring the lilac

flowers, lost no opportunity to call to her, after removing his hat, of course: "Bonjour, Madame!"

"Bonjour, Monsieur!" she replied in a quiet voice from the other side. Thinking that it might be an acquaintance, she edged closer to the aperture in the fence and looked out toward the street. "O, la, la!" she cried, puckering her lips. "I don't know him! He is insane! Or maybe—" And she remained suspended on the thread of hope.

Quite contented, he continued on his way without paying attention to what the elderly woman had said or to someone who had hastened his footsteps to overtake him. That someone was a stout, robust old man dressed in white. His linen suit had become short from excessive laundering and so tight that it barely fit, squeezing his flabby abundance of flesh so that he moved with difficulty. Without doubt, it was with great effort that he fastened the single button on his coat. He wore a white cap on his head, and the green lining of his visor cast two green reflections on his shining rosy cheeks, which appeared oily. Anyone would have been surprised to know that this old man was the owner of three houses and one of the oldest and best merchants in town. An amateur chanter and volunteer trustee of the church, he had been affected at sight of this stranger, suffering as he had earlier during mass, and about whom he had heard so much. All kinds of rumors had been spread about the stranger. Some said that he was a Russian spy, and that his performances were only a ruse to cast ashes in the eyes of people so they would consider him insane and thus allow him to proceed with his business unmolested. Others called him an agent of Tito; and still others said whatever they could conceive. Later, the old man learned that the stranger had found work in the offices of the Franco-Ethiopian Railroad Company. However, because he was always pre-occupied, he made countless errors, and they were obliged to release him. It could have been that his French was not so good. Later, the company people felt compassionate and rehired him; not in the offices this time, but in one of their warehouses, and at a smaller salary.

It was after this occurrence that the stranger began to enter the *Asmara* in the evenings, the bar which the proprietress Amal maintained with some kind of respectability. Standing beside the bar, he would drink several glasses of anisette, pay for these, greet —with his hat, of course—and take to the streets. He walked for hours without a specific destination, and without hurry, turning by chance sometimes to right, sometimes to left, walking until midnight when the second siren sounded. If circulation on the streets had not been prohibited, he would perhaps have continued walking until morning. During these hours, the streets were deserted, half-dark, and he resembled a drifting shadow.

Those night strolls caused some people to conclude that he was an evil man. They asked: "Why should he be roaming about in the dark, deserted places, a man of his age, instead of lying down in his home to rest after his day's work?"

They failed to consider that perhaps that empty, alien, inhospitable home was unable to contain him; that perhaps those naked walls repelled him; and that the ceiling, made of asbestos cloth to conceal the zinc-plates of the roof, smothered his heart like a marble tombstone. They even failed to consider how unbearable it could be not to have someone in the house with whom to exchange a word in one's native tongue. Each man knows within himself, for what reasons he acts one way and not another. And the secret of this embittered man was concealed deeply, a secret which ruled over him and guided his life. It was this secret that Mr. Poulopoulos, the vigorous old man from Kalamata, now sought to uncover; and he ran quickly to overtake the stranger who greeted the passers-by with his hat.

It was no simple curiosity which propelled him. He had known many lands and men of many races, a true Sinbad the Sailor, multilingual, astute, experienced. He had a treasure in money, knowledge, and goodness for his fellowman. And it was a joy to him to become acquainted with someone new and to penetrate this man's secret world. It was like penetrating an unexpected, concealed garden full of exotic plants, creatures, and birds.

Today, in church, as he saw the stranger beating himself like the shipwrecked man is beat by the waves and his attempts to grasp at some higher power as he would a precipice on the wind-swept beach, his heart broke; he sensed compassion for the stranger. He felt like going beside him to raise him from the stone slabs and ask softly: "What is troubling you, my brother?" But he was embarrassed before all those people; so he waited until the liturgy was concluded. Before he could count the offerings, record and lock them away in the candle cupboard, the stranger had eluded him.

The stranger was neither difficult to become acquainted with nor conservative in his words. Together they entered the bar

Asmara, where the proprietress Amal sent them two glasses of
pernot with ice. The bar was quiet at this hour. Aside from a group
of Swedish airmen who were already drunk and slobbering over the
dark entertainers, and another group of four stout Dutchmen, rosy-
faced, bald, blue-eyed, middle-aged men who were amused by the
games of the Swedes, there was no one else there. One of the Dutchmen sang, every so often, in a high-pitched tremulous voice:

> *Tout va bien, tout va bien,*
> *Madame la Marquise. . . .*

To express her deepest appreciation, Amal would not allow
the boy to serve the patrons of her bar, but opened the bottles of
blonde beer herself and served it, raising the bottle high in order
to obtain a five-finger crown of foam. The Dutchmen grabbed the
glasses and emptied them in a minute, licking the foam off their
lips with delight, glancing with hungry eyes at the sunburned
curves of the proprietress, who had dissolved like sugar in water
and was fondling their bald heads with laughing eyes, full of
promises.

Mr. Poulopoulos touched his small glass to that of the stranger
and gulped down the pernot because his throat was dry. He had
been in church all night; you see, he had been assisting Father
Jason at matins. But the stranger also emptied his glass to refresh
himself from the heat, which every afternoon soared to exceeding
heights in this town. They looked at one another and laughed.

"How do you like this land?" the old man from Morea asked
to begin the conversation.

"I like it immensely. It has a significant advantage for me, its
peacefulness. After the frightful agitation of the last war and the
nervous breakdowns resulting from these great turmoils, we need
peace and quiet. We might thus be able to pass the remainder of
our days with a bit of tranquillity, since absolute tranquillity is impossible for us in this world."

"You are right. Tranquillity is a great virtue in these unquiet
times we live. I have been here for thirty years and am quite content. Only that it is too hot."

"I like the heat. In my country—I am from Yugoslavia, you
know—I suffered from the cold every winter. I used to say that I
should have been born in the south. Generally, I have always felt
that I never did adjust to this world. I found it very harsh, in-

human, not only insofar as men were concerned, but nature itself. However, despite everything, before the war I lived relatively well with my wife in Zagreb—I was a judge. Then the war came—"

Both men took off their hats. The old man saw the thick grey, wiry hair of the Yugoslavian, and the stranger saw the hairless, arched, shiny bald head of his companion.

The stranger's voice was full of bitterness. He talked with difficulty, often interrupting himself, often hesitating as he searched to find the most appropiate words in French. The man from Morea had heard and read many identical stories. The war, the disintegration of the front lines of the Yugoslavians, which left the side of Greece vulnerable and brought the German tanks to Thessaloniki— all these were known facts. But now he was hearing how the Yugoslavian had escaped with many Englishmen and fellow-officers to the south. They had cut across the entire length of Greece, from the Axios River in the north to Kalamata in the south. At the arched coastline in the south, they had given their final battle.

When the old man heard the name of Kalamata so unexpectedly, he felt his heart fluttering ardently in his breast, as though he were suddenly seeing his deceased mother again standing alive before him.

"So you came to know Kalamata? But that is my native homeland. I was born there, and grew up there—I fished at its beautiful coastline—"

He caught the Serbian by the hands and shook him hard, overcome with joy that he had at last found someone who had known the land in which he had first seen the light. He ordered more pernots and danced up and down in his chair, wiggling restlessly, and emitting small joyous grunts.

The Serbian, amazed somewhat by this outburst of joy from his new friend, continued: "Yes, it appeared to be a very beautiful beach. But its beauty was soon covered by the storm of battle. That day became one of graves and hell. The kaleidoscopic pebbles, where formerly little angels must have played with their tiny buckets and shovels, digging wells and building ovens, and where the fishermen had spread their peaceful nets to dry, were covered with empty cartridges and shells; bits of flesh and carcasses without a soul. In the night, submarines came and carried away all the men they could. I was caught and imprisoned. After much wandering, I found myself locked in the concentration camp of Dachau. There, hunger, darkness, dampness, cold, sickness, floggings, horror, and death. Death at night, death in the daytime; morning, noon, and night; death in its most horrible aspects. What a savage beast man becomes!"

The old man from Kalamata listened without looking at the Serbian. He had fixed his gaze on the dirty blue oilcloth of the table, and his thoughts traveled to other places, to far distant places.

After a while, he shook his head negatively, knitting his heavy grey brows with displeasure. He was saying to himself: "No, no, I do not agree one bit. Try as I might, I am unable to imagine that beautiful beach in such a horrible plight as you present it to me. I had a magic illusion enclosed within me, entirely my own, my secret treasure, and you came with those empty cartridges and shells and blood and pieces of flesh to mar it, to give it a bad stench, to make it loathsome. No, my man, no! You have no right, in spite of my sympathy for you, and I do heartily feel sorry for all the dreadful horrors you have undergone, but leave me, I beg you, with my talisman uncontaminated by blood and fierceness, free of smoke and gunpowder. Let it shine with sweet light in the darkness of barbarity."

The blue oilcloth of the table expanded, expanded, until it encircled him. It began to move pulsatingly, to rise and fall, to take on brilliancy, clarity, and depth. There, the green reeds in the bottom of the water swayed unceasingly, carried along by the soft pushing of the water, while he oscillated on the gleaming breast of the sea, which swelled and dipped softly, like the breast of a sleeping girl. The breeze tickled his ears and, circulating sharply over his forested naked chest and arms, caused the hairs to undulate from their very roots in an exhilarating shudder. In his nostrils he sensed the wrath of brine and in his mouth the taste of sea-urchin and limpet. The sea danced, swinging her blue satin gown; the foamy lace of her under-slip swayed over the subdued beach, leaving behind a long silky trail.

"What did you say, Sir? They made sugar from the bones and soap from human fat? A! No, no! I beg you, stop aligning such horrors. Proprietress Amal, two more pernots. With these two, I believe that makes ten? Excellent. Would you like a second piece of ice in your glass? Pernot tastes like ouzo, which we're accustomed to drinking in my country; only that this is yellow and ouzo turned milky white when you poured a little water into it. And there were the small plates of fried smelts with their delight-

ful aroma, hot as they were, and some cheese and black, salt
olives—all of which gave you a devilish appetite."

"A la votre santé, Monsieur!"

Over there, we used to say, "Eviva!" The tables were arrange
on the beach beneath the jujuge trees down by the waves of th
sea. Now and then, the salt water refreshed them. And in th
winter, the sirocco caused the sea to swell, the waves to bea
against the doors as though to order coffee at the Panhelleni
There were many tables, all identical; round, green, iron table
with three legs which always, now the one, now the other, san
deeper into the sand, tilting the small glasses with the ouzo. Th
tables were all anxious to contain people in the evenings. Th
women chattered, the children ran around and twittered. In th
center, on stage, the small orchestra played Viennese waltzes an
old romantic songs.

Later, he would go for a walk to Antivrahiona and on down t
the green harbor light. (Was the light at Antivrahiona green an
the one at the Great Mole red, or vice versa?) Ah, miserable year
If he were to ask, perhaps the Serbian could tell him the color c
of the lights on the right and on the left side of the entrance to th
harbor. The Serbians, too, have a sea and boats. He remembere
a Serbian boat which had come to anchor across Kiskila's coffe
house to unload wood. Entire mountains of boards and beam
were raised on the beaches. Look, he even remembered the nam
of that boat. *Herkerova-Ergegobina* was written in large letters o
her masts. He even remembered that, beneath the name, writte
on the stern, was the word *Split*, and that the boat had four deck
two upper and two lower. But was it the Serbian ship which ha
four decks or the Norwegian, the *Rolf-Jawrl*, which unloade
herring from Bergen? He was confused again. Ouf! And what did h
care now about the color of the harbor lights and which of th
two ships had four decks? No, he would not ask the Serbian. Le
him continue to relate his macabre story about the Czech girl wh
had given birth to a dead baby at Dachau because the priso
guards had kicked her in the belly. What a mania that Christia
had for relating such shuddering events! For an hour now that wa
all he had talked about. Let him talk. He was talking to himself
he was listening to himself.

"Proprietress Amal, two more pernots, please. And some ice-
Does this make twelve? Ouf! I am perspiring!" Well, where wa
he? Ah, yes, he had gone for a walk to Antivrahiona—no matte

ow about the color of the harbor light—and he was greeting his
cquaintances who were promenading there and those others who
·ere seated on the benches, talking and laughing. Some others sat
reaming quietly. A boat might be leaving the harbor, lighted like
ie candelabra of the church of Papanti; it would whistle low, and
ontinue to become smaller and smaller, until it moved slowly out
f sight, an ephemeral happiness which became submerged in the
·a of forgetfulness.

Red lights to attract the fish would move slowly over the
iallow places, casting snake-like reflections on the dark waters.
he rocks would absorb the sea with a gurgle, like old addicts their
arghile. Yellow phosphorescent lights would come and go on those
iossy, cube-shaped rocks, and young people, girls and boys, would
ng from boats, while far in the distance, in the waters of Mani,
ie boat of the Gragonaios family sat like a diamond crown on the
·et, crow-black hair of night.

The voice of the Serbian came from afar, a monotonous mur-
iur, call it, which served as an accompaniment to the reveries of
ie old man from Kalamata. At one moment, the Serbian stopped
ilking. He caught the old man by the arms; he suddenly shook
im violently and asked in great excitement:

"Do you see this eye, which has been destroyed? I lost it there,
·ith their fists— They had taken us out into the yard for a bit of
unshine. I thought to wash out my shirt in the trough because it
·as so greasy it had stuck like glue to my back. As I was stooped
ver doing my laundering, I did not see a fat guard passing by; so
failed to stand erect to salute him. 'Why don't you salute, swine?'
e cried fiercely. Disconcerted, I stood at attention. His face had
ecome red and flames were flying from his bleached eyes. 'I'm
orry. I did not see you,' I replied in French, because I did not
now German. Then he rushed upon me with clenched fists and
egan to fling them into my face as though they were iron weights.
staggered and fell. Two other German soldiers, who happened to
·e near by, rushed over and also attacked me. All three kicked and
tepped on me until I fainted. It was forty-eight hours before I
egained consciousness. I was in bed for a month. I lost my eye at
hat time, in that place. I am amazed at how I was able to endure,
who always was so delicate and so inexperienced. It is unbeliev-
ble how much man can endure—"

The old man listened carefully to this story. He thought, un-
oubtedly, there was some connection between this experience at

the camp of Dachau and the mania the man had for greetir everyone. However, he understood that it was improper to questic him further because the Serbian was now wiping the good ey with his handkerchief. His lower lip trembled.

"I will never ask," the old man thought, and they parted fc that day.

A week later the old man from Morea became convinced th; he had not been wrong in his diagnosis.

It was the night during which the Ethiopians lighted the hug fire in the center of the dead torrent and danced for joy becau; the heavy rains were over at last. The *Asmara* bar, brightly lighte with a variety of colored lamps and decorated with phoen branches, was enjoying moments of glory. Tonight, the proprietre Amal sparkled like a copper-fly in her strapless lamé gown, wea ing, furthermore, with great pride, wide, heavy golden bracelets four fingers deep—, a necklace with golden tassles, and long, fak diamond earrings. Indian jonquils, thrust in a double row in h(thick, curly, ebony hair, resembled a royal diadem, which accen tuated her wisely calculated movements with a tone of dignit Around her, playing the role of ladies-in-waiting, chirped a grou of girls with dark complexions, dressed in the loudest colors, i sparkling sequins and beads, in natural and artificial flowers, i tulle and ribbons. All the tables were filled with young, wel attired Ethiopians, who were wild about drink, dance, and womer and with Italians who had come with their foreign families—unwe Ethiopian mothers and coffee-milk children; with Frenchmen an Frenchwoman—*liberté, égalité, fraternité;* with some equally i; toxicated Americans and Englishmen; with Germans who gathere around like girls who had never been out before; with straw colored Swedes; and with frightened Muslim Arabs and Hindu who occupied the tables all night long with a single sherbet—fc which reason the proprietress Amal disliked them; and with othe varieties of Orientals. Smoke and heavy fragrances permeated th warm air of the low-ceilinged room. From the megaphone, howle the swings, sambas, and raspas, all of which the Africans enjo immensely. "Biz, biz, biz!—" Nor did anyone pause for breath.

Huddled in a corner, the old man from Kalamata, the Serbiar and his younger brother, who worked as an engineer in Addi Ababa, and who had only recently arrived to visit with his brothe were smoking and drinking whiskey, and gazing curiously at th dancing couples squeezed on the narrow dance floor. Howeve from the drinks and the lack of oxygen, they felt faint in the

and went outside for a breath of air and for a look at the big fire
and the dance of joy.

The night was clear, full of stars and noises. They took the
road leading to the violent stream, the torrent. From its banks
came the tremulous sound of a symphony of tropical crickets and
the sweetest, most deceiving noise of concealed poisonous snakes,
which, to one unacquainted with it, sounds like the chirping of
young birds.

They were walking slowly with knees weak from too many
drinks and from age. The old man from Kalamata heard the story
of the Serbian again, this time related by the brother. The canvas
was identical, gloomy, only that a few enlightening touches were
added.

When Germany knelt and surrendered, whatever prisoners had
endured the martyrdom and survived, were liberated. Dusan—for
so the Greeting One was called—returned to Zagreb, a pale shadow
of his former self, dull-witted, with horror imprisoned in his mind,
with hollowed cheeks, dead lips tightly sealed, and twenty years
added to his true age. His wife was terrified when she saw him.
On his back he carried a knapstack, but in his head he carried fear
and that mania for greeting everyone.

They took him to all the doctors, even to the famous specialists
in Paris; they gave him medical treatment, electrotherapy, hot
baths, but nothing, nothing helped! Fear had accepted him in her
employment forever. Fear had enclosed him within an invisible
web and was dragging him through her dark domain.

"And how was it you came to this place?" asked Mr. Poulopoulos.

"We were not in agreement with the new order in our country;
so we took the bitter path of expatriation. Fortunately, we found a
peaceful refuge in this hospitable and civil country, which accepted
us with such kindness along with hundreds of other refugees from
the Iron Curtain."

As they were talking, they had approached a row of automobiles, purposely parked some distance from the big fire. A great
many Europeans had come to partake of the joy of the Ethiopians.
Small children, sitting on the hoods of the cars, screamed and
clapped their hands while their small faces sparkled with the reflections of the fire rising to the sky, a tall, many-tongued fire, which,
with its flying sparks and its bright smoke, resembled a golden,
haunted oak-tree. Around the fire, the Ethiopians were singing
and dancing their ancient breathless, masculine dance. From out of

the night, from the roots of the hills, thousands of moving lights sprouted and joined with one another before dashing toward the fire. When the dark merry-makers were twenty steps from the fire, they cast into it their lighted torches, which created bright arcs diving into fiery arms.

Dusan had proceeded ahead of the other two and was looking at the strange sight with a smile.

The brother suddenly asked Mr. Poulopoulos: "Do you know German?"

"No. Why?"

"So I can give you a vivid portrayal of the shock my brother has received from the day of his flogging. At any rate, to explain, I will use the identical expression to him which the German prison guard used at that time. Watch!" And going closer to his brother, he called in an unexpectedly savage voice: "*Warum grüssen sie mich nicht, Schwein?*"

Dusan jumped suddenly and turned around like a man who had lost his mind, took off his hat, and greeted incessantly with bows, now to the right, now to left, in back of him, in front of him, wherever he could. O, he was a tragic automaton there before the fire of joy. For a long time, he greeted in this fashion. It finally became imperative that his brother take hold of him to make him stop.

"That is enough, Dusan; enough! You have greeted enough."

The old man from Kalamata remained speechless, his soul embittered and burdened.

They advanced closer to the fire, as close as the raging crowd of dancers would allow. The excessive blaze licked their faces, and they were perspiring from the heat and giddy from the perpetual circling of the dance, and deafened by the noises.

The faces of everyone were red, except that of Dusan. His face had become white, dripping with cold perspiration, as the marble face of a bust on a tombstone. He had not recovered yet. Perhaps his heart was not beating, and his blood had frozen. He was not in company with the other two. His good eye was opened wide, and the iris played uneasily, strangely, insanely. His brother caught his hands.

"Be quiet, Dusan. Nothing is wrong," he said. "Forgive me. I played a bad joke on you. But you must react now to your fear. Such a long time has elapsed since then. Entire years. There is no reason for you to be greeting everyone. No one is going to say a word to you. Do you hear? No one. And throw away that old hat.

They are no longer in style. There, look! Do you see anyone wearing a hat? You are the only one. Throw it into the fire and burn it. Besides, it is old now. It is shameful for you to wear that old hat. Throw it into the fire. Your fear will burn with the hat."

Dusan turned and looked at his brother like a small child. He took off his hat slowly and observed it carefully, turning it this way and that, examining it as though it were a new hat some merchant was offering him and he was about to make the purchase.

"Come, have courage!" the younger brother said.

Dusan looked at his brother again and at the old man from Kalamata, as though he were returning to this world after a short visit to the gloomy, cold kingdom of the dead. Color was slowly mounting to his face, and even a faint smile sparkled on it in the reflection of the fire.

"Come. Burn your fear!" the brother repeated.

The hat oscillated a little—perhaps the hand holding it was trembling—and suddenly it flew outward, made a beautiful curve, and fell into the fire, which swallowed it unsatedly.

"Bravo, bravo-o-o!" the other two shouted, clapping their hands with emotion. They caught Dusan and kissed his cheeks; then, taking hold of his hands—as though they had already planned this earlier—they rushed into the human torrent which was passing before them; they mingled with the Ethiopians, and the tide of shouting and dancing carried them along. Shortly, however, they were forced to pull aside for lack of air, trampled underfoot, but also quite contented.

"What did I, miserable wretch, want to get my whiskers caught in the wadding!" the voice of the old man from Kalamata was heard saying, while he brushed the dirt off his clothing with his hands.

Several days went by and the old man failed to see the brothers. One sunset, as the evening sirens were sounding and all the streets had overflowed with laborers, the old man from Kalamata discerned, in the distance, a white hat bobbing up and down, greeting that swarm of ants. It was an imitation panama hat, *made in Japan,* one of those that the native vendors, loaded to their ears with variegated products from the land of setting sun which had flooded Africa, were selling in the streets. Colorful wares, cheap and vulgar.

"No, in the name of God—" the old man cried, jumping in place. He felt something crumbling within him.

He had not been deceived. It was he, Dusan, who was once again greeting the passers-by with his new hat. The same as before!

Demetrios Yiakos

(1914-   )

Yiakos was born in Agrinion in 1914. He studied law and literature, as well as French, at the University of Athens. Today, he is Chairman of the Board of the Department of Archeology at the Ministry of the Deputy Prime Minister, and also a member of the Administrative Council of the Greek Writers Association.

He has published three volumes of short stories, a novel, and four volumes of critical essays, *I. M. Panayotopoulos, Lyrical Writers of Roumeli, Literary Exercises,* and *Forms and Themes of Literature.*

He writes with an intensely human feeling and lyricism which is often suspended between dream and reality. His early works were inspired by the later struggles of the Greek people for freedom. Today, he has achieved a universal awareness of the moral and intellectual problems of man. His classical background never allows him to be classified among writers who are spiritually tormented over contemporary events. He is never arrogant as he faces the changeable proclamations of aesthetic movements, nor does he sense the terror that grips our times. In fact, his is a pathological optimism, and it moves him to proclaim in both his narrative and critical works the deep faith he has in man, whose destiny is to receive only the best from life.

The Path of Dawn

They walked in the night. And they were four in all. John Baxter and those others. He did not know their names, nor did he ever hope to learn them. Whenever he asked, chiefly through signs rather than language, all three kept their mouths sealed as though in concert. Nor did their clothing, those garments of a ragamuffin, reveal anything. Their sole possessions were a photograph of two children and of a woman, an old newspaper which had seen better days now folded in eight, and an empty box of cigarettes on which were scribbled three or four numbers. A fortuitous arrangement, or did these numbers represent some code?

"Come, tell me," he shouted. "Why do you remain silent?"

Not a sound from them. And John Baxter thought: "Are they human beings or are they statues which someone overlooked in the dusk?"

He had captured them while they were eating. Without coats or weapons, they kept out of sight behind the hill where, seated on the grass, they had opened their bags and were munching on what they had to eat.

It was cold. A strong wind blew from this side of the hill, penetrating a man's body clear through to the bones. The sky above was overcast, indicating rain. But they continued to eat without being concerned in the least, as though no war were in progress, as though they were at home or at a picnic in the country.

He stood observing them from a distance, bent forward, distrustful, as though he were death lying in ambush for them. But he sensed no hatred in his heart; on the contrary, he envied these men. He regarded them with pleasure, because they reminded him of the holy hour in the evening where, far away, in a trusting household, his father, mother, and brothers would be quietly preparing for their evening meal. And overhead, the evening star would be shining, while the herd would be resting peacefully in the yard, their lowing having ceased by now, and their rompings and savagery forgotten. The soft voice of his father would be leading in the evening prayer: "Bless us, O Lord, this food and drink."

They had not shifted positions, though they continued to eat.

They were like marble figures, a small representation of eternity. How wonderful to eat your bread thus, while death waited outside; while the moments rolled away heavily, like hours, like years. And all the time you would remain there like marble, motionless. Could you endure for long? Would death feel any compassion for you? But death is there; he has discovered you; he seeks you out—

As he crawled forward to take them by surprise, so engrossed were they in their meal, he carried this strange representation within him. He considered firing a shot, but an unseen hand withheld him. Was it the hand of his father or his mother? It was an old, gnarled hand. It touched him softly from within the shadows; it radiated overhead like the evening star and now extended toward him— It commanded him sweetly, softly: "Don't, my child! What are you about to do? Have you forgotten?"

"Yes, Mother, I swear to you that I will never touch a man while he is taking food. I swear to you. I had no intention of destroying them— Only, may God enlighten them not to do something foolish— I want to be able to kiss your hand with pure lips when I return home. When I return, I do not want to say to you: There, see? I, John, the sickly and consumptive, have stained my hands with blood— I have killed a man! I do not want to say this, Mother— And I swear to you, I will never destroy them!"

His hand became unnerved. The men continued to eat. Mess plates, canteen, quiet voices, soft laughter. A second picture, long forgotten, flashed through Baxter's mind, glided down his hand, and withheld it for a second time. High noon it was in the large public square. The sun bent toward the earth, spraying it with hot mist. The breath was fiery, and human flesh melted, became beads of perspiration which dripped to the ground from the forehead, the naked chest, the forested palms of the hands. He had been a child then, sauntering along until he came to rest like a column in the shade. At the time, it had been the day-laborers who had been taking their meal, at high noon, there in the middle of the unconstructed road. They had laid open their packages, unfolded their soiled napkins, spread the newspapers on the gravel, and then neatly arranged the olives, cheese, and water on them. They began to break bread in pieces with hands that were coarse and perspiring. Slowly, they had carried the bread to their mouths, a bread moistened with saline perspiration. "My son, show respect to the day-laborers while they are taking food. This is the reward of their labors. These workers preserve life and build roads to gratify you as you walk over them."

How could he aim? How could he strike? Those three men standing across from him were not soldiers; they were day-laborers who had become disjointed by the burden of their labors. And they were taking food. The holy hour was being contaminated by war. He did not shoot; he shouted instead. The men were startled; they froze. One man continued to chew; another held onto his canteen with no time for a second drink of water. The canteen slipped through his fingers. Nor did he stoop to pick it up. He stood dumb and motionless.

The third man stood up. He turned quickly to take flight.

"Halt!" cried Baxter.

He shot once in the air as he commanded: "Your hands high!"

The strangers turned to statues, their hands uplifted toward heaven as though in prayer, a triple, penetrating prayer.

"Now lower your hands!" Baxter said, motioning to make himself understood.

They obeyed. A dreadful hour. This was the law of war. Where should he begin? How should he address them? How should he proceed?

He had flashed the light up to their eyes in scrutiny. The photographs, the newspaper, the empty packet. He looked straight into their eyes. One had blue eyes; the other two black. Six glass beads, dark and penetrating, were gazing at him motionless. The bright beam of light scarcely had time to fasten on them before it was reflected back to nail him stupidly in place. Those glances contained hatred, a glassy hatred, which became steel and pierced his heart.

He had addressed them in his own tongue. It had never occurred to him that they might be foreigners, his enemies. He changed at once to ask in their own language, somewhat slower this time: "Come, tell me, who are you? Why don't you speak?"

The glass beads had nailed him. A shadow walked within him; the darkness, the silence. He found it essential to keep talking, to keep shouting, more as a form of self-encouragement, more to cast off the shadow raging inwardly. And he talked, shouted, broke forth with countless threats; he cursed, in their language, in his own.

From the three men, complete silence. Only the pupils of their eyes sparkled, as though they had something to disclose. Then quickly the glances were silenced, turned away, faded in the night, became dull glances. They had observed his fear. Encouraged by this, they persisted in their silence with an obstinacy which generates a second, a reactionary, obstinacy.

He took two steps forward and came closer. The statues moved now, but they made no effort to speak. He brought his hands forward; the column of light in his hand fell obliquely to shine down on the swampy waters. Then he crossed his hands, one over the other, to indicate handcuffs. With tight fists, he hastily moved his elbows back and forth as though to ask them: "Are you prisoners? And how did you manage to escape? Tell me—"

Not a word from them.

"Don't you understand me? Or don't you want to talk?"

He repeated the words in his own language. He detested talking in a foreign tongue, a fact he did not conceal from them.

"I hate your language," he told them. "I detest everything that is arrogant, as I also detest your dumb silence."

Only then did the beady eyes move. They glanced at one another sidewise. They glanced at his uniform, and again at one another. Were they perhaps attempting to reply that his words were incomprehensible to them? Or were they agreeing to remain silent?

"If you are under the misapprehension that you are going to act this way with me, that you will break my nerves, let me tell you this: you will never succeed! Only, be careful that this does not work to your own detriment in the end—"

A mouth moved as though to say something. But when the man looked at the other four beads, he closed his mouth again, even tighter than before.

"Well, why don't you speak?" he repeated after a while. "Aren't you human? I don't want you to reveal any secrets. I'm only asking for a single word, a foreign word, a different word; something that is not associated with the war and the battle. Say anything. Just so it is a word to reveal that you are also human—"

Only silence from them. Only the beads stared at him, dark, deep, and savage.

"Come, let's move on!" he said finally.

His hands trembled slightly. Was it because of anger, or because of the night and the loneliness? The beam from the flashlight danced up and down. It had lost considerably from its firmness. And an agitation, a shudder caressed his body.

He projected the beam of light on the khaki coat and pointed the revolver. They followed him. He motioned them to walk ahead; they obeyed. They walked in the night now, a total of eight military boots, which tracked the swampy waters underfoot and wounded the earth's back with their nails. Had anyone observed them, he would have thought they were companions, so close to one another were they walking. But they could never be companions, since one had asked for companionship and three had refused. Besides, how could that be? Companionship meant equality. And in this case, John Baxter was master; he controlled their footsteps, and they obeyed. Furthermore, they were unarmed, while he was armed.

But what meaning was there in this? The night belonged to everyone; a dark, treacherous spider, ready to capture them in its web. The eight military boots walked on, latched to the shadows as though they were moving through a dark, endless cave. It was like riding on a train which was moving through a tunnel, and jumping suddenly from light into darkness; half a minute, a whole minute, endless hours. Only here, he sensed that these men were beside him. He could not see them, nor could they see him. Yet, he was aware of their bulk and breathing. Only the sense of touch operated, as though he was blind. And a cigarette which burned faintly, a pale flicker which also walked beside him, barely half a meter away. He attempted to offer a cigarette to the others so they could join him and add to the number of sparks, even though minute. But the others lifted their heads proudly; they refused with a motion. You? No. You? No. You? Nothing. He cursed, he swore. And then hastily, he advanced in the night. He wanted to get out of the tunnel that much sooner; he wanted to catch the light. But he could not. The darkness choked him. It nailed him down.

All four were walking through an endless tunnel, dark and silent. The sky was black, indicating rain, and the ground was dark with mud-puddles. As far as eye could discern in the distance ahead, there was nothing; on either side, nothing. It was as though they were living a few days before the firmament was created out of chaos. But Baxter had already issued a warning before the storm broke. Let them beware. If anyone made the slightest movement, if anyone rebelled in the least, he would not survive! Did they understand the warning or not? Only God knew. They would be to blame in case of an unfortunate accident. John Baxter indicated this in every way he could: with motions, with sign language, with his revolver. Still they remained silent and attentive. They continued to walk through the tunnel, the three in front and Baxter in the rear. They expressed a silent awareness that he was now guiding their destinies. Should he so desire, he could kill them without reason. If they made a single false move, he would touch the trigger with his finger and three living bodies would be sprawled on the ground dead. Who would know? And who would come forward to accuse him? Had he acquired these men from some specified place? Could anyone account for them? They were his spoils of war; thus he could dispose of them as he pleased. He was master over them now. They belonged to him; their lives or their deaths were in his hands. He had become a god and walked in the field at night. Three ants were crawling. He could stretch his legs so and crush them with his heels; smash them. And they deserved to be smashed because of the strange manner in which they were behaving toward him. Not a sound, not even a cigarette. And to say that he had mistreated them. Everything but that, as God was his witness. He had done everything possible to be on friendly terms with them, to make them human again. What! Did they expect him to make escape possible? Ah! enough is enough! War is war. Would they have allowed him to escape, if he had been in their predicament. He saw this; he comprehended it from their attitudes. Ah! but, in truth, they were going too far, all three of them. Arrogant, disdainful, as though they were the victors. Look at their hatred! Look at their malice! They were not human beings; they were savage beasts. What if he had fallen into their hands instead? They would have killed him outright. But he had not killed them. And why not? Was it out of desire for trouble? Or was it out of philanthropy? Is there such a thing as philanthropy in war? Not to mention the mine fields. How was he going to lead them back to camp? How was he to get them through? Was he to look after them now, or after his own skin? So— Suppose he did succeed in getting them into camp? What would the others do with them in camp? Three more, three less— What did it matter! They would only be a headache. Fuss and bother and inquiries. Come here, John Baxter. Where did you discover these men? Where did you pick them up? And you. How came you to sprout over there? Why this? Why that? Run here; run there. They would only be a source of trouble. As though he had little enough of trouble already.

Thus, a single shot and all would come to an end. And Baxter would be at peace. But what kind of peace is that with three souls strung around his neck? To hell with it! Why had he decided to capture them? Why hadn't he left them where they were, gorging themselves on hardtack? They would have been asleep by now, and snoring. And he would have been going about his mission, spying in a foreign uniform. See now the kind of trouble he had purchased for himself. How much better to rid himself of these men.

He took aim. Searching through the darkness, he discerned three shadows. God forgive me, he said to himself. This is the law of war; a hard law to be sure, but nonetheless a law. When they were passing this law, they never consulted me. They never even had me in mind. As for my mother— What does my mother know, illiterate as they had left her.

He prepared to fire. The three shadows walked unsuspectingly. One shot and all would be over. A shot at a barely moving target, from the rear. He would hit the target, by God; he could not miss at such close range and as fatigued as their footsteps were. All three would fall with the first shot. This would mean a release from cares; theirs and his. And after a while, the report: Private John Baxter, thirty-sixth regiment, company three. I have the honor— Ah! no! It was no honor. Was it essential that he tell them anything? Would that not only add to his troubles? They were foreigners, three unknown men, three hateful enemies— For attacking a soldier— For insubordination— For attempting to escape— I take— Ah! no! This was their destiny.

Because they were eating—

Because they were fighting—

Let the darkness feast on them now! Thus, no cat around, no damage!

Come, John, why do you hesitate? Who will see you? Who will ever learn that the decision was yours alone? You are a god at this moment; you are the devil; you are whatever in hell you want to be. Only end it quickly. Why do you hesitate? The storm will break at any moment now; thus do not delay. Guide the destinies of these men at last. Complete their destinies! One shot, and all will be over—

"Death!" he shouted. "Death!"

The first shot was fired accidentally. It hit the ground at their feet.

At that moment the storm broke in fury. Was that essential now? Lightning furrowed the sky. Thunder clattered through it as though to destroy the sky. The rain fell to earth, slowly and windless at first, and resembled moistened downy fur which caresses the cheeks. Later, as it became denser, it fell headlong. He could not endure so much rain. It choked his voice and stopped his breath as it poured over him like a shower bath. The wind dashed into his mouth, stopped up his nostrils, held his body rigid. Or, what was closer to reality, the rain attempted to overthrow him. And then, just try to advance before such a windstorm. The rain poured furiously; the thunder refused to abate, the lightning whipped the earth to reveal four human wretches swimming through the mud. O, God, he could endure it no longer! He would be sprawled heavily on the ground. Well, so much the better. He would perish along with the others. He would find peace—

The shot had come with the thunder and lightning. He had not hit the men; he had aimed at the mud. The foreigners quickened their footsteps. They sought to separate. Baxter called out, he commanded, he cursed. But who could hear him in this storm? His hands were full of water, his heart was flooded with tears, his boots sank in the mud—Water dripped from his revolver, which had become a pipe from which the water mocked him, stroked him from all sides, and pulled him down to earth.

"Forward, run!" he shouted to them. "Let's find refuge some place."

But those three men advanced without concern, without suspicion, still silent. They were three shadows, three drenched ghosts which merged with the night, but which continued to advance. One of the three fell slightly behind, and he appeared to be limping.

"Forward, run!" Baxter shouted again.

But how could they hear him in this rainstorm? They walked slowly, two in front, the third lagging behind. He could not fire another shot. What had been done was already done. He could not go through that again. It was essential now that they hasten their steps to find shelter somewhere, to escape the rain. Later, he would see—

They found themselves in a cave. Or more appropriately, an opening on the far side of the hill. They entered quickly and shook off the water. John Baxter laid his revolver aside. He sensed someone falling to the ground. He flashed his light, then propped it in a hole so that it shone like a lantern. The four men eyed one another strangely, the one of the ground and the three standing up.

"And now?" he asked them. "What do we do now?"

From them, silence. They continued to look at him strangely and maintained their silence.

"What have you to say?" he asked the wounded man.

He also remained silent, secretly stifling a moan. That was when Baxter noticed him. This was the one from whom he had taken the photograph with one or two children and the woman.

"I also have a son," Baxter said. "An only son. Would you like a cigarette?"

"No—"

At last! Baxter heard human speech— In fact, the word was in his own language. O, God! This was a good sign! It would be possible now to find some way to communicate, to become friendly.

But, no! He was deceived. When he asked, "How many children have you?" the other man replied, "No!"

"What do you mean, *No*?" Baxter shouted. "These children here, and this woman," he continued, pointing to the photograph. "Aren't they all yours?"

"No—"

"Consider yourself fortunate, poor wretch, that I took an oath to my mother— Consider yourself fortunate that you are wounded— Otherwise, I would explain this *No* and *No*— Come, untie his leggings," he ordered the others. "Tie his wound—"

They obeyed him. He gave them his tin cup, his wet handkerchief. They washed their companion's wound; they cleansed it and covered it with tobacco from the cigarette he had offered earlier to the wounded man. Then they bandaged the wound. The wounded man expressed relief. A soft sigh escaped through his lips. Was it a sigh of joy or of pain?

"Thankful," he turned and said to the others with hushed breath.

"Why do you conceal it from me that you have children?" John Baxter asked quietly.

"I don't want your compassion. I have never learned to beg—"

"But you have my compassion. You have not begged for it!"

"I don't want it, I tell you. I will not become a target for your pity— Only for your revolver—"

Baxter bent down. He caught the wounded man's hand gently.

"You're hot," he said with a painful smile. "You must have a fever. Why don't you consider your children, your wife?"

"I told you once, and I'm telling you again," the wounded man cried. "I have no children! I have no wife! I want you to know that I am not married!"

"But I saw. I understood—"

"You understood nothing. You're a fool! The woman and children belong to them. They do not belong to me— And leave me alone, please—"

A little later, the wounded man said more softly. "Even so, it was dark. What would you see in the dark?"

"I also have a son," John Baxter murmured. "Why do you conceal the fact that you have one, too? Tomorrow, or the day after, the war will end. Our children might become friends. Why don't you want this?"

"I already told you— The devil take it, I have no children! I am talking to you in English."

"Are you English?"

"I am an Englishman."

"O, the devil you say! Then what do you think I am? Do you know?"

The wounded man fixed his eyes on Baxter's uniform. "Only you know," he said.

"My friends, I am also an Englishman. Disregard my uniform. They made me wear this deliberately so I could spy. Wait, you will see everything shortly."

Baxter took off his helmet. He was on the point of taking off his uniform.

"If that's the case, then I do have children," the wounded man smiled faintly. "And the woman there is my wife."

Baxter bent down to embrace him. "I also have a son," he repeated. "Do you know the charming poem by Frank Hardy? I will recite it for you so you can see how well it applies to both of us."

And Baxter recited the poem at once, even to its title.

To My Son

A tear had appeared on the tip of Baxter's eyelashes. Turning, he saw tears in the wounded man's eyes as well.

"Are you an Englishman?" Baxter asked again.

"An Englishman."

"And the rest of you," he asked the others. "Are you all Englishmen?"

"Englishmen."

"O, the devil you say! Why did you conceal this from me? Why didn't you speak? Are you aware that I was about to kill you?"

"We knew everything. We knew where you were taking us. That is why we were silent. We had gone AWOL from camp. You captured us— It was a long time before we understood the rest—"

"It always takes a long time for men to communicate— They walk side by side, but they are so far separated—"

The three men laughed. Baxter also laughed, bitterly.

Outside, the dawn was rose-colored. The storm had passed and day was breaking. At first, nothing could be discerned clearly. Only a kind of suspension half-way between the dark and the grey light of dawn. Something which resembled a soft, opaque line becoming brighter as it traversed the mountainside. Shortly, however, the horizon burst into a radiant flame; the sky sprinkled blue patches over the muddy earth. The sun now touched and caressed the hilltop. It was a large sun, an earth in itself, and it was encircled by a dazzling, rosy-gold light. A much taller, much fainter disc reflected behind the sun on the hilltop across the way and scattered a strong, endless, blinding light. Everything appeared to be in flames, shooting high like fireworks, swimming in a soft dust. The hills had lost their magnitude to become soft shadows floating over the earth, something obscure, ephemeral like a dream vision. And within this vision, a bright, radiant path was slowly revealed, a path full of people, of men and children celebrating with rattles and bugles, with flags—

"The path of dawn has appeared," one of the men said.

"Truly, it has appeared," echoed all the others. "Just look!"

They came out of the cave to have a better look. They stood slightly to one side so that the wounded man could also see the path of dawn.

All four stood there dazzled. No one spoke. They only gazed at the sight—and remained silent.

PART II

DRAMA

Gregorios Xenopoulos

(1867–1951)

Born in Constantinople in 1867, Gregorios Xenopoulos was brought to the island of his father, Zante, when he was only a year old. There he pursued his early education and developed a fondness for the island landscape and the islanders, both to feature so prominently in his early fiction. In 1883 he moved to Athens to study mathematics at the university, but devoted himself to literature instead. He wrote short stories, novels, plays, and essays. For years, he edited a children's magazine called *Education of Children* and later founded the literary magazine *Nea Estia,* which still remains one of the leading magazines in Greece.

Xenopoulos was one of the most prolific writers of modern Greece. His first novel, *Margarita Stefa* (1893), shows the influence of Zola's naturalism. It was written in the vernacular and established him at once as an author of great importance. He wrote with narrative ease and a keen sense of observation, paying attention to detail so that his episodes create miniature pictures unified by character and point to his dominant theme that love is the most important force in the world, transcending every barrier, but mostly that of class. Most of his novels are titled after their heroines, but not all have a happy ending.

At a time when the modern Greek theater was presenting no new plays, Xenopoulos appeared to become the father of neo-Hellenic drama. His plays are still produced in Greece with as much delight as when they first appeared. Early, he recognized that audiences wanted to be entertained, and so he revealed the daily life of the times without pretence or concealment of follies and foibles. But neither did he satirize events or conditions. Contemporary Athenian life was being portrayed for the first time in plots and with characters, speaking in the vernacular and often in dialect, who were familiar types. He was optimistic about the human condition, and thus never exposed human weaknesses.

Among his important works are: *The Stepmother* (1897); *Stella Violanti* (1909); *The Red Cliff* (1915); *Laoura* (1921); *Aphrodite* (1922); *Isabella* (1923); *The Patch of Decadence* (1928); *Secret Engagement* (1929); and *Among Three Women* (1930). Best known among his plays are: *Photini Santri* (1908) and *Die Versuchung* (1910). In *The Secret of Countesss Valeraina* (1904), though not a very successful play, he did what Pinero had done in *The Second Mrs. Tanqueray,* that is, Xenopoulos wrote for the Greek people, describing the Greek way of life as it was at the end of the nineteenth and the early part of the twentieth centuries.

Divine Dream

A One-Act Comedy

CHARACTERS

MORSIMOS, *a wealthy Athenian, formerly a banker, a frustrated tragedian*

CANCER, *a frustrated architect*

ARCHIAS, *a frustrated sculptor*

PHILOCLES, *a frustrated orator who lisps*

GLAUCE, *daughter to* MORSIMOS, *eighteen years of age*

NIKIAS, *young son to the great Sophocles*

PASINOË, *nurse to* GLAUCE, *middle-aged*

MYRSA, *slave girl to* GLAUCE, *young and beautiful*

THRASIS, *old slave to* MORSIMOS

The SCENE *is in Athens at the home of* MORSIMOS *during the time of Pericles.*

The SETTING: *A large courtyard opening out of the men's quarters. On the right is a path leading to the doorkeeper's room and the outer gate. On the left is a door to the women's quarters. In the distance there is a peristyle, on which the doors of two bedrooms can be seen, covered by a curtain. In the center of the peristyle, between the two doors, is an aperture opening out on a small lane which stops at the iron gate of the garden. On the peristyle, the roof of the bedrooms forms a terrace, an invisible stairway leading up to it from the garden. Almost in the center of the courtyard is an altar and several statues of Dionysus, Zeus, and Athena; one or two tripods; and closer to stage front a table with various chairs around it. The Acropolis with the newly built Parthenon is visible in the distance beyond the terrace. It is a summer evening, a half hour before sunset. Gradually, darkness falls.*

(NOTE: *None of the characters is historical. Even* NIKIAS *is an imaginary brother of Iophon and Ariston, the known sons of Sophocles.*)

As the curtain rises, GLAUCE *enters through the door to the women's quarters. In her hand she carries an embroidery hoop on which is a piece of cloth she is embroidering. Her nurse,* PASINOË, *follows close behind.*

GLAUCE. Let us sit here. When Father is away, isn't the entire house our own? What is the difference whether it is the men's quarters or the women's quarters!

PASINOË. Even when he is here. It is only when his visitor happens to be a young man—

GLAUCE. (*Cheerfully*) That is because all of Father's friends are old men—(*She sits smilingly on a chair beside the table*) Wonderful!

MYRSA. (*Enters through the same door carrying a basket of multicolored threads and other paraphernalia used in embroidering, a metal-backed hand mirror, etc.*) Shall I leave these here, my lady?

GLAUCE. (*Short silence. Then, as though awakening*) Yes.

MYRSA. (*Lays the basket on the table*) Would you like me to bring something else, my lady?

GLAUCE. (*Absent-mindedly at first*) No, Myrsa. You may go. If I need anything, I will call you. (MYRSA *bows and leaves the room.* GLAUCE *begins to work on her embroidery. After a while she sighs and raises her head, resting it against the chest of* PASINOË, *who is standing behind her chair*) Pasinoë, just as we have planned!

PASINOË. (*Nods her head slightly*) Of course!

GLAUCE. (*Cheerfully, turning her head to look at* PASINOË. *She takes* PASINOË'*s right hand in her left one*) When Thrasis sees him from a distance, he must inform me so I can go up on the terrace. I would prefer to go to the outer gate, but I am afraid—

PASINOË. O no! It isn't proper! You can see him from upstairs. Only, you must pretend to be watering the flowers so that no one will suspect anything—

GLAUCE. (*Cheerfully, dropping* PASINOË'*s hand*) Who will suspect? Our house is secluded here, and few people ever travel on this road.

VOICE OFFSTAGE. Figs for sale—Fi—i—i—igs for sale—!

GLAUCE. Oh, occasionally a vendor passes by.

PASINOË. Do you want me to buy some figs?

GLAUCE. No. If anyone is selling fish, Father said to buy some.

PASINOË. No one will pass by at this hour. The fishermen come in the morning. (*A short silence.* GLAUCE *works on her embroidery.* PASINOË *looks on, leaning over a chair*)

GLAUCE. (*Suddenly*) Oh! But what is the matter with me today! I cannot even work here—I have made another mistake. Instead of red, I have used blue. Goddess Athena, help me!

PASINOË. (*Without looking at her*) You are tired.

GLAUCE. This is enough. (*Places her embroidery on the table and rises*) I am almost through. Later, after I have had some rest.

PASINOË. After you have seen him and are calm again, you shrewd girl!

GLAUCE. (*Suddenly and with unexpected joy*) O, my eye is fluttering! My right eye—Terribly— (*She rubs her right eye*) Is that a good sign, Pasinoë?

PASINOË. (*Seriously*) Your right eye, you said? It is a very good sign. You are about to see him.

GLAUCE. I know I am about to see him; but what is to be the outcome? The problem is: will anything come of this? Will my father ever consent to let me marry the son of Sophocles, his enemy?

PASINOË. But I told you—

GLAUCE. (*Facing* PASINOË) Well, if Pericles gives him some kind of promise today; if they accept his trilogy for the coming Dionysia; then something may come of this. If, however, Father becomes discouraged; if they exclude him again; then woe is me! He will never listen to this.

PASINOË. (*Sitting down*) Don't say it. When he sees how good the young man is, and how handsome and wealthy—

GLAUCE. (*Walks around restlessly*) How unfortunate! The son of Sophocles! Of all his enemies, he believes that Sophocles—and he is not wrong in this—is the most dangerous.

PASINOË. I hear him mention a man called Aeschylus. And one called Euripides—

GLAUCE. O, Aeschylus is dead. He is no longer afraid of of him. And Euripides is very young. He is only now making his appearance. Sophocles! Sophocles! That is the one! How afraid I am! I assure you, Pasinoë, that I would never have given my heart to him, had I known that he was the son of Sophocles.

PASINOË. (*Smiling*) Well—Could you have done otherwise?

GLAUCE. You are right! That takes place against our will. It comes from God. But Nikias is so handsome—If you could have seen him the day I first saw him! How striking he was on his horse! He stood apart from all the horsemen at the religious procession! He resembled a statue, one of those they have placed at the metope of the temple. He was even more handsome than Alcibiades!

PASINOË. I believe it. But you, too, my sweet Glauce, were outstanding among the virgins surrounding the new veil of the goddess. (*Raises her hands in a supplicating gesture*) Blessed be her grace!

GLAUCE. (*Boisterously gay, as though she has forgotten all her fears*) And what a coincidence! His horse became frightened just as he was passing before me! It touched me! I became frightened and fell. Nikias dismounted at once and helped me to my feet. A single moment. For a moment only he held me in his arms. Love found an opportunity at that moment. to pierce both of us with the same arrow!

PASINOË. It was meant to happen. Perhaps nothing will come of this affair—

GLAUCE. (*Discomfited again*) Ah, but he is late—(*She runs to the door of the women's quarters and calls out*) Myrsa!

MYRSA. (*Enters immediately from the women's quarters*) What is it?

GLAUCE. (*Quickly*) Go outside for a moment and see what Thrasis is doing. And say that I am expecting him here. Ask if anyone has come.

MYRSA. Certainly, my lady. (*She takes a step toward right to leave the room*)

GLAUCE. Wait! Will you remember everything?

MYRAS. (*Stops shortly*) I remember, my lady. If he has seen anyone, and that you are expecting Thrasis here.

GLAUCE. Very well. Go! (MYRSA *leaves the room*)

PASINOË. Did you notice how well she caught your meaning?

GLAUCE. (*Shaking her head*) She caught my meaning. But will my father—?

PASINOË. Again? But didn't we settle that? Your father will agree because the gods want it. (*She rises*) Didn't the affair begin at the Panathenaia? It will end well!

MYRSA. (*Returns on the run*) My lady, I didn't see anything or anyone. The master hasn't returned either. I told Thrasis that you are expecting him here.

GLAUCE. Very well. Run into the garden now and cut some poppies.

MYRSA. But will I find any? They are all withered now, my lady.

GLAUCE. Look carefully. You might find some. (MYRSA *leaves through the garden gate*)

PASINOË. Do you want the poppies for your embroidery?

GLAUCE. No! I want to tell my fortune.

PASINOË. (*Smiles*) But didn't you tell your fortune at noon? And didn't you see how the moist pear seed flew out of your hand, and how high it flew when you squeezed it with your finger? Not that seed alone. Many pear seeds. All of them.

GLAUCE. The pear, yes. But let us ask the poppies as well.

PASINOË. My dear Glauce. You torment yourself all day long with these things.

GLAUCE. Do not scold me, Pasinoë. This is what I want!

MYRSA. (*Returns with two poppies in her hand*) These were all I found!

GLAUCE. (*Runs beside her*) A, yes! Give them to me! (*Takes the poppies*) Now we shall see! (*She kisses the poppies and places them on the altar, whispering a prayer.* PASINOË *and* MYRSA *gather around her.* GLAUCE *pulls a petal; she forms a balloon and strikes it against her forehead, but it makes no sound*) Nothing!

PASINOË. Try another one!

GLAUCE. (*Strikes a second petal. This one bursts with a loud sound. Happily*) There it is!

PASINOË. Did you see?

GLAUCE. Give me another petal! (*She strikes another petal, which bursts even more loudly. With wild enthusiasm*) It will come about! It will come about! (*Dances around*)

PASINOË. There are no more petals. That is enough now. Of the three, two burst with a sound. And how loud it was!

GLAUCE. They made me deaf! My ears are still ringing! (*Laughs and sits down*)

PASINOË. Well, then, have no fear. The day is not far off when we will be decorating our door with myrtle, and I—I, who nursed you, who watched you grow up—I will go to carry back the water from Callirrhoe for your bridal bath. There, until the wedding day, which is approaching. What month is it now? It is almost here. Five on six more moons. And my Glauce, a beautiful bride, dressed all in gold, will be flying from here to another nest!

GLAUCE. (*Her head resting on the breast of* PASINOË) Yes, but with her Pasinoë.

PASINOË. Of course. Do you think I would leave you alone?

MYRSA. And with me, too, my lady!

PASINOË. (*To* MYRSA) With you, too. Only you must be careful at the home of the bridegroom. She broke another glass today. And it was hand-painted. She received a beating from Thrasis.

GLAUCE. (*Thoughtfully*) And poor Father? Is he to live alone?

PASINOË. Don't cry over him! The master has Thrasis; he loves him like a father. Besides, he is still young and very wealthy. I have a feeling that he will marry as soon as you are married.

GLAUCE. (*Gaily*) How funny! It seems so strange to think of father married! Do you believe that mania of his will ever leave room for other thoughts? Even about me—O, here comes Thrasis! (*Runs right*)

THRASIS. (*Entering right; and before he can speak to* GLAUCE, *he points to* MYRSA) You get out of here, careless one, before I thrash you again! (MYRSA *exits in embarrassment. To* GLAUCE) He has come.

GLAUCE. (*Joyfully*) At once! I will go up to the terrace. (*Primping herself hastily*)

THRASIS. No! He has something important to say to you, and he can't shout it from down below.

GLAUCE. So?

THRASIS. (*Imposingly*) He begs you—He begs you very much to receive him here for a minute.

GLAUCE. Here? O, no, no! I am afraid!

PASINOË. (*Goes beside* GLAUCE) It isn't proper!

THRASIS. But—But he begged me very hard!

GLAUCE. What are you saying, Thrasis! And suppose my father comes in unexpectedly?

THRASIS. O, the master will be late. Didn't he go to the home of Pericles? By the time it is his turn to enter the house—

GLAUCE. You are wrong. Pericles has known Morsimos for many years. When he hears the name Morsimos, he will receive him at once.

THRASIS. Very well. What if he does happen to come home this early? I will be on watch. There's the garden. I will take the visitor out through the garden. I will let him stand on my back to jump over the wall.

PASINOË. So they will consider him a thief.

THRASIS. It is deserted on that side.

GLAUCE. And what will the gatekeeper say?

THRASIS. Not a word! I have given him a whole two-drachma piece.

GLAUCE. (*Softly*) Rascal! And for you, how much?

THRASIS. Do not worry about me. Come, shall I bring him in? The man is waiting!

GLAUCE.   And the dog?

THRASIS.   She won't bark. I threw her some pieces of meat that even I envied!

GLAUCE.   (*Laughing*) Hm! He knows you well, doesn't he? (*Determined*) Very well, bring him in! But tell him he can only remain here for three minutes. Not three and a half. Only three!

THRASIS.   And three is too many! I will tell him two and a half minutes. (*Exits happily through the right door*)

GLAUCE.   The old fox! (*She repairs herself, looking into the mirror*)

PASINOË.   You didn't do right!

GLAUCE.   Now you tell me! It is too late. Come, you must go too. I wish to be alone.

PASINOË.   I will go. But *I* intend to stand behind the door, I want you to know.

GLAUCE.   Stand wherever you want. Only don't let yourself be visible.

PASINOË.   (*As she is leaving*) Glauce! No embraces and no kisses. It isn't proper!

GLAUCE.   Do not worry. I know! (*As she hears footsteps outside*) O, go away, go away! They are coming! (GLAUCE *runs quickly to the table, takes the mirror from the basket, pats her hair, replaces the mirror, jumps back, and takes a pose that is demonstrably indifferent*)

NIKIAS.   Greetings, Glauce!

GLAUCE.   (*Softly*) Greetings!

NIKIAS.   I thank you for granting me my plea to meet with you here for five minutes.

GLAUCE.   (*Incontrollably, taking a step forward*) He told you five! I only said three!

NIKIAS.   (*Smiling*) Even three! (*Takes a step toward her*) Even one minute is enough to make me the happiest of mortals!

GLAUCE.   What is it you want to tell me? Say it quickly because I am expecting my father to arrive at any moment.

NIKIAS.   (*Takes another step toward her*) I am sending my friend Archias to your father tonight to ask for you.

GLAUCE.   (*Animatedly. She also takes another step toward him*) Is he a matchmaker?

NIKIAS.   No. He is a sculptor.

GLAUCE.   A! He is a friend of my father. I believe I have heard his name mentioned here.

NIKIAS.   Archias knows your father by name only. But he is a

great friend of the architect Cancer and the orator Philocles, who
are Morsimos' closest friends.

GLAUCE. Yes, they are his friends. I know them.

NIKIAS. This is what I had to tell you. I hope you are pleased.

GLAUCE. Yes, Nikias, I am. I am very pleased. But my happiness is intermixed with fear. I am afraid that Morsimos will turn
down your offer.

NIKIAS. (*Terrified*) Why? Has he perhaps selected someone
else for you?

GLAUCE. No! But because the man I have selected is the son
of Sophocles!

NIKIAS. (*Proudly*) How is that? But my father is the most
famous man in the city, after Pericles, and one of the wealthiest
Athenians!

GLAUCE. I know that. But, you see, Morsimos also writes
tragedies.

NIKIAS. Yes, Archias told me something like that. But what
does that mean? Competitors they might be, but they are noble as
their ambitions, as their work. Not enemies who cannot become
related through marriage! (*He laughs*)

GLAUCE. Unfortunately! Morsimos believes that Sophocles is
the reason they won't produce his trilogy.

NIKIAS. (*Seriously*) That Sophocles, in other words, is perse-
cuting him, plotting against him, and undermining him? (*Proudly*)
My father would never condescend to such things. Nor does he have
to! He was victorious over Aeschylus at the age of thirty. He is no
longer afraid of anyone! Not even Euripides.

GLAUCE. (*Agitated*) I imagine that—I believe that—I said
nothing against your father! But, since my father has this impression—(*She becomes tearful*)

NIKIAS. (*Looks at her tenderly, as though regretting he spoke
as he did*) O, do not be sorrowful, Glauce. If Morsimos has this impression, we will make him change it.

GLAUCE. (*Drying her eyes*) How?

NIKIAS. We will find a way. It will not be so difficult to make
him see the truth.

GLAUCE. This is what you think, because you do not know the
mania my father has! Could you ever reject your father?

NIKIAS. As my brother Iophon did? Never!

GLAUCE. So you see! (*She continues to be sorrowful*)

NIKIAS. (*Looks at her thoughtfully*) No—I still cannot find the
obstacle so important. Do not be sad, Glauce! If it becomes neces-

sary, we will do what you say—We will misrepresent things. We will find a way. (*He places his arms around her waist*) Aphrodite will inspire us.

GLAUCE. (*Cheerfully correcting him*) Hymen!

NIKIAS. (*Smiling*) Hymen! At any rate, Archias will know how to talk to him. We will wait to see what reply your father gives. Glauce, is the first minute over?

GLAUCE. O, and the second minute. We have only one minute left.

NIKIAS. (*Looks around. Sees the embroidery on the table and picks it up in his hand*) Did you embroider this?

GLAUCE. Yes. Do you like it.

NIKIAS. (*Tightens his embrace and pulls her closer to him*) Magnificent. These flowers look real. I can almost smell them. They have taken something from you—from your lily-white hands, from your rosy cheeks, from your fragrant breath.

GLAUCE. If my flowers are beautiful, that is because I am embroidering them for you while thinking about you.

NIKIAS. Truly? And I? Will I find something to give you that is as exquisite as this?

GLAUCE. You have given me your love. Do not write about it any more on the walls and trees.

NIKIAS. (*Shamefully*) Yes, that is unnecessary now. At the beginning, however, I could find no better way to express my love.

GLAUCE. Lucky my father remained close to the house during those days. What would he have said had he seen your inscriptions?

NIKIAS. If he sees them now, he won't say a thing. Archias will be here before evening. And I hope that, before long, the beautiful Glauce will be mine! (*Suddenly, he embraces her and quickly kisses her on the cheek*)

GLAUCE. (*Without resisting*) O, no kisses! Hymen will become angry.

PASINOË. (*Appearing at that moment from left*) You called me, my lady?

THRASIS. (*Running in terrified*) The master! The master! (*The lovers separate, greatly agitated*)

GLAUCE. In the garden!

THRASIS. (*To NIKIAS*) This way, master. This way. (*Points to stage back*)

NIKIAS. (*Departing in a hurry. To GLAUCE*) Have hope! For a short while!

GLAUCE. (*After seeing* NIKIAS *as far as the peristyle, she returns*) Pasinoë! It will come about! Nikias will find a way!

PASINOË. Yes. I heard everything. But you never should have allowed him to touch you!

GLAUCE. Sh! Father! (*Runs to him*) Father! (*She embraces him effusively*) What news?

MORSIMOS. (*Darkly. He pushes* GLAUCE *aside gently and advances*) No news. What are you doing here?

PASINOË. Glauce was embroidering. There is more light here in the afternoon, and it is cooler in the courtyard.

MORSIMOS. And Thrasis? Where is he?

GLAUCE. I don't know. He was here. But—Father, did you see Pericles?

MORSIMOS. Better that I had not seen him!

GLAUCE. (*Sadly*) A! Didn't he read your work?

MORSIMOS. (*Approaching the table and laying down his manuscript*) He claims to have read it. But—I am sure he gave it to Aspasia to read! And she told him—The devil take her! I know as much about weaving as that Milesian knows about dramatic art!

THRASIS. (*Has entered on the terrace above where he walks around noiselessly, listening*) O, we have been rejected again, master?

MORSIMOS. You close your mouth! What are you doing up there?

THRASIS. I am getting a breath of fresh air.

MORSIMOS. Impudent one! You see your master has returned home. Why don't you come to ask what he wants?

THRASIS. If you want anything, call Myrsa. I am tired!

MORSIMOS. You are insane!

GLAUCE. Leave him alone, Father! Tell me what it is you want.

MORSIMOS. Nothing. Leave me!

GLAUCE. You are sad—So your trilogy will not be performed this year either at the Dionysia?

MORSIMOS. Well, of course! With the finger of Sophocles in there again!

GLAUCE. (*Motioning to* PASINOË. *Softly*) How unfortunate for me! (*Aloud*) Do you think so, Father? Is it Sophocles again? I don't believe it—

MORSIMOS. You are in no position to know and to believe. Do you at least know who might be writing such improper words about you on all the walls and trees of the neighborhood?

GLAUCE. (*Agitated*) No! I don't know!

MORSIMOS. Nikias, he says. "Nikias loves Glauce!" "Glauce is beautiful!" Did you see those inscriptions?

GLAUCE. I saw them, but—I wasn't concerned. Anyone can write. How am I to blame?

MORSIMOS. (*Severely*) You should have told me! The slaves don't know how to read—

THRASIS. (*From the terrace where he is seated*) O, if only I knew how to read and had read all those words! I myself would have taken care of that handsome youth!

MORSIMOS. Who is it? Do you know any Nikias in the neighborhood?

THRASIS. No. He could be from some other neighborhood.

MORSIMOS. Whoever he is, he has not conducted himself properly. One writes such words for loose women, loose girls, not for modest and honorable virgins!

GLAUCE. Do not say that, Father! Today, they write such words for all women.

MORSIMOS. Perhaps. This period we live in, and the way we have degenerated! But I do not want such words written for my daughter. I will not allow it!

THRASIS. Never mind, master! I will be on guard. I'll tell it to the gatekeeper and, one of these times, we will catch that cunning one.

GLAUCE. (*Unconsciously*) He will never write anything again!

MORSIMOS. And how do you know?

GLAUCE. (*Shaken*) Well—So long as I pay no attention.

MORSIMOS. Be careful, Glauce! You have no mother to advise you. But you are of age and have reason to guide you. And you, Pasinoë, be on guard! I will not say another word to either of you. Go now! I wish to be alone—Take your belongings with you, Glauce. Go ahead!

(GLAUCE *gathers her belongings as* PASINOË *helps her. They leave together, sadly.* MORSIMOS *sits at the table and unties his manuscript.*)

MORSIMOS. (*Murmurs*) Those miserable wretches! Those schemers! Those intriguers! Because they are worthless themselves, they undermine the value of another!

THRASIS. (*From the terrace, ironically*) Tripped up again!

MORSIMOS. Let me see—Is it all here or have they kept part of my manuscript? (*He turns the pages*)

THRASIS. Is the written page so dear?

MORSIMOS. (*Paying no attention to* THRASIS) One should expect anything from such enemies. (*He continues turning the pages*) "Penelope—" "Penelope—" Hm—Hm— "Return—" "Return—" (*Silence*)

SHRILL VOICE OFFSTAGE. Crushed olives for sa—a—a—ale!

MORSIMOS. Thrasis, they are selling olives. If they are good, buy some! (*He continues to turn pages*) "Return—" "Return—" A! How beautiful that chorus is—! And then they tell you that—

THRASIS. (*Rises on the terrace and simultaneously shouts down the street, left*) Vendor—! You there with the olives—! Wait—! (*Goes down into the garden and shortly returns to the courtyard through the gate. To* MORSIMOS) Master, give me a sheet of paper to put the olives in!

MORSIMOS. (*Quickly*) I have no paper! Get a plate from the doorkeeper's room!

THRASIS. Give me a sheet of paper! You have so many there!

MORSIMOS. (*Stunned*) Profane man! You want a sheet of paper from my Trilogy to wrap olives!

THRASIS. Well now! Pericles read it and even he rejected it.

MORSIMOS. (*Rises angrily and chases* THRASIS, *who exits right*) Aspasia read it! Didn't you hear? It was Aspasia! Idiot! (*Returning*) That old man has become unbearable! (*Sits and begins to turn pages again*) "Return—" It is all here— "Telemachus—" "Telemachus—"

(*To the actor. The Trilogy supposedly contains three tragedies: 1) Penelope, 2) The Return, and 3) Telemachus. Each has the same number of pages.*

CANCER *and* PHILOCLES *enter from right. On hearing their footsteps,* MORSIMOS *suspiciously collects his manuscript; but on seeing these are his friends entering, he becomes calm and rises.*)

MORSIMOS. (*Distressed*) Come in!

CANCER. (*Sadly*) We won't ask what news you have because your servant, who is outside buying olives, has already told us.

MORSIMOS. Did you expect it, my good friends?

PHILOCLES. I did. Didn't I tell you that Pericles is not the just man that people call him? (PHILOCLES *talks with a lisp and gestures nervously. An interpretation of this character is left to the actor*)

MORSIMOS. I must admit I thought—

PHILOCLES. And you were deceived!

CANCER. What did he say was wrong with your Trilogy? Tell us.

MORSIMOS. He found many faults. Sit down! (*All three are seated*) First of all, he didn't like the myth. Even babies, he said, know the *Odyssey*. Yes, but I do not imitate Homer! I innovate! The characters are the same, but the myth is modified. I do not show Penelope as the faithful wife. Like any other woman who is left without a man for so many years, I imagine that she fell in love with the most handsome of her suitors—

CANCER. Yes—Somewhat daring, but therein lies the originality.

MORSIMOS. And my Odysseus differs from Homer's. After all those wanderings, he returns to his homeland with new, with different ideas—It is pointless to tell you the rest, because you know my work—Then, he didn't like the verse form. He found it unusual. And the language he found very contemporary, almost vulgar. Anyway, he did not approve. So here I am, rejected again!

CANCER. Most unjust!

PHILOCLES. Naturally! You are not one of the favorites, the flatterers, "our friends"—Today, you may be an architect like Cancer, a sculptor like Archias, a poet like Morsimos. But if you are not a friend of Cephalaras, you remain neglected forever.

THRASIS. (*Returns from right, carrying a plate of olives*) That vendor certainly has excellent olives! They are from the groves at Colonnus. Will you sample one?

(*They all take an olive without interrupting their conversation. THRASIS leaves the place, goes to the back room, and returns with a napkin, which he passes around for each man to wipe his fingers.*)

MORSIMOS. A! I forgot! Pericles is also afraid of the innovation of a fifth character. Now, how is it that Sophocles could have added a third and Aristophanes a fourth character? Don't I have the right to innovate, to advance? This is funny!

CANCER. When they want to avoid doing something they find all kinds of excuses. Everything is wrong.

THRASIS. (*Who has remained in the courtyard and is walking around in back, playing with the napkin*) That is an old story!

PHILOCLES. Well, success will never be ours, if *he* isn't out of the way. *He* is responsible for all the bad luck. But I have faith in my friend and fellow politician, Thucydides. O, yes! Mark my words. The people will become enlightened soon, and then Pericles will be ostracized. Then, all the authority will pass into the hands of Thucydides.

THRASIS *(Ironically, from a distance)* And into ours!

MORSIMOS. Let us hope so. For twelve years, I have been carrying my Trilogy from leader to leader and from choragus to choragus. I will continue to carry it! With faith, with persistence, and with patience.

THRASIS. So long as that does not fatigue you—

MORSIMOS. Certainly, some day justice will be done. And then, I will not submit my *Return* only to have them cast it aside so they can perform an *Oedipus* or an *Antigone*.

CANCER. Well—To tell the truth—These tragedies by Sophocles do show some ability, but—

MORSIMOS. *(Interrupts him, indignantly)* What kind of ability? What ability? *Oedipus Tyrannus?* O, just gods! An improbable and foolish myth. A tangled skein of arbitrary coincidences for the entertainment of the foolish!

THRASIS. Tangled skein? What is he saying?

PHILOCLES. *(Makes a sign to* CANCER*)* Most assuredly.

MORSIMOS. And that *Antigone?* A tolerable myth, I admit, but so badly constructed and unexplored! And how ill-conceived is that suicide of Haemon in the end!

THRASIS. Ill-conceived suicide! What is he saying? *(Louder, impudently)* I did not see the *Antigone,* but when I saw *Oedipus,* my hair stood on end!

MORSIMOS. *(Angrily)* Thrasis! Go away! Why do you interfere in conversations you do not understand? Go! *(*THRASIS *exits to the room in back, but shortly reappears and continues to follow the conversation)*

PHILOCLES. Is your servant with the opposition, Morsimos?

MORSIMOS. He takes liberties because, he says, I was born in his hands. And I tolerate his contradictions and impudences in order to cultivate my patience, in the same manner that Socrates tolerates his wife, more or less. *(They all laugh)* What is there to say! Until now, our country has not produced any other dramatists except Choerilus, Pratinas, and Phrynichus. In fact, these three will live throughout the ages—

CANCER. But even Aeschylus—

MORSIMOS. *(Interrupting)* Which Aeschylus? That clumsy writer, who doesn't know anything about the construction of a play;

that chatterer, that soap bubble! Eloquent words, and no play. But
the theater demands a play. Aeschylus finally realized this. But did
you see the inscription on his tombstone? He boasts of nothing but
his military prowess at Marathon. It would be well for Sophocles
to recognize that he is nothing more than a general.

PHILOCLES. And not one of the best. A friend of Pericles. That
speaks for itself. (*A short silence*)

CANCER. The time will come for justice to prevail. And then
I will not submit a plan for a Parthenon like the one I showed you
so they can reject it and give preference to that ridiculous plan of
Ictinus! (*He points to the Acropolis*)

THRASIS. Ridiculous? O blasphemy!

MORSIMOS. Well, Ictinus does have some ability. At least, he
has done something—

CANCER. Absolutely nothing! Callicrates did everything. Callicrates executed the plans, after he had made the corrections, at least
to those plans he could correct. Ictinus, the enemy of the Straight
Line! If you ask for a foot measurement, he will convert even that
into a curve. What a mania for curves!

PHILOCLES. (*Making a sign to* MORSIMOS) You are right. No
one can say that the Parthenon is straight.

CANCER. Straight? Anything but straight! Place something, say
a lamp, on the edge of one of the steps, then go to the opposite
side and bend over. You can't even see the lamp! That is how
curved, how inflated, the steps are in the center.

MORSIMOS. That is what I heard, too!

CANCER. And what does Ictinus have to say about this? That
he makes curved lines so the object will appear to be straight when
viewed from a distance. (*He laughs*) And what about the object
when seen at close range? Are we not supposed to look at it at
close range? (*They all laugh*)

THRASIS. (*Loudly*) For me, the Parthenon is straight at close
range and at a distance!

MORSIMOS. (*To* THRASIS) Are you back again? Thrasis, you
will be whipped!

THRASIS. And if I am whipped, will that make the Parthenon
crooked?

MORSIMOS. Go away from here! (THRASIS *conceals himself,
then re-enters*)

CANCER. The old Hecatompedon was more beautiful! Modest,
simple, proportionate, and—straight, straight! These men built a

temple which is huge, disproportionate, and overburdened. Too many statues, too much sculpture, too many images! And gold and silver, and colors, and precious stones. Such extravagance and lack of taste! Luxury and barbarism!

PHILOCLES. The times! The times! The Athenians have started to build their houses in the same manner. Sculpturing on the outside, frescoes on the inside— (*He points around the house of* MORSIMOS) Look at the old Athenian home. Simple, modest, precious.

CANCER. They are going to build a Propylaea now.

PHILOCLES. With the money from the Allies. Certainly—How else will the friends become wealthy?

PHILOCLES. (*Rises; speaks rhetorically*) And yet, that is their political slogan: "Public works! Public works!" What kind of public works, and how expensive, is a matter of indifference to them! My dear friends, disregarded and neglected! We live during the worst period our city, our Greece, and our world, have ever known. And Pericles is to blame! (*He sits down*)

MORSIMOS. Those who leave to go to Sicily or Macedonia— even to the Great King—do very well indeed. Since our homeland is so unjust—Archileus invited me to come where he is. I will go!

THRASIS. (*Aside*) Who does he say has invited him? O, what fancies!

PHILOCLES. Pericles is to blame! But where will he go? So long as Thucydides and I keep well! If he doesn't have us assassinated (*in a lower voice*) as he did Ephialtes.

THRASIS. (*Horrified*) What—? (*Loudly*) Master, even if I am whipped—

MORSIMOS. Are you back again?

THRASIS. Back again, and I will speak! This is the most splendid period that Thrasis, who is seventy years old, and the world have ever seen! As for Ephialtes, he was not assassinated by Pericles, but—

MORSIMOS. (*Rising angrily*) That is enough—! That is enough—Not another word. Out of here! Leave, impudent one! (*Chases him.* THRASIS *exits right and does not re-enter*)

PHILOCLES. (*Rises; speaks rhetorically*) Did you hear him? Only a man like Thrasis can defend the tyrant and his period! He has enlarged the city, but diminished the stature of its men. This hegemony is an injustice and a decadence. We were in a better position before when we were lesser men, and poorer, but honest. Hegemony is now leading the city toward a war which will destroy it. Unless Athena enlightenes the people to listen to Thucydides. (*In a lower voice*) Enough. It is time to leave you, Morsimos. Let us go, Cancer.

CANCER. Yes. (*Rises*)

MORSIMOS. (*Rises*) But why so early?

CANCER. At any moment now, a friend will come to tell you something.

MORSIMOS. Who?

CANCER. You know him. It is Archias, the great sculptor, whose works you were admiring a few days ago in his studio.

PHILOCLES. Disregarded and neglected, as are all who have true value today.

MORSIMOS. O, how I admire Archias. How sorry I was not to have found him in his studio so we could meet. And how happy I am that—But why don't you remain? Is he going to tell me a secret?

CANCER. So it seems. We would stay to introduce you to one another, but it is unnecessary. And because we must meet someone before it is too dark—

MORSIMOS. Very well. I will not detain you any longer. Go, my friends. I hope we can talk again tomorrow. Good luck! (*They greet one another.* MORSIMOS *leads them to the door at right. He looks toward the entrance of the hallway and calls out severely*) Come here, you—Come here—!

THRASIS. (*Enters right, humbly*) What is it, master?

MORSIMOS. (*Imitating* THRASIS) "What is it, master—?" Look at that expression! One would think that you were the most humble and most faithful house servant. What was this all about today? Tell me.

THRASIS. Forgive me, master, but I cannot listen to eccentricities. Nor can I watch you struggling and becoming embittered without reason.

MORSIMOS. Without reason? Do you find my efforts to be futile?

THRASIS. Master, my dear master! You know how I love you as though you were my own child. True, I am impudent and sometimes I pretend not to hear you, but it is because I love you and want only the best for you!

MORSIMOS. All I need would be for you to wish me evil luck! (*He sits down and bends over his manuscript*)

THRASIS. Don't pay attention to those imbeciles! They will involve you in some foul business, and then you will beat your brains. Listen to me; I know; I see. I, who love you. So forget everything;

leave all these things alone. Do you know why they produce the plays of others and not yours? It is because their plays are better! Even Pericles told you—

MORSIMOS. Athena! Give me patience to listen! (*He turns pages*)

THRASIS. Forget everything, I said. Look after your house, your property, your daughter! Marry her off, and later you must marry, too. You are still young, but you have almost become an old man like me. You have here in your house a certain Myrsa, a girl like cool waters—a slave purchased by your own hands—and you do not even turn to look at her. You do nothing at all of wining and dining, singing and dancing! Everyone else, poor men and old men, socialize. They enjoy life. You—You know nothing except these—(*Points to the manuscripts*) And what are you doing? What? (*The dog barks outside*)

MORSIMOS. (*Who has been listening all the time to* THRASIS, *but with head bent over his manuscripts. Raises his head now*) A, yes! The dog is barking. That must be the visitor I am expecting. Go bring him here! And you sleep thinking—(*while* THRASIS *is moving toward the exit right*)—that you are now going to do with me as you see fit. (THRASIS *exits right*)

MORSIMOS. (*Alone, thoughtfully*) But could he be right? Is it possible that I am at an impasse and should turn back? (*He rises*) No, never! This Trilogy is a masterpiece! I will continue with my battle until people learn of the work!

(THRASIS *and* ARCHIAS *enter from right. The servant leads in the visitor and then withdraws.*)

ARCHIAS. Greetings, Morsimos! I am delighted to be passing over the threshold of your home.

MORSIMOS. It is Archias, certainly, the great sculptor! Our friends told me—I am proud to welcome you to my poor house. My best greetings!

ARCHIAS. And may the gods be kind! I do not know if I am a great sculptor, but I do know that Morsimos is a great poet.

MORSIMOS. Be seated, Archias. (*They sit down*) I had the pleasure of seeing your work, so I know to whom I am speaking. But you have never seen mine.

ARCHIAS. I have not seen your work, but our friends, who have read the plays, told me about them. And, certainly, I will soon be seeing and admiring these plays in the theater.

MORSIMOS. (*Shaking his head*) I am a man to whom an injustice has been done, Archias. (THRASIS *re-enters, goes to stage back, and follows the conversation from that point*)

ARCHIAS. And am I less so? Such is the case today with the best men. You, me, the excellent Cancer—

MORSIMOS. And the brilliant Philocles. Such a politic mind, such a rhetorician—

THRASIS. (*Aside*) Who can delight in that hoarse-voiced rooster, that lisper!

MORSIMOS. And they have never entrusted him with a single post, a mission, an embassy, a command of an army. He is always bypassed. It is always someone else!

ARCHIAS. But I also sent the model for the statue of Athena for the Parthenon—Did you see it? But Pheidias was preferred.

THRASIS. (*Aside*) Hm—He is like the others! Each with his own miserable problem—

MORSIMOS. Well, of course *he* was the friend!

ARCHIAS. Yes, the friend. Everything for the friends! O, how happy I am to have found someone who has suffered as I have, and who thinks as I do! Such men are rare in these times when everyone in our city has become decadent. For Pheidias, everything; for me, nothing. Naturally. I would never have been capable of setting up a wooden atrocity thirty feet tall, which would touch the roof of the temple! What a megalomania! What a mania for height!

MORSIMOS. Pheidias, of course, is a good sculptor, we must admit, but—

ARCHIAS. What kind of goodness has he? Is there a sculptor without good taste? He has converted Athens into a barbaric idol, overburdened with thousands of ornaments. Ornaments on the shield, on the breastplate, the dress, the helmet—on everything! He was compensated very handsomely, it is true. Because, between us, aside from the talents he received (*Lowers his voice*) he also stole half the gold he was given for the dress.

MORSIMOS. O, and perhaps half the ivory.

ARCHIAS. It is true that he made the dress so it could be taken off to be weighed. But what is the significance of that? And from the original weight, he deducts the loss in casting and workmanship. And that, my friend, raises questions!

MORSIMOS. Many questions!

ARCHIAS. And between us—

MORSIMOS. Speak freely, my friend. Speak freely.

ARCHIAS. I would never be capable of receiving women of the street on the Acropolis, of the kind who go up there pretending to be admiring the artworks so they can be presented to Pericles for his selection of mistresses—

THRASIS. (*Aside*) Pericles does very well. He is not like my master!

MORSIMOS. That is a slanderous remark. I know it well. And then we expect justice, with our purity and honesty. For twelve years I have been seeking justice, Archias, my friend.

ARCHIAS. O! Have you been writing tragedies for twelve years, and they still haven't accepted one?

MORSIMOS. Yes. Originally, I was a banker. In those days, even Pericles deposited his money in my bank. My father Myrtilos, a famous locksmith from Alopekis, left me a sizeable fortune. I increased it by working hard. And then, I saw a dream.

ARCHIAS. What dream?

MORSIMOS. Dionysus appeared to me in a dream. He was the god of our home, which was near his temple. We always paid him special honors. So, he appeared to me in a dream—What am I saying? I was awake; I saw him very much alive! And he said to me: "This is enough, Morsimos. You have now acquired all you need. It is time to look after yourself!"

ARCHIAS. A Divine Dream!

MORSIMOS. Yes, but what did it mean? Should I build a temple to the god? He already had a temple. Should I plant vineyards for him? Our district was full of vineyards. Should I drink wine to become drunk, to make merry—?

THRASIS. (*Aside*) That was it! That was what he meant, you poor wretch!

MORSIMOS. Certainly not! I broke my head, but I found what he meant. He was not pleased—as I was not pleased—with the tragedians who were celebrating his festive days, and he was selecting me to honor him more appropriately. And I began to write tragedies.

THRASIS. (*Aside*) Hollow the hour!

MORSIMOS. You know the rest. My story is the same as yours. So be it. I don't wish to take advantage of your kindness any longer by relating about injustices, intrigues of my enemies, which would make you shudder—Our friends told me that you had something to say to me. Is it good?

ARCHIAS. I hope so. (*He looks around. His glance falls on* THRASIS.)

MORSIMOS. Thrasis, go outside. (THRASIS *exits from right. A short silence*)

ARCHIAS. Morsimos, do you have a daughter called Glauce?

MORSIMOS. Yes. My beloved Glauce, my orphan. Her mother left her to me at the age of ten. She is the most valuable possession I have. Or rather, the only possession I have.

ARCHIAS. The best of luck, Morsimos. A young man, a brilliant young man from a famous family, a handsome and wealthy youth, saw your daughter at the Panathenaia and—he is asking to make her his wife.

MORSIMOS. Yes—? And you, Archias?

ARCHIAS. (*Smiling*) I am certainly not a matchmaker. But, because the young man happens to be a good friend of mine—he is kind enough to come to my studio to pose as a model—and because, from our common friends I happen to know who you are and what you think about me, I was bold enough today—

MORSIMOS. O, it is a great honor to me to have such a matchmaker. And the bridegroom—Who is he?

ARCHIAS. It is Nikias, the son of Sophocles, the youngest brother of Iophon and Ariston, by the great poet's second wife.

MORSIMOS. (*Jumps to his feet*) Son of Sophocles? Son of my enemy—? And he dares to ask for my daughter as his wife. Never! Never!

ARCHIAS. (*Rises. Confused*) Forgive me—! I did not know that Sophocles was your enemy—I never imagined—

MORSIMOS. You should have known it—! You should have imagined it—! What have I been talking about all this time? Which others are my enemies? Who hasn't given me any peace? Aeschylus, Sophocles, and that sullen, aged youth Euripides. And I am to give my daughter to the worst of these? (*Beside himself*) Never! Never!

ARCHIAS. Do not be vexed, Morsimos! For the sake of the gods—! I only made a proposal to you—You are free to accept or reject it—But—Why should you? Even though the father is an enemy, can't the son be a friend? And if the son marries your daughter, is it not possible that the father can also become a friend—? And look how the father has already given his son permission to ask for your daughter. He does not know you, but he asked about you; he learned who you were, and he gave his consent.

MORSIMOS. (*Surprised*) Who—? Sophocles did not know me—? He did not know *me*—? And is he only now finding out about me—? What are you saying to me—?

ARCHIAS. I don't know—That is what Nikias told me—

MORSIMOS. He told you lies—! But that is of no consequence! Even had he told the truth, my answer would still be the same. No, never—! I do not want this match—! It is disagreeable to me, Archias, that our friendship should start out so badly, but I cannot act otherwise. (*He begins calmly, but slowly becomes irritated*) Tell your young friend that Morsimos thanks him for the honor he has bestowed upon him, but he refuses to become related through marriage with his enemies, who have fought against him with such cowardice—even though they now pretend not to even know me. Nor, in the final analysis, with a man (*beside himself with rage now*) who leaves his house with a cloak on, then returns without it because he has been attacked in the fields and runs away leaving the cloak behind, and the lover later steals back the cloak from the attackers! We are a different breed of people, Athenians of the old stock, moral and honest! Honest—! Honest—!

ARCHIAS. Very well; very well. It isn't necessary—

MORSIMOS. It is necessary. I must justify my rejection to a matchmaker like Archias. I believe you see how impossible this match is! I certainly have nothing against you—You only carried out your duty to your friend—But—But—

ARCHIAS. That is enough, Morsimos. (*With greater dignity*) I will relay your answer to my unfortunate friend, certainly without telling him all you told me in your anger. I wish your daughter a better fortune, and you, whatever you desire. Farewell, Morsimos.

MORSIMOS. Farewell! (ARCHIAS *exits from right;* MORSIMOS *walks with him to the door and returns. Paces up and down furiously. Aside*) That is all I need—! That is all I need—! To give my Glauce to his son—! (*Goes to the door of the women's quarters, opens it, and calls out*) Myrsa—! (*Paces up and down again*)

MYRSA. (*Runs in from left*) Here I am!

MORSIMOS. (*Without looking at her*) So that's who it was—! Very well, he will see—! (*Notices* MYRSA) What do you want?

MYRSA. Master! Didn't you call me?

MORSIMOS. A, yes! Tell your mistress to come here. Tell the nurse to come with her. (MYRSA *bows and exits.* MORSIMOS *stands now and waits*)

(GLAUCE *and* PASINOË *enter shortly from left.*)

MORSIMOS. Glauce! We have discovered who that impudent fellow is who dares to write your name on the walls! It is the son of—Whose son do you think?

GLAUCE. I don't know—

MORSIMOS. (*With disgust*) Of Sophocles!

GLAUCE. O—!

MORSIMOS. Yes! His son! He just sent one of his friends to ask for you in marriage.

GLAUCE. Did he?

MORSIMOS. You understand, I gave him the answer I should have given and sent him back from where he came.

GLAUCE. Why, Father?

MORSIMOS. Must you ask—? Then, tell me, Pasinoë. Do men give their beloved daughters to the sons of their enemies?

GLAUCE. But are you certain, Father, that Sophocles is your enemy?

MORSIMOS. Then what is he? A friend?

GLAUCE. He is not your friend, but—Does he plot against you; does he persecute you? Sophocles is not such a man—

MORSIMOS. Who told you that? How do you know?

GLAUCE. Everyone says so.

MORSIMOS. And where do you see everyone? How do you hear everyone? A, Glauce! It seems to me that those signs on the walls have turned your head—It is not unlikely that you even saw the one who wrote those words and talked with him—

GLAUCE. O, no, Father!

MORSIMOS. Be careful, Glauce. Your words make me suspicious—Pasinoë—!

PASINOË. No, Master. Glauce has seen no one and talked with no one.

MORSIMOS. I don't believe that, but it is of no consequence. It is enough that, from now on, she will see no one nor talk with anyone. Glauce! You are not to take a single step out of this house until the day I marry you off to the man of my choice! Not even to go to the temple! Don't ever let me find you out of doors, nor up on the terrace! And you are not even to step down here to the men's quarters. In your courtyard and in your rooms. Nowhere else. Do you hear?

GLAUCE. (*Head bowed*) As you wish, Father.

MORSIMOS. (*Softens*) And don't you worry. Our friends have handsome sons, and other men might see you next year at the Panathenaia. (*He is interrupted*) What is that?

(*A disturbance is heard outside and scuffling. The dog is barking ferociously. It appears that someone is being dragged as he resists. Loud voices of* THRASIS, NIKIAS, *and the doorkeeper. They make out the words:* "Come here, you wicked boy!" *and* "Let me go—!")

THRASIS. (*From outside*) Master! I caught the one who has been writing on the walls—! Come here—! Come here—!

NIKIAS. (*From outside*) Let me go!

MORSIMOS. (*Shaken. To the women who are standing by frightened*) Go away! Get inside quickly! (*He pushes them.* GLAUCE *and* PASINOË *leave from left.* MORSIMOS *closes the door and goes right*)

(THRASIS, *meanwhile, enters, dragging a resisting* NIKIAS *by force. This scuffling is feigned.*)

NIKIAS. (*Loudly*) What do you want? Where are you taking me? (*In a lower voice*) Release me now!

THRASIS. Here, wicked boy—! This is my master, Morsimos! You settle matters with him!

MORSIMOS. (*With dignity*) Release him, Thrasis!

THRASIS. (*Releases* NIKIAS *and points to him*) Here he is! I was on guard outside, and I caught him as he was writing on the wall with a nail—How strong he is! If it had not been for the door-keeper and the dog—

MORSIMOS. (*Interrupting him*) Very well, Thrasis! You have performed your duty. (*He looks at* NIKIAS, *who is standing proudly.* THRASIS *leaves, secretly making a sign to* NIKIAS *that he will stand outside. A short silence. The two men look at one another.*) Your improper words would have been unforgivable, but I forgive them because you also sent a matchmaker. The one atones for the other. I have nothing more to say to you. Go, and try to meet with Archias so he can give you my answer to your proposal.

NIKIAS. I saw Archias a little while ago, and he told me.

MORSIMOS. (*Coldly*) So much the better. Now go!

NIKIAS. Not before I have said something.

MORSIMOS. Nothing! I ask your pardon for the violence of my servant, but not for having spoken so badly against your father!

NIKIAS. Yes, your enemy—Do you imagine that my own thoughts are any different?

MORSIMOS. I am not concerned with whether you think he is my enemy or not.

NIKIAS. Your enemy and that of many others, Morsimos! In that, I agree with my brother Iophon. Sophocles existed once, but no longer. It is time now for better men to come along. And you, Morsimos, as I hear, write excellent tragedies. And so does my brother Iophon, and I—

MORSIMOS. (*Amazed*) You, too?

NIKIAS.   Certainly! But my father has no intention of allowing us to appear. I know everything. It isn't necessary for you to tell me Sophocles thinks that dramatic art has had the final word with *Oedipus Tyrannus* and *Antigone*.

MORSIMOS.   (*Piqued*) What word! We were not aware of such a thing! (*He turns and looks ahead*)

THRASIS.   (*From the corner of the hallway where he cannot be seen; softly to* NIKIAS) We are doing well! Go ahead!

NIKIAS.   (*Making a sign slyly to* THRASIS) And what is *Oedipus?*

THRASIS.   (*Softly*) A tangled skein of thread!

NIKIAS.   A tangled thread of improbable coincidences so that the foolish can be entertained.

MORSIMOS.   (*Continues to look ahead*) That is what I say!

NIKIAS.   And that *Antigone?* And that suicide of Haemon at the end?

THRASIS.   (*Whistling*) Ill-devised!

NIKIAS.   (*Supplementing*) So ill-devised!

MORSIMOS.   (*Still looking ahead*) That is what I say!

NIKIAS.   And yet he persists. Imagine what that *Oedipus at Colonnus*, which he is now writing, will be like!

MORSIMOS.   (*Loudly. Turning toward* NIKIAS) He is now writing *Oedipus at Colonnus?*

NIKIAS.   O, for ten years he has been tormenting himself with it! He writes and he erases, and writes—But he can no longer direct even his own business, and he expects to write a tragedy, which demands the greatest intellectual power?

MORSIMOS.   What perseverance! What a mania!

NIKIAS.   Let him write! No one told him that he could write. Perhaps his last work will be, as he claims, his masterpiece. (*Without awareness, he stresses the last word with pride*) But not so he will not allow others to appear by using his influence—and we must admit that he is powerful and influential. (*Again proudly*) Iophon could tolerate this no longer! Nor I!

MORSIMOS.   Nor I!

THRASIS.   (*Softly*) Magnificent!

NIKIAS.   (*Advancing with courage*) You know that Iophon has withdrawn? He has his own home now. I will do the same. I will take my portion and leave—And—We can become allies, if you want. You, Iophon, and I. Don't you think that the three of us will be victorious very quickly?

Morsimos. (*Enchanted*) O, but certainly—I have a Trilogy ready, which—

Nikias. (*Interrupting him*) I know. *Penelope, The Return,* and—

Thrasis. (*Whispering*) *Telemachus!*

Nikias. And *Telemachus*. Your friends assure everyone that it is a masterpiece, and I believe it—!

Morsimos. But Pericles—

Nikias. Forget Pericles! He will fall. In a short time we will have Thucydides, who is our friend.

Morsimos. (*Most enchanted*) A! Are you also of the party of Thucydides?

Nikias. And of Philocles. Most certainly!

Morsimos. How good! Look how observant youth is! Without doubt, Pericles has a great mind—Who says the contrary—?

Nikias. O, and he is a very great man!

Morsimos. But what is the use?

Nikias. What is the use—? But your Trilogy, Morsimos, must be finished off with a satyr play.

Morsimos. Do you think so?

Nikias. O, that is essential today! What would you say, Morsimos, if I proposed to you—as an ally—that we write the satyr play together? We could call it *Eumaeus the Swineherd!*

Morsimos. *Eumaeus?* What a wonderful idea! (*Ecstatically*) It will take place in the country and the forests. The nymphs, satyrs, Silenus, and Pan will come out—! Dionysus himself will come out! Yes, that is it! But how did you ever think of it?

Nikias. The love for Glauce—! Do you still think you cannot make me your—son?

Morsimos. (*Enthusiastically*) With all my heart! You are a magnificent youth! And without doubt, it was Dionysus, my guardian, who sent Glauce on your path—! Come to my arms! (*He embraces* Nikias) And let us go in! I want you to become engaged at once! (*Dragging* Nikias *along by the hand, he opens the door to the women's quarters, and they exit as* Morsimos *calls out joyfully*) Glauce—! Glauce—! We have caught the one who has been writing on the walls—!

Thrasis. (*Joyfully, capering about, rubbing his hands, he emerges from his concealment and goes toward the door to the women's quarters. He stands there a minute as though he wants to see, to hear, and then returns*) There—! That is done! O, now, if only the other would also take place so we can find peace—! (*Before the statue of Dionysus*) Great God! Guardian! Perform a miracle! (*Thoughtfully advances to the altar. He sees the poppies and absently takes up a petal, forms it into a balloon and strikes it against his forehead. It does not burst with a loud sound. Spitefully, he selects another petal and strikes this against his forehead. It bursts loudly*) There it is! It will take place!

MORSIMOS.   (*Returning*) Did you see, you grouchy, suspicious one, to where your fame has spread, and what is about to happen now!

THRASIS.   O, certainly, I know! Now that you have become an ally with the sons of Sophocles. At last, that cruelly tormented Trilogy of yours will be produced!

MORSIMOS.   You are close! We have beaten them, Thrasis. It is over!

THRASIS.   Very well; very well. But—have you left them alone in there?

MORSIMOS.   Pasinoë is with them. Let the chidlren talk together for a while—Later, I will call him out so we can draw up an agreement concerning everything—A, what a day! It started out badly, but it is ending beautifully! However, it has fatigued me. Let me sit down—(*He reclines on a chair and closes his eyes. It is starting to grow dark*) Thrasis—! Have the lamps ready—And the street lamp—Later, you will escort Nikias to his home— (*He falls asleep*)

THRASIS.   Not I. One of his slaves is waiting for him at the door.

(THRASIS *goes to stage back and prepares the lamps.* MORSIMOS *sleeps for a few minutes. It is dark in the courtyard. The Acropolis reflects the last rosy rays of twilight.*)

MORSIMOS.   (*Suddenly, awakening fearfully and rising to his feet, crying loudly*) A! O! No—! No—! It is not possible—! A dream—! A bad dream—! Help—! Help—!

(THRASIS *runs toward him with a lighted lamp in his hand, coming from the back, and from right come* NIKIAS, GLAUCE, PASINOË, *and* MYRSA, *the last two also carrying lighted lamps in their hands*)

THRASIS.   Master—!
GLAUCE.   Father—! What is it?

PASINOË.   (*Simultaneously*) Master—!

MORSIMOS.   (*Sees them, still fearfully, then slowly recovers and becomes calm*) Nothing! I fell asleep for a minute and I saw—I saw a long dream. Gods! How can a person see so much in so short a time? O, but that was no ordinary dream! It was a Divine Dream, like the other one!

GLAUCE.   But what did you see, Father?

MORSIMOS.   I saw—I saw—the Future!

NIKIAS.   The Future?

MORSIMOS.   Yes! On the wings of the dream I traveled into Time and found myself returned here again, under the Acropolis, but some six hundred Olympiad years later!

GLAUCE.   O, how much time! And how was our city at that time?

MORSIMOS.   A different city! Unrecognizable! But the Parthenon was there in place, still the same! It was no longer a temple, but it was intact. The Athenians preserved it with reverence as the most precious, the most holy thing they possessed—and they say that the world has never seen a more perfect work of art—and this after six hundred Olympiad years! They continue to admire Pericles, Pheidias, Ictinus; and they claimed that this period—our period!— was the Golden Age of Mankind—! And what else, my children; what else—! In a theater much different from ours today, a theater where women were acting as well, the Athenians were rushing to see *Agamemnon!*

NIKIAS.   By Aeschylus?

MORSIMOS.   By Aeschylus, my Nikias! And everyone said, even the babies, that Aeschylus, Sophocles, and Euripides—yes, yes!— were the greatest tragedians of the world! What about Choerilus, I asked them? No answer—Pratinas—? Phyrinichus—? A someone called Morsimos—? All unknown! They have all vanished! They are all dead!

NIKIAS.   Don't you ever believe it, Morsimos! Is it possible? A dream—

MORSIMOS.   (*Rising*) No, Nikias, I believe it. I believe everything! It was a Divine Dream, and it was sent to me by Dionysus to dispel my delusions about the first dream. I had misunderstood him. Dionysus was telling me to drink, to enjoy life, and I had supposed that he wanted me to write tragedies! This period is truly a great one—My enemies are alive, and they will remain immortal, while I—I—

NIKIAS. But what is that you are saying, Morsimos? Now that
we have become allies—? Or are we not going to write *Eumaeus*
together?

MORSIMOS. Do not be afraid! I will give you Glauce because
you are a brilliant young man and—because you are the son of
Sophocles. But—*Eumaeus* I will never write, neither with you nor
by myself—! A person does not return to a delusion once he has
seen the truth—! Thrasis! You were right! Take this! (*He gives the
manuscript to* THRASIS)

THRASIS. (*Joyfully*) What shall I do with it?

MORSIMOS. It is wrapping paper!

THRASIS. We have found peace!

CURTAIN

George Theotokas

(1906–66)

George Theotokas was born in Constantinople in 1906. He studied law at the Universities of Athens, Sorbonne, and London, and began practicing in 1931. Simultaneously, he devoted himself to literature and the theater, to which he served as director for some time. In his writings, he is chiefly preoccupied with the sociological problems of the bourgeois middle class. His essay, *Free Spirit* (1929), with its ideological and literary controversies, a reaction against the excessive lyricism to that time, became the manifesto of the generation of the thirties. He was a most articulate writer, subordinating any interplay of fantasy to the entire architectural concept of his creation. An important work is *The Demon* (1938), in which he analyzes the modern Greek temperament and character with keen perception and artistry. The essays of Theotokas are characterized mainly by their refutation, search for the inner man, and awareness of the critical hours of his times. In theory and practice he attempts always to include folk tradition in the intellectual literary productions of Greece.

His important works include: *Idle Hours* (1931); *Forward to the Social Problem* (1932); *Argo* (1936); *Euripedes Pentozalis* (1937); *Leonis* (1940); *Theater A* (1944); *Poems Between the Wars* (1944); *Theater B* (1947); *Sacred Way* (1950); *Essay On America* (1954); *Problems of Our Times* (1956); and *Neo-Hellenic Folk Theater* (1965).

The Game of Folly vs. Wisdom

A Comedy

To Socrates Karantinos

CHARACTERS

KYR ANDRONIKOS
DUKE OF PARONAXIA
MAVRIANOS, KONSTANTIS, *noblemen of Byzantium*
IGNATIOS, STAVRAKIOS, LEONTIOS, *Senators*
FIRST SERVANT, SECOND SERVANT
OFFICER
ARETE
ZAMBETA
MAROULINA
FIRST ATTENDANT, SECOND ATTENDANT, THIRD ATTENDANT
THE BIRD OF SONGS
NOBLEMAN, NOBLE LADIES, SENATORS, SERVANTS, HERALDS

The action takes place in the Byzantium of legend and song.

ACT I

As the curtain rises, we hear the boisterous laughter and voices of men at a banquet. A table laid out with food is visible. At the head of the table sits KING ANDRONIKOS, *surrounded by the* DUKE OF PARONAXIA *and other noblemen. The* KING *is attired in red; the* DUKE *is adorned and infatuated like a peacock. Servants move about distributing large chunks of meat and analogous portions of wine. The conversation is in the tone of voice of men who are half-intoxicated. After each address, glasses are drained.*

FIRST NOBLEMAN. Long live the girls of all nations and religions who are deflowered wherever Kyr Andronikos passes, our King with God's charity, magnificent be His grace!

NOBLEMEN. A long, long, long life!

SECOND NOBLEMAN. Long live the married and the divorced women, and the unfortunate widows, whose modesty has been exalted by our greatly renowned Lord with a royal act!

NOBLEMEN. A long life! To a long life!

THIRD NOBLEMAN. Long live the good fathers of the Polis and of Romania, whose homes, thanks to the intervention of Kyr Andronikos, have been enriched with royal children.

NOBLEMEN. A long life!

THIRD NOBLEMAN. He disperses his blue blood with chivalry and ennobles the nation. For this, his reign will go down in history as a significant event. The unforgettable symbol of his reign, in the minds of later generations, will be the deer horns our Emperor has ordered suspended in the halls of the Forum as a trophy from his great hunting expeditions.

NOBLEMEN. A long life!

FOURTH NOBLEMAN. And a long life to us who have had the good fortune to be instructed by him in a manner befitting those bold enough to live a life of happiness and pleasure.

NOBLEMEN. Hurrah for happiness! Hurrah for pleasure!

DUKE. Hurrah for History! To a long life!

NOBLEMEN. (*Amid the clamor of revelry, the voices of various noblemen are distinguished as they alternately speak the following phrases. This same procedure is followed later under similar circumstances*) Hurrah for the wine from Samos! Hurrah for the wine from Santorini! Hurrah for the *mavrodaphni* wine! Hurrah for the *retsina* wine! Mix them all as Kyr Andronikos mixes his countless love affairs! (*They mix the wines*) Hurrah to the intoxication of countless love affairs!

DUKE. Hurrah to the horns! To a long life!

NOBLEMEN. (*Chanting*) I will open my mouth to relate countless marvels. Come, noblemen; come to hear about the accomplishments of Kyr Andronikos, about the horns on the men of the Byzantine Empire.

SERVANT. (*To a companion who appears to be an apprentice*) The man has a weakness, and they're constantly reminding him about it. He loves women. That's no sin.

SECOND SERVANT. Is that so?

FIRST SERVANT. Whenever he sees an attractive girl—she doesn't have to be beautiful—there, just so she's tolerably attractive—around thirty-five or under—say forty at the most—he cannot contain himself.

SECOND SERVANT. Imagine that!

FIRST SERVANT. Only that she be a woman, and it doesn't matter what she looks like! He takes off her girdle in the wink of an eye!

SECOND SERVANT. What strange carryings-on!

FIRST SERVANT. He doesn't do it on purpose. It's his nature. And what have we to lose? When Kyr Andronikos is happy, all Orthodoxy lives a golden life. No one can recall such festivities in our country. Wherever you turn, you see smiling faces; you hear smacking kisses behind doors; and you smell flowing wine everywhere. Why, even as I look at you in all your disarray, I feel the urge to take hold of you and dance with you, as though you were Belthandro's Chrysantza. (*He takes the* SECOND SERVANT *by the hand, while holding a platter in the other, and dances*)

SECOND SERVANT. Don't! They'll scold us!

FIRST SERVANT. And wait until you hear something else! Sometimes at night, he is deluded and attacks women. Last week, during a wild midnight, as he was wandering through the halls of the Palace, he stumbled over the grandmother of the Chancellor.

SECOND SERVANT. And then?

FIRST SERVANT. And then? What do you mean, and then? It happened!

SECOND SERVANT. Merciful God!

FIRST SERVANT. The poor Chancellor was quite disconcerted. I too went to console the woman. "Grandmother," I said, "who would have thought that such a thing could have happened to you at your age!" And do you know what she replied? "E, come now! Don't exaggerate! I'm not that decrepit!" At seventy-eight, if you please!

SECOND SERVANT. And what more we'll hear today!

FIRST SERVANT. Stop! I believe they're about to make a speech.

ANDRONIKOS. My good attendants. The wine, of course, allows my tongue a certain freedom, a removal somewhat from court formality. So I will speak bluntly, as is proper to a King and Emperor who is drunk, who is addressing his bosom companions. Yes, it is true; it is no exaggeration. I do incline somewhat toward women.

NOBLEMEN. Hear! Hear!

ANDRONIKOS. When I sit and think, strange reflections come to my mind. I look upon women as unfamiliar, inconceivable creatures, as animals of a different species, a different skin, speaking another language and looking on the world from another point of view. But their eyes, their voices, the way they walk, their essence— everything about them goes to my head.

NOBLEMEN. They go to his head! They go to his head!

ANDRONIKOS. It is an indescribable state. But I have no objection. I declare this to you formally. I am reconciled with God. I love you too. I accept you. The world is strange; the strangest thing that can be conceived by man's mind. But I feel that it is an orderly world.

NOBLEMEN. He loves us! He accepts us! The world is orderly! Everything is orderly!

ANDRONIKOS. Thus, I say, each man should be on good terms with God. That is most important. Hurrah for men who accept life!

NOBLEMEN. Hurrah for life! Hurrah for life!

DUKE. Stop! Stop! I will speak seriously. The subject we are discussing is one of lofty politics.

NOBLEMEN. Lofty politics! Lofty politics! Lofty politics!

DUKE. Of all the calamities that can befall nations, which is the worst?

NOBLEMEN. Which? Which? Which?

DUKE. The worst, without doubt, is that which causes our poor women suddenly to become embittered and difficult and go into a rage and fail to accept life. I know all this better than anyone else after three marriages blessed by God, after escorting three angel creatures to the grave. (*The* DUKE *is in tears. Noblemen rise to console him*)

NOBLEMEN. Come, come! There's nothing wrong! Don't take it so hard! Have a drink and everything will be all right!

(*The* DUKE *drinks wine and recovers.*)

DUKE. Then you will agree that in our Greek-speaking world there is a large number of women who are crabby, acrid, sour, embittered, poisoned, and who will fail to accept life. I ask you, who is to blame?

NOBLEMEN. Very true. Who is to blame? Who is to blame?

DUKE. I speak to you on authority. Our population is to blame. It has yet to learn how to graft properly. Women can be grafted like uncultivated trees. There is an art to grafting.

NOBLEMEN. Hurrah for art! Hurrah for art!

DUKE. And here is Kyr Andronikos! What does Kyr Andronikos do? He knows the art of grafting women. No sooner does he take them in hand, then they become docile; they become human. You would think something has been set loose within them, and then—mysteriously—they accept everything; they find everthing to be orderly. So Kyr Andronikos races wherever he can. He is attempting to bring you back on the straight path. The result—

NOBLEMEN. The result! The result!

DUKE. Where we saw worthless, sterile earth before, now gurgling fountains suddenly bubble over, gardens blossom, birds sing. Whatever was inanimate as a rock, now becomes animate. Wherever inconsistency, harshness, and anger reigned, now kindness, understanding, forgiveness abound. People are becoming peaceful. The Polis is becoming beautiful. People are becoming pleasant.

NOBLEMEN (*Chanting*) Carnations from Chios, chestnuts from Broussa, honey from Athens, plums from Damascus, the height of Olympus and Athos, the grafting of Kyr Andronikos—Most exquisite things!

(KONSTANTIS *and* MAVRIANOS *enter, austere and ostentatious in dress and manner. They stand aside.*)

FIRST SERVANT. (*To his companion*) See those men who just entered? They belong to the opposition party, the Wisdom party.

SECOND SERVANT. And what do they want, dressed as they are in dark clothing?

FIRST SERVANT. They want to change the form of government so that fools will no longer rule, so that the prudent shall take their place.

SECOND SERVANT. And what will happen when the wise ones come?

FIRST SERVANT. Seriousness. Self-importance. No more banquets. You will have to take a stand on important issues. In other words, you will have to select a cosmo-theory.

SECOND SERVANT. And what will I do with this cosmo-theory?

FIRST SERVANT. Just let her sit there. She doesn't ask for food. You will bring her forth periodically so that no one will say you don't conduct yourself properly.

SECOND SERVANT. And where will I find her?

FIRST SERVANT. Don't worry. Their trunks are loaded. They distribute positions, securities, instructions, and systems as easily as Kyr Andronikos distributes wine and something else. But the hour has not arrived yet. As long as the revelry holds out, we will continue to have our fun. (*He takes the* SECOND SERVANT *by the hand, and they exit dancing*)

KONSTANTIS. (*To* MAVRIANOS) Look at the regime of Folly with all its impertinence.

MAVRIANOS. What's to be expected from an era which has no principles and no faith, an era which subverts Reason and Morality?

KONSTANTIS. Men who have known Truth have no right to despair. The day will come when History will turn the page.

MAVRIANOS. I hope so.

DUKE. (*To* KYR ANDRONIKOS) My long-lived Lord, I see the opposition party pacing up and down and murmuring around here. Be careful. They might be cooking up some kind of revolution.

(KONSTANTIS *and* MAVRIANOS *extend greetings to everyone.*)

ANDRONIKOS. Let the noblemen come to my table. I know nothing of parties while I am drinking.

DUKE. Come, my Lords. The King invites you to his table.

KONSTANTIS. We are honored.

MAVRIANOS. The pleasure is ours. (*They sit at the table*)

ANDRONIKOS. Give the noblemen something to drink! My Lords, long live the mistresses of your thoughts.

KONSTANTIS. We thank you.

MAVRIANOS. And I as well.

ANDRONIKOS. Let the glasses be refilled. Long live the beautiful ladies you have desired and continue to desire, and all those others who are destined one day to be kissed by you.

NOBLEMEN. To a long, long life!

ANDRONIKOS. One more toast. Long live love! Long live those who serve love!

NOBLEMEN. Long, long, long live!

FIRST NOBLEMAN. To Kyr Andronikos, thrice-excellent one, created like an angel, beloved by everyone!

SECOND NOBLEMAN. No woman has ever resisted him!

THIRD NOBLEMAN. Not a single woman in the entire Empire can resist him, if he desires to seduce her, be she young girl, a middle-aged woman, or a grandmother—

FOURTH NOBLEMAN. Not even the niece of the Patriarch, nor the cousin of the Pope—

DUKE. Nor the godmother of the Devil—No, I say, and let all the parties hear it. There's not a girl, not a woman, of whichever station in life, who doesn't long to be grafted by our Lord, Kyr Andronikos. Long may he live!

ANDRONIKOS. Duke of Paronaxia, leave us in peace!

NOBLEMEN. He speaks the truth! He speaks the truth!

ANDRONIKOS. I say, let the court flattery cease! (*To the two newcomers*) Certainly—and I don't conceal it—this does intrigue me. I can't deny that I find a kind of pleasure in it. I say that everyone should act according to the desires of his heart so that he may be at peace with the heavens. But no one must think that I am neglecting my duties. (*To the others*) Isn't that right? What have you to say?

NOBLEMEN. Of course! Of course! His duties! His duties!

ANDRONIKOS. One opinion, to which my most learned political advisors subscribe, has it that the women in our country suffer and so inject us with poison because we do not know how to graft them properly.

NOBLEMEN. Certainly! Certainly! The graft! The art! The graft!

ANDRONIKOS. So, as they say, I am aiding the cause. I am instructing the people.

NOBLEMEN. He is instructing the people! He is instructing the people!

MAVRIANOS. Blissful Lord, it isn't my business to instruct you in your duty toward the Empire and the people you rule. However, certain words expressed around this table, which you ignored and didn't deny, compel me—with all due respect to the distinguished company—to make an observation for reasons of moral order.

NOBLEMEN. Silence! Hear! He will make an observation! For reasons of moral order!

MAVRIANOS. It was said earlier that there isn't a woman or a young girl in all your Empire to thwart you, should you be inclined to seduce her. That's what I think I heard. Or am I perhaps mistaken?

DUKE. No, my Lord, you are not mistaken. I stated that fact, my long-lived Lord, and I repeat it, in case you failed to hear it. I repeat it.

NOBLEMEN. We also said it! We repeat it!

MAVRIANOS. Most excellent Lord, my principles command me to oppose this view publicly because I know, with absolute certainty, that at least one woman in this land can be seduced by no one. I say, no one!

NOBLEMEN. Who? Who? Tell us who she is! Tell us who she is!

MAVRIANOS. I have no objection to telling you who she is. My sister Arete.

NOBLEMEN. His sister Arete! His sister Arete! Who knows her? Who has seen his sister Arete?

KONSTANTIS. I know her. I have seen her. I have spoken with her.

NOBLEMEN. So? So?

KONSTANTIS. So, without any reservations, I confirm the opinion of Lord Mavrianos. The entire life of his sister Arete proclaims her name very loudly. Her spiritual and intellectual superiority is unsurpassable. Her purity is as indestructible as the walls around the royal Polis. She spends her time in her castle and her hanging gardens on the banks of the Bosporus, surrounded by her attendants and her white-haired mentors, who inspire her thoughts with the fountains of wisdom of the ages. Her only passion is learning. She has been taught rhetoric, philosophy, theology—

NOBLEMEN. Theology! Did you hear! Theology!

KONSTANTIS. Mathematics, astronomy—

NOBLEMEN. Astronomy! Astronomy!

KONSTANTIS. She can repeat from memory countless passages from Homer, the choruses of all the tragedians, and the speeches of Demosthenes and Cicero. And as for marriage, she has declared to her brother that she will abide by his decision. She will follow his advice blindly. I also believe that it is impossible for such a maiden to ever fall into the sins of the flesh. Therefore, the opinion expressed by the brilliant Duke of Paronaxia appears to me to be unacceptable.

DUKE. I believe—I believe—I will tell you at once what I believe—

ANDRONIKOS. Sit down, Duke of Paronaxia! It isn't necessary that you believe in anything at the moment—Lord Mavrianos, we are discussing something nonexistent. No one is conspiring against the peace and reputation of your sister.

MAVRIANOS. That's not the point, most eminent Lord. It was said earlier that you can seduce any woman in our land whenever you desire. And I am replying to you that no one can seduce my sister.

DUKE. But this is a challenge! Good gracious! My dear, this is a challenge!

ANDRONIKOS. Quiet, Duke of Paronaxia! Lord Mavrianos, I do not like the manner with which you talk at my table. But since you insist on discussing this topic, I will reply to you very bluntly. Modesty is superfluous among men. I have yet to meet the woman who will reject me, whether I appear to her as a King, or an officer of the Palace, or a fiddler, or a merchant, or a foreign traveler, or under some other disguise. However, I don't know your sister and, to end this conversation, I promise never to pass by her castle.

MAVRIANOS.   I thank you, most glorious Lord, for your generosity to me. However—and I hope you won't take offense—I repeat and maintain that it matters little if you pass by her castle or not.

DUKE.   Haven't I already said that this was a challenge!

ANDRONIKOS.   My Lord, be careful with your words because I might take them seriously.

MAVRIANOS.   Take them seriously, eminent Lord. I ask you to take them seriously. What could be more serious for me in the world than the principles I profess and the reputation of my sister?

ANDRONIKOS.   My Lord, you are boring me with your sister.

MAVRIANOS.   It doesn't bore me, world-desired Lord, to uphold my honor and that of my sister.

NOBLEMEN.   If he seduces her? If he seduces your sister?

DUKE.   Then tell us! If he seduces your sister tonight at midnight?

MAVRIANOS.   If you seduce her? Did you say you would seduce my sister, my Lord, blessed by God?

ANDRONIKOS.   That's what I said. If I seduce her, how will you feel? Seduce her, in fact, without revealing my royal office so that no member of your party can say that I abused my power to frighten a helpless creature.

MAVRIANOS.   If you seduce her, King, you can have my head!

ANDRONIKOS.   Do you hear, my Lords? Tell me please. Will I be to blame if I have his head tomorrow morning? Will you cry again that I am violent and cantankerous, that I am governed by irrational passions and such-like?

NOBLEMEN.   No! No! We will say nothing! Have his head!

DUKE.   Have his head so it will teach him a lesson!

KONSTANTIS.   (*Aside to* MAVRIANOS) Ask him what kind of wager he will lose if he doesn't succeed in seducing her. You need a reciprocal wager. And this is an opportunity.

MAVRIANOS.   If you don't succeed in seducing her, King, what is your wager?

ANDRONIKOS.   (*Laughs*) My wager? My crown!

NOBLEMEN.   Did you hear what he said? His crown? If he doesn't succeed, he will lose his crown!

DUKE.   That's all we need! To make this a constitutional issue! How well these men here have managed everything with their sisters! Tomorrow, the stock market will again be in a state of confusion!

NOBLEMEN. Bah! Nonsense! It suffices for Kyr Andronikos to be in the mood! What were we just saying? Did any woman ever reject him? Who ever heard of such a thing!

ANDRONIKOS. Go to the women's quarters. Find one or two senators and bring them here so that our wager will take an official character. (*Two noblemen exit*) Those present are witnesses, Lord Mavrianos, that I attempted to save you from this adventure.

MAVRIANOS. My fate and the fate of the Empire are in the hands of Arete.

KONSTANTIS. (*To* MAVRIANOS) Hold fast to your principles, my friend! I am beside you!

MAVRIANOS. My confidence is unshaken!

KONSTANTIS. That is most important. From this point on, let History be the judge!

MAVRIANOS. Let History be the judge!

DUKE. Wonderful! Excellent! No sooner do we begin to forget about the war, the revolution, History, and the rest of it, and begin to enjoy ourselves, then here comes another crisis and confusion. And all this for what? For a slip of a girl no one has ever seen, and who could even be a hunchback.

(*The two noblemen return with the three senators,* IGNATIOS, STAVRAKIOS, *and* LEONTIOS. *All three are elderly, shortsighted, and limping, especially* LEONTIOS.)

IGNATIOS. I smell wine, Stravrakios.

STAVRAKIOS. I divine a banquet, Ignatios. Do you see women anywhere?

IGNATIOS. I neither see nor hear them. It seems to be a bachelor banquet, a conference on important matters of State. Look after Leontios. See that he doesn't fall over something.

STAVRAKIOS. Wait here, Leontios. Where are you going in such a hurry?

LEONTIOS. I thought the dancer Pulcheria passed by quite naked. Or could it have been Roxandra? Naked women resemble one another like little Negroes.

STAVRAKIOS. You are seeing visions. We didn't come here for dancing and entertainment, but for a conference with Kyr Andronikos.

LEONTIOS. Who is Kyr Andronikos?

STAVRAKIOS. The Emperor-King.

LEONTIOS. I knew him as Manuel.

STAVRAKIOS. Manuel died years ago. You gave the funeral

oration. Leontios, I suspect that your memory is beginning to have lapses. Perhaps it is from old age.

IGNATIOS.   Did you say something?

STAVRAKIOS.   We were conversing on a historical matter.

ANDRONIKOS.   Noble Senators, I greet you. (*The* SENATORS *acknowledge the greeting*) I called you here to witness, with your presence, a wager I made with Mavrianos.

IGNATIOS.   (*To the other two*) He has made a wager with someone called Mavrianos.

STAVRAKIOS.   What did you call him?

IGNATIOS.   Mavrianos.

LEONTIOS.   I knew Manuel. The great King Manuel!

ANDRONIKOS.   The Lord Mavrianos has a sister called Arete.

IGNATIOS.   Long may she live!

ANDRONIKOS.   She lives on the Bosporus, in a castle with hanging gardens.

IGNATIOS.   (*To the other two*) He is talking about the sister of Mavrianos. Her name is Arete.

LEONTIOS.   Manuel!

ANDRONIKOS.   The wager is as follows: I will attempt to seduce the noble lady Arete on this night, on her own bed, without revealing my royal office. If I succeed, the Lord Mavrianos will lose his head tomorrow morning. If I fail, I will lose my crown. Do you understand?

IGNATIOS.   Certainly! Of course! (*To the others*) The matter is simple. If he succeeds, he takes the head of Mavrianos; if he loses, they take his crown.

STAVRAKIOS.   And then what happens?

IGNATIOS.   Another king.

LEONTIOS.   Which king? Manuel?

IGNATIOS.   Manuel died. Be quiet! We understood, my Lord, ruler by divine right.

ANDRONIKOS.   You will convene the Senate tomorrow morning. I will appear and bring proof of the success of my experiment.

IGNATIOS.   As you command, providential Lord.

ANDRONIKOS.   Are we agreed, Lord Mavrianos?

MAVRIANOS.   Agreed, eminent Ruler.

ANDRONIKOS.   My Lords, I greet you—Duke of Paronaxia, I will require your company as soon as you are sober.

(KYR ANDRONIKOS *and the* DUKE OF PARONAXIA *exit. The* KING'S *companions withdraw.*)

LEONTIOS. I heard something about a bed.

IGNATIOS. Kyr Andronikos has placed a wager to seduce the sister of Lord Mavrianos on her own bed.

LEONTIOS. Why don't we go to see?

IGNATIOS. He will bring us proof tomorrow.

LEONTIOS. Isn't it more substantial proof if we saw the seduction with our own eyes?

IGNATIOS. That's not in the terms of the wager.

LEONTIOS. A bad legal procedure! A bad legal procedure!

IGNATIOS. That's how matters were decided. We can't change them now.

LEONTIOS. A bad legal procedure! What did you say this king is called?

IGNATIOS. Andronikos.

LEONTIOS. Andronikos? How is one to remember them all? Andronikos—Manuel—Andronikos—

(The SENATORS *exit shuffling.*)

KONSTANTIS. (*To* MAVRIANOS.) My friend, even now History has vindicated you. If you succeed, Prudence will be victorious; the Empire will be saved. If, on the other hand—

MAVRIANOS. If?

KONSTANTIS. I only say if—in case the devil should accidentally break his leg tonight—

MAVRIANOS. Do you believe such a thing can happen? You? You?

KONSTANTIS. I? God forbid! Never.

MAVRIANOS. Then why did you say it?

KONSTANTIS. I say it out of a dialectical need, so that my syllogism can be complete.

MAVRIANOS. Continue.

KONSTANTIS. If—all I said before takes place, your name will be engraved in gold letters in the catalogue of martyrs for Arete— I mean the idea of Arete-Virtue, not the person. You will be mentioned along with Harmodius and Brutus. Your example will light our way like a shining beacon in the night. You will exalt the party. We needed a heroic deed to make our cause a holy one. I rejoice with all my soul that historical fate granted me the favor of entrusting this role to my most bosom friend. Let's go now to plan with those who share our convictions what tactics we should follow, should the throne be widowed tomorrow, so that control of power never leaves our hands again.

ACT II

The same afternoon in a room in the castle of ARETE. *Two doors open out of this room.* ARETE *is reading.* ZAMBETA, *companion of* ARETE, *older in years, and three other women attendants are working on a large piece of embroidery as they sing.*

SONG.   Down in Rhodes, in the fair isle of Rhodes,
A Frank fell in love with a Byzantine maid.
"Marry him, daughter, 'cause he wears a helmet."
"For husband, Mother, I want no Frank."
"Marry him, daughter, he has countless florins."
"I want no husband who wears no mustache."

ZAMBETA.   Be careful, girls, not to drop a stitch or you will have to rip the whole thing. Observe the pattern and count correctly.

ATTENDANTS.   One, two, three—One, two, three—One, two, three—

FIRST ATTENDANT.   Dear Lady, aren't you going to tell us what you're reading so we ignorant ones can learn something from you.

ARETE.   I'm reading the story of Helen of Sparta.

FIRST ATTENDANT.   Is that the one who eloped with her lover—Paris I think they called him—and whose husband the king started a war to bring her back? You told us that story once last winter.

ARETE.   That's the one. The wife of Menelaos.

SECOND ATTENDANT.   She must have been very beautiful to have had so many things written about her in books!

ARETE.   Very beautiful. But she brought inconceivable suffering to the world. For ten years the Greeks and Trojans persisted in killing one another on her account.

ATTENDANTS.   Ten years! My Lady, ten years!

ARETE.   Such are the results of foolishness. Women should never desert their husbands!

ATTENDANTS.   My dear, of course not! Who ever heard of such a thing! O, O, O! Such coquetry! (*They embroider*) One, two, three—One, two, three—One, two, three—

ZAMBETA.   Dear Mistress, you told us a story about a lady with a difficult name, and I became highly incensed. I believe she was Helen's sister.

ARETE.   Clytemnestra.

ZAMBETA.   Of course, I think that's what she was called

Wasn't she the one who killed her husband the King with a dagger?

ARETE. Yes, she killed him so she could marry her lover Aegisthos.

ZAMBETA. Dear me! What women in that family!

ARETE. Don't you fret. She paid a heavy price for this deed. Her son Orestes killed both her lover and her in order to avenge his father's blood.

ATTENDANTS. Her son! Did you hear? She was killed by her son!

ARETE. These deeds are paid in full. Women should never kill their husbands.

ATTENDANTS. How very true! For such a deed to be permitted? A wife to kill her husband! (*They continue to embroider*) One, two, three—one, two, three—One, two, three—

THIRD ATTENDANT. (*Dreamily*) I like the story of Digenis Akritas. He was handsome. He was strong. He was a brave man.

ZAMBETA. He's nothing to brag about! He was all for debauchery and immoralities!

THIRD ATTENDANT. What did he do wrong? He fell in love with the Lady Eudocia, her father wouldn't consent to her marrying him, so he abducted her—with her consent—and then married her. Where is the sin in that?

ZAMBETA. Ask our Lady to tell you how he seduced one woman after another. Am I not right, dear Lady?

ARETE. Zambeta is right. Since Eudocia acted as she did in consenting to be abducted as though she were a girl of the streets, her husband soon became bored with her. Because—I want you to bear this in mind—men have no respect for women who lack self-respect. The result was that Digenis Akritas very shortly acquired girl friends. First the daughter of the Emir Aplorabdis, then Maxima the Amazon, and who knows how many others. Girls should not elope and then marry without the consent of their parents.

ATTENDANTS. That's right. Ah, that's right! (*They embroider*) One, two, three—One, two, three—One, two, three—

(*The* BIRD OF SONGS *appears at the window and begins to sing*)

ZAMBETA. My Lady, my Lady, turn around slowly and see who has remembered us.

ARETE. What? Do you think it is that fine-feathered friend, the Bird of Songs? Are you sure?

ZAMBETA. Of course I'm sure. Look at him carefully.

ARETE. You're right. I recognize his human eyes. What a long time since we've seen him.

ZAMBETA. Ever since he came to sing us that song about the two mountains who were quarreling. "Olympos and Kissavos, the two mountains are fighting—" To tell the truth, I never did understand what two mountains had to fight over!

FIRST ATTENDANT. Olympos and Kissavos? I recall that he said Giona and Parnassos.

SECOND ATTENDANT. And, if I'm not mistaken, I heard them called Helicon and Kithairon.

THIRD ATTENDANT. And I, my dear, heard about the extensive war that took place one day between Helmos and Taygetos.

ZAMBETA. To this person he relates the story in one manner and to another in a different manner. He does these things. Don't take everything seriously. It may be that nothing more took place than a simple quarrel between Kyr Lykabettos and the Acropolis in Athens, and the Bird was exaggerating.

ARETE. Be careful, girls, not to frighten him away just as he has arrived here. Let's see. Will he have something to relate today? Little bird, will you give us human speech? Will you tell us about the mountains that are quarreling? Will you tell us about Kyr North Wind who is menacing the ships? Or about the mother with the nine sons and the one daughter? Or about the famous Bridge of Arta?

(The BIRD sings.)

ZAMBETA. *(To the attendants)* He sometimes brings messages from faraway places. He also makes forecasts. He gives warning so that you can be aware of what awaits you and so be on guard. Then, you believe only what you want and ignore the rest. Sometimes, he comes with his two brothers, and they sing in chorus: "Three little birds sat on the tower of Arete—"

(The BIRD flaps its wings.)

ARETE. Silence! I think he is about to speak!

BIRD. The King Andronikos and all his noble lords
    Together wined and dined in the City's Palaces.
    Topics for gossip they had none, and so they turned to
      talk
    About the loveliness in maids and also the virtuous
      maidens.

And then Mavrianos began to talk, to boast about his
sister.

"The kind of sister that I have, no other has her equal.
She's never been kissed nor pinched, she'll never go
astray."

Soon as the Emperor heard these words, he turned to
him and said:

"Should I seduce her Mavrianos, what wager will you
forfeit?"

"Should you seduce her, Emperor, then you can have
my head.

But if she will not be seduced, what wager will you
forfeit?"

"My kingdom will I forfeit, sir, and with it my golden
crown."

(*The* BIRD *flies away. The audience is greatly amused.*)

ARETE.   Did you hear, ladies? Did you hear what he said?

FIRST ATTENDANT.   We heard. O horror! Are we deaf not to
have heard?

SECOND ATTENDANT.   Can't you see us quivering like fish?

THIRD ATTENDANT.   Ah! Now what was that all about? I'm
going to faint!

ZAMBETA.   Hang on to her. This is no time for fainting! That's
all we need!

(*They take hold of the attendant, and she recovers.*)

ARETE.   Those people are out of their minds! They've lost their
minds completely! Did you see how they insulted me—Me!—to be
discussing my virtue at their banquet; to be wagering over my
dignity! They have done this to me!

ZAMBETA.   Dear Lady, it seems to me from this account that
your brother is gambling with his head. Stop all this about dignity
and let's consider what we're going to do.

ARETE.   What we're going to do? It would serve him right if
I were another kind of sister, then he'd see! To make a joking
matter of my honor! To sport with the dignity of our family! And
with whom, please? With Kyr Andronikos! With that degenerate
man! With that dreadful man who makes everyone blush at the
mention of his name! I'm to be disgraced like that?

THIRD ATTENDANT. Ah, why does Kyr Andronikos do these things? Why?

ZAMBETA. Why? Because he's a villain, a dishonest man, an arch-imposter. Because he's the seducer of women. Because he can never quench his thirst, even should he drink the blood of all of us, the anti-Christ!

THIRD ATTENDANT. Ah! Handsome as he is and shining like an archangel of God, how we all could have loved him, if he only didn't behave in such a fashion! Ah, why does he do these things?

SECOND ATTENDANT. To seduce the girls, and then to cut off their brothers' heads!

FIRST ATTENDANT. My dear, what carryings-on among the aristocrasy! What carryings-on!

ZAMBETA. Don't worry; his turn will come! Some girl will come along who is more clever than we are, and she will put both his feet into one shoe. In the end, these deceivers, these faithless, these mockers of the gods, are caught worse than the others!

ARETE. Will someone like that come along? Is that what you think? In other words, you believe that no one has yet been found to put both of Kyr Andronikos' feet into one boot?

ZAMBETA. Dear Lady, what are you trying to say? What is running through your mind?

ARETE. You know very well what is running through my mind. No, my dear! I won't be taken in by something like that! To have such a disgrace occur to me! Men shall pay for this! And since they're sending me their King as envoy of their masculine villainy and cunning, he will pay for the entire race of men.

ZAMBETA. Light of my eyes, graceful as a twig, my dear, what are you saying? Aren't we going to leave at once? Aren't we going to rush down to your boat, to hoist sails, before that untamed beast appears?

ARETE. To hoist sails? To desert in the face of danger? Zambeta, you don't know me very well! (*The* ATTENDANTS *make various exclamations*) I will remain here to confront him.

ZAMBETA. My dear Lady, he is an imp, a dragon, a Charon who takes away the souls; he is a devil with horns and tail! How are you to confront him? Have mercy, Mother Mary!

FIRST ATTENDANT. Horrors! Don't do such a thing, dear Lady!

SECOND ATTENDANT. Have pity on us. We are frightened!

THIRD ATTENDANT. Ah! Why have you no compassion for us, sweet Lady?

SECOND ATTENDANT. Gentle Lady!

FIRST ATTENDANT. Most beloved Lady!

ARETE. Let this grumbling cease! I give the orders here and not my servants! I will fight, and I will win!

FIRST ATTENDANT. What catastrophe has befallen us!

SECOND ATTENDANT. What a storm has overtaken us!

THIRD ATTENDANT. Ah! What will our eyes witness!

FIRST ATTENDANT. What misfortune awaits us!

ARETE. Stop, I said! Not only will I make him lose his wager, but I will dishonor him as well; I will humiliate him in the East and in the West! I will avenge all the women he has tortured! I will avenge the blood! I will re-establish female honor in our land! The God of women is sending me an idea for salvation. Run to the gardens and bring here my humblest woman gardener, the lowest peasant, the most ignorant, the most stupid! Why do you stand there and look at me with open mouths? Run and do as I tell you!

(*The* ATTENDANTS *exit.*)

ZAMBETA. My dear Lady, dear Lady, have you considered well how you are to proceed? Are you going to play with fire? You will be burned, my dear.

ARETE. He will see with whom he is about to engage! At last, he will understand that there are different types of women! He will learn the meaning of love, honor, name, dignity, and self-respect!

ZAMBETA. Ah, my dear, have you ever seen him?

ARETE. No. After what I've heard about him, I've never had the desire to see him. I've never consented to stand where he was about to pass!

ZAMBETA. Ah! Neither have I seen him, and I hope I never will! But haven't you heard, dear one, what they say? That when he looks into your eyes, your blood boils and you melt like wax? Ah! The thought alone makes my heart fail me! May I sit down? (*She sits down*)

ARETE. I'm not one of those who melt easily. When something concerns my dignity, I am like iron; I am like stone!

ZAMBETA. Ah! I begin to suspect that I'm not stone or iron at all. Only the thought that he is approaching here, and I feel as though I have already melted.

ARETE. Ha! Let me laugh! If you only knew how sorry I am

for you! How well the women would have clung to their reputations,
if they were all like you!

(*The three* ATTENDANTS *enter dragging* MAROULINA *by the
hand. She is a lovely ignorant girl. Her hair is the same color as that
of* ARETE.)

ARETE. (*To* MAROULINA) Come here. What is your name?

MAROULINA. Maroulina.

ARETE. How old are you? (MAROULINA *laughs*) I said nothing
funny. I am asking you your age.

MAROULINA. I don't know.

ZAMBETA. My dear, she's as dumb as a brick! Where did you
go to find her?

ARETE. Have you ever seen a king? (MAROULINA *giggles*) Don't
you know what a king is?

MAROULINA. He is the one who makes war.

ARETE. Precisely. Shortly, a king will come here; and if you
don't do as I tell you, he will cut off your head. (MAROULINA *bursts
into tears*) Silence! If you attend to me, no harm will come to you,
and I will fill you with sweets. Now, we will dress you like a lady
and seat you on this couch to receive the king as though you are
the Lady of the Castle. When he appears, you will greet him like
this, with a motion of your head. He will speak to you. You will
say nothing, because once you've opened your mouth, he'll see
through our trick, and he'll punish all of us. We will tell him that
you have been ill and cannot speak a word. You'll only smile at
him. Here, like this. Later, we'll lead you to my room to sleep on
my bed. After dark, the king will come seeking you in the bedroom,
and you will let him do whatever he wants.

MAROULINA. What will he do?

ARETE. He will also lie down.

MAROULINA. Is he sick?

ZAMBETA. Ah! We can do without such sickness in here. I
feel faint just listening to this! Let me sit down! (*She sits down*)

ARETE. He is not sick at all. In fact, he's crazy about playing
games in the dark. That's why he'll come to find you. To play with
you. (MAROULINA *giggles*) Now, you'll remain quiet, like a good
girl, and you'll let him play all his games without making any noise
and commotion in the night.

MAROULINA. How will we play? With our hands? With our
feet? With our lips?

ARETE. She's not as stupid as you represented her to be. You'll play, I think, in as many ways as a man's mind can conceive. But as we said. Not a word! (MAROULINA *giggles*) Don't forget yourself and strike up a conversation with him.

MAROULINA.   My dear Mistress, who feels like talking when she is playing games?

ZAMBETA.   Silence, shameless hussy! Aren't you ashamed of yourself?

ARETE.   It was fated, it seems, that my room should witness such a spectacle. So be it! I am making a sacrifice, which will be acknowledged someday, for the honor of my name and that of all the women of my race. Without sacrifices, nothing of any consequence has ever taken place in History! Remember that!

FIRST ATTENDANT.   Of course, my dear.

ATTENDANTS.   Of course.

FIRST ATTENDANT.   Can such sacrifices ever be forgotten?

(*The* BIRD *appears at the window, flaps its wings, and sings.*)

BIRD: The Emperor Andronikos, astride a white she-mule,
Appears on the main highway, draws nearer to the garden.
Following close behind, the Duke, laden with heavy bundles,
Bearing books immense in bulk, as well as pen and paper.
The pen warbles a song, and the pieces of paper crackle:
"Greetings, solemn women, maidens devoted to study,
You most pensive maidens, instructed in higher learning!
King Andronikos is come this way to perfect your education!"

(*The* BIRD *flies away.*)

ARETE.   Hurry, we barely have time. (*She takes off her garment*) Clothe her in my garment and put on my jewelry. Bring me the dress of a servant. Seat her on the couch! There! Place a footstool under her feet. Sit back! Assume a pose! Comb her hair the way I wear mine! Don't become flustered! Pin my diamonds in her hair! Be quick! (*Her orders are carried out quickly. The* ATTENDANTS *now place the large diamond which* ARETE *had formerly worn in her own braids in* MAROULINA'S *hair. In the meantime,* ARETE *puts on the simple dress that has been brought for her*) Kyr Andronikos is coming to supplement our education. Let him come! We're here, and how we're expecting him. Tomorrow morning, we'll see who will emerge from this story the better educated. (*A servant enters and becomes flustered at sight of* MAROULINA, *adorned as she is and seated in the place of the Mistress of the Castle*) Why do you look at us like a simpleton? This is the Mistress of the Castle tonight, and no one is to say a word. This is my command. Do you understand me?

MALE SERVANT.   Ye— ye— yes, Mistress.

ARETE.   Now, what do you want?

SERVANT.   Two—students—are down below—and—they are—seeking—permission—to receive—your hospitality—for tonight—

ARETE.   So! So! So!

SERVANT.   —because—there is—no time—to enter the Polis—before—nightfall—and they are—afraid that—

ARETE.   They are afraid that they might encounter evil on the public road. Isn't that what they said?

SERVANT.   Ye—es!

ARETE.   I will extend them hospitality with pleasure. Let them come in! (*The* SERVANT *exits*) Strike a little better pose, Maroulina! Don't forget who you are supposed to be at this moment. Pretend you are a very important person. There! But you will smile to him from time to time, as we agreed. You three stand behind her; you Zambeta on her left, and I on her right.

(*The orders are executed.* KYR ANDRONIKOS *and the* DUKE OF PARONAXIA *enter, attired as students. The* DUKE *is carrying books and a pen. They bow many times in greeting. The women return the greetings.* MAROULINA *nods her head and smiles as best she can.*)

ZAMBETA.   My heart is breaking! My blood is boiling! Ah, I'm melting, my dear!

ATTENDANTS.   Ah!

THIRD ATTENDANT.   Why does Kyr Andronikos behave as he does? Why?

ARETE.   Silence!

ANDRONIKOS.   Most noble Mistress of the Castle, my name is Parthenios. (*He bows deeply*) And my companion's name is Sophronios. (*The* DUKE *bows in greeting*) We thank you from the bottom of our hearts for the generous hospitality you consented to grant us. We were ignorant of whose castle it was that unexpectedly appeared on our path. When we asked the servants, and they informed us that it belonged to the famous noble Lady Arete, we were astonished at our marvelous good fortune. We are students of Greek letters; we have traveled to famous Institutes, from Greece to Syria, and everywhere we heard talk about your great learning and your keen ability to decipher the secrets of the ancient texts. Since we are here in your house tonight, we would consider it a great privilege to hear your opinions on the manner in which Homer's meter should be read, on the syntax of Thucydides, on the laws of the tragedies, and on the teachings of the divine Plato. Because, of course, we of the younger generation are all Platonists today.

DUKE. Platonists, of course. Platonists!

ANDRONIKOS. As a small token of our gratitude and our esteem for you, permit us to deposit some dictionaries at your feet, some grammar books, linguistics books, and other references works which might be useful in your studies.

(*The* DUKE OF PARONAXIA *comes forth and deposits his books before* MAROULINA. *They make quite a pile on the floor.* MAROULINA *starts to giggle, but* ARETE *pinches her and she stops.*)

DUKE. (*Aside to* KYR ANDRONIKOS) I'm really impressed with this noble lady.

ANDRONIKOS. She's not bad for what we've come here to do. Her servant on the right would have suited me equally well. In fact, I believe even more.

DUKE. I prefer the noble Lady. She has color. She has breasts. She has dignity. Servants are not my type.

ARETE. My good men, our noble Lady thanks you for your beautiful words and precious gifts, but she cannot tell you so with her own mouth, nor can she converse with you on the subjects with which you are concerned. She has been under a strange illness these last few days. She has become tongue-tied, and the doctors have ordered that we not attempt to make her talk because something terrible might happen to her. The only thing that helps is to take her to bed very early, to caress her, and to sweeten her life as much as possible. It seems that she will regain her speech little by little with this kind of therapy.

DUKE. (*Aside to* KYR ANDRONIKOS) See what I told you about leaving the books behind, long-lived Lord. Of what value have they been to us? You only made me carry them all that way in the heat of summer.

ANDRONIKOS. We have created an atmosphere of trust. The Lady is already displaying great benevolence toward me. (*To* ARETE) Lovely maiden, your words afflict my heart. We wish now that fate had not pushed us in the direction of philology but in medicine so we could hasten to participate in the recovery of such a beautiful sick lady. One doesn't know what to admire most in her, her spiritual graces or her beauty. (MAROULINA *again tries to giggle, but* ARETE *pinches her as before*) But even without physicians, we are not incapable, believe me, of finding means essential to sweetening the life of those we love.

ZAMBETA.   Now I understand what it means to be Andronikos! It's a great thing! If only I could sit down somewhere!

ATTENDANTS.   Ah!

THIRD ATTENDANT.   How he behaves! How he talks! Why does he feel no compassion? Why?

DUKE.   (*Aside to* KYR ANDRONIKOS) It seems to me that she is also disposed toward me. Did you see how she looked at me?

ANDRONIKOS.   Duke of Paronaxia, don't make this an occasion for dissension! Everything here must be carried out with all dignity.

DUKE.   Certainly. With formality, my Lord! Formality above all.

ARETE.   Your words, my good men, have created a most excellent impression on my mistress. Without question, she will have a very pleasant night, knowing that there are two such select, well-mannered and highly educated people on the same floor.

(KYR ANDRONIKOS *and the* DUKE *bow in greeting.* MAROULINA *returns the greeting. She is about to make a remark, but* ARETE *pinches her and she stops.*)

ZAMBETA.   A great thing!

ARETE   (*Aside*) It seems to me that it's time I put an end to this conversation. (*To* KYR ANDRONIKOS) Now, with your permission, we will bid you good night because it is getting dark, and it is time to lead our mistress to her room. (*She points to one of the doors*) Zambeta, see that whatever is necessary for a good dinner is brought out for these two good men.

ZAMBETA.   I'll go. Ah! (*She exits*)

ARETE.   Girls, give your mistress some help here. Good night, my good men, from my Lady and me.

ANDRONIKOS.   Good night, Ladies. Sleep well. Pleasant dreams.

DUKE.   Think of us, and we will think of you.

ATTENDANTS.   Good night. Ah!

(*They bid one another good night.* ARETE *and her* ATTENDANTS *lead* MAROULINA *toward the opposite door, in the direction of* ARETE's *bedroom. At the doorway,* MAROULINA *pauses, glances back at* KYR ANDRONIKOS *and attempts to smile.* ARETE *and the women lead her through the doorway.*)

DUKE. The sister of our good friend Mavrianos is not bad. You'll not be wasting your night, esteemed Lord. By Babylon, I envy you a little.

ANDRONIKOS. I will win my wager without difficulty. In fact, the entire episode no longer has any special meaning. Even though, to tell the truth, I am somewhat intoxicated. Everything is beginning to appear extremely pleasant and marvelous. This castle, the night which is approaching, the first stars I see sparkling in the twilight—you! Only, I have yet to understand which of these women has incited this mood tonight.

DUKE. For God's sake! Long-lived Lord, put these disturbing thoughts aside and proceed to win your wager. Had it been only a question of attending to one's own amusement, I, too, would have had something to say, because the mistress of the castle cast such glances at me that I have the hiccups. But we have come here for a political reason; in fact, for reasons of State. Your duty, illustrious Lord. Your duty!

(ARETE *and her three* ATTENDANTS *come out of* MAROULINA'S *room and cross the stage. They greet the men.*)

ATTENDANTS. Ah!

ANDRONIKOS. Very well. I know my business. I will go where duty calls me as soon as it is dark. In the meantime, the best thing you can do is to go to the room assigned to us and don't stick your nose out till morning. If you start walking around at night, I'm afraid you might commit some grave error.

DUKE. As you command, my bravest Lord. That way, I'll be fresh as fresh in the morning at the execution.

ANDRONIKOS. Which execution?

DUKE. Well, aren't you beheading Mavrianos under the terms of the wager?

ANDRONIKOS. Leave me in peace! The lesson he'll receive will be sufficient. At best, I might dispatch him to one of the embassies among the Moslems. As for the young lady, my heart cannot endure to abandon her in grief after the reception they have given us here. As you can see, I'm in the best of humor today. I'm considering marrying her off to one of my attendants so that everything will be concealed under the cloak of a noble marriage. (*He is thoughtful for a moment*) But wait! No need to look elsewhere! It seems to me that twelve months have passed since your third wife died. What do you say? Will you marry Arete? I'll be responsible to see that you have permission for your fourth marriage.

DUKE. That I should marry—Hm! Hm!

ANDRONIKOS. You are reluctant?

DUKE. Hm! Hm!

ANDRONIKOS. Weren't you praising her all this time! Didn't you just tell me that you envy me because I'm going to spend the night beside her?

DUKE. Of course, the noble Lady Arete is not bad, and she suits me perfectly. Should I marry her, she would be of considerable solace to me in life. She would help me to forget my grief and bitterness, those three deaths which have poisoned my soul—

ANDRONIKOS. Stop burdening me with your soul and your three deaths and explain clearly what you are trying to say.

DUKE. My Lord, you must understand the position of your humble subject. Everyone in the Polis will know that you have slept with her. True, you've slept one or more times with the wives of most of your nobles, cabinet members, generals, and admirals. Everyone is informed about these; however, no one knows anything officially. The formalities have been preserved. But in this case, the situation assumes a public character, sanctioned by the decision of the Senate. How will I take care of the formalities, my Lord? Formalities! They are everything!

ANDRONIKOS. Tell me, if I give her a dowry, won't all the formalities be preserved?

DUKE. You will give her a dowry, you say?

ANDRONIKOS. I don't know. This castle has affected me strangely. I feel an inclination to be law-abiding. Yes, I will give you three of the Cyclades Islands: Syros, Tinos, and Mykonos. Add Delos with its antiquities for good measure.

DUKE. Barren islands, my Lord. Do you think the islands have anything left over for good measure? They barely support their inhabitants. If Andros were to be included—I'm not saying—but maybe one could consider the matter, not for profit, but only to grant you your wish.

ANDRONIKOS. Rascal, you have caught me at a moment when I am possessed by love of beauty and love for the human race. Very well, I will also include Andros.

(ZAMBETA *enters with servants carrying the food. They go to the bedroom of* KYR ANDRONIKOS.)

DUKE. (*Counts on his fingers*) We said Syros, Tinos, Mykonos, Delos, and Andros—

(ZAMBETA *and the servants return, cross the stage, and exit.*)

ZAMBETA. Ah!

DUKE. This castle sighs from every direction. They don't give you time to make a true assessment. Didn't we say five islands, my Lord?

ANDRONIKOS. So we said, and that is all. Have your dinner now and then go to sleep while I attend to my business.

DUKE. Good night, myrtle-crowned King.

ANDRONIKOS. A good night to you, glorious heir to my reign of this night.

DUKE. I think that I, too, will sigh. Ah! (*He enters his bedroom*)

ANDRONIKOS. A strange night. It appears that some mystery has enclosed me. The sweetness of the world has made a prisoner of me. It rises within me like fermenting wine. I feel as happy as though, for the first time in my life, I was finding myself alone with a girl in such a garden, on such a night, in the intoxication of the fragrances and warm breaths of love. But it is a disturbed happiness. I will be taking one woman while desiring another. It isn't the first time that such complications have occurred to me. But this castle has thoroughly confused me with its gentle mystery, its strange innocence, its sighs behind every door and window. (*Music is heard*) Something enchants me. It almost consumes me and yet disturbs me. Something is obscure within me. Kyr Andronikos, what's the matter with you? You're beginning to act strangely. I suspect that tonight you are inclining toward sentimentality and won't admit it.

(*It is dark. The moon gives light to the room.*)

VOICES. Guards, hurry!

ANDRONIKOS. It's evident that this moon is mocking me. Its brilliance is suspect. And it has pursed its lips in a manner I know quite well. I've seen it a thousand times before, mocking others because of me. Kyr Andronikos, do you know that you are being duped?

VOICES. Guards, hurry!

ANDRONIKOS. (*To the moon*) Please stop that, Lady Moon! Don't do such things to me! What are you trying to say? What is so comical about this situation? Is it simply because you've caught me at a moment of sentimental weakness? It's been your fault, every time this has happened to me. You know it well. You, with your flattery, your shrewd, your crafty tricks! You know well that tomorrow morning I'll be laughing over your actions. No, you say? You don't mean that? Then what do you mean by assuming such an expression, as though tonight I am a victim of some mockery! Are you trying to make me afraid of women? I, Kyr Andronikos, should hesitate at the door of a woman who smiled at me and who I know well has not locked her door? You are deceived!

(*He enters* MAROULINA's *room. The music stops.* ARETE *and* ZAMBETA *appear, out of breath.* ZAMBETA *goes to* MAROULINA's *door to eavesdrop.*)

ARETE.   So! Well! What do you think?

ZAMBETA.   It's a great thing!

ARETE.   We were fated to see this affair! To experience it! This scandal! This debauchery! This impudence right under our noses! In my own room!

ZAMBETA.   My dear, it's a great thing!

(ARETE, *walking in the dark, stumbles over the pile of books. Angered, she kicks them with her foot; she picks them up and tosses them around the room.*)

ARETE.   (*To the books*) I'm sick of you! I'm tired of you! Clear my house! Empty my corner! Get you gone! Get lost from my sight! Don't ever let me see you again! Don't let me know about you! I'm tired of you!

ACT III

The Senate hall on the following morning. Members of the Court are gathered together. The murmur of conversation is heard. KONSTANTIS *and* MAVRIANOS *stand in a corner.*

FIRST SERVANT.   (*To his companion*) We can't describe what went on last night with all the wagering. The taverns were open all night long; and from one to the other the Polis was wagering on whether Kyr Andronikos had slept or not. The Wisdom Party, you see, has become unyielding.

SECOND SERVANT.   Even the schools for girls were wagering. And the old-folks homes. And even the insurance companies. They accepted huge sums of money as collateral.

SECOND SERVANT. Such carryings-on! Such carryings-on!

A NOBLEMAN. Ten to one in favor of Kyr Andronikos.

SECOND NOBLEMAN. I'll take that!

FIRST SERVANT. They are even wagering in here.

THIRD NOBLEMAN. Twenty to one in favor of Kyr Andronikos!

FOURTH NOBLEMAN. I'll take that wager!

A NOBLEWOMAN. A hundred to one in favor of Kyr Andronikos! (*From different areas come gasps of surprise*) I said a hundred to one!

THE CROWD. (*From different areas*) I'll take that! I'll take that! I'll take that!

NOBLEWOMAN. I'll hold the money. A hundred to one!

HERALD. The Senate!

(*Enter* IGNATIOS, STAVRAKIOS *and several other senators. They sit on their thrones.* IGNATIOS *presides.*)

IGNATIOS. Silence from the audience! The meeting is about to convene. The agenda refers to a wager made yesterday by our Lord, Kyr Andronikos—long may he live—with the nobleman Mavrianos. Everyone is aware of the terms.

LEONTIOS. Who made the wager?

IGNATIOS. You were present, Leontios, and later we explained everything to you in detail. Have you forgotten?

STAVRAKIOS. It seems that his memory presents lapses. On account of old age. (*He bends over and explains everything to* LEONTIOS *privately.* LEONTIOS *finally remembers everything and begins to laugh.*)

LEONTIOS. Did anyone witness the scene?

IGNATIOS. The elements of proof will be brought to the audience.

LEONTIOS. A bad legal procedure! A bad legal procedure! We should have witnessed the event. Next time we must go to witness the scene.

IGNATIOS. Are both parties present?

MAVRIANOS. At the commands of the Senate, Illustrious One.

IGNATIOS. Who are you?

MAVRIANOS. Mavrianos. With head high, I am ready to receive my fate, whether it be of victory or of death, only, in the one instance and in the other, to receive glory because I am fighting for Reason and Morality.

THE CROWD. Did you hear? Reason! Morality! Reason and Morality!

KONSTANTIS.   (*To* MAVRIANOS) Friend, continue to bear your-self with courage as you have begun. Weigh the words you are about to speak. History is attending you. Always bear this in mind.

VOICES FROM THE CROWD.   He comes! He comes! He comes!

FIRST NOBLEMAN.   Even his ears are laughing. He shines like the prince in the fairy tale.

FIRST NOBLEMAN.   We have won!

THIRD NOBLEMAN.   How could anyone doubt it? Otherwise, we would have been insane to have made such extravagant wagers. But we know him well.

OTHER NOBLEMEN.   We know him well! We know him!

(KYR ANDRONIKOS *enters with the* DUKE, *who bears himself proudly. The* KING *sits on his throne.*)

ANDRONIKOS.   Noble Senators, it seems foolish to me that a man in such a responsible position in society should come to brag publicly about his successes in love like an apprentice writer. Nor am I accustomed to revealing the secrets of women. But the wager which is responsible for this gathering has taken unusual propor-tions. Ever since yesterday, there has been much talk in the Polis about an affair of State, and I hear that huge sums of money are at stake. Then I am obliged to resolve the problem at once and in an explicit manner. The Lady Arete willingly responded to my offer of love last night, even though I didn't reveal my royal office to her.

THE CROWD.   (*Whenever the crowd responds, a great clamor and voices are discerned*) We had no doubt! Bravo! Bravo! Long may you live! A healthy, joyous life to you! May you be made of iron! Of steel! A stone-breaker!

ANDRONIKOS.   So that I can be in order, I have even brought you tangible proof. It's one of her braids adorned with a rare dia-mond, easily identifiable. I cut it off with her consent, telling her that I wished to have some kind of affirmation of the love we shared. (*He gives the braid of hair with the diamond to* IGNATIOS. *All the senators bend over to look at it*)

THE CROWD.   Long may you live!

LEONTIOS.   What did they say?

IGNATIOS.   They are applauding Kyr Andronikos for having won the wager. He has brought us her braid of hair.

LEONTIOS.   Whose braid of hair? Pulcheria's?

IGNATIOS.   No, Arete's. Have you forgotten again? (*They ex-plain once more to* LEONTIOS. *He remembers, and he examines the braid of hair with great excitement*)

ANDRONIKOS. I wish to make one final announcement. Arete's virtue will not be jeopardized. My faithful subject and companion, the Duke of Paronaxia, desires to honor both me and her, who at this moment is unknowingly stamped with the royal chrism. He voluntarily begged me to permit him to marry her, thereby concealing under his distinguished name whatever occurred last night. I accepted his plea, and I publicly thank my good Duke for the wise solution he has found to this problem.

THE CROWD. Congratulations! Bravo! And to nobler accomplishments! His loyalty is admirable! A great coup! The Duke will be advanced! He will go far!

(NOBLEMEN *approach the* DUKE *and greet him with respect.*)

KONSTANTIS. (*To* MAVRIANOS) Are those really her hair and diamond?

MAVRIANOS. They are.

KONSTANTIS. So we've been deceived!

MAVRIANOS. So it seems.

KONSTANTIS. "O Zeus, why then did you let women dwell under the light of the sun, those evil forgeries. . . ." We should have thought of these words of the ancient tragedian while there was yet time. We could have arrived at a compromise, at some halfway solution. Unfortunately, our bright ideas often come to us after the event.

MAVRIANOS. And it isn't only that I've lost my family honor, but, as it appears, I'm also going to lose my head.

KONSTANTIS. The matter of your family is somehow reconciled by the solution they have presented to us. As for your head, what am I to say? Such are the historical battles. Whoever sets out to impose Truth on mankind, should know in advance that it is possible he may lose his head on the way. But politics is full of surprises, and something may yet happen. Be careful, however, of what you say because everything is being recorded in the minds of those present, and later generations will be informed about everything down to the minutest detail.

ANDRONIKOS. Noble Senators, I believe that the matter has been exhausted. We can now adjourn the meeting and everyone go on about his business.

THE CROWD. Very well, but what about the execution? Isn't there going to be an execution? The people are waiting for the execution!

DUKE. (*Aside to* KYR ANDRONIKOS) They are expecting the execution. Didn't I tell you?

ANDRONIKOS. I'm in no mood. Tell them to leave me alone!

DUKE. Be careful, my Lord. It isn't right to disappoint public opinion over such insignificant matters. What's the price of one head to you? Why are you so stingy? We talked about economy, but we don't have to be so extreme.

LEONTIOS. Who are they going to execute?

STAVRAKIOS. Lord Mavrianos. He's lost the wager.

LEONTIOS. He's lost the wager? Then— (*He laughs*) To the stake! To the stake! To the stake!

IGNATIOS. Since the crowd is so impatient, I propose a good dismemberment by four horses so that everyone can at least see a splendid spectacle.

THE CROWD. Wonderful! Wonderful! A dismemberment! A dismemberment!

DUKE. Will it make any difference to you if we use eight horses? Are we even going to economize on the horses?

CROWD. Excellent! Wonderful! We want eight horses! Eight horses!

LEONTIOS. (*Rising*) Let's find a front seat!

IGNATIOS. (*Holds him back*) Sit down. Kyr Andronikos hasn't replied yet.

(MAVRIANOS *raises his hand.*)

STAVRAKIOS. The nobleman Mavrianos asks for the floor. He may have a suggestion to make on the manner of his execution.

IGNATIOS. Let Mavrianos speak. Let him voice his suggestion.

MAVRIANOS. My Lord, King and Emperor, a death such as that awaiting me is certainly not dishonorable. I have performed no injustice, either against common law or against politics. I believed and continue to believe in eternal ideals, in Reason, in Morality, in History. I have fought an honorable battle against a great honored opponent. I have lost. I'm proud to pay my debt, bringing honor to my name, my principles, my friends (KONSTANTIS *bows*) and, above all, to the lawful Master of our Empire.

KONSTANTIS. (*Aside to* MAVRIANOS) You've made a great impression. Now, subtly present your petition for mercy.

MAVRIANOS. In one way or another, we are all destined to die one day. I consider it preferable to die with honor. And if I petition for a favor at this moment, believe me it is because of love for order and because the customs of judicial law must be observed, and not because of an expression of human weakness in the face of death.

KONSTANTIS. (*To the* CROWD) Ever since yesterday, it seems to me that we've done nothing but prove to the people how little we value death.

MAVRIANOS. Furthermore, my Lord, it is obvious that I have no other argument to present in support of my petition except to appeal to your generosity, which is known throughout the Universe. I have lost the wager; there is no doubt of this. Another man might readily have appealed to your friendship for his sister. He would have explained that this tender creature cannot possibly withstand, within so short a time, such tremendous emotions; for instance, your royal generosity which she came to know during the past night, the important wedding you are now preparing for her, and finally the death of her only beloved brother. Someone else, I say, would have appealed to your chivalry and would have begged you to lighten the sister's burden, not the brother's. But my sister has deeply embittered me, and my family honor forbids me to bring her into this conversation.

KONSTANTIS. Nor, of course, did such a thing enter our minds!

MAVRIANOS. There's nothing left for me to do, great King, but to leave my problem to your right and equitable judgment. Anything you decide to do will be most beneficial to the Empire and to society.

VOICES OFFSTAGE. Execution! Execution! Execution!

KONSTANTIS. (*Aside to* KYR ANDRONIKOS.) My Lord, we give you three lions of Arabia from our stables and as many Indian buffaloes of prime quality so you can present your people today with a spectacle such as has never been seen in the Hippodrome since the days of Theodora. Let them delight in a battle between royal animals and blood of prime quality.

ANDRONIKOS. That's an idea! What do you say, Duke of Paronaxia?

DUKE. Imperfect solution, my Lord. You know very well that nothing satisfies the people like the sweet sight of human blood. But, since you so desire, let us increase the number of wild animals so we can at least attempt to deceive them with quantity.

KONSTANTIS. We'll double them.

DUKE. Noblemen and noble Ladies, listen to the great news! Today, at the usual hour, we will give you so excellent a performance at the Hippodrome that even our grandfathers won't recall ever having seen its equal before. Six lions from Arabia will fight six Indian buffaloes, all of prime size. You'll see enough blood to satisfy you. And what blood! Of incomparable quality!

THE CROWD. And the execution of Mavrianos? When will Mavrianos be executed?

DUKE. Leave Mavrianos out of this! Don't you understand that Kyr Andronikos wants to grant him mercy? So it pleases him. He offers you such indemnity and you complain! Six Arabian lions, six Indian buffaloes! Stop talking and run to find a seat!

THE CROWD. Bravo! Bravo! A royal bounty! Six Arabian lions! Six Indian buffaloes! Let's run to find a seat! Let's not be last again!

(*The* CROWD *turns to leave*)

DUKE. And so, ladies and gentlemen, one can say that the comedy has ended in the best possible manner, that is, with a noble wedding full of hope, with public festivities, and with the reconciliation of the two parties. What remains now is to pray that all comedies end as conveniently as ours.

HERALD. The noble Lady Arete!

(*The* CROWD *stands still.* ARETE *enters, attired as a noblewoman and carrying flowers.* ZAMBETA, MAROULINA *attired as a gardener, and three* ATTENDANTS, *accompany her. The* CROWD *remarks on the entrance of* ARETE.)

FEMALE GOSSIP. Arete, my dear! Arete! So that's her? I imagined her to be much younger.

MALE GOSSIP. She's not bad! A sweet face! A nice waistline! She has an excellent shape.

FEMALE GOSSIPS. She doesn't look bad from behind. She hasn't very shapely legs.

MALE GOSSIPS. She has all the curves she needs. Perhaps she could have been fuller in the breasts.

FEMALE GOSSIPS. She has circles under her eyes! Naturally, you can see what a night she's had! They don't call him Kyr Andronikos for nothing!

MALE GOSSIPS. Look! Look! Her ankles are exposed! Marvelous ankles!

LEONTIOS. Are those women?

STAVRAKIOS. It's the noble Lady Arete with her attendants. The sister of Mavrianos. The wager, remember?

LEONTIOS. Ah, of course! She's the one who— (*He laughs*) Let's go see! Let's get close!

IGNATIOS. Be seated! We are at a meeting.

ARETE. Health and happiness, noble Lords! I bring you flowers from my garden to decorate your meeting place.

THE CROWD. How fine! What wonderful breeding! In spite of what happened, she still shows breeding!

ARETE. But what is the matter with my brother that he is in such bad humor and looks so glum?

KONSTANTIS. My Lady, if you don't know already, let me inform you now. Your brother came near to losing his head just now; he barely escaped from the clutches of death. So, it's difficult that you should see him in a gay mood today.

ARETE. So! And how did this come about? Did he become involved in a political argument which displeased our long-lived King, great be his grace? Did he kill someone under the influence of wine? Or was it over the dark eyes of some beautiful woman?

KONSTANTIS. Mavrianos, an honest, law-abiding nobleman of the rarest quality, could not have been mixed in politics against the will of our Lord, nor could he have committed murder. He almost lost his head on account of a braid with a large diamond in it, missing from your head and in the hands of the esteemed Senate at this moment.

(IGNATIOS *displays the braid of hair from a distance.* LEONTIOS *dances up and down in his seat.*)

ARETE. For goodness sake, my lords! My braid of hair is missing? (*She displays her braids. A surprise from the audience*) My diamond, of course, is missing. But here's how it happened— Maroulina, come here, poor child! (MAROULINA *approaches*)

DUKE. (*Aside to* KYR ANDRONIKOS) Are you aware of something, my Lord?

ANDRONIKOS. I think I am aware of something, Duke of Paronaxia.

ARETE. This innocent creature is the child of my lowliest gardener, and I have taken her under my protection. Yesterday, I noticed that she was enamored of my diamond, and I gave it to her to play with for a night. The unfortunate girl pinned it in her hair the way she had seen me wearing it, and she went to sleep. Ah! What a sleep that was! A nightmare! What uproar! (*She caresses* MAROULINA)

ANDRONIKOS. (*Aside to the* DUKE) Are you aware of anything, Duke of Paronaxia?

DUKE. Am I aware of anything? From the moment this herd

of geese walked in here, I became aware of everything. The women are suffocating us, my great-powered Lord.

ANDRONIKOS.   You are probably right, Duke of Paronaxia.

DUKE.   We were bound to slip on a mellon rind at some point, my Lord. We've become too involved with love. We went too far, brother! Couldn't we have behaved ourselves a little?

ANDRONIKOS.   There's nothing left to do now but to fold our hands and enjoy the sight, forgetting that it is we who are paying for the damages. There's a humorous side to the situation, Duke of Paronaxia.

DUKE.   You're telling me! Let's cast aside all troubles and become engrossed in philosophy and in loftier thoughts! A little more and we would have advanced to Reason and Morality!

ARETE.   My noble Lords, this innocent creature, this harmless and tender creature, was seduced during the night by a man who appeared at my castle pretending to be a scholar of Greek letters, but whom we all recognized at once as an officer of the Palace from the way he walked and from the glances he gave us. Then, as soon as this godless man had accomplished his barbaric act, he cut from this unfortunate servant of mine—who knows for what inexplicable reason—a braid of her hair which had on it the diamond you were talking about earlier. (*She takes the braid of hair from the hands of* IGNATIOS *and matches it with* MAROULINA's *hair*)

ZAMBETA.   It's a great thing!

ATTENDANTS.   Ah!

CROWD.   Unheard of! Inconceivable! Unbelievable! The insurance companies are going bankrupt! An economic crisis!

ARETE.   We came to register a complaint to the respected Senate because, with our female minds, we consider that it isn't right for such occurrences to take place in our Empire, that is, that such men in disguise should enter our peaceful homes and seduce innocent girls who haven't even provoked them. Is this how our land henceforth shall repay prudence, modesty, and dignity of families?

THE CROWD.   Astonishing! Everything is dissolving! Let laws be passed! Let new men govern us!

ARETE.   Maroulina, unfortunate child, do you see that villain who took advantage of you? (MAROULINA *giggles*) This is no time for joking. Do you recognize him anywhere around here?

MAROULINA.   Mistress, don't you see him? Is he a man not to be recognized?

ARETE. Oh! Where should I look for him? Do you think I can recall what he looked like?

MAROULINA. Isn't it the one over there in red?

THE CROWD. What degradation! What decadence! What catastrophe! With a gardener! With a servant girl! Kyr Andronikos! He who had the most famous women of our century for his mistresses! Eudocia Comnena! Philippa, Princess of Antioch! Theodora, Queen of Jerusalem! And so many others! The most beautiful! The most sparkling! The highest! And now he has descended to a gardener! He is finished! Done and gone!

IGNATIOS. Silence from the audience! Trust the Senate and everything will work out all right! Don't become rattled! We'll take care of everything! We'll attend to everything!

THE CROWD. A gardener! A gardener! A gardener!

LEONTIOS. Do you see a gardener anywhere?

STAVRAKIOS. There she is. She slept with Kyr Andronikos. By mistake.

LEONTIOS. By mistake? How by mistake?

STAVRAKIOS. He thought she was the other one. He's lost the wager.

LEONTIOS. What wager?

STAVRAKIOS Have you forgotten again? (*He explains to* LEON-TIOS, *who bursts out laughing*)

LEONTIOS. A gardener! A gardener! (*He becomes sober and stands up*) This is a matter of State!

ANDRONIKOS. Noble Senators, it is indeed obvious that a matter of State exists in the Polis.

VOICES OFFSTAGE. A panic in the stock market! All stocks are tumbling! The insurance companies are going bankrupt! The banks are failing! Crisis! Crisis! Crisis! Crisis!

ANDRONIKOS. The crown is hereby transferred to the princes of the Comneni family who are not yet of age. It is now your business to elect a Regent. Until that moment, however, I still exercise my royal authority fully. Let the crowd then withhold its nervousness in order to hear my final commands!

THE CROWD. Let us hear! Let us hear! Let us see what he is planning! Let us see how a man like Kyr Andronikos falls from his throne!

ANDRONIKOS. Last night, this young lady here, Maroulina as she is called, assumed nobility through a royal act. Now, our good Duke of Paronaxia will marry her and thus her advancement will also be sanctioned through the blessings of the Church. Isn't that right, Duke?

DUKE. What did you say?

ANDRONIKOS. Aren't you going to marry Maroulina today?

DUKE. Me?

ANDRONIKOS. (*Aside*) Infamous one! Didn't we agree that I should give you three Cyclades Islands?

DUKE. We agreed on four, my long-lived Lord. In fact, with the island of Delos, that makes five. But we made these arrangements when we thought you were spending last night with the noble Arete, the sister of Mavrianos. Not with the gardener!

ANDRONIKOS. Look me in the eyes, Duke of Paronaxia! I believe I am still King of the Romans or the Greeks, whichever you want to say!

DUKE. Of both the Romans and the Greeks and of the entire East, divine Lord. Did I say anything to the contrary?

ANDRONIKOS. And I think I can still make heads roll until the Regent has been elected!

DUKE. Cut them off, my Lord! With health and joy! How have I offended you?

ANDRONIKOS. And can't I ennoble a commoner, make her a noblewoman of the Kingdom!

DUKE. Of course! A thousand times so! But you must also understand me, famous Lord! If Maroulina had in fact been Mavrianos' sister, just think of my benefit in becoming a member of such a family! I would have shared in her property! Now, however, who am I marrying, if you please? And what are four Cyclades Islands today? Were you at least to include Euboia as well!

ANDRONIKOS. You are blackmailing me, treacherous man!

DUKE. We must also live, my Lord. Don't desire everything for yourselves, you most favored men of the Universe.

ANDRONIKOS. I give you half of Euboia so we can have done!

DUKE. Certainly, half of Euboia with the town of Calchis, with the bridge and all rights to the tolls.

ANDRONIKOS. (*Unites the hands of the* DUKE *and* MAROULINA) Noble Senators, to show my pleasure to those of my good subjects who marry with my consent, I have decided—and this is my final royal decree—I have decided, I repeat, to give the bride a dowry. So, I give her four Cyclades Islands—

DUKE. Five, if you please. Five Cyclades Islands—

ANDRONIKOS. Five Cyclades Islands. In other words, Andros,

Syros, Tinos, Mykonos, and Delos, and half of Euboia with the town of Calchis—I leave you now in good health! (*He exits*)

THE CROWD. The Duke was clever! An industrious man! An immense talent for diplomacy! The Empire needs such leaders!

DUKE. Naturally, along with Calchis goes the bridge and the right to tolls. His Highness had no need to say this. We aren't talking with stupid people. Whoever has brains, comprehends this well enough.

A NOBLEMAN. Do you know why Kyr Andronikos did this? For the benefit of a posthumous fame. So that no one will say he slept with a gardener. Instead, they will say he slept with the Duchess of Paronaxia. Do you understand? He loses his throne, but he saves his honor. That's how these Commeni are! Thoroughbred rascals! (*Shouts*)

SECOND NOBLEMAN. (*To* KONSTANTIS) My Lord Konstantis, we are floundering. We have exceeded our wagers in overbidding amounts which we won't be able to pay. The insurance companies are going bankrupt. The banks are in danger. The entire economy of the land is in danger.

KONSTANTIS. The situation is serious. Very serious. Very, very serious!

NOBLEMEN. What's to be done? How do you see the situation?

KONSTANTIS. First of all, the political situation must be resolved. A Regent must be elected. An honorable man, competent, strong, with clear ideas, and naturally, with an excellent knowledge of economics.

NOBLEMEN. And how do you think he would have confronted the economic crisis?

KONSTANTIS. If I were in his place, I would declare a judicial moratorium.

NOBLEMEN. (*To those beside them*) A judicial moratorium! Did you hear? If Lord Konstantis is elected Regent, he will declare a judicial moratorium at once! It's the only solution! The only salvation!

VOICES OF NOBLEMEN. A judicial moratorium! This is the solution! The only solution! The program of Konstantis! Let Konstantis be elected Regent to declare a judicial moratorium! For the salvation of the land! For the honor of the Empire! For the good of the people! It's a historical necessity! We want Konstantis! We want Konstantis!

VOICES OFFSTAGE. A judicial moratorium! A judicial moratorium! Salvation for the land! Honor for the Empire! A demand from the people! A historical necessity! Konstantis as Regent! (*Rythmically as at a demonstration*) Kon-stan-tis! Kon-stan-tis! Kon-stan-tis!— (*The noise from the people continues to the end of the Act*)

KONSTANTIS.   (*To* MAVRIANOS) My friend, we prevail! Listen! Our hour has arrived! The voice of the people elevates us to power. We will put our program into practice! We will bring salvation! We will bring liberation! We will restore! We will bring reforms! We will rebuild!

MAVRIANOS.   (*To* ARETE) My praiseworthy sister! My incomparable sister! How proud I am of you! Our party is grateful to you! History is proud of you! Your indestructible virtue justifies our struggles, solidifies our ideas, extols Reason, saves Morality! Let me kiss you!

ARETE.   (*Pushing him away*) I'm bored with you! Don't vex me! I don't want to see you or hear mention of any of you! You and your ideas and your party and your History, all bore me! I never want to sense you near me! (*She exits angrily. The women run after her*)

ACT IV
Scene I

The following day in the garden of ARETE. *She is pacing up and down very sadly. Her three attendants accompany her at a short distance. From time to time* ARETE *sighs and the three attendants echo her sigh.*

ARETE.   Ah!
ATTENDANTS.   Ah!
FIRST ATTENDANT.   She never closed her eyes all night long. And such tears—as large as plums!
SECOND ATTENDANT.   Isn't the situation one for tears? Isn't it one to sigh over?
THIRD ATTENDANT.   My dear, why should we women do such things? Why?
ARETE.   Ah!
ATTENDANTS.   Ah!

FIRST ATTENDANT. And now, as though she hasn't enough troubles, they want to marry her off. Lord Mavrianos said yesterday before the entire court that he had decided to give her in marriage to Lord Konstantis. The wedding has been set for tomorrow morning. They claimed that this was the proper thing to do. Virtuous women should marry serious-minded men. Such couples, with their reputations, will give the example and so reform society.

SECOND ATTENDANT. My dear, does it matter if society is not reformed?

THIRD ATTENDANT. My dear, why should we women be like this? Never to undertand what it is we want? One day to want one thing and the next day something else! Why, my dear?

ARETE. Ah!

ATTENDANTS. Ah!

FIRST ATTENDANT. What can I say, girls? That Konstantis is a good and saintly man? In fact, they claim that he will become Regent. But to have him for a husband all day and all night long— he appears to be a bit dry. While the other one—let me not mention his name—

SECOND ATTENDANT. Don't! Don't! Don't remind me of him!

FIRST ATTENDANT. And, in fact, if you heard what Maroulina had to say about him! She's no longer tongue-tied. Where formerly she couldn't even say good morning, now she delivers a whole lecture.

SECOND ATTENDANT. Don't mention her! It looks as though the world was created for the likes of her!

THIRD ATTENDANT. My dear, why can't we women conceal our emotions? If we only knew what was happening to us! Why, my dear? Why?

ARETE. Ah!

ATTENDANTS. Ah!

(ZAMBETA *enters out of breath.*)

ZAMBETA. My Lady! My Lady!

ARETE. Zambeta, what news do you bring from the Polis?

ZAMBETA. Ah! Let me catch my breath!

(ARETE *motions to her attendants to leave. They exit. She sits beside* ZAMBETA *on the bench.*)

ARETE. Will you speak?

ZAMBETA. Ah! My Lady! Where should I begin, and where

should I end? First of all, Kyr Konstantis was elected Regent. This might be of interest to you, since your brother has ordered you to marry him. You will be our Regentress, commanding over everything.

ARETE.   Leave me alone, with my wedding and my Regency! Is that what we're going to talk about now? Next, what have you to say?

ZAMBETA.   The entire Polis is talking about you, about your virtue, your purity, your modesty. You have become a symbol, my Lady. The Wisdom Party swears in your name. They will hang your picture in all the girls' schools.

ARETE.   Continue, Zambeta. Please stop annoying me!

ZAMBETA.   Kyr Konstantis has proclaimed an edict. I've memorized it! "Nations of the Empire, I bring you a world-historic message. The regime of Folly has capitulated following the general outcry of serious men and virtuous women. From the Adriatic and the Danube to the Caucusus and the Euphrates, Wisdom triumphs and redeems and glorifies Byzantium. Rejoice in the victory of Reason over Matter, of disciplined Morality over the barbaric anarchy of the senses. In the future, there will be laws for everything—"

ARETE.   Ah! Stop talking about the edict and all the laws and tell me what happened to that unspeakable, that most wretched man—

ZAMBETA.   Ah! Mistress, how can I tell you when I can't find words! My dear, they have put him in irons!

ARETE.   Kyr Andronikos in irons!

ZAMBETA.   In irons, in the tower of the Golden Gate. Three battalions guard him so he won't escape. And now they are considering what to do with him. Some say they should cut off his nose, as is the custom when a king falls. But the implacable supporters of the Wisdom Party contend that, even without a nose, he can continue quite well to carry on the business he conducted to the present and plunged the entire Empire into debauchery. For this reason, they say it would be more politic to cut off something else. You understand, my dear. And yet, they are not certain, because the most horrified men claim that, from such a man, you can expect anything, and it isn't improbable that one day his power will sprout again. And then, God save us from his vengeance!

ARETE.   My dear, they are out of their minds! Out of their minds!

(The BIRD appears, flaps its wings, and sings.)

ZAMBETA. My Lady, there it is again! The Bird of Songs!

ARETE. (*To the* BIRD) A! Of course! You were all that was lacking at this moment!

BIRD. Clear is the water, bride-to-be, brilliant is the moon,
   Charming the youth escorting you, and one so very enviable.
   To the home of your new relatives, to the district you'll be going,
   Stand stately as the cypress tree, become rooted as the holmoak,
   Blossom like an apple tree, a luscious apple tree, and bear as many fruit.
   With nine sons may you be blessed and with one apple-daughter.

ZAMBETA. Dear Lady, he came to sing you a nuptial song!

ARETE. A nuptial song! (*To the* BIRD) The way you've managed everything! With your moonlights and your elm trees and your nine sons and all the rest of it!

BIRD. The brilliant star that's journeying all the way to the Pleiades,
   The one that shines to point my way straight into your courtyard.
   Twice I knock upon your door and five times on your window.
   Arise, Arete, and attire yourself in dresses all of gold.
   Forty carriages now transport the gifts for your wedding.

ZAMBETA. And that uncharacteristic habit he has of talking about the stars and the Pleiades while it is still high noon!

ARETE. It is poetic license! But he isn't to blame! We're to blame for listening to him. (*To the* BIRD) Curse you! You've ruined everything! Aren't you a bit ashamed of your ancestry? They say you descend from Homer! (*The* BIRD *flaps his wings and sings*) It's better that you go to find Kyr Andronikos! You who came in such haste to bring news that he was coming to instruct me out of his books! Now, let's see how he's instructing himself where he is! (*The* BIRD *continues to sing*) I'm tired of you! Do you hear me? I'm tired of you!

(*The* BIRD *flies away. A* SERVANT *enters.*)

SERVANT. The Illustrious Duchess of Paronaxia!

ARETE. Let her enter. (MAROULINA *enters, richly dressed*)
Come, Maroulina. Don't be embarrassed! Sit down. It isn't proper
for a Duchess to remain standing. (MAROULINA *sits down and begins
to giggle*) This is no time to laugh, Maroulina. It's time to cry!
(MAROULINA *bursts into tears*) Have you heard the news about Kyr
Andronikos?

MAROULINA. I've heard.

ARETE. They have him in irons. And they want to cut off his
nose and—

MAROULINA. Yes, my dear. (*She is in tears*) Mistress, can't you
think of something to do?

ARETE. What should I do? It seems to me I've done enough
already, and thus we've prospered!

MAROULINA. My dear, let's release him from prison!

ARETE. Release him from prison and let him roam the world,
free to seduce and abandon? Have you thought of this, Maroulina?

MAROULINA. I've thought about it, my dear. I think about it
all the time.

ARETE. Zambeta, do you hear what this industrious Duchess
of Paronaxia is saying? On the first day, in fact, of her wedding, to
what her thoughts turn, what she plots, what she prays for? A way
for Kyr Andronikos to escape his prison!

ZAMBETA. My dear Mistress, aren't you, too, on the eve of your
own wedding, praying for the same thing?

ARETE. Zambeta, I didn't expect this of you! Such insolence!
Such injustice! As though my own troubles weren't enough, I must
have you here saying such things to me! Let's see what else you'll
find to say! (*Greatly agitated*) Say on, Zambeta! Go on! What can
we do?

MAROULINA. Mistress, just as you disguised me the other
night and all those other things happened, can't you disguise me
again so we can do something now?

ARETE. Disguise her! She wants me to disguise her! Yes, my
dear, I'll disguise you! Come with me! Have the horses saddled!

(*They exit quickly.*)

Scene II

In prison. KYR ANDRONIKOS *sits in chains. The* BIRD OF SONGS
stands between the bars of the window.

ANDRONIKOS. (*To the* BIRD) Look what has happened to me! See the situation? To put me in irons! Because by mistake I went with the gardener and not with the noble Lady, whom, furthermore, I did prefer! A very complicated story. Let's see what words you'll find to sing about this! (*The* BIRD *sings*) Wretched verse-maker, I have a feeling you're waiting ready to unleash a fountain of fifteen-syllable verses. What do you care? Just so it's a song, and it doesn't matter what it's all about! You flew here on the double as soon as you smelled a sensational topic; a consequential, royal topic. (*The* BIRD *sings, flapping its wings*) If I were to tell you the entire truth, I don't know but that my kingship wasn't only one role among the thousands of other roles. I altered character so often, I no longer know when I was the real me. (*The* BIRD *attempts to sing something*) I suspect what you are about to say. That the role doesn't matter, and that essentially I was the same man. For instance, what? (*The* BIRD *sings*) A young boy? You say that I was an overgrown boy? How amusing! (KYR ANDRONIKOS *laughs*) So be it. A young boy, if you wish! I love it. I enjoy it. I am happy. In my own way, of course. They can't forgive me that. Happiness perturbs them as a scandal, as a provocation, as an insult to society. But I have no complaints. I accept everything. Life, men, love, hate. Isn't that happiness? (*The* BIRD *flaps his wings*) You have reservations. No, my pet, stop pretending. Dialectics is not your business. Your business is singing, and nothing more. Sing on, then. Come, the music—You hesitate—Don't you know how to begin, how to end—? You're waiting for a solution. Something will happen. Something always happens. You'll see!

(*The door opens.* ARETE *appears with* ZAMBETA, MAROULINA *disguised as a monk, and an officer. The* BIRD *flies away.*)

ARETE. (*To the* OFFICER) I've already explained, Captain, that I have orders from the highest church officials to attempt to convert this unfortunate man who is possessed of the devil, so that the evil spirits may leave his body, and, should he die, so his soul will find peace. Again, were he to live for several more years, whole or in part, so he can dedicate himself to the spiritual and, with his example, help also in reforming society. That's why I brought the saintly monk with me. But along with liberating his mind, you must also release the prisoner because the Word of God loses its power when one hears it while he is bound. The soul must be free to receive the divine teachings.

OFFICER. Lady, your name is assurance enough! The entire
Polis knows you by now as the symbol of womanly wisdom. I will
release him, and we will be on guard outside, should you need us,
three battalions on foot and on horseback. As soon as you have
completed making him wise, call me so I can bind him again. (*He
exits after having released* KYR ANDRONIKOS *from his chains.* KYR
ANDRONIKOS *stretches and appears easily to have recovered his
good spirits*)

ARETE. Give me the monk's robe and the cap, Maroulina.
(MAROULINA *carries out her orders*) My Lord, we haven't much
time. You will put on the church robe and leave this place at once,
before anyone has time to think about what is going on. You will
mount the black horse, which is mine, climb over the walls of the
City and jump over the trench to proceed on your way with the
blessings of God.

ANDRONIKOS. I will wear the robe. I will mount the horse. I
will jump over the trench. Wonderful! A clever plan! Let it come
to pass then. (*He puts on the monk's robe, looks out the window*)
The black horse. Of course. It's a magnificent animal, my Lady.

ARETE. My proceeding must appear strange to you, my Lord.

ANDRONIKOS. Your proceeding? Your proceeding? Ah! Of
course! That you are helping me to escape from this place. Isn't
that what you mean?

ARETE. You must be thinking about our other two encounters,
those of yesterday and the day before.

ANDRONIKOS. Two other encounters? Ah! Certainly! (*Truly
absentminded*) In your castle. And in the Senate. Just imagine! I
had almost forgotten them.

ARETE. Who knows what impression you've formed of me!
Of my mind!

ANDRONIKOS. Of you? Of your mind? A very good impression,
my Lady. You are intelligent. You have ideas. A strange proceeding?
But to tell you the truth, everything I see always appears strange
to me. Everything astonishes me. But I like everything. I accept
everything. And you, most assuredly, I accept you.

ARETE. You accept me! Listen to what he is saying. He
accepts me!

ANDRONIKOS. What a pity that I have no time. We could
have become better acquainted. I regret this from the bottom of
my heart, believe me. You have charm, you have vivacity. I like
you. But I like all of you. I feel as though I have known you for a
long time. I have already grown accustomed to you. However, let's

not become melancholy. This is a small world. It's not impossible that we shall meet again. (*He kisses her*)

ARETE. My Lord! My Lord! Andronikos! (*But as she pronounces his name,* ANDRONIKOS *has already departed. All three women rush to the window*) There he is! There he is!

ZAMBETA. He's running toward the horses!

MAROULINA. The soldiers are in turmoil!

ARETE. They don't understand what kind of priest can be running like a madman!

ZAMBETA. He's throwing off the monk's robe!

MAROULINA. He's mounting the black horse!

ARETE. Ah! Now they recognize him! (*A trumpet is heard*) They are sounding an alarm! They are running from all sides!

ZAMBETA. He's getting ready to jump!

MAROULINA. He's jumping!

ARETE. He jumped! With one spring, he flew over the walls and the trench. He's disappearing toward the valley of Thrace! There goes Kyr Andronikos!

ZAMBETA. He's off!

MAROULINA. He flew like a bird!

ZAMBETA. He, too, became a bird.

ARETE. He became a song!

(*Enter* KONSTANTIS, MAVRIANOS, *the* DUKE OF PARONAXIA, *and attendants.*)

MAVRIANOS. You here, Sister, on the eve of your wedding to the Regent? And after the highest example of morality and wisdom that you gave to the Universe yesterday? How do you explain your conduct, please?

DUKE. Duchess of Paronaxia, what are you doing in this cell? I want to know how your behavior is consistent with the laws of matrimonial honor.

MAVRIANOS. Men of the Polis and of all the Empire, guard your women! Kyr Andronikos is free! Kyr Andronikos is roaming!

VOICES. Shut your doors and windows! Guard your families! Kyr Andronikos is roaming!

MAVRIANOS. Be careful who you take into your houses! He is full of guile and in disguise! He is a shrewd devil! Kyr Andronikos is roaming!

VOICES. Be careful of tricks and cunning! He is roaming! He is roaming!

DUKE. Duchess of Paronaxia, remain beside me! (*He grabs*

MAROULINA *by the hand*) Here! Where I can see you! Where I can touch you! Know that for a man in my position nothing is more important than conjugal honor!

MAROULINA. Kyr Andronikos is roaming!

ZAMBETA. Ah! Just to know that he is roaming makes me go limp. This is a very, very, great thing!

ARETE. He is roaming! He flies! Like a bird! Free of his chains and his royal office and the Polis and Empire. He is free to fly from branch to branch. The entire world belongs to him now. In Syria, in Jerusalem, in the lands of the East, in Venice, in France, in Castile—the women of the entire Universe must have shivered in their sleep and wakefulness. Kyr Andronikos is roaming!

KONSTANTIS. It certainly is a strange event! Wisdom set a trap for Folly, caught her on the branch, and shut her in a cage. But, before Wisdom could rejoice in her victory, she repented, opened the cage door, and allowed Folly to fly away.

MAROULINA. Did you see how he flew away?

ZAMBETA. My dear, what is this feeling I have? Ah!

KONSTANTIS. Seriously, I don't understand why you did such a thing, Arete!

ARETE. It just came over me. Can I explain it!

KONSTANTIS. If you meant to go away with him, I could have understood; I could have seen some logical explanation to your actions. But as it is, my Reason is perplexed.

ARETE. My fate, it seems, was that I should remain with the wise. But I am thinking of something now. If there were no Folly in the world, the essence of folly, the taste of folly; if folly were no scattered everywhere around us in the air we breathe, how could we have endured our wisdom, we serious-minded women?

ZAMBETA and MAROULINA. Ah!

KONSTANTIS. My friends, Wisdom demands that we put an end to this episode. In an instance such as this one, the best polic is for everyone to close his eyes. Without doubt, we have been enriched today by an experience which shall be useful to us in th future. But I recommend that we no longer insist on pursuing thi topic and that we return to our usual tasks.

(*They exit. The Stage remains empty. The* BIRD OF SONG *appears again.*)

BIRD. King Andronikos has broken loose from the chains tha
        had him bound,

High over the city walls he's jumped and vanished in the
valley.

He furrows hills and mountains; the world belongs to
him,

And gardens full in blossom, and all the rosy beaches,

And all the golden cities, both in the East and West.

Rejoice, young maidens, rejoice old dames, rejoice you
married women,

Ladies of Byzantium, mistresses of all Europe,

And you, as well, my prudent maids, and you light-
headed dames

Frothing white mares and frenzied female cats!

The Emperor Andronikos is traveling again in freedom,

He sports and laughs and trifles with you all,

He loves you all collectively and separately each one.

Pandelis Prevelakis

(1909–   )

Pandelis Prevelakis was born in Rethimnon, Crete, in 1909. He studied at the University of Athens, at the College of Literature at the University of Paris, and at the Institute of Arts and Archeology at the University of Paris. Since 1935 he has been professor of art history at the School of Fine Arts in Athens. He has written poetry, novels, plays, and aesthetic and literary criticism. Many of his poems and novels have been translated into French, German, and English. His play *In the Hands of the Living God* (1955) was performed at the National Greek Theater in 1957, and *The Last Tournament* in 1966.

Prevelakis first appeared in literature with the long poem "Soldiers" (1938); in 1930 he published the historical monograph *Domenicos Theotokopoulos*. In all his work he expresses his own anxieties with a warm sensitivity and a courageous temperament. The language he speaks is the unpolished language of the Cretan peasants. Prevelakis called the novelette, *Death of de Medici* (1939), a "mythical story," as though by the very term he wished to define the creative process from the inception of the myth to its passage through the creative conscience and to the final emergence of form, unified in all aspects. His critical volume, *Nikos Kazantzakis and His Odyssey* (available in English translation of Philip Sherrard, 1958, 1961) is a debt paid to his old master.

His selected works include: *The Naked Poetry* (1941); *The Chronicle of a City* (1938); *Abandoned Crete* (1945); *The Cretan: The Tree* (1948); *The Cretan: First Liberation* (1949); *The Cretan: The City* (1950); *The Sacred Massacre* (1952); *Lazaros* (1954); and the critical volumes *The Italian Renaissance and Art* (1935), *Art in Modern Greece* (1938), and *El Greco in Rome* (1941).

The Last Tournament
(A Tragedy in Three Days)

CHARACTERS

LORENZO DE' MEDICI, *merchant-prince of Florence, aged 29*
GIULIANO DE' MEDICI, *brother to Lorenzo, aged 25*
LUCREZIA TORNABUONI, *mother to Lorenzo and Giuliano*
AGNOLO POLIZIANO, *poet and friend of the Medici, aged 24*
CARDINAL RAFFAELO RIARIO, *nephew to Pope Sixtus IV, aged about 30*
FRANCESCO SALVIATI, *Archbishop of Pisa*
JACOPO DE' PAZZI, *nephew to Jacopo*
BERNARDO BANDINI, *a Florentine democrat*
GIOVANNI BATTISTA DA MONTESECCO, *a hired assassin*
ANTONIO MAFFEI, *a priest in the Cardinal's retinue*
STEFANO DA BAGNONE, *a priest in the Cardinal's retinue*
MARIA, NANNINA, *and* BIANCA, *older sisters to Lorenzo and Giuliano*
LEOPETTO ROSSI, *husband to Maria*
BERNARDO RUCCELLAI, *husband to Nannina*
GUGLIELMO DE' PAZZI, *husband to Bianca*
BACCIO, *Captain of the Medici's bodyguard*
ANTONIA RIDOLFI, *mistress to Giuliano*
ANTONIO RIDOLFI, *a citizen of Florence*
SERVANTS *to the Medici and the Pazzi*
A PRIEST *and an* ALTAR BOY
FLORENTINE CITIZENS

The action of the play is set in Florence and Fiesole and extends over three days, Good Friday to Easter Sunday, April 24 to 26, 1478.

FIRST DAY

PART ONE

The curtain rises on a large hall in Renaissance style in the Palazzo Pazzi in Florence. Doors to the right and left; backstage, three arched windows. Night.

SCENE I

Two SERVANTS, *one elderly and distinguished, the other young and uncouth.*

FIRST SERVANT. (*Goes to close the windows, followed by the* SECOND SERVANT *carrying two lighted candelabra.* FIRST SERVANT *leans out of the center window and breathes in the air*) Ah! What a night! Makes one want to be young again—When I was twenty a night like this would have sent me over a garden wall into the arms of a girl among the roses—Too bad, too bad—All I'm good for now is to stand and stare as my masters enjoy themselves. Did you see Giuliano's Tournament?

SECOND SERVANT. (*Places the candelabra on two consoles at opposite sides of the room behind low wide vases of roses*) No, I wasn't in Florence at the time. But I've seen him out hunting. Mighty fine he looks on horseback with his falcons and his dogs around him. Just like Saint George, I say.

FIRST SERVANT. That Tournament was something! You should have seen young Giuliano riding by under our windows, all dressed up in gold and silver, and all his knights cantering after him. And afterward, on the field, charging against all the other lords and knocking them out of their saddle one by one! God bless him! A man could serve such a master with all his heart and soul. (*He places the chairs in a semicircle, their backs to the windows*)

SECOND SERVANT. (*Assisting him*) Was there plenty of free food and drink at the Tournament? That's what I'd like to know. What's the good of that carnival parade with all those painted hussies up there on the floats? Give *me* food and drink and a good fling on the same dance floor. Show me a bloody bullfight, murderers, and cutthroats strung up on gibbets and heretics sizzling at the stake. That's *my* idea of a good time.

(*The door to the* LEFT *opens softly.* CARDINAL RIARIO *peers in stealthily and listens to the conversation without revealing himself.*)

FIRST SERVANT. You miserable clod! D'you mean to tell me you saw all those lovely princesses sitting on their thrones of flowers, each one drawn by six fine horses—You saw that wonderful sight and didn't get a thrill? And when the two Medici, the Lord Lorenzo and the Lord Giuliano rode by shining like a pair of stars, you didn't bow your pate down to the ground and worship them?

SECOND SERVANT. Who d'you think is the best? Lorenzo or Giuliano?

FIRST SERVANT. Come, lad, which do you prefer—the Sun or the Moon?

SCENE II

The TWO SERVANTS *and* CARDINAL RIARIO.

CARDINAL. Good evening, friends. What time did Signor Jacopo say for us to meet?

FIRST SERVANT. Good evening to your Excellency. My master ordered me to light the candles at ten.

CARDINAL. Has the Archbishop of Pisa arrived yet?

FIRST SERVANT. Just a moment ago I heard his mule clattering across the courtyard.

CARDINAL. (*Moving back toward the door*) So you love the tyrants of Florence? (*Slight pause*) Yet they say that a faithful dog licks the hand that feeds it. Don't you like the house where you make your living? Don't you care for your old master and his ten sons and nephews?

FIRST SERVANT. We were only saying how handsome and splendid the young Medici Lord looked. That's all, Sir. Your Excellency knows best how Florence deals with tyranny.

CARDINAL. That's better. (*Makes a vague sign of blessing*) And that is why the Holy Father sends his blessing from Rome to his beloved children in Florence. (*Exits through door*)

SCENE III

ARCHBISHOP SALVIATI, JACOPO DE' PAZZI, FRANCESCO DE' PAZZI, GUGLIELMO DE' PAZZI, BERNARDO BANDINI, GIOVANNI BATTISTA DA MONTESECCO.

(*They enter through the right door and take their seats in a semicircle, the* ARCHBISHOP *and old* JACOPO *in the center, leaving an empty seat between them for* CARDINAL RIARIO. JACOPO *signals to the servants to leave. The* LEFT *door opens suddenly and* CARDINAL RIARIO *enters.*)

CARDINAL. In the name of God and with the blessings of the Holy Father! From the Rock of Peter Sixtus IV has his eyes fixed upon us. "I have a good thought for my beloved son Jacopo de' Pazzi," he told me the other day in Rome, as I was taking my leave of him to come and meet you. "I want him to rule Florence under the law of God—(*turning to* ARCHBISHOP SALVIATI) and for that pillar of the Church, the Archbishop of Pizza, I have a mightier See under the dome elevated by Brunelleschi." (*Changing tone*) But, we are brought together in this place today by our fear of God, our sense of honor and our love of Freedom. And hospitality is offered to us by the House which is the very soul of Florence. When the little people hear the name of Pazzi, they put their hand over their heart and bow in reverence. When the Medici hears the name of Pazzi, his gall flows in rage. Ages ago, when the first hut was built on the banks of the Arno, Pazzi and Honor walked hand in hand. When the rest of Italy still lived in caves, Pazzi ate out of plates of gold—

JACOPO. Hearing my name so exalted makes me impatient to learn what duty has been assigned to me by the Holy Father, uncle of your Excellency.

CARDINAL. The grandeur of the duty which falls to your House (*he turns his eyes towards the other two Pazzi*) can be measured only by the extent of Florence's misfortunes. Look around you and behold! Faith has been trodden down by man's insolence. Honor has been debauched by money. Virtue—where can it be found? Courage, compassion, humility—where have they flown? Gone is the fear of God, gone all reverence for things holy. A naked blade is esteemed more effective than the wrath of the Lord or the majesty of the Law. Fallen idols have risen from the earth which covered them. The Medici no longer lights a candle before the Crucifix, but only before a manuscript of the *Iliad*. Heresy stalks abroad shamelessly. The reverent processions of the Church have yielded their place to carnival ribaldry. All the things which our forebears cherished most, all have been besmirched. The Temple is rocked to its foundations, thrones totter, standards are overthrown. Man wants to marry, to have children, and to die without the ministrations of the Church. He has trampled society underfoot, he has set the family at nothing, he scoffs at divine law. The spirit of Lucifer searches, enquires, mocks; it glories in its independence. The Commandments are forgotten, the laws torn up! The ideals which until yesterday governed the lives of men are now held for vain shadows and contemptible bugbears—

ARCHBISHOP. Your God-inspired words paint a picture of the

sickness of the age. We hang upon your lips to hear the remedy which the Holy Father ordains.

CARDINAL. When the cause of all the ill is removed the remedy will follow.

JACOPO. Is there but one single cause?

CARDINAL. The cause is one imputable to one man's guilt.

JACOPO. One man's guilt? What man?

CARDINAL. One man with two heads. (*Pause*) I want to ask you something, Signor Jacopo, since you are the wisest among us and of the old blood of this glorious state. Who rules Florence today?

JACOPO. What a question! Why, Lorenzo de' Medici, of course, with his brother Giuliano ever at his side.

CARDINAL. And who ruled before Lorenzo and Giuliano?

JACOPO. Piero de' Medici.

CARDINAL. And before Piero de' Medici?

JACOPO. Cosimo de' Medici.

CARDINAL. One more question. Does the disease go back further than this dynasty?

JACOPO. I would say that the evil started and grew under the Medici.

BANDINI. Speak up, man! Admit it. Democracy has been destroyed by the cowardice of the citizens—For all that, we brag that Florence once produced men with the love of freedom and an indomitable spirit in their hearts!

CARDINAL. I fear that outside the Kingdom of God, man is constrained to exchange one tyrant for another. But here, in the person of Jacopo, a stout defender of the Faith, the Holy Father has found a vessel of choice, and his hand goes out to him in blessing—

JACOPO. Your Excellency fills me with trepidation. The Medici are the lawful rulers of Florence.

BANDINI. I refuse to recognize a tyrant as the lawful ruler of the state. He is its worst enemy. Arms, conspiracy, violence—all means are legitimate against him. There is no more sacred sacrifice than the slaughter of a tyrant!

FRANCESCO DE' PAZZI. Where are Florence's Harmodius and Aristogeiton? Where the modern Brutus? Surely, the nobility of the undertaking will fire the blood of every stout man. Let me say this to you, Uncle, whom I honor like a father: lay aside your scruples. The spirit of the Pazzi calls for decisive action. Heed it now!

JACOPO. The crime—It's the crime that frightens me!

BANDINI. Honor is the highest judge of a citizen's acts. He who lives for honor disregards danger, threats and pain!

JACOPO. I fear God.

CARDINAL. (*With official unction*) O Vessel of Choice! I bring absolution from the Holy Father.

JACOPO. (*Shuddering*) O-oh!

BANDINI. (*Jumping to his feet*) We have taken our decision like responsible citizens. (*He looks* FRANCESCO DE' PAZZI *in the eyes and gives him his hand*) The Pope's absolution shall be the first laurel to crown our great and free undertaking!

MONTESECCO. What am I doing here?

CARDINAL. Your tried experience and your willing advice as a free citizen make your presence valuable in this hour. (*To* GUGLI-ELMO) And you, in whom the blood of the Pazzi is watered by your allegiance with the Medici—

GUGLIELMO. If that is your Excellency's opinion of me, why do you put my irresolution to the test?

CARDINAL. We want you to share in the accomplishment and the glory of a great undertaking in which your House is about to engage.

GUGLIELMO. I promise to keep the secret. But I cannot share further in action. How could I ever look my wife in the eyes, if I were to lift a killer's hand against her brothers? The sacred bonds of marriage—

CARDINAL. Enough, little man! Your domestic bliss has drugged you. You have gone back into your mother's womb! You eat, drink, and sleep, and never have you considered your debt to God and your duty to the state. And, as for life's enigma—that's something for the frustrated to solve.

JACOPO. No truer word was spoken. Frustration—Lack—Lack of power, lack of money; that's the motive of our actions. As for this fatted calf, let your Excellency leave him to his mediocrity, and let us examine the difficulties in our bold undertaking. If my conscience no longer troubles me, my common sense still has some doubts.

CARDINAL. (*To* ARCHBISHOP SALVIATI) Let us hear from you, Archbishop. (*He crosses his arms*)

ARCHBISHOP. By my silence, I let you run the course I have myself already run. At the point on which we are all agreed, it only remains for me to unfold the plan of the deed which History will record under the title: "The Hound of God rends the Unicorn of the Renaissance—" The soldiers of the Pope, their hands upon their sword-hilts, are waiting in Rome to hear the trumpet call of their valliant leader Girolamo Riario, his Excellency's brother, in order to fall upon the new Babylon in their terrible onslaught. Two mercenary armies are encamped less than a day's march from here. The Duke of Milan, that old confederate and accomplice of the Medici, has been destroyed in his den by brave tryannicides. Within the gates of Florence, hatred for the tyrants has brough revolt to a ferment. In the wake of the champions of Freedom will follow the usual retinue of Revolution: Utopians, adventurers, the starving, assassins, honest citizens, and the rabble that always rejoices in turbulence—(*Pause*) Tomorrow morning, Holy Saturday, our most glorious Cardinal Riario with his retainers will enter the Villa of the Medici in Fiesole as the guest at a banquet to be given by the two tyrants. Among the retainers our experienced, intrepid, and trusted associates, Giovanni Battista da Montesecco will, of course, be present. (*He turns toward Montesecco, who puts his hand upon his sword and growls aggressively*) The Cardinal's retinue—his deacons, his secretaries, and his cup-bearers, will be armed. When his Excellency lifts his cup to drink to the health of the Medici, our faithful collaborators will push forward and perform the sacrifice so pleasing in the eyes of God—

JACOPO. Your Eminence! I beg—I beg your mercy for the innocent victim. There is but one tyrant, Lorenzo. Giuliano lives in luxury and dreams. His sacrifice is not necessary to our purpose.

CARDINAL. Giuliano a dreamer! Call him, rather, the icy, calculating Spirit which causes Dogma to pale. In all Italy there is no man more godless than Giuliano.

BANDINI. That creature hates both God and man; he hates good works and ideas and laws from the very core of his precious incorruptible intellect.

JACOPO. But take pity on his youthful beauty.

CARDINAL. Yes, if 'twere possible to take his life and leave the flawless image standing!

FRANCESCO DE' PAZZI. The double-headed monster must be severed at the root of the neck. Else the people will hear: "Lorenzo is dead," and will shout: "Long live Giuliano!"

JACOPO. His death may further our mission, but I am thinking of how history will judge us.

BANDINI. The greatness of our undertaking will force history's commendation.

ARCHBISHOP. History has a soft voice for victors. Let us examine the issue of our enterprise. Facts speak louder than the figments of the mind. Our success will win praise. Only failure is blamed.

CARDINAL. Proceed with the plan.

ARCHBISHOP. The cry of Freedom winds its way from the place of sacrifice to the Villa Laveggi where the Pazzi clan are assembled. The great bell on the Tower of the Signoria tolls out the joyous tidings. Thenceforth, only the voice of the people is heard. Houses, workshops, streets, and squares all resound with shouts of "Liberty!"

BANDINI. That's where I come in. By my hand Democracy will chastise the hirelings of the tyrants after Destiny has awarded *their* death to more favored avengers.

ARCHBISHOP. If help is needed, our army of mercenaries will reinforce the people's wrath. Lorenzo Giustini will advance from Imola and Niccolo da Tolentino from Todi. The soldiers of the Pope have already unfurled their banners.

JACOPO. I enter this horrible arena pure in heart. Love of Freedom is my only motive. My soul shudders at the sacrifice. Yet our great decision already instills new life into my old body. Forward, then! To our mighty task! In the name of God and with the blessing of the Holy Father.

CARDINAL. (*Unfolds his arms and lifts his right hand to bless them*) Let us take an oath. (*All rise*)

ARCHBISHOP. In the name of the Universal Creator! (*He offers the cross he wears and the confederates press the finger tips of their right hand upon it*) I swear to slay the tryants of Florence—

THE OTHERS. (*Repeat the words, excepting* GUGLIELMO, *who draws back*)

ARCHBISHOP. —to obey the commands of the Most Holy Father, Pope Sixtus IV—

THE OTHERS. (*Repeat after him, excepting* BANDINI, *who withdraws*)

ARCHBISHOP. —and to assist in establishing in Florence the Polity of God.

THE OTHERS. (*Repeat after him, excepting* BANDINI)

BANDINI. (*With emphasis*) I swear to slay the tyrants, to give freedom to the citizens, and to make Democracy triumph.

CARDINAL. (*Spreading out his hands to stop further talk*) Our purpose is a common purpose. We are bound by oath. The wrath of God and the excommunication of the Pope will fall upon the coward and the perjurer! Forward to our task!

ALL. Forward!

CARDINAL. (*Blesses them*) *Dominus vobiscum! Dominus vobiscum!*

(ARCHBISHOP SALVIATI, FRANCESCO DE' PAZZI, BERNARDO BANDINI, *and* GIOVANNI DA MONTESECCO *leave by the* RIGHT *door.* GUGLIELMO DE' PAZZI *looks around in bewilderment.*)

SCENE IV

CARDINAL RIARIO, JACOPO DE' PAZZI, *and* GUGLIELMO DE' PAZZI.

CARDINAL. (*To* GUGLIELMO) I wish to relieve your conscience of all misgivings regarding the task we have begun, and also to remove any suspicions of treachery on your part; so I shall detain you until tomorrow afternoon in the apartments which the hospitality of my good friend (*indicates* JACOPO) has assigned me. When you hear the people celebrating our success in the streets, you will be free to run out and join them to forget your cowardice. (*He pushes* GUGLIELMO *before him, and they leave by the* LEFT *door*)

SCENE V

JACOPO *alone.*

JACOPO. (*Looking toward the door through which the* CARDINAL *exited*) May the crime be on his head! He planned it without passion!

FIRST DAY

PART TWO

Nighttime. A large, bare, white-walled room in the Villa Medici at Fiesole. LEFT: *a door.* BACKSTAGE: *a wide low window through which a dark sky and the cypresses in the garden are visible. A black and white (or red and white) chequered floor. A Florentine chest, a writing table, and a chair are the only pieces of furniture. The room is lit by a seven-branched chandelier.*

SCENE VI

GIULIANO DE' MEDICI. *The priest,* ANTONIO MAFFEI.

GIULIANO *is seated at the table studying a book. Through the window, suddenly, comes the song of a nightingale.* GIULIANO *lifts his eyes from his book and listens. The scene is filled, as it were, by the song of the bird and the silent ecstasy of the man.*

The door opens quietly and ANTONIO MAFFEI *enters. At first he does not notice* GIULIANO *at the table and looks around him.*

ANTONIO. A cell! Truly a monk's cell!

(GIULIANO *rises. He is dressed in black. There is an expression of complete indifference on his face.*)

ANTONIO. My Lord—Will your Lordship pardon the intrusion of a priest led here by the love of Christ?

GIULIANO. 'Tis a strange hour to choose.

ANTONIO. I was pressed for time. (*Correcting himself*) Time is ever pressing.

GIULIANO. Your words hit the very thought in my mind, which your entry interrupted. If it is the love of Christ which has brought you here, what, pray, is the purpose of your visit?

ANTONIO. I have come to take your sins upon my head.

GIULIANO. It is seven years since I have been to confession. My conscience is not divorced from my actions. You are wasting your time.

ANTONIO. A dulled conscience is but one more sin. But I have not come as a confessor; only as one who follows the example of the Lamb.

GIULIANO. I judge you Roman by your speech. Do you belong to any Order?

ANTONIO. I am a priest of the Church of the Resurrection in Rome, and I belong to the retinue of Cardinal Riario, who will be your Excellency's guest tomorrow.

GIULIANO. So? I was expecting to find the Cardinal accompanied by retainers worthy of his fame, by valiant soldiers, philosophers, poets, and artists. Not by devotees of the Lamb.

ANTONIO. Who knows what higher Will ordained that I should be the most humble follower in a company which is indeed such as your Excellency imagined?

GIULIANO. I would have you tell me more about yourself, so that I may judge how best to listen to your message.

ANTONIO. From early childhood, I was reared in a monastery as a mendicant friar. I never ate, drank, nor slept my fill, and my soul became even, imperturbable, and numb from want. This is the strength with which I guide my flock to salvation and combat the wolves let loose by the idolatry of my age.

GIULIANO. Ha! Now I understand. You have come to beard the wolf in his den.

ANTONIO. I have come to take your sins upon my head for the love of Him Whom they hung on the Cross. It is true that I imagined you plunged in lust and luxury and encompassed by the trappings of vanity, and now that I have come into this cell I am at a loss.

GAULIANO. Where else could a spirit, freed from all self-delusion, make its abode?

ANTONIO. A small Crucifix upon that wall would give light and meaning to your exercises.

GIULIANO. Ready-made sentiments have no place here—One would imagine that you think I'm on the brink of death. Why this sudden urgency? When you came through the door, you were the picture of a confessor preceding the executioner.

ANTONIO. (*Perturbed*) Oh!

GIULIANO. There's no need for you to be offended. The hand that deals out death also proffers absolution. That's the theory of Divine Providence, isn't it?

ANTONIO. Shame on your scoffing! Only the insubordinate mind reads absurdity into the manifestations of God's infinite wisdom.

GIULIANO. Once again, Priest, your barb has hit the mark. 'Tis Mind insubordinate that dwells within this cell.

ANTONIO. Blasphemy upon blasphemy! How well I see that I am indeed the destined instrument of a higher will. Suffer me to take your sins upon me without delay, before the sword of Vengeance flashes.

GIULIANO. If this blasphemy of mine is to bring down the flashing sword of Vengeance, let me tell you, my friend, that for many a long year already have I immersed myself in the impartial world of pure intellect. As one would cast off useless raiment, so have I put aside Faith, doctrines, idols—the coward's blindfolds. And now, alone, I strive to pierce the darkness and uncover whatever lies behind the world's turmoil—far back, beyond the confines of history, in the deep unknown where the first Principle set the Machine in motion.

ANTONIO. O spirit of Lucifer! O accursed rebel! To think that so evil a thing dwells within this chaste cell.

GIULIANO. Dwells a man who beats against the walls of his own limitations but with them he is proud, free, and his own master.

ANTONIO. No! He is doomed!

GIULIANO. Maybe he *is* doomed, if you consider the discouragements which constantly thwart him in his striving. Even so, he would not barter his damnation for all the sanctioned odors of your paradise of submission and blessedness.

ANTONIO. (*In a frenzy*) I see it—I see the sword of Vengeance swinging above the head of the apostate—And I am shaken in my purpose—O Blessed Savior, give me the strength to accomplish the task for which Thy Hand has guided me—hither— (*To* GIULIANO) You are condemned to die—

GIULIANO. (*Gives him a sharp, suspicious glance, then resumes his equanimity*) I know that Destiny will suppress me. It will abolish the exception for which I stand and will assert its majesty. Therein lies the greatness of free man—or maybe, this greatness, too, is but a vain figment.

ANTONIO. I knew it—I knew all the time that you would refuse the Holy Mystery of Confession. But you *are* going to die, and another, living in repentance, will redeem your sins. God's will be done. (*He places his hand beneath his robe*)

GIULIANO. (*Calmly, with outstretched hand*) If you're about to draw your dagger, I warn you that I'm determined to stop you, for tonight. I am expecting a visit from one of the great minds of our time who enjoys our friendly discourse. And later, my brother will come here. I don't intend to miss their company, which always gives me exquisite pleasure.

ANTONIO. (*Drawing a scroll from under his robe*) Permit me to read this— (*He makes the sign of the cross*) In nomine Patris, et Filii— "I, Antonio Maffei, unworthy servant of Christ, priest of the Church of Santa Anastasia in Rome, declare that I do willingly offer to the soul of my brother Giuliano de' Medici all the good works I have accomplished either in the dispensation of charity or the forgiveness of my enemies, ever since I forsook death in order to espouse life. I offer him all my days and nights of fasting, all my tears, all my flagellations, and the holy fruit of the Masses which my lips have chanted. I bestow upon him also all the prayers and supplications which I have offered to my Lord and God.

"In return for these I accept his sins, his agony, and his pain.

"Done in the Villa of the Medici, adjacent to the city of Florence, in the year of our Lord the One Thousandth Four Hundred and Seventy-eight, in the month of April, on the night of the Twenty-fourth to the morning of the Twenty-fifth day." (*Pause*)

This document is to be placed upon your breast, beneath your folded hands, when you are laid in your coffin.

GIULIANO. Well, has the weight been lifted from your conscience? Do you feel that you've done your duty, as a good priest, toward one who is doomed?

ANTONIO. (*Kneels, trembling from head to foot, and seeks to kiss* GIULIANO'S *feet*) Go forward blameless henceforth. (*He rises*)

GIULIANO. If your logic is not a madman's raving, it is incumbent on me to die instantly before I incur new debts not included in your quittance. (*He takes the priest by the shoulders*) When am I to die?

ANTONIO. No one knows when death awaits him. He may await you at the turning of the road, or at the end of a long journeying. Let me go on my way.

GIULIANO. Antonio Maffei! For your visit and your strange mission, I ought to deliver you to the torturer until you confess the secret which oppresses you. That is what my office as ruler of the city dictates. On the other hand, for the one-sided covenant you offer me, I ought to proclaim you my benefactor. In either case, it is a question of perspective. However, from my own vantage point, Antonio, I despise the ravings of a monk as much as I abhor the high-mindedness of a ruler. So, go your ways, it has been a pleasant evening. I'll keep your paper. I find your Latin quite charming.

(*Exit* ANTONIO *slowly, bowed down as it were by a great burden.*)

SCENE VII

GUILIANO *and the poet* AGNOLO POLIZIANO.

POLIZIANO. (*Entering like a whirlwind*) O Wonderful Life! "A full life and noble meditation"—Let this be our theme for tonight—My sweet Lord, I've missed you these long eighteen months I've been away.

GIULIANO. Welcome! Welcome to the full-throated nightingale! (*They embrace*) And how, pray, do you suggest that we give substance to your theme?

POLIZIANO. Let us with one heart and twin accomplishment continue our poem, "The Tournament of Giuliano." Already we have written one thousand four hundred lines. And in them a radiant world has been created: Love, Beauty, Art, and Victory.

GIULIANO. And you call that "a full life and noble meditation"? Why, the cow does as much when she chews the cud. She recalls the moment when her maw was full and meditates upon her high predestination—There is but one certain end to a full life—glut. And as for high meditation, I can bear witness—from the center of pure reason to which a full life and its consequences have brought me—that it may be summed up in one postulate: To verify every proposition, whether from others proceeding or from within oneself.

POLIZIANO. (*Half in jest, half seriously*) Mercy, I beg! Mercy for Life and Poesie!

GIULIANO. True, they are sered by the burning rays of pure light. They only thrive in mist. But here, my friend (*indicating his cell*) you have entered the realm of absolute lucidity, where an ascete is waging a war on Vagueness and Intoxication.

POLIZIANO. But, then, is Man's experience to count for nothing? What of the systems, the institutions distilled by the ages? Must all be revised? Doesn't life's all-powerful urge mean anything?

GIULIANO. I stake all my honor on being open-minded. Without fear and without passion. I have thrown down every wall raised up by human cowardice—religions, morals, institutions, systems—in order that free horizons may extend around me. And from there begins my inhuman surveyal, the growth of the pure matter that I was in the hour of my birth. The world believes me to be a Florentine, a Christian, a lover of the arts, and a ruler. How deep the error! That which is but chance, uncontrolled coincidence, it takes for the essence of Giuliano. The prompter who until yesterday spoke through my lips they accepted as the real Giuliano de' Medici. The ready-made thoughts, the ready-made desires, which occasion and place dictated, they took for the offering of my spirit—But I, out of the authority and substance bequeathed to me by my ancestors, retain only these privileges: To be aware of the vital falsehoods forged by rulers, and to stand beyond the confines of Necessity. From that pedestal, as a requital to those who set it up for me, I seek Truth: the Truth of Truth. I seek the reason of my creation, the purpose of my life! (*In exaltation*) I press forward *toward* the

Impenetrable, I stretch my arms out *toward* the veil of Mystery. I knock on the gates of Death!

POLIZIANO. Giuliano, your words are godless. They fill me with terror. Do you not ever think of the day of Judgment?

GIULIANO. I am delivered. The ashes which have fallen upon the face of the world are the price of my expiation. Do you remember our songs, our revels, our banquets, and our hunting parties? Our loves and our pleasures? The endless illumination which surrounded our youth? All has passed through my fingers like dust and ashes. Susa, Athens, Carthage—dust and ashes. The more one gratifies the senses, the more surely shall one reap the harvest of dust and ashes. Kings and Princes, lords of the earth, should all end their lives as hermits in the desert.

POLIZIANO. And many have. But in a spirit of submission, not of revolt. Therefore, they died in peace.

GIULIANO. Fools! They died annihilated as individuals, engulfed by the divinity which their terror created. But, Agnolo Poliziano, have you ever thought of the glory—the terrible glory—of absolute freedom. The absolute loneliness? The absolute self-determination? Have you ever reflected upon the apotheosis of the Individual?

POLIZIANO. Many of your words find an echo within me and give me wings; and many terrify me.

GIULIANO. Poet! You are dazzled by the spectacle of the world. You will never know satiety. Your senses will ensnare your spirit to the end.

POLIZIANO. Don't take me for a clashing cymbal. In every phenomenon I see a sign.

GIULIANO. (*Laughing*) Signs in phenomena, forsooth! Messages from the Invisible! Voluptuous mysticism! You rave, innocent soul!

(*A pause. The nightingale's song is heard through the open window.*)

GIULIANO. (*Reflectively*) Once I used to listen to the call of Nature in the song of the nightingale—a call to an awakening from torpor, a call to love and creation.

POLIZIANO. (*With affection and admiration*) My sweet Lord! In your countenance Nature glorifies herself. I am not afraid of being called a flatterer, if I proclaim how much I adore you. Shake off, dear heart, your oppressive thoughts! Come back into the dance of life! (*He recites the following verses which are his and contain intimate memories for both*)

> Come flowering May, come leafy May,
> Come Spring that calls to lovers,
> Come lads and maids, your tribute pay
> With roses
> And with posies
> To Love and May.

Oh, Giuliano, 'tis but six days to May Day. All the young folk will go out into the hills, and the slopes will echo to their songs as they dance with festive garlands in their hair. Sweet Lord, be with us once again to lead the dance!

GIULIANO.   Tempter, desist! I ask for no pity, but pray have some consideration for the stress of my endeavor. Tempt me not, knowing my erstwhile love of life and all its pleasures—For even the holiest hermit in his rugged loneliness sometimes remembers life's enchanting delights.

SCENE VIII

The same. LORENZO DE' MEDICI.
An attendant wearing the livery of the Medici opens the door and announces with formality.

ATTENDANT.   My Lord of Medici! (*He bows before* LORENZO, *then retires*)

LORENZO.   (*Homely, but arresting of mien, with long hair drawn back over the nape of his neck, and an air of authority*) Good evening to you. (*He gives his hand to* POLIZIANO) I'm glad to find you here, Poliziano. We shall celebrate Easter together, then on Monday I must leave you. I have to go first to Milan to see if the new Duke loves us well. Thence to the King of Naples, with whom we shall exchange new pledges of friendship. Thus fortified by two alliances, I'll call upon the Pope in Rome and talk with him. For some time past, I've had the feeling that the old fox has his eye upon our vineyard. Scarecrows amid the vines will not suffice to keep him out. It will do him good to see the vine-grower himself, face to face. I expect to be absent four or five months. You, Giuliano, will have to forego your studies and step into my shoes. It's time you began to get a taste of the bitter fruit of power.

GIULIANO. Four generations of Medici have tasted it. Its juice carries the intoxication of old wine and has caused them to forget their worthlessness. And now, they have bequeathed to us—their blessing and their curse—the task of following in their footsteps. But deep in me here (*he points to his breast*) a glut has settled which makes me loathe the actions, the habits, and the mission of my kind. So do not speak to me of power. The fumes from its wine do not rise to my head. Passion finds no outlet in deeds.

LORENZO. You are sick from skepticism and doubt—twin monsters of idleness. Your mind spins in a vacuum, like a top. Take hold of yourself, man, and leap like a vintager into the wine press! There you'll see whether the fumes from the foaming must take hold of you or not!

GIULIANO. I despise the intoxication of empty agitation. I thirst for certainties and not for self-forgetfulness. Let others act, conquer, succeed—defying the Skeleton with the uplifted scythe that grins at them at every turn of the road. To them belongs power, wealth, and glory. But let them leave me alone to devote myself entirely to my cold passion.

LORENZO. If only things could be as you say! It would be well if you could fix your gaze upon the absolute and ignore all earthly agitation! But, alas, it is not possible. The world is made for temporary life—with all its impurities and worries. But set aside your fruitless agony. Your blood calls for action, and I will provide the certainties for your mind.

GIULIANO. Alas, we have killed the certainties. You, I, Poliziano, the philosophers, the poets, and the Greeks who have come to us from Byzantium. Before our time religion linked creation with the Creator and united man with the universe. But our faithfulness has split them asunder. *Hic incipit tragoedia!* Henceforth, who shall reveal to us the purpose of life? I seek the answer in my mind. I have no other door to knock on.

LORENZO. The people is unshaken in its faith. Do you remember our old nurse? How deep her roots went into the ground, and how generously she spread her shade! She was like the tree, unpruned by human hand, which spreads its branches far and wide. Greater than we—far wiser—was she; immortal as life itself. She would distinguish right from wrong, or what was beautiful from what was ugly as readily as night from day. With all the arrogance of my youth and all my learning, there were many times when I felt myself helpless before her and as stunted as a capon. That's the People for you! And it is on the People's strength that I still lean today and realize my ideal as ruler of the state.

GIULIANO.   I respect the People and marvel at your readiness to usurp its strength. But to us, ever since we have abandoned faith, the gods have turned a double face. We have lost the integrity of mind which makes the People so strong, as you have said. The People spreads out beneath—it is earth wide and indivisible, while we—we are above, nothing but a thin rind of frost.

LORENZO.   In politics, what is important is the *result*. I found myself swirling in the sea's foam. The winds beat down upon me. But the tideless waters of the deep beneath me sustain me. Do you find anything unreasonable in this?

GIULIANO.   Unreasonable? No. But I find it shameless and vain that you should lay claim to leadership when you are devoid of purpose.

LORENZO.   I devoid of purpose? My whole body is a-tremble when I think of it. The aim I pursue is to unite Italy as a nation. Queen Isabella is uniting Spain under her rule. Louis is uniting France. I foresee a world at peace and local hatreds forgotten, and peoples united as nations competing for the attainment of a higher ideal. I see wars giving way before bloodless struggles. I see science, letters, art, at the service of the citizen. The Rebirth of Europe completed. I see a new Ethic arising, illumined by the light of Reason. And our new Culture extending from one end of the Continent to the other. A new Rule of Life for man, a new Ideal, which will spur him on to surpass himself—Is that nothing? Is that really vain and shameless?

GIULIANO.   You are drunk with the fumes of action no less than the generations of Medici which preceded you. The tables of your law spell equality, yet you put the citizens of Volterra to the sword; they call for brotherhood, yet you allow your people to waste away in want and disease. Where then are the ideas that Marsilio Ficino, the new Plato, taught you? Where the Christian spirit our mother instilled in us? All is forgotten! And the reason? The reason is that which you yourself gave when you said that the actions of the Ruler can only be judged by results. Opportunism and Expediency. In other words, suppression of the Ideal. Do you remember the time when we were so intoxicated with ancient Greek culture that we offered a prayer to Pan in the words of Socrates? "O Pan and deities of the place!" Our innocent lips said, "Grant to us the inner beauty. Vouchsafe that our outward being shall always be in harmony with our inner and that we may always esteem the wise man wealthy; and that we may never carry upon our persons more gold than a prudent man would!" O guileless years! O idle dreams!—My blood freezes when I consider how your conscience is divorced from your acts. Even those ancient monsters, the Roman Emperors, might boast a greater conformity between their souls and their deeds. Only this evening, I was reading in Suetonius: (*He takes up a book and reads*) "A thousand conflicting plans surged in his mind. Should he slaughter the Gauls living in Rome? Should he again set fire to the city? Should he let loose the wild beasts? Or transfer the capital to Alexandria? All these projects appeared to him to be grand, admirable, and easy." There's a picture of undiluted action for you! Such is the destiny of the godless tyrant!

LORENZO. Heavens above! One drop from his poison is sufficient to vitiate all desire for action. But, Giuliano, where does your philosophy lead? Have you no thought for the history of your House? Have you no feeling for Florence? Don't you need Florence in order to extend the conquests of your spirit?

GIULIANO. (*Carried away by his own words*) I cannot abide the darkness! I will not give myself over to delusion! Give me laws, give me certainties! I am dedicated to purity.

LORENZO. (*Fatherly*) Man's lot is your doom. Absolute freedom breeds death.

GIULIANO. (*In a dream*) My loneliness and independence hold me in ravishment—I am oblivious of the indecent din of clashing kingdoms—The shades of Homer call me to their Elysian fields! The immaterial warriors burnish their armor, unsubstantial hunters pursue a shadowy prey—The future? It does not exist for me! The present? It is inscrutable—

LORENZO. (*More fatherly*) Take pity on yourself. You are inviting death—

(*Dawn glimmers through the window. Its ghostly light creeps over their faces.*)

SCENE IX

The same. LUCREZIA TORNABUONI.

LUCREZIA. (*Opens the door violently and appears with her hair disheveled, in a gray nightrobe*) I smell death! The house stinks like an ossuary! What are you three up to? 'Tis the dawn of a Holy Day. Go to the Chapel and pray before you go to bed—Why do you look at me like that? (*Seeing* Suetonius *on the table*) I'll have your impious books burned. I'll poison the Greeks you brought to Florence. I'll light bonfires for heretics! Out! Out! All night I heard you in my sleep dragging the chains of the damned—Christ, come to my aid!—They'll drive me mad, as they used to when they were children—

GIULIANO.   And I, too, Mother, saw you in my sleep last night. I held you in my arms.

LUCREZIA.   Oh! To see your mother in a dream means Earth. And Earth means a grave. My Giuliano! Giuliano! (*She seizes him by the hand and drags him from the room as if to save him from death*)

END OF THE FIRST DAY

SECOND DAY

PART ONE

Evening in Fiesole. The Villa Laveggi, owned by the Pazzi. A large hall in the basement, serving as an armory. High up in the wall, backstage, two small windows with iron bars. The door spaces reveal thick, strong walls. A door, left, leads out of the Villa; a door, right, to an adjacent room where other conspirators await. At the beginning of the act their noisy clamor is heard; then it subsides as they seem to be eavesdropping on the chief conspirators on stage.

SCENE I

JACOPO.   It's better—It's better that things turned out this way. (*He holds his head in his hands*) The grandeur of the exploit caused my spirit to soar, but the crime involved has plagued it down into the abyss.

ARCHBISHOP.   He who obeys the Church of Rome commits no crime.

BANDINI.   You talk as though we had failed. Our fingers are in the dough; now we go ahead and knead the bread. (*To* SALVIATI) What news from the Cardinal?

ARCHBISHOP. He bids us await his arrival before doing anything. Merely a postponement. There's no failure.

BANDINI. Thank goodness for that. Luck's on my side. (*Lifts his right arm*) For twenty years I've been flexing this arm to strike down the tyrants. To let them fall by Montesecco's sword would have been an insult to Democracy.

FRANCESCO DE' PAZZI. I stand by you, for honor and for glory! A page in History is ours! The deed is at hand! The fulfillment of years of brotherly preparation!

ARCHBISHOP. Let us await the Cardinal—

JACOPO. I had always dreamed of the spirit of Democracy as being strong and just, not pitiless and violent.

ARCHBISHOP. (*Furious*) Don't damp their ardor.

JACOPO. I always knew the Princes of the Church were insatiable and intolerant, but I never imagined them so ruthless.

ARCHBISHOP. The Cardinal is here. (*He points to the door at left, where* MONTESECCO'S *heavy tread is heard descending the stone steps*)

SCENE II

The same. The CARDINAL *and* MONTESECCO.

CARDINAL. (*His eyes aflame*) Are you all here? Has anyone in the city moved yet? No one is to stir. Our plan hasn't gone forward. But I have a new and better one.

ARCHBISHOP. That's what I was just saying. A slight postponement.

MONTESECCO. (*Unfastens his sword and places it on a cask of gunpowder standing on a corner*) We were out of luck.

CARDINAL. Young Giuliano went out hunting this morning— Whoever heard of such impiety? To go hunting on this holy day!— He was wounded in the thigh by a boar and didn't go to the banquet where—

ARCHBISHOP. The heretic! Hunting today!

BANDINI. And what about Lorenzo? Wasn't the principal offender at the point of your sword?

CARDINAL. Both our pledge and our reason bade us keep to our original decision. For, if the people heard the cry, "Lorenzo is dead!" they would have shouted, "Long live Giuliano!" (*Turning to* FRANCESCO DE' PAZZI) That's what we decided, wasn't it?

FRANCESCO DE' PAZZI. An oath is an oath.

BANDINI. If I had been there, I would have burst into his bedchamber and torn him apart on his bed.

CARDINAL. His mother was standing in front of his door like a guardian spirit, or rather, like a snarling sheepdog. I had the greatest difficulty in persuading her to let me go in alone.

BANDINI. And didn't your Excellency have a dagger on you?

CARDINAL. I looked to see whether his wound was serious and asked him whether he would go down into the City tomorrow to attend the Second Easter Mass. My insistence and expediency, no doubt, convinced him that he must not disregard his duty as a Christian.

BANDINI. So?

CARDINAL. So our next meeting will take place at their palace where Lorenzo has invited me with my retinue to see his collections. From there we shall go to the Cathedral together.

JACOPO. (*Sadly*) The Eagle's claws reach out for the birds— Will not your Excellency grant a short delay?

CARDINAL. A delay? But that would be our undoing! Tomorrow night our mercenaries will be beating on the gates of Florence. What will happen if the Medici are still in power?

JACOPO. If we wish, two couriers can halt Lorenzo Giustini outside Imola and Niccolo da Tolentino in the outskirts of Todi.

CARDINAL. Our decision cannot be changed. The Pope is plethoric. A fit of anger or a disappointment might kill him.

JACOPO. I beg your Excellency for a short delay. Otherwise, I shall withdraw from the venture with all my kin.

FRANCESCO DE' PAZZI. (*Protesting*) Uncle!

CARDINAL. In Florence there are eighty noble Houses, and from each at least one pretender will aspire to power, if 'tis heard the Medici are overthrown without your help.

JACOPO. No one hates the Medici more than I.

CARDINAL. You say you hate them? What further persuasion do you need? (*To the* ARCHBISHOP) Is your Reverence ever firm in your resolve?

ARCHBISHOP. Firm as a rock.

CARDINAL. Listen then to my plan. (*With emphasis*) In the Cathedral, during elevation of the Host, when the congregation is kneeling with heads bowed, Harmodius and Aristogeiton (*points to* FRANCESCO DE' PAZZI *and* BERNARDO BANDINI) will strike Giuliano from behind (*makes the motion of striking*) and our new Brutus (*points to* MONTESECCO) will strike Lorenzo.

(JACOPO *sways, as if about to faint. The* ARCHBISHOP *supports him.*)

BANDINI. (*Embracing* FRANCESCO *with enthusiasm*) Here's the page which History will write about the two brothers-in-arms—the new tyrannicides!

MONTESECCO. (*Awe-stricken*) No! Not I! I'll commit a thousand murders, but not sacrilege!

(*The* ARCHBISHOP *assists* JACOPO *to the gunpowder cask where he sits to the end of the scene.*)

CARDINAL. (*To* MONTESECCO) Our mission has the blessing and absolution of the Pope. Do you think that you will be the first tyrannicide to carry out his assignment in a church? The citizens of Fabriano slew their tyrants at the appointed moment when the Priest was intoning the words of the Creed: "*Et incarnatus est—*." The Milanese slaughtered their Duke, Giovanni-Maria Visconti, in the doorway of St. Gothard's. Duke Galeazzo-Maria Sforza was done to death in St. Stephen's. Will you say that the heroic slayers of these tyrants were all sacrilegious? Galeazzo's avengers actually attended the first Mass and made a vow to the Saint before shedding the oppressor's blood.

MONTESECCO. Call me assassin, pimp, robber, and perjurer. I've committed crimes by the dozen. But I won't commit sacrilege! I have a soul to hand over to God.

CARDINAL. And you're the man who said to me: "I'd crucify Christ all over again to please you!" Swine! Butcher! Hell-scum!

MONTESECCO. Today your Excellency curses me in Tuscan. Yesterday you blessed me in Latin. My memory will retain only the idiom of the Church.

CARDINAL. In the name of the Pope, I place you in my custody from this moment. (*To* FRANCESCO DE' PAZZI) Take him into the next room and bring me the two priests in my retinue.

SCENE III

The same, excepting MONTESECCO. *The priests,* ANTONIO MAF-FEI *and* STEFANO DE BAGNONE.

CARDINAL. (*To the priests*) A single hesitation and our venture will follow the course of the conspiracy of the Pitti. Instead of historic figures, we shall become the laughing-stock of the world

—those of us, that is, whose heads do not roll—Montesecco is afraid to go forward with us in the act of sacrifice imposed by circumstances. The Church of Rome entrusts her children—

STEFANO DE BAGNONE. (*Pointing to the door*) We heard your Excellency expound the new plan.

CARDINAL. So? You who are accustomed to holy places—

ANTONIO MAFFEI. (*His face expresses agony*) To which of the two tyrants does your Excellency destine my murderous hand?

CARDINAL. (*Indicating the two priests*) You two will strike Lorenzo. Francesco de' Pazzi and Bernardo Bandini will slay Giuliano.

ANTONIO. (*With a sigh of relief*) So be it!

STEFANO. (*Lifting his hands to heaven*) So be it!

ALL. (*Together*) So be it!

SECOND DAY

PART TWO

Night. A sumptuous hall in the Palazzo Medici in Florence. Decor in Renaissance style. The walls are in dark red brocade panels. Paintings and sculpture are in evidence. Front stage lighted by tall candlestands. Backstage in semidarkness.

SCENE IV

LUCRECIA *and* GIULIANO.

Before the curtain rises, LUCREZIA's *voice is heard echoing her cry at the end of the final scene in the First Day:* "My GIULIANO! GIULIANO!" *The curtain goes up slowly, and* LUCREZIA *is seen moving about in agitation.*

LUCREZIA. My Giuliano! Giuliano!

GIULIANO. (*Advances slowly from the gloomy depths of the hall. He holds a book in his hand*) Here I am. Why are you so agitated? Like the ancient sage I might say? "Do not disturb my—"

LUCREZIA. (*Taking him in her arms and searching his body*) This anguish is driving me crazy. I can't rid my mind of its forebodings. And your sister Bianca has only added to my terrors—Her husband disappeared last night, and when he returned home this afternoon, the first thing he did was to inquire after his wife's brother. When he heard later that you had been wounded, he went white as a shroud and asked whether the culprits had been seized— before he found out that the boar had struck you—Giuliano, Pazzi is up to something. I'm sure of it!

GIULIANO. Pazzi! You needn't worry. After all, each of our sisters has disarmed a foe for us. Maria holds Rossi in check, Nannina, Ruccelai and Bianca, Pazzi. The fortunate tyrant possesses daughters and sisters to place in the house of his enemies— Marriage in the service of policy—a fine invention! So, when you see Bianca greet her for me with the name, "Brave Judith!"

LUCREZIA. You're turning my pain into ridicule. Answer me! Have you noticed anything unusual around you?

GIULIANO. (*Laughing*) Let me go on with my philosophy. The new Judith looks the man in the eyes and makes a God of him for his wondrous works—be he banker, tradesman, or soldier. Modern Holofernes is tamed, settles down, and puts on weight, and smugly enjoys his self-deception. (*Passionately*) Yet God has placed the dreaded spark in here—here, between the brows! Has given him power to search and find! (*Sarcastically*) But the new Judith prefers to take a lover. Her worship provides another with delusions. That was it! A trick of the eyes—(*Changes his mood*) Greetings to our dear Guglielmo too! I'm sending him this copy of Dante. (*Hands her the book he is holding*) Let him read the third canto of the "Inferno" and solve this riddle: In what verse was his brother-in-law thinking of him?

LUCREZIA. (*Giving back the book*) Take it back! I won't budge from here! (*She darts about the hall like a bloodhound*) Are your bodyguards below? (*She feels his sides*) Are you wearing your coat of mail? I tell you, I'm going crazy with fear!

GIULIANO. (*Sarcastic*) Compose yourself. One of my stature is not destroyed without the heavens being filled with signs. Has the sun been dimmed; is the moon leering? My horses in their stalls have not refused their oats. They shed no tears like Caesar's steeds on the eve of his destruction. Nor have the other birds pounced on the golden-crested wren carrying the laurel branch in its beak! There are no omens. What surer proof of my security? Compose yourself.

LUCREZIA. (*Looking at him as if dazed by his appearance*) You are rocking like a pillar that is about to fall. (*She sways to emphasize her words*) And yet, you scoff! I'm going to find your brother.

GIULIANO. (*With an expression of indifference makes a gesture as if to say:* "*Do as you please*")

LUCREZIA. (*Turning back*) Come, let me kiss you (*Composed*) Your calm has suddenly passed into my heart. Forgive my cowardice. Fasting has weakened me. Tomorrow, I must prepare a feast for you two which will astound all Florence! (*Exits*)

SCENE V

GIULIANO. *alone.*

GIULIANO. This I ought surely to call provocation. If he has heard me, he must be sharpening his scythe at this moment. But why should I speak in parables? Death conquered the life in my heart at the very time my calm brought relief to my mother. O strange coincidence! An omen, it would seem. In the clear sky a dagger, point downward, dripping blood, supported by two twigs— Well, my biographer can record this heraldic fantasy of mine. Let him discourse upon the warm-blooded zest for life which was mine in the cruel hour of Spring—even more cruel amid the roses of Florence. Let him say a few words about my youthful years and many about lovely Simonetta who returned my adoration until the weeds grew through her sockets. Better he should name her Venus—Botticelli was on his knees when he painted her—May she rest in peace! Gone two years already—Who would ever have believed it! And I am still in her husband's debt, according to the laws of honor. I'll dedicate to him my last thought, and in it the weight that bears down my whole life. And I'll bequeath him the crown which her white hands placed upon my brow on the day of my victory at the Tournament. For me, I shall take with me an immaterial caress from her lips and a memory of the soft fragrance of her hair. I hope it will be said that the account was settled equitably—But Love and Guilty Conscience come to confuse in me the reasons of my life and death. Ofttimes, I called myself Spirit and I must be consistent now. The anguish of spiritual endeavor— pure, unadulterated—this alone has drained the life within me. The tears it drew forth from my eyes would fill a lake beside the rose petal dewdrops which I shed for my lost love. Apollo was my God. In his light, History seemed to me but hoarfrost, dissipated by the sun a thousand years ago. This irrevocable revelation became my New Chart of Time. Henceforth, I lived only for the Light. I have

ever sought for light in my solitude and inhuman life. It is light
that I seek behind the shadow of death. Light behind the impenetrable curtain—Men will measure the extent of my yearning by the
utterness of my dedication.

Scene VI

GIULIANO *and* BACCIO.

GIULIANO. The executioner! He's the man. Twenty-four hours
after the confessor—His bloody hand will lift the impenetrable curtain— (*With hauteur*) Here end, here is accomplished the great
adventure of Knowledge. (*He hastily unbuttons his doublet, unfastens his coat of mail, unbuckles his sword and throws all into a
chest. He takes off his medallion, kisses it, and throws it away too.
With his forefinger he describes a circle over his white shirt around
the position of his heart.*) Gian-Battista da Montesecco, minister
of Destiny for me, here is your target!

(*The door* BACKSTAGE *opens and* MONTESECCO, *clad in full
armor, enters. He advances and stops at some distance from*
GIULIANO.)

Scene VII

GIULIANO *and* MONTESECCO.

GIULIANO. Approach. Don't hesitate.
MONTESECCO. (*Taking a step forward crosses his arms over his
chest and bows*) At your command, my Lord.
GIULIANO. Destiny commands, Montesecco. Proceed.
MONTESECCO. I entrust my life to the fair-mindedness and
generosity of your Excellency, after I have revealed my terrible
secret.
GIULIANO. (*Irritated and, as it were, disappointed*) Well then,
speak!
MONTESECCO. The Pope in Rome, his two nephews—Girolamo
Riario and the Cardinal—and the Pazzi clan are plotting the murder
of your Excellency and the Lord Lorenzo tomorrow morning at the
second Mass in the Cathedral. (GIULIANO *starts, in spite of himself*)

Francesco de' Pazzi and Bernardo Bandini have undertaken to slay you. The Lord Lorenzo's murder will be done by the two priests in the Cardinal's retinue. The time fixed for the crime is when—

GIULIANO.   Cease, man! They'll never reach that time. By God, they won't! You say they want to kill Lorenzo and me? To wipe out our House?

MONTESECCO.   Yes, my Lord.

GIULIANO.   To crush Florence! To let loose the Pope's soldiery in our houses, to rape our women and plunder our goods! To tear down our flag from the Castle and hoist the Papal Banner! And men of Florence have been found to take part in this affair— (*He paces up and down in great agitation*) They're blinded by hatred. And they give their hand to their worst enemy. (*Turns back to* MON-TESECCO) Montesecco! From this moment, I take you into my service. Your life and pay are guaranteed. I require your loyalty until the end of the war which the Medici will wage against the Pope.

MONTESECCO.   My loyalty? You have it since the moment I refused the Cardinal's demand that I become your murderer. As for war, it's music to my ears. In its din I forget the weakness of the flesh. I am swept away by its mighty whirlwind.

GIULIANO.   With these words of yours you have won my heart more than by the secret you revealed to me. Baccio tells me you're old pals. Go and stay with him in the guardroom and keep your mouth sewed up about all we've said until I give you further orders.

(MONTESECCO *bows and exits.*)

SCENE VIII

GIULIANO *alone. He strides up and down the room.*

GIULIANO.   The call of my blood, the love of Florence, and the urge of vengeance. These are my motives. O pitfalls of the Evil One!—I might add the lust of war and thirst for glory; terrible pitfalls! Half an hour ago, if I were offered the kingdom of the whole world, I should not have taken my eyes off my purpose. What then has intervened? What nerve has slackened within me? (*Light suddenly dawns on his conscience*) The blackguards! The cunning knaves! With their treachery they have lighted my anger! Anger has obscured my spirit and made me react to impulse. An eye for an eye!—A philosophy meet for cave men. But I, am I not he who stood at the center of Indifference, in the kingdom of Impersonal Thought, in the sphere of Pure Intellect? Pitfalls of the Evil One! For an instant my foot was suspended over your teeth. But I'm still standing and master of my Destiny!

(*Enter* LORENZO.)

SCENE IX

GIULIANO *and* LORENZO.

LORENZO. I've given orders for the ancient manuscripts to be taken out of their cases. I'm having the signet brought out too; and we'll get all the coins laid out on velvet. I want that barbarian to be impressed tomorrow. Together with his envy he can take back to his Holiness the Pope an appreciation of the strength of the House of Medici.

GIULIANO. (*Feigning calm*) What hour has been fixed for the visit?

LORENZO. They'll come at ten, and at noon we'll all go together to the second Mass. The Cardinal is very pleased you took his hint and are coming along with us.

GIULIANO. I'd much prefer to be far away from Florence. I'm already upset by all this fuss. I'd like it even more if *you* were to be absent. It's too much honor for that barbarian to be entertained by two Medici. After all, why shouldn't you leave for Milan at once? I'm sure I can summon up the energy to step into your shoes, as you asked me to. A short spate in office might possibly drive the ghosts of lethargy out of my spirit. What do you say?

LORENZO. I find you acting very strangely. So was our mother a short while ago. If I weren't so tired, I'd stop to probe your mood. You may have a little fever from your wound. But I'm grateful to you for your good tidings. Good night.

GIULIANO. A *good* night, indeed! (*He rushes after* LORENZO, *picks up his cloak by the hem and kisses it*)

LORENZO. (*Takes* GIULIANO *in his arms and embraces him with feeling*) Your decision has already cured you of your unhealthy dreaming. The future is ours! Go and get some sleep now.

GIULIANO. Sleep! That, by God, would indeed be the sleep of the unruffled sage!

(*Exit* LORENZO.)

SCENE X

GIULIANO *alone.*

GIULIANO. (*Pulls the bell-cord and orders the servant who enters*) Get Baccio to come here and then go upstairs and ask Agnolo Poliziano to be good enough to come down. (*He walks to and fro with his hand to his forehead*) That was the most difficult hour of my life! O abyss! O loneliness!

SCENE XI

GIULIANO *and* BACCIO.

GIULIANO. Is Montesecco in the guardroom?

BACCIO. Yes, my Lord.

GIULIANO. You will take him, and you will both go to the deepest cellar under the palace. Your excuse will be that you are going to bring up some arms. You are to lock him in there securely until tomorrow night. Without bread. Without water. And he is to communicate with no one. For twenty-four hours. No longer. My order is to be carried out scrupulously and without question. Do you understand me? When you release him, you will give him this purse (*takes a purse from his pocket*) and you will say to him. This comes to you with Giuliano's thanks—Can I rest assured that my orders will be carried out exactly as I have said?

BACCIO. I obey my master blindly.

GIULIANO. Your obedience is not enough. I must have your manly oath.

BACCIO. (*Places his right hand on his sword-hilt*) I swear it on my sword.

GIULIANO. Give me your hand.

(*Exit* BACCIO. *Enter* POLIZIANO.)

SCENE XII

GIULIANO *and* POLIZIANO.

GIULIANO. Have I taken you out of your sleep or disturbed your wakefulness? Forgive me, anyway. I have a decision to impart to you, and I'm going to test your friendship. It was you, wasn't it, who wanted us to go on with our poem, "The Tournament of Giuliano"? Yet, that was a poem about the carefree deeds of youth. Impressions, Poliziano, moments, evanescent tricks of sunlight on the waters! What would you say if I were to give you the material for a poem immovable as a primitive statue—one of those statues with their legs all of one piece, austere, unbending, eyes staring out into the unprobed infinite? Would this not be more worthy of the great spiritual travail nurtured by our godless age?

POLIZIANO. My sweet Lord! My whole hearth as been dedicated to the poem of your golden years. There was the image of our age. Your life of overflowing vitality, your wealth, the arts you fostered—The resurrection of the ancient gods, your tender love, and old Plato's philosophy—Such material bound up in the sweetest Tuscan tongue made a poem which we both thought would be immortal. And now you want us to leave it in the middle?

GIULIANO. I want still more. I want to ask your consent to burn it.

POLIZIANO. (*Falling to his knees and clasping* GIULIANO's *legs*) You haven't burned it already! Tell me the truth! Better you took a knife and pierced this heart whose beats have forged its rhythm!

GIULIANO. (*Raising him up*) How far apart our souls have wandered, Poliziano. Yet once they were so closely bound! Now one of us speaks and the other scarcely hears him. However—fear not! I didn't have the courage to pull away the whole foundation of your life from under you. And yet, I find the strength to draw a curtain of darkness over my whole lineage. The poem is yours. You'll find it over there in the chest—doomed to remain unfinished. But will you keep, I wonder, a place in your heart for your old collaborator? He has one last favor to ask of you which will not offend your poet's sensibility.

POLIZIANO. Speak, my sweet Lord. My life is yours.

GIULIANO. (*Gravely*) Fix your eyes upon me. Be the mirror of my every action. Engrave precisely in your memory my every movement, my every step. Imagine that we, both together, form a single acrobat studying his inner self in concentration. I want to unfold before you the triumphant refutation of my ere-now inaction: one perfect act—unsullied, harmonious, self-imposed. Whatever your memory records put into purest Tuscan and relate in manly style, shorn of ornament and overstatement. Let it be like the stone walls round our gardens when the rain has washed them clean. And call this poem, "Giuliano's Last Joust," or better and more simply, "The Hidden Conflict." It will carry its own message and awaken pity and fear in the spectator. That is the favor I ask of your friendship. And my friendship for you already rejoices that our two names will be linked over a question mark—the stamp of every poem of our times.

POLIZIANO. You frighten me. Yet I won't refuse your favor.

GIULIANO. Come, let me kiss you. (*Kisses him on the mouth as though blowing his life's breath into him*) Put my soul into the impression of my every act—

SCENE XIII

The same. LUCREZIA.

LUCREZIA. You here, Poliziano? Oh, now I am completely calm and reassured.

GIULIANO. You're calm because today 'tis I that rule my destiny. Yesterday, others controlled it. Their shameless contumely cast its shadow over your spirit.

LUCREZIA. I owe my peace of mind to my prayers. My knees bear witness to the hours I spent bowed at my *prie dieu*. (*Ecstatic*) My soul soared very high with fearless wings and rested in the Empyrean of the Blessed.

GIULIANO. O happy people, you! One genuflexion and lo! You're in touch with powers unknown to others, save through the broker, Death. Each time that I down here have concentrated on my self's enigma, I have swum in the vertigo of the bottomless abyss.

LUCREZIA. It's those Greek tutors of yours. They've killed the Faith within you. But age will lead you back to its maternal warmth.

GIULIANO. What if I withdraw twenty or thirty years from the horrible course you predict? Then I retain the fullness of my spirit, and go forward to the generative sacrifice with the garland of youth upon my brow. This I call a sublime fate, worthy of being sung by poets!

LUCREZIA. Your words act like a spell on the stainless calm of my spirit. O Giuliano! I beg you, dim the light that sears your soul. Come, let me put you to bed. (*She leads him by the hand*). Good night, Poliziano.

GIULIANO. Good night, my lady. Good night, my Lord. (*Exits by a side door.* GIULIANO *turns silently and bids him farewell with a sign of the hand.*)

SCENE XIV

LUCREZIA *and* GIULIANO.

GIULIANO. (*As* LUCREZIA *leads him backstage to the dimmed depths of the hall which seem like a bridal chamber*) You bring back to me the taste—the atmosphere of my dream two nights ago— forgetfulness within a mother's arms! What lethargy creeps over me! Come Sleep and bring me Light!

END OF THE SECOND DAY

THIRD DAY

PART ONE

Morning at the Palazzo Medici. Same setting as in Part Two of the Second Day. The hall is decorated in festive manner. Garlands of flowers and wreaths of flowers and fruit hang from the walls. Among the paintings which were barely visible in the half-light of the preceding act, we now recognize three masterpieces by Botticelli: "The Birth of Venus" and "Venus and Mars" hanging on the wall to the LEFT *(or on an easel), and to the* RIGHT *on the wall (or on an easel) "Primavera." All on the stage are in holiday dress.* NOBLEMEN *wear short swords.*

SCENE I

LORENZO DE' MEDICI, CARDINAL RIARIO, FRANCESCO DE' PAZZI, GUGLIELMO DE' PAZZI, BERNARDO BANDINI, ANTONIO MAFFEI, STEFANO DE BAGNONE, AGNOLO POLIZIANO, TWO ATTENDANTS *wearing the full livery of the House of Medici.*

When the curtain rises the hum of conversation is heard as the two men approach from the door, CENTER BACK. *The two attendants lift the heavy draperies, and the whole company comes forward led by* LORENZO, *with the* CARDINAL *on his right.*

CARDINAL. Magnificent! Truly worthy of the name of Medici! I thought my artistic sophistication had reached saturation point. But here (*with a gleam of envy and greed*) . . . here my appetite is whetted anew. Your palace is a second Vatican.

LORENZO. Your Excellency's most gracious words are welcome indeed, but I wonder if His Holiness would like to hear you compare the collections of an amateur with the treasures heaped at the foot of his throne by the innumerable multitude of the Faithful.

CARDINAL. (*With worldly smugness*) *Mutatis mutandis!* Poetic license may take even the sun as a standard of comparison.

LORENZO. (*With hidden mockery*) Yes, we do find ourselves in a poetic milieu—My dear Poliziano, would you be so kind as to interpret for his Excellency these silent poems (*indicates the three paintings*) which the brush of Botticelli extracted from your lips?

CARDINAL. Ah, yes indeed. *Mutum est pictura poema.* A painting is a silent poem. (*To* POLIZIANO) I hang from the lips which inspire such art.

POLIZIANO. (*Standing before the first painting*) This painting depicts the Birth of Venus. The source of its inspiration is to be found in divine Homer—

CARDINAL. (*Turning with a knowing look toward the two priests*) Divine Homer—hm—Supposing we call him—and more accurately so—*blind* Homer, since he was born before the Redemption.

POLIZIANO. (*Unruffled*) The theme comes from the Homeric hymn "To Aphrodite." Cyprus acclaims the golden-crowned goddess, as she stands on the shell wafted by the breath of Zephyrus on the waves of the sea. Our good Lord Giuliano, in ordering the painting, sought to do honor to one dead—

CARDINAL (*In mock offense*) Oh, you're attributing an impious motive to your most Christian Lord.

POLIZIANO. (*Unperturbed*) . . . But the artist brought to light a more general idea. Observe the *ceaseless motion* of the sea and the shell upon which the Goddess *sways* with the rhythm of the wave; notice the winds, personified, as they *fly*, the roses that *fall* from heaven, the Nymph as she *runs* with the unfurled robe, *blown* by Zephyrus, to cover the nude deity—Are not all these expressions of eternal Transformation?

CARDINAL. In truth! The very picture of the instability of worldly things.

POLIZIANO. Venus personifies the Senses. Life in accordance with the senses. The world of phenomena—That world, according to the philosophy of the Lord Giuliano, cannot but end in satiation. The senses, left to their own capacities, are quickly blunted before man's life is expended—The second painting (*leading the* CARDINAL *and his followers to the "Mars and Venus"*) depicts Mars sleeping beneath the exhausted gaze of Venus. The sleeping man is likewise exhausted, extenuated, and his limbs are shriveled. Little Fauns darting from the woods, filch his arms and blow their mockery into his ear through a conch. Venus, now clothed from head to foot like a nun, observes pitilessly the degradation of the male—

CARDINAL. In this I recognize a Christian thought. The artist has the blessing of the Church and may count on its support.

SCENE II

The same. GIULIANO.

As the party moves to view the third painting, the door in the back opens, the attendants lift the draperies and GIULIANO *enters. He too is in festive attire but wears no sword. He is very pale, and in his hair he wears a wreath of violets sprinkled with pearls.*

POLIZIANO. (*With unaffected delight*) Our Lord Giuliano!

GIULIANO. (*Greeting the* CARDINAL) I salute the spirit of the Age!—I've arrived just in time to be your guide. For the third picture, I have an interpretation of my own to give. New sparks seem to burst in my mind all the time—(*To* GUGLIELMO, *intently, as though conveying the meaning* "*Et tu Brute!*") You here, too! Did you receive my greeting and the riddle I set for you?

GUGLIELMO. (*Coldly*) That's why I came.

GIULIANO. (*Giving him his hand*) I hope that your contribution will be judged according to its merit. (*He salutes the other guests. For an instant he looks intently and in silence at* MAFFEI)

LORENZO. (*As* GIULIANO *approaches him last*) Ah, Giuliano— That wreath you're wearing—I don't say it isn't very becoming. But when you came in you looked to me rather like a sacrificial victim about to be led to the altar.

GIULIANO. Then I'll take it off at once. (*He removes the wreath and holds it hesitatingly in his hand. To the* CARDINAL) May I present it together with its pearly as an offering to the Church of one of your priests? (*The* CARDINAL *makes an unctuous gesture of acceptance.* GIULIANO, *turning to the two priests, says to* ANTONIO MAFFEI) Who is the patron saint of your parish?

ANTONIO. (*Uncomfortably*) Santa Anastasia.

GIULIANO. She is my last hope. The "Victim" dedicates his garland to her. (*Gives* MAFFEI *the wreath. Turns to the* CARDINAL) I must make a short introduction before I interpret the third painting. You know very well that a single interpretation is not sufficient to exhaust the many meanings of a work of art. We must authenticate our interpretation—For a long time, I contemplated art after the manner of my friend Poliziano: as a poet and maker of myths. And even today that outlook is among the most pleasing to me. I always preferred it to the spectacles of the bookworm. Not that he is devoid of great qualities. But his frightful shortcomings are capable of plucking life of its feathers and defiling its essence. You all know the schoolman, the man of learning—how vain he is, how stubborn, pedantic and petty. If the curled lip of my scorn could stretch from one end of this hall to the other, it would still be too short to express my revulsion—But let us forget the Philistines! Life has been gracious and cruel to me. These two pictures (*indicating the "Birth of Venus" and "Mars and Venus"*) epitomize the first part of my biography. In the second part, I have come to realize the meaning of freedom and self-control—also my infinite loneliness. My thoughts winged unimpeded from the most forgotten past to the remotest future; they fed me with an illusion of eternity. And yet, my being was beaten about in torture between two walls—birth and certain death. This contradiction almost reft me of my senses. I sought an outlet—a fusion with something more durable than I. I desired as it were an extension of self. Like Ganymede, I turned my eyes toward heaven and prayed that Jupiter might seize me in his claws. But I have been betrayed by my human limitations. A thousand years of torturing search bears down upon my heart and presses it toward the Mystery of the World—

CARDINAL. Intellect has ever poisoned the race of man. The sin of Knowledge cannot be expiated until the end of time. You are the victim of self-punishment. Occasionally, you find relief in some system created by your arrogance. Then it falls apart, and the sense of anarchy tortures you with greater force.

GIULIANO. Let us be patient awhile, and soon we shall find a light to lead us out of the impasse.

CARDINAL. 'Tis not *patience*; 'tis *submission* that you need.

GIULIANO. (*Interrupting*) Ah, no! Not that! I've gone through the Catechism. I've learned the Ecclesiastes by heart. But no more of those. The vital life is dead forever. I carry my norm within me.

CARDINAL. (*Shocked*) You have the audacity!

GIULIANO. I begged your indulgence for an Introduction. Now, I come to my main theme. (*Indicates the first painting*) I have lived through the pleasures of a dying civilization which suddenly squanders all that it has amassed through the ages. (*Indicates the second painting*) I have exhausted all the senses had to offer. (*Stands before the "Primavera." With solemnity*) Nature taught me the principle of generative sacrifice. "If the grain of wheat perish not—" This painting symbolizes resurrection after death, the promised Spring. (*He gives* LORENZO *a look of deep affection, commanding his attention*) My brother and I have always sallied forth at our Tournaments under one emblem: a dry laurel burgeoning with green shoots. And beneath it the device: "*Le Temps Revient.*" Time comes back. (*Points to the picture*) Venus, the Graces, Mercury, all that is decor, but the hidden meaning is that one dies to be reborn. For that rebirth of a people, the Prince must undergo the horrible ritual.

CARDINAL. We do not understand.

GIULIANO. I have left certain legacies to my faithful Poliziano. He will present them in due course. Like a sheaf of Apollo's sunbeams, they will illumine the acts I still have to perform. Then will it be proved that the liberated soul soars above the nets and snares of its fellowmen. And that it can turn their guile to its advantage. Draw honey from poison. Convert the enemy into a collaborator.

CARDINAL. Behind your brow there lies, no doubt, a secret and, with it, a light. But arrogance has ever been a provocation to the gods.

GIULIANO. The gods have no power over men who have built up their own pyre and already have their foot upon its first step.

CARDINAL. The full meaning of your words still escapes me, but I am relieved at hearing you.

GIULIANO. (*Takes him by the arm and draws him aside. The members of the* CARDINAL's *retinue look at each other anxiously*) When the victim freely elects to be sacrificed, his slayer may well feel relief—Don't be perturbed. My contempt for the compassion of the common herd is the warrant of your safety. (*Releases the* CARDINAL's *arm abruptly. To the others*) Come! Let us be going. The hour is nigh!

POLIZIANO. We are awaiting our gracious Lady, your mother.

LORENZO. (*To* GIULIANO) I can't compliment you on the

bewilderment you've succeeded in spreading among us. The fever from your wound must still be irritating you.

GIULIANO. At any rate the conclusion to it all is a cheerful one: A new birth! Renascence! The word has dinned in my ears often enough without my ever being able to see in it more than the self-complacency of my contemporaries. Poor souls! They expect to build without first throwing down. In this at least Christ who died upon the Cross is my teacher.

CARDINAL. What blasphemy!

GIULIANO. A teacher! Nothing more. There is not the slightest analogy beyond this. The Jews, the Pharisees, the crucifiers have no counterpart among us.

ONE OF THE ATTENDANTS. (*Announcing*) Her Ladyship our Mistress.

(LUCREZIA *followed by her three daughters stands in the great doorway. Tall and stately, they fill it imposingly. The tableau recalls the Florentine ladies in the mural by Ghirlandajo in the Church of Santa Maria Novella, entitled "The Birth of the Virgin."*)

SCENE III

The same. LUCREZIA TOURNABUONI *and her three daughters,* MARIA, NANNINA, *and* BIANCA. *All in gala dress.*

LUCREZIA. My dutiful greetings to your Excellency. (LU-CREZIA *and her daughters bow their heads as the* CARDINAL *blesses them*) Greetings also to all who have come with you and to my beloved fellow citizens.

GIULIANO. An impressive company, indeed! (*His eyes slowly move over all present*) Almost every reason for existence is represented here! (*Aside*) Everything I have rejected, everything that dust and ashes have covered over, one by one—

LORENZO. Time for us to go! It's almost noon. (*To the* CARDI-NAL) Your Excellency takes precedence. (*The attendant takes* LORENZO's *cloak from a chair and throws it over his shoulders*)

(CARDINAL RIARIO, *with* LORENZO *to his right, advances to the door backstage.* LUCREZIA *and her daughters follow; then her son-in-law,* GUGLIELMO DE' PAZZI, *the two priests and* AGNOLO

POLIZIANO. *The two attendants wait for the rest of the company to pass, but* GIULIANO *signals to them to proceed. They also depart.*)

SCENE IV

GIULIANO, FRANCESCO DE' PAZZI, *and* BERNARDO BANDINI.

GIULIANO. (*Taking* PAZZI *and* BANDINI *by the arms at the last moment prevents them from following the others*) Stay! We shall follow separately. I want to take this opportunity to appoint you my collaborators *now* in a plan which I shall reveal to you after the service.

FRANCESCO. (*Feigning affectionate friendship, takes* GIULIANO *by the waist to see if he is wearing his coat of mail*) My dear Giuliano! It won't be the first time that our hearts have been fired in the same cause!

GIULIANO. What are you searching me for? I never wear a coat of mail when I've been to confession! (*Laughs*) Besides, I can't get into it any more. (*He puffs out his chest*) I've put on quite a lot of beef lately. My trainer tells me I must cut down on exercise if I don't want to disfigure my body with a load of wrestler's muscle.

BANDINI. I admire you more for your intellectual exercises. You certainly put the Cardinal in a spot! Whatever did you say to him when you took him aside? He turned quite pale.

GIULIANO. Oh, perhaps I made him envy me for a moment. But let us go. You go ahead and I'll catch up with you at the front door.

(*Exit* PAZZI *and* BANDINI.)

SCENE V

GIULIANO *alone*.

GIULIANO. House of my Fathers! Shades of my ancestors! Forgive me if I drag down in my sacrifice your true offspring, my brother! Forgive the pride to which your labors have elevated me! Forgive the seething surge which your blood has stirred in my veins!—Time presses. Time revolves. *Le Temps Revient.* Who knows by what future name the soul of the Medici will make itself heard? (*Goes to the window*) Towers, domes, mountain slopes! Let me gaze upon you for the last time! (*Bends out*) Streets, courtyards, flowering gardens! (*Slight pause as if in meditation*) Farewell! O vain Imagination, art thou then the child of my spirit? (*He advances slowly toward the door in back. As he goes the curtain of a side door is drawn apart and* ANTONIA GORINI *darts in. Consternation appears on her face.* GIULIANO, *hearing the rustle of her dress, stops short without turning, as though expecting to be stabbed*)

SCENE VI

GIULIANO *and* ANTONIA, *dressed as a peasant girl.*

ANTONIA.   Giuliano! Turn around and look at me a moment. It is I, Antonia, whose ears have heard words that burn and yet refresh.

GIULIANO.   (*Turning abruptly*) You! How did you get up here? Only this moment I sent out a thought to you when I was looking at the gardens in bloom. That is where I want to know you, for there you are a closed bud, a quiet pool untouched by the scorching heat of summer. What are you doing here? What business has your innocence in this place?

ANTONIA.   My angel! If you didn't seem to be in such a hurry, I would reveal to you the sweet secret that has brought me to your palace from our distant nest where you've forgotten me.

GIULIANO.   (*With a gesture of impatience*) What horrible words! For heaven's sake, spare me "sweet secrets" and "nests." Woman should offer herself silently, like ripe fruit. I have only a few seconds to myself before going to an important meeting. Can you speak clearly and briefly?

ANTONIA.   Modesty holds me back. In this great, unfriendly mansion, I cannot tell you to your face the secret which my body's warmth is sweetening.

GIULIANO.   (*Resignedly*) I have always paid in coin for the utter hopelessness, the inadequate joys brought to me by women. Antonia, will you please tell me plainly what you mean?

ANTONIA.   (*With a look of subconscious possessiveness*) My body is preparing for you a new and tender bond with life.

GIULIANO. Oh!—O treacherous Nature! O shameless Force! And as for you, woman, who has put these words into your mouth? What hand has led you here in this hour?

ANTONIA. (*Straining with all her soul to draw some sympathy from* GIULIANO) Surely, *my* lips should be the first to tell you this?

GIULIANO. I wish you had waited for the sun to set. To go down in his splendor. To draw Night over him like a shroud. Couldn't you have waited *one* day?

ANTONIA. The joyful spirit of Easterday gave me the courage to run to you. All through Holy Week, I wept—I felt so wretched—

GIULIANO. Miserable humanity! Worthless humanity! All your emotions are conditioned by a *mise-en-scène*. (*To* ANTONIA) Couldn't you have managed for just *once* to fix your spirit upon the absolute of Love? Upon its annihilating omnipotence?

ANTONIA. I'm your slave. Order me to die.

GIULIANO. That's the answer! You fall when I fall—But then, we should offer a misleading spectacle to mankind. You see, I have always worshiped uprightness—I don't know any longer what to ask of you—I was a falling star burning itself out in its onrush. Your eruption has stopped me in my course. Now I have to bring my decision to a birth.

ANTONIA. Dear Heart! You confuse me so much. Tell me to die, and I'll die.

GIULIANO. (*Making up his mind*) Conquer Nature within your body! Do the Giuliano in your womb that which my faithful colleagues are going to do to me today. That is my last word. Good luck! (*He hurries to the door upstage.* ANTONIA *sinks to the ground sobbing*)

THIRD DAY

PART TWO

Noon. Inside the Cathedral of Santa Maria del Fiore in Florence. The scene is in the shape of a horseshoe, the curve upstage, in the center of which stands the Altar. The sanctuary is separated from the Choir by two steps and a low railing, with a small double gate in the center. A subdued light descends from the dome above the Choir. Large doors in the walls on either side. Before the curtain rises, organ music is heard for some time.

The curtain rises. The organ continues playing. A priest stands before the altar officiating in Latin. CARDINAL RIARIO *is on a throne in the sanctuary, to the* LEFT. *In the Choir, in front of the railing, stands* GIULIANO, *to the* LEFT *also. Behind him* FRANCESCO DE' PAZZI *and* BERNARDO BANDINI. *Opposite him, to the* RIGHT, LORENZO *and behind him the two priests,* ANTONIO MAFFEI *and* STEFANO DE BAGNONE; *also* POLIZIANO. *In the middle of the stage,* LUCREZIA, *alone. Behind her in a row her three daughters,* MARIA, NANNINA, *and* BIANCA. *Behind them stand their husbands,* LEOPETTO ROSSI, BERNARDO RUCCELLAI, *and* GUGLIELMO DE' PAZZI. *Between the preceding and the audience a dense gathering of worshipers.*

SCENE VII

The priest turned toward the altar continues with his office. He takes the Wafer and then the Ciborium and intones the mystic words of the Consecration. The Acolyte serves him. A silver bell tinkles announcing the Elevation of the Host. The priest turns and offers the Body of Christ to the adoration of the faithful. The congregation of men and women is kneeling with heads bowed.

FRANCESCO DE' PAZZI *and* BERNARDO BANDINI *rise abruptly, with swords drawn.* BANDINI *strikes with violence at the head of* GIULIANO, *who is kneelinng.* GIULIANO *falls prostrate without a word.* PAZZI *leaps forward and plunges his sword in his breast.* BANDINI *strikes furiously at his victim.*

At the same moment the two priests of the CARDINAL'S *retinue leap forward, drawing their daggers from beneath their robes, and strike at* LORENZO. *He does not fall but, rising from his kneeling posture, draws his sword and turns on his assailants, using his cloak as a shield over his arm.* MAFFEI'S *dagger has inflicted a skin wound on his shoulder.*

LORENZO. *(Defending himself)* I'm no animal for slaughter! *(To the congregation)* Shut the doors! Seize the assassins!

BANDINI. *(Rushes furiously, with bloody sword, at* LORENZO. ANTONIO RIDOLFI *throws himself, unarmed, in his path and checks him)* Liberty! Liberty! Strike down the tyrants!

(POLIZIANO, *with drawn sword, advances between* LORENZO *and* BANDINI. LORENZO *seizes the opportunity to vault over the railing into the Sanctuary. The priest and the acolyte run down into the Choir and lose themselves in the crowd.*)

CARDINAL. (*Lifting his scarlet robes in terror, climbs onto the Altar and throws his arms around the Cross. To* LORENZO) Not here! You'll never dare. That would be the end of you and Florence!

LORENZO. (*Ignoring him, lifts his sword*) Shut the doors! Seize the assassins!

(FRANCESCO DE' PAZZI *and* BERNARDO BANDINI *have already escaped by the* LEFT *door, and the two priests by the* RIGHT. *The congregation is in the throes of panic. The three husbands of* LUCREZIA's *daughters are attempting to drag their wives away from the scene, but they resist, turning toward their brother's corpse over which* LUCREZIA *is now kneeling.*)

LUCREZIA. My son! My child! What have they done to you? The savages have butchered you!

THE THREE SISTERS. (*Falling to their knees, beside their mother*) Giuliano! Dearest brother! O Giuliano!

(GUGLIELMO DE' PAZZI *runs to the* RIGHT *door as if to close it and also makes his escape.* ROSSI *and* RUCCELLAI *running behind him close the heavy door. Citizens have closed the* LEFT *door.*)

LUCREZIA. O blackest day! (*Fondling the corpse and lifting it to see if there is still any life left in it, she drags it to the* CENTER *of stage*) Light of my life, you have gone out forever!

THE THREE SISTERS. Alas! Alack! Forever! Forever!

LORENZO. (*To* POLIZIANO, *who is still beside him in the Sanctuary*) You, get the Cardinal down from there and lock him up in the vestry until I return. (*To the Congregation in a steady voice*) Citizens of Florence! This is Florence speaking to you!—This hideous slaughter is the work of a conspiracy, not of a Revolution. Florence has not turned her back on the Medici. (*He goes down among the crowd*) Whoever is on my side will show it now! Let us go and halt the conspiracy in the city—

A CITIZEN. Long live the Medici! Lead the way! We follow you!

THE CONGREGATION. (*Some men with uplifted swords gather around* LORENZO)

(LORENZO *approaches* GIULIANO'S *corpse in silence.*)

LUCREZIA. Look at him, Lorenzo! See how the beasts have mangled him! Nineteen thrusts they dealt him, the lawless dogs! May they be accursed and damned forever! (*To the congregation*) Christian people! Look, you too! Hacked to pieces with nineteen sword-thrusts! Could none of you have stopped their murderous hands? My child! My little boy! Where did the snarling beasts find room to set their ravenous teeth on your frail body? Sprig of my heart! My youngest one! What pain you gave me when I bore you! Yet, is there surfeit of pain for me to bear now that your undoing tears my heart apart!—

THE THREE SISTERS. Ah, pity, pity! Dearest Giuliano! You are gone who were our fondest pride! Gone! Who now will hear the sound of your horn? The prancing of your horses? The eager barking of your dogs? Gone! Lost to Florence!

LORENZO. I shall return to do you honor. Our faithful Florence will give you worthy burial—Come, citizens, we've business to do.

(LORENZO, ROSSI, RUCCELLAI, *the priest and the acolyte and all the men, excepting* POLIZIANO, *leave by the* RIGHT *door. The women divide themselves into two groups (semi-choruses) with* LUCREZIA *and her daughters in the* CENTER, *kneeling by the corpse. All have their faces turned toward the audience. As this arrangement proceeds,* POLIZIANO, *sword in hand, forces the* CARDINAL *down from the Altar and pushes him into the Vestry through a door in the* LEFT *wall of the Sanctuary next to the throne. Then he returns to the corpse.*)

SCENE VIII

LUCREZIA, *her* THREE DAUGHTERS, POLIZIANO, CHORUS OF WOMEN.

POLIZIANO. My sweet Lord! So foully stricken down by murderous hands— (*Staring at the blood*) So much blood—What waste—In slaying one so enamored of Death!—Oh, yes, at the last I had divined your dark, cherished secret. Your Hidden Conflict was revealed to me—I saw you for what you were—the Victim

going to the sacrifice! For three long days you challenged that vast
Nothingness which at last engulfed you. For three days you changed
your own dirge. And now—now Earth has returned to Earth—Dust
to Dust. My sweet Lord! Stretched out lifeless upon the ground
you are become that shadow of yourself which followed you darkly
wherever you went—Never, ah! never to come to life again!

LUCREZIA *and* DAUGHTERS. (*In unison*) Never, ah! never
again!

SEMI-CHORUS OF WOMEN. (*Right*)

O Florence, pour forth from the fountains of anguish,
    For him who hath passed to the realms of the blest,
The tears, bitter tears, as now thou dost languish
    With heartbreak and weeping and beating of breast.

SEMI-CHORUS OF WOMEN. (*Left*)

Thou art gone, gone forever, O favored of heaven,
    Gone, O beloved; swift eagle in flight
Their wing has been seared by the blast of the levin;
    I am orphaned, abandoned, lost in the night.

SEMI-CHORUS OF WOMEN. (*Right*)

O weep for the dear one so cruelly taken,
    Weep mother bereft, weep sister forlorn—
Than widows more lonely, I sisters foresaken—
    And bury your grief in a night without dawn.

LUCREZIA *and* DAUGHTERS. Woe, ah woe! A night without dawn
verily engulfs me!

SEMI-CHORUS. (*Left*)

Thy vengeance, thy vengeance forget not, O Florence!
    Blood calleth for blood and the slayer shall fall
Like cattle in slaughter. In sacred abhorrence
    Our sons come to punish the Great with the Small!

SEMI-CHORUS. (*Right*)

They are nigh! They come heeding the bronze-tolling urge
    Of the bell, and the ax is uplifted for felling;
Lo! Vengeance uncoils at the call of the dirge
    Of a mother in grief—unrelenting, compelling.

LUCREZIA. My Lorenzo tarries not! I hear the dread blows

of his ax! At his call the faithful citizens of Florence have left their Easter board. Hark! Hark to their mighty roar!

(*The roar of the approaching crowd is heard. It bursts into the Cathedral through both doors like the seething ocean into a landlocked bay. Gradually, the tumult subsides.* ANTONIA GORINI *appears on the fringe of the crowd, but she is too shy to show herself or to approach the corpse. She follows everything with despair written on her face. The men gather on one side, the women on the other. Enter* LORENZO *and his two brothers-in-law with swords drawn.*)

SCENE IX

The same. The CROWD, ANTONIA GORINI, LORENZO, *and his* BROTHERS-IN-LAW.

LORENZO.   (*Enters by door to the* RIGHT; *goes to the steps of the Sanctuary.*) Citizens of Florence! The conspiracy has been crushed, and the Sword of the Republic will lop off the heads of the poisonous Hydra! Our gallant Commander, Petrucci, has already dealt with the Archbishop of Pisa and his ruffians, when they went to get the keys of the city from him, thinking that the assassins had accomplished their godless task in here. Their bloody bodies now swing from the windows of the Signoria. Pazzi and his treacherous brood have made off to the mountains. But their fate awaits them there. Either the wolves or the countryfolk will get them. For our farmers all swear by the name of Medici. The land has its jaws open to swallow them, and the sea is sharpening its claws on the rocks to clutch them. Should anyone of them succeed in making port, the gold of the Republic in the palm of every seaman will surely haul him back. This I now pledge: The heads of the fugitives shall be placed in one pan of the scales, and an equal weight of gold in the other. That is the reward I offer—As for the abominable criminal of all, I have him locked up in here—in the Vestry!

THE CROWD.   Where is he? Hand him over! We'll have his blood!

LORENZO.   No, friends. Don't ask for this. I want to send him back to his master, the miscreant Pope. Rome is the heart of this conspiracy. Let him go back there, cowed like ancient Xerxes, and beat his breast at the foot of the Throne.

THE CROWD.   A curse on the villain! May his soul burn in Hell!

LORENZO. And another conspirator, one Montesecco by name, a hired assassin, has been in jail since yesterday. Good Baccio, vigilant Captain of my Guard, suspected his actions and put him behind bars. By now, no doubt, Baccio has wrapped up his head ready to be sent over to the Signoria to be hoisted aloft alongside the others— (*Changing his tone*) Well, so much for the measures we've taken to punish the offenders. 'Tis time now to dedicate our thoughts to the innocent victim—

CHORUS OF WOMEN.
> Thy words pour soothing balm upon my heart.
> Blood-guilt the guilt of blood doth now release.
> O gentle soul, that crooked swords did part
> From this fair body, rest at last in peace!

LORENZO. (*Turning to GIULIANO's body*) Now fain would I be alone with you, dearest brother—Fain would I dedicate myself wholly to thoughts of you, even as the lovely widow at midnight draws the coverlet over her head to dream in a darkness made more dark of the dear one she has lost—The gods ever take the best first of all into their bosom—And you, my brother, were the loftiest branch our Tree brought forth—the tenderest shoot of the old fir's topmost limb. Higher than titles, birth, worldly honors. O young blood fired by that Spirit! The spirit of purity that sought purity in death! You have taken upon yourself the sins of your race and the errors of your city. O Redeemer of Florence! Each utterance of yours opened up a hidden secret, each act resolved a mystery. The afflictions of our time have passed through the filter of your spirit—have been made lighter by your sacrifice. O Holy Victim! You have returned the people to its faith, more strongly confirmed in it. To the ruler you have revealed the sanctity of the Law. To the poet you have shown the lustrous poesy of Truth Absolute. Redeemer of Florence! Martyr in the City's cause more worthy of reverence even than the warrior slain upon the battlements! Prophet of a new humanity! Saint of a new holiness!

CHORUS OF MEN.
> Purest dewdrop of white fire,
> Gem that kindlest men's desire,
> Holding captive in thy prism
> Starlight's radiant mysticism.
> Shattered splendor!—O the pity!—
> For the safety of our City.

Eagle soaring proud on high,
Or songbird of a softer sky,
Or that Consecrated Dove
Harbinger of God's dear Love.
Shattered pinions!—O the pity!—
For the safety of our City!

Christ in Heaven protecteth thee,
Lofty limb of noble Tree,
Sovran, Prince and Prophet too,
Who wast ever pure and true.
Shattered scepter!—O the pity!—
For the safety of our City.

CHORUS OF WOMEN.   (*Turning to face the men*)
Husband, thou art my leader and my guide!
A golden Eagle scanning the heavens wide!
Thine eye is fearless turning to the sun.
A web of lightning in my veins is spun.
By words that burn truth in my heart at last,
And doubt and error from me now are cast.
This bier which erst I looked on through my tears
Has shed its tragic shroud and now appears
With shining sail uplifted on a cloud,
And skims o'er heaven's ocean light and proud.

Hushed, thou art my leader—young or old—
Out of the Battle's steam thou comest bold,
Turning thy fearless eye toward the sun—
A Golden Eagle, in pride of guerdon won.

LORENZO.   (*Pointing to the Cathedral door*) Take down that panel on which the sculptors of Florence have carved the Passion of Christ. 'Twill make a fitting bier to bear so noble a body.

(*Four citizens unhinge the panel and carry it to the center of the stage. GIULIANO's corpse is laid upon it.*)

LUCREZIA.   Ah! Ah! You tear my heart out! Don't take him away from me! Bury me with him! Bury me with my dear one in my arms!

A SISTER.   Ah me! Ah me! See what is left of the tall cypress!

(*Citizens lift the bier on their shoulders*)

LORENZO. (*Raising his mother by the arms*) Once did you bear his weight within your body. Come now, place here your shoulder—Bear him this last time.

LUCREZIA. (*Places her shoulder beneath the bier at the front LEFT corner. The citizen she replaces retires*) My child! My child! See how your dream comes true!

LORENZO. I shall raise it on the other side. (*To POLIZIANO and ANTONIO RIDOLFI*) You two, who saved my life from the murderous dagger, bear him up in the rear. By your self-sacrifice you have known one aspect of his perfect goodness. Henceforth, your heirs shall have the privilege of burying the lawful rulers of Florence in token of your loyalty and honor. (*He shoulders the bier. POLIZIANO and RIDOLFI follow suit*)

(*The procession moves forward in the direction of the spectators. In the rear ANTONIA GORINI follows in a trance. The procession wheels around and advances toward the RIGHT door.*)

CHORUS OF MEN AND WOMEN. (*Chanting*)
Behold the aged Dame, and at her side,
Her noble son, yoked in a tragic team;
Bowed down they go. Indifferent to pride,
Fate bends on lordly necks the harness beam.

(*Canons roar.*)

Lo! Heaven flashes and the thunder peals,
And now God hangs a ladder from the sky,
To our young Prince, Lo! He the Throne reveals
Where he shall sit among the Just on high.

CURTAIN

Translation by André Michalopoulos

Loukis Akritas

(1909–65)

With his first novel, *Young Man with Excellent References* (1935), Loukis Akritas assumed an enviable position in modern Greek literature. This work was an outcry of the afflicted urban youth between the two great wars, a generation which oscillated between unemployment and deep misery. *Young Man* was a "novel of penury and privation," recalling Knut Hamsun's *Hunger* or Maxim Gorky's *In Strange Hands*. And this outcry, though immature, Akritas succeeded in expressing artistically.

In his second novel, *Valley* (1936), the Cypriot author, with an obviously pulsating style and a tight expression, sought to perfect the harsh picture of modern Greek life by portraying the adventures of the provincial world. In *Those With Weapons* (1947), his third novel, he gave the most synthesized, as well as the most humanistic portrayal of the Albanian War in 1940. Among his theatrical works are included *He Who Loves, Torments, Hostages,* and *Theodora.*

Hostages

A Tragedy

CHARACTERS

OLD Man *of the Prologue*
KOSMAS, *chief Elder of the village*
LAMBRINOS
ARETE, *mother to* LAMBRINOS
PHOTINE, *betrothed to* LAMBRINOS
STURM, *leader of the conquering troops*
FOUR ELDERS
THREE WOMEN
THREE YOUNG GIRLS
WIFE TO LIAKOS
LEFTERIS, *a youth*
A YOUNG GIRL, *his sister*
A FOREIGN OFFICER
TWO FOREIGN SOLDIERS
A CROWD, *gradually swelling, of youths, young girls, children,*
    foreign soldiers, etc.

SCENE: *In a village near the border. A modest Byzantine church*
    gives an austere and unified appearance to the scene. Crum-
    bling steps lead to the center door of the Church. Houses on
    a mountainside are visible to right and left of stage, and a
    winding lane leading up the mountainside. The CROWD *is*
    able to move freely at right and left. The particular dances
    of the play can be accompanied by folk music. Byzantine
    melodies are heard during the ritualistic moments.

The open-air theater, naturally, lends itself far better to this
play. There is no CURTAIN.

PROLOGUE

(*An* OLD MAN, *about seventy, rises from the audience, slowly*
approaches the stage, and stands surveying the audience as
though in greeting.)

419

OLD MAN. Welcome, compatriots. Around this churchyard today, the villagers will perform a play called *Hostages*. It is not the
story of kings, nor is it a skillful development of plot, the kind befitting a serious play, with all the elaborate stage directions, with
powders and music. Nor does it develop along well-formulated,
distinctive speeches. Even those beautiful visions do not appear in
our midst; nor alas, does the play contain happy contrivances.

This is a simple, primitive play. It is as coarse as I am. And at
first glance, it is not a very important play. The man who wrote it
evidently knew little more about the theater than you who are
watching it, or than—I. He is not a playwright. He sat down to
write the story of our village, if such a story can ever become a
play. The blessed man, for example, did not even take the trouble
to explain when all these events we are about to hear occurred.
Was it two thousand years ago? A thousand? Perhaps five hundred
or a hundred years ago? Or could they have taken place yesterday—? And may it please God that no similar world catastrophe
ever occurs again—The playwright groups together women, children, and old men, on the one hand, while on the other, he juxta-
poses the invaders with their countless names, stars which have
descended for plunder during the last three thousand years.

I see someone over there asking himself: Then what are we to
hear? Well, I, who have heard the play before, give you this answer:
This story is a memorial to your own people, to all those who sacrificed their lives that you might remain masters of yours. Keep
them in mind and permit your souls to rejoice that you have your
roots in a strong race.

A, yes, and one thing more. Many migratory laborers have
come to watch the performance. Make room for them. It is only
right that they should be given a good seat. Our own villagers can
even sit here on the steps; they can sit anywhere. And should they
feel inclined to interject something at the proper moment, no one
will interfere. This theater belongs to them. *Hostages* is dedicated
to all men, to the actors in the play and to the spectators, even
though, until yesterday, they were enemies.

ACT I

(*A tall, skeleton-thin woman,* ARETE, *emerges from the door of
the church. She appears older than she actually is. Dressed in
black, a kerchief wound tightly around her head and partly*

concealing her face, she stands on the church steps, making the sign of the Cross. She speaks softly, almost ritualistically: "May God—May God banish the evil . . . !" She sits down, not so much to rest as to think.

At the same moment, an old man, KOSMAS, *enters from right. His cape is thrown over his shoulders. He bears himself with ancient dignity and thus resembles an Apostle who descended from the templum. He ascends the steps slowly and stands at the top step. Extending his hand, he lays it on the shoulder of* ARETE, *who has silently bowed her head. The picture resembles a funeral pose.*)

KOSMAS. If we are to lament our fate at this point, Arete, how will we endure when the storm actually breaks? If you respect me as leader of the village and as the cousin of your deceased husband, you will heed to what I say. Stand firm. Do not give fear the opportunity to prostrate your spirit. And remember this: We are old and, whether it be today or tomorrow, our hour approaches when we must bow before the judgment of God. At the brink of the grave, all creatures on this earth should stand with dignity—

ARETE. Kosmas, as leader of the village and as the first cousin of my husband, I doubly value your judgment. You have always stood counselor to me in my unfortunate circumstances. However, the thing I foresee advancing directly toward us, seizes and holds me in a tight grip; it suffocates my heart. Much as I want to be optimistic in my thoughts, I cannot be. I cannot listen to empty solaces. I already envision it. His father's fate is tugging at him. And Lambrinos is all that sustains me; he is the man of my house, my only son.

KOSMAS. Arete, you speak about evil—And it is a crime against God that you should implicate your son's name—

ARETE. No, no—Let the evil fall into the bottomless sea and be drowned there. (*She crosses herself*) O God, do not permit a new catastrophe to lodge in our house! Life has given me countless sufferings—Have you, at any rate, spoken to him as you promised?

KOSMAS. Yes, I spoke to him today.

ARETE. And what did my son have to say? The truth is bitter, but it is far better that I know.

KOSMAS. I will tell you the whole truth, Arete. Lambrinos listened to me for a long time. I explained that his plans are insane. He cannot possibly reach the other side—

ARETE. As you say, his plans are insane!

KOSMAS. When a man goes out on a limb, what can he do against the millions? The old days are gone—

ARETE. True, very true. And what was his reply? What?

KOSMAS. He looked at me the way your late husband did before he went out with the rebels to attack the contrabandists, the Bulgarian rebels.

ARETE. Poor me! Didn't I already tell you? And he didn't open his mouth to speak to you? Didn't he even show some consideration for your judgment?

KOSMAS. He stopped for a moment to scrutinize me, as though searching my heart to discover if I was actually speaking the truth. Then he spread his body like an eagle—May God watch over Lambrinos; he has surpassed his father—Then he replied: "Old man Kosmas, you are my second father, and I know how deeply grieved you will be if I should go astray." "Certainly," I said. "Don't worry, then," he said. "I will never dishonor my family nor our village!" And I said: "Who will dare to utter such an insult! The bullet is rooted in your body—"

ARETE. And what did he tell you? What?

KOSMAS. He said that it was a miracle he had been saved. Others were killed!

ARETE. Is he ashamed of having lived?

KOSMAS. He meant that this was one more reason why he should perform his duty, as he called it. When you listen to what this strange duty is, you begin to wonder whether the one speaking is more sensible or more foolish.

ARETE. O-hou. Didn't I say a while ago that he is moving toward his father's destiny?

KOSMAS. He told me that his father came to him in a dream, carrying firearms and gleaming like an Archangel. He stood beside Lambrinos, and after touching him with a sparkling cutlass, pointed toward the border and smiled proudly. Lambrinos says that he heard his father give him this advice: "My son, sometimes there is joy even in death!" It was like a song. Then his father pierced the night like a shooting star and went in the direction where he had killed the contrabandists, and where he was to be killed later through treachery—

ARETE. O-hou! You drive a knife through my heart! A knife! Foolish me, I am to blame for everything. Ever since he was a baby, I brought him up with the image of his father carrying firearms always before him. Deprived by death, I sought to bring my

husband back to life, to resurrect him in our home, to hear him
breathe again, my life and my protector. And all the while I inflamed the boy with my hatred for his father's murderers. "Accursed
be the hand that struck him down! Accursed!" What was a child to
think? I shaped my child like putty in firearms and hatred. Wasn't
I the one who brought his father to him in his dreams, carrying
firearms? Wasn't I the one who gave him the black-handled dagger
to take back his father's blood? Wasn't I the one who taught him
to listen for dead men's voices? What was my son expected to do
when he had grown to manhood?

KOSMAS.   Arete, dry your eyes and conceal your tears in your
heart. There, your son is coming toward us. Photine is behind him.
It would be better if you two women spoke to him. A son listens
more attentively to the appeals of his mother and his beloved than
he does to the words of an old man. I will go into the church to
light a candle. May Saint George help our land—

(KOSMAS *advances slowly toward the door of the church.*
ARETE *dries her eyes with the back of her hand.* LAMBRINOS
and PHOTINE *enter from left.* LAMBRINOS *is a tall, dark, brawny
young man. He carries an old soldier's cloak over his shoulders.
His hair is windblown and resembles a lion's mane. His face
has taken on a premature austerity; it is almost sad. He has a
sparkling gaze.* PHOTINE *is stately with loose blonde hair, and
she walks lightly in the full maturity of her deep love.*)

ARETE.   Welcome, my children.

LAMBRINOS.   (*Offering his mother a rose*) A good honor to
you, Mother. This rose is from father's grave, the first rose of the
year to blossom from his heart.

ARETE.   (*Taking the rose, she looks at it for some time, then
tucks it in her bosom*) Would to God, my son, that thoughts of
your father make you gentle and lead you to virtue.

LAMBRINOS.   As you say, Mother, he always directs me on a
virtuous path. It seems that any man who walks on earth with
courage cannot depart from us very readily.

ARETE.   Yes, of course. But it is one thing to remember someone you've loved when he's buried in the ground, and quite another
thing to see him alive before your eyes.

LAMBRINOS.   At any rate, whenever I remember my father, my
spirit becomes dauntless again.

ARETE.   One man alive, my son, is worth all the dead buried
in the ground. You were a year old when the villagers brought

me your butchered father. They stretched him out on the sun porch. Our house was overrun by death; some three meters long. Tell me, what was the result of all this? The earth swallowed his youth! And the two of us, without a man in the house, decayed all alone in our unprotected condition—I'm not saying that a man must not stand with dignity, but only to that point where lightning will not scorch him. No, he must stand taller.

LAMBRINOS. Mother, everything I say appears strange to you, and likewise, everything you say appears strange to me. Speak openly.

ARETE. My love, may God take years from my life and give them to you in hours. Don't ever again speak words which will have the power to bind you to action, because then, instead of safeguarding yourself, you will bare your breast at the first signs of fury and lay yourself open to assault.

PHOTINE. But what is the matter today? Have you heard something? Has something happened? Speak! I cannot endure it.

ARETE. Nothing, by the God who hears me; nothing has happened! Here, the rose Lambrinos gave me brought back the past. And I am relating the sufferings of the living. And then, with the foreigners who have overrun our country, our fate has become burdensome; as burdensome as it can possibly be. I repeat, this is all the meaning there is to what I said earlier: The wise man does not go about provoking his restless destiny. He is careful. He should even be careful of the foreigner's shadow. The farther away he remains, the better. My son, I want you to plant roots. The time has come for you to marry—

LAMBRINOS. Good, good! Don't you fret, and it will be so. Think back to the legends you used to tell me, because you will have countless grandchildren to raise. Come, Mother, raise your head. Drown your sorrows and smile.

(PHOTINE *bows her head in embarrassment, while* ARETE *goes to her with some ecstasy and embraces and kisses her.*)

ARETE. You are like the swallow, my daughter, and my heart is overjoyed at the sight of you. Would to God that my grandchildren resemble you. There is no greater happiness in all the world than this. May God's blessings be upon you, my children.

(ARETE *turns to leave.* LAMBRINOS *stops her.*)

LAMBRINOS. And now, I want you to promise—
ARETE. Whatever you wish, my son.

LAMBRINOS. While Photine is under your roof, I want you to
show her the same consideration that I show her. And Photine, too,
must show you the same consideration.

ARETE. If I said something, my tongue is to blame, not my
heart. (*To* PHOTINE) Do you have any complaints, my daughter?

PHOTINE. If I have complaints, may God who is listening
scorch me to death! You have been more than a second mother to
me. You took me into your home as an orphan when my own parents were uprooted—

ARETE. Yes, yes, it is as you say. And you are my daughter
twice over, the support of my generation and the sprout—

LAMBRINOS. I want no more. All three of us are united in life
and in death!

ARETE. I am leaving now. If I could, I would run like a young
girl. God be with you.

(ARETE *exits.* PHOTINE *moves closer to* LAMBRINOS; *she looks
into his eyes for a long moment. She rubs her head against his.
Her voice is happy; at times it becomes heavy with an overflowing love.*)

PHOTINE. Sometimes you're hard, my precious, as hard as
steel; sometimes you're soft like the wingless bird. Today, you're
soft like the light of dawn. And wherever you stand, it becomes
like the day of Easter!

LAMBRINOS. I thank God, my darling, for bringing me into
this life to find you.

(*A distant rumbling is heard. Both stop to listen. The rumbling
fades.*)

PHOTINE. Let it be a lie that the invaders have reached our
borders.

LAMBRINOS. I've told you before: stop thinking about it—

PHOTINE. They say that wherever the curse leads their footsteps, the villages are turned to ashes and cinders. And innocent
blood flows like a raging river.

LAMBRINOS. Let them say—

PHOTINE. I even heard that—

LAMBRINOS. Photine, be still!

(*An uncomfortable silence intervenes.* PHOTINE *bends her body
forward, as though in a pose of true supplication. And she is
almost in tears.*)

LAMBRINOS. Would you like us to build a small hut, only large enough for the two of us, beside the spring, there where the water nestles to sleep? And we'll plant squash around the hut, or lilies. Isn't it all the same?

PHOTINE. O, how I love the large, milky-white, cone-shaped lilies—

LAMBRINOS. And two walnut trees to climb side by side, straight up to the sky, their branches intertwined.

PHOTINE. I will plant your tree, and you will plant mine.

LAMBRINOS. I say that we should begin at once to clear the rocks from the place and plant the corn. Plenty of corn. We will have children, and children have mouths which must be fed.

PHOTINE. (*Silent again*) Tell me. Which is worse, war or enslavement?

LAMBRINOS. Enslavement. Is there any doubt?

PHOTINE. That is what I say. You become a slave to the enslaved. (*She suddenly bursts into tears*) O, I am losing my mind!

LAMBRINOS. Photine, I want you to be brave!

PHOTINE. Don't worry. I will be brave.

LAMBRINOS. You are not to cry in difficult hours.

PHOTINE. Here, I am drying my eyes. The foreigners will never see me in tears—

LAMBRINOS. Be sharply resolute. Grit your teeth—

PHOTINE. You will never have to bow on my account.

LAMBRINOS. I have always been certain of that—Thank you.

PHOTINE. Go ahead. Do what your heart dictates. What am I but a part of you. Forgive the way I behave—

LAMBRINOS. Never forget what I am going to say: The world is so wide. It is a pity that it must become a narrow noose around our necks because of men's thoughtlessness or cowardice.

(*From right and left the old men of the village enter, walking in step. Some wear caps over their heads, others kerchiefs. Four or five, whose beards are white, are wearing their capes; they are dignified, patient, gentle, and wise. They take positions to right and left of the church steps and sit without order. KOSMAS slowly descends from the church. To his greetings the old men nod their heads. In the meantime, PHOTINE exits and LAMBRINOS moves apart. He sits down and remains thoughtful and motionless.*)

FIRST ELDER. Old-man Kosmas, have you heard anything to brighten my heart?

KOSMAS. It seems that the invaders have advanced and taken over our cities and seaports. They have laid open the joints of our land; they are striking at the very heart to shatter our Homeland.

SECOND ELDER. Two hours ago I met a traveler passing through. "A good hour to you, Old Man," he said. "And to you, young man. Would you like to stop over at my house to rest, and later you can continue on your way?" "No," he replied; "the enemy will be here at any minute now. It is better that I go on!" "And where," I asked him, "is the enemy?" "Close by. They will be here today. Take care of yourselves." That's what he said; I'm relating what I heard. And may God on high and the Saint who protects us raise their hands to strike those who are striking us—

THIRD ELDER. You, Lambrinos, the educated member of the village, tell me: Why is it that the same thing always occurs to Greece, ever since she was first created?

LAMBRINOS. The slaves of every land have always hated our Homeland; in fact, they hate every country which holds its head high. Thus, under numerous unconcerned pretexts, every generation sends its diversified armies to our borders, two or three times. The various starving armies sometimes arrive from the East, sometimes from the West, and sometimes they descend from the sky. They come to plunder whatever stands in the way of their lunacy.

KOSMAS. Yes, but as far as I know, their endeavors have been futile for thousands of years. With a single voice, our people attack the pirate wherever they find him, on land and on sea, until they destroy him.

SECOND ELDER. Once, during my youth, I said to the old mountaineer Liakouras: "You have no guns and you lack bullets. Then what is the secret of your slaughter of the Turks?" "Our secret has never been disclosed," Liakouras replied. "Yes, but tell me so I can learn your secret, too." Just then a youth who was sitting beside him jumped to his feet and said, "They call it freedom, the pride and joy of every man, of whichever time in history."

FIRST ELDER. Nothing can supplant what life has taught me these seventy years.

KOSMAS. Our Homeland prefers to fall a thousand times over rather than to bow before a master. The life of an enslaved man is a suffocating death, three times over—

FIRST ELDER. Then there is nothing left but to tighten our lips and to attack, wherever we encounter them.

THIRD ELDER. O God, we supplicate your Grace because we are weak.

KOSMAS.   Extend Your hand and bless our Homeland!

THE ELDERS.   (*In chorus*) Extend Your hand and bless our Homeland!

(*Voices are heard offstage, which become an uproar, a wailing; they are cries of women approaching the church. Some of the Elders sit at ease; three or four sit on center stage as though rooted to earth. Others ascend the steps and gaze far into the distance. LAMBRINOS, his body rigid as a column, stands higher than the rest. Most of the people are gazing at him with great pride.*)

KOSMAS.   What do you see, Lambrinos?

LAMBRINOS.   Women and children climbing in our direction.

SECOND ELDER.   (*Calling loudly*) Eh, Women! Eh, Women!

LAMBRINOS.   Your blessings, fellow villagers. May we meet again safely!

KOSMAS.   Wait, Lambrinos! Do not go!

LAMBRINOS.   Farewell! Health and joy to you!

FIRST ELDER.   May the blessings of God be with you!

(*LAMBRINOS exits from one side, while the women enter from the opposite side like a frightened herd. Some are shouting, some crying; the old women are simultaneously lamenting. One can only distinguish such phrases as: "Woe to us!" "Where are we to go!" "Who will conceal us?" "The foreigners will kill us—" etc.*)

KOSMAS.   The invaders!

(*The women in unison and in a variety of voices, which slowly blend into one, reply: "The invaders!"*)

FIRST WOMAN.   They are on their way to the village. They are already here!

FIRST YOUNG GIRL.   And they are like wolves. They are coming in this direction, armed like devils.

SECOND YOUNG GIRL.   They carry heavy shining firearms. They will descend on us and devour us.

THIRD YOUNG GIRL.   Their iron strikes with fury. The earth trembles wherever they walk. I hear their cruel footsteps in my heart.

FIRST WOMAN.   The wolves will soon be here!

SECOND WOMAN.   The wolves have come!

THIRD WOMAN. I advise you to hide!

(The women, with separate voices, which gradually blend into a single voice, cry: "Hide!")

KOSMAS. Women, you are disturbing our line of thought. There is no comprehensible meaning to your cries. Speak, you there, Old Woman, after you have bridled your fears!

THIRD WOMAN. Futile words—Hide while there is yet time!

KOSMAS. *(To the* THIRD WOMAN*)* Stop! *(To the* OLD WOMAN*)* You speak!

FIRST OLD WOMAN. What should I, a miserable creature, know more than the others know. My limbs have become paralyzed, poor woman, and I have come crawling to bring you the news—They are tall, blond, red-faced, with savage, unsmiling faces; square faces, which resemble bulls before they have been castrated—O God, how I tremble!

FIRST WOMAN. Let us go; let us go while there is yet time.

SECOND OLD WOMAN. I see them making slaves of my daughters!

FIRST YOUNG GIRL. Women, these are cruel masters who have descended on us. Only death can save us!

SECOND OLD WOMAN. And where will they take the men, Holy Mother Protectress?

FIRST WOMAN. I am leaving. I am taking my two children and leaving.

KOSMAS. You are going nowhere. You will remain here with the others.

FIRST WOMAN. They say that old men are wise. Through that wisdom of yours, you risk losing the respect of your children, because, once this war is over, they will call you cowards. Consider this well. The conquerors will soon be here.

KOSMAS. All those who have come to this land, my daughter, have departed in shame. No matter who they were; no matter who they are!

FIRST OLD WOMAN. And what do you counsel, Elder?

KOSMAS. The only counsel I give you, women, is that you remain as quiet as serpents. There will be time to discharge your poison.

FIRST WOMAN. And even if I leave, where will I go? Who will take me in? I will remain here. I have already said so.

(The FIRST WOMAN *draws away and begins a soft lament.*

*Other women join the lament, while the sound of heavy foot
steps is heard approaching.)*

SECOND OLD WOMAN. As the animals smell the tracks of death
so I, pitiable and star-crossed, see disaster enshrouding us.

KOSMAS. Women, leave off lamenting. You are certainly justified, but laments are futile. Conceal your suffering, and above all
exhibit no fear. Stand there behind the men. A nation which con-
fronts its destiny without fear is never defeated. Our honor will
be lost if fear makes the slightest movement in your eyes. Look
the enemy squarely in the eyes. Not we, but they must bow.

*(The women, stifling their sobs, proceed to hide behind the
men. Simultaneously, the sound of a bugle is heard, a deep
rhythmic song, followed by heavy footsteps. STURM enters
followed by his attendants. He is tall, squarely-built, and unyielding; he wears a helmet with a long plume. The officers
accompanying him and the men who fill the stage differ little
from their leader. As STURM enters the villagers fall back in
alarm. The ELDERS are in the front line and two steps before
them is KOSMAS. An icy silence ensues, overflowing with hatred
The conquerors stand before the steps of the church, slightly
higher, erect, provocative in their arrogance. They are the new
masters.)*

STURM. I am called Sturm!
VILLAGERS. Sturm!

(The bugle call of victory is heard offstage.)

STURM. And I conquer this land in the name of the Fatherland. From this day on, I will be master wherever your language
is spoken. I derive my power from these iron-clad men standing
beside me like weapon-bound columns. We can destroy any resistance. We plant terror everywhere. Anyone who dares to raise his
head, in which his decadent brain has hatched a cunning plot
will see our sword fall heavily and without compunction. Know this
from the beginning. We have torn our hearts from our breasts
and have supplanted them with steel, steel! We have only one aim:
to become masters of the world!

KOSMAS. Strangers, your arrogance appears to have increased
from the moment you stepped on Greek soil.

STURM. Old man, I honor your land. And know this before
you begin to contradict me: it is an honorable ear which will listen
to you.

KOSMAS. Then, I have only one reply to make: Never, but never, will you become rooted on our soil!

VILLAGERS. O, O—

STURM. Words, boastful words. Even the armies of devils cannot resist the brave arm of the soldiers I command.

KOSMAS. In this land, Stranger, every mountain has its flag and every cave its hiding place.

STURM. And I, in turn, will scorch your mountains. And if necessary I will shatter every rock with dynamite. Every head that opposes me will rot as the starving wolf rots and loses its hair. I am still able to discern each secret being hatched in your houses. My power has many eyes, and woe to you!

VILLAGERS. Woe to us!

STURM. Now, it is to your advantage, not to mine, to show that you are an intelligent race. The time is past when words were the spirit of the world. And you, first of all, who speak in behalf of all the others, know that the best thing you can do is to bridle your tongue.

KOSMAS. Not before I have told you what you are entitled to know. You are entering into my home with guile; you are an uninvited guest; and I, the owner of that house, insist on being heard.

STURM. Do not forget, however, that often my sword gives the reply.

KOSMAS. All of our people, Stranger, have died by means of a bullet, an honorable bullet, and not by means of fraud. And if you consider it courageous to kill an old man who seeks to speak freely, my Homeland will boast about the dead, and your Fatherland will sense the shame of it.

STURM. Your words are taking an unwholesome direction. Be careful!

KOSMAS. My silence will be of no benefit to you. One of the others who is listening to us would shoot a more poisonous word through your heart.

STURM. That is enough! I know what you have to say: that slavery has never become rooted in your land. I have been taught your history in school. But my country is not far behind. She too fights and seeks to live.

KOSMAS. Stranger, the tops of the mountains of my land have never been enslaved for thousands of years; their spirit has never bowed—

STURM. Yes, but our spirit also has breadth, and it surpasses the boundaries of your thoughts.

KOSMAS. My thoughts tell me that the world wants no master.
STURM. The world has always had a master, and now it is our
turn to become masters.
KOSMAS. And I tell you that injustice can lead you nowhere.
STURM. You waste time talking about justice. I hold Greece,
and this suffices me.

(*Suddenly, gunshots are heard; the crowd of villagers scatter
for a moment, then gather behind the men.* STURM *stands motionless; two officers exit. A messenger enters and says something like an inarticulate cry.* STURM *becomes furious; he
mounts higher. A young girl runs in from right.*)

YOUNG GIRL. They have torn the flag of the foreigners!
VILLAGERS. The flag!
YOUNG GIRL. Yes. They have torn it into a thousand pieces!
VILLAGERS. O, O—

(*An officer enters. From a distance, the voice of* LAMBRINOS *is
heard.* KOSMAS *mounts the steps and stands beside* STURM, *confronting his hatred.* KOSMAS *stands undecided for a moment,
then mounts higher.*)

STURM. He has escaped, eh! The slave has escaped! And is he
boasting about it now?

(KOSMAS *listens attentively. He repeats the words that echo
from the ravine.*)

KOSMAS. Lambrinos is his name.
VILLAGERS. Lambrinos.
STURM. Shut up!
KOSMAS. (*Repeating*) Wherever you go, you will find me
there before you!
STURM. That is precisely what I want. That is what I want!
I swear that even death will not deprive me of him. And you,
slaves, do not smile! You will pay for this insult to the flag. I
promise that whoever delivers him to me will gain my favor at
once. And you, army of depraved men,I command that you bar the
doors of your houses. From this moment, the world for you extends
only as far as the limits of your village. And everyone, old men,
women, children—You are all Hostages!

(KOSMAS *descends the steps slowly. He again hesitates when
he is on the same level with* STURM, *then continues to descend*

unperturbed. The women of the village encircle him and accompany him toward the exit. Except for STURM, *the other foreigners step aside to allow the villagers to pass.*)

STURM. Let what has just occurred be a lesson to you. Consider the extent of my duty. This is a difficult land we have conquered. Never forget it. And always be on guard. Opinions of old men are dangerous. Bitterness in woman is dangerous. Fear in her children breeds hatred. And the untrod mountains of this land mean ruin. Should you see a smile on a frightened face, even on that of a child, do not mistake it for a sign of friendship. The Greek people are clever with their snares, and their words are full of deceit. Most of all, never speak about justice in this land. Your sword is Law. If we can maintain the spirit of Greece under submission, then we will find the path to the world opened wide to us.

(*A heavy military march as they exit.*)

ACT II

SCENE: *The same.*

(*A young boy of fifteen enters. He looks around and sighs. Then he enters the church to reappear before long. His face is shining now. He sings a kelphtic song softly. Little by little, the song emerges from the very depths of the youth, heavy and bitter, a song provoked by enslavement.*)

YOUNG BOY. Mother, hear me say, no more I'll labor for the stranger,
Tomorrow morning, I'll arise, gird round my waist my armor,
And hasten to the hideout to join there with the *klephtes,*
The other brave young men, together to give battle,
To fight the whole day through, to kill the stranger.

(*While the boy is singing, his sister, a girl of about twelve years, enters. She appears to have been searching for him.*

She listens to his song for a while. When the boy stops singing, he jumps up, and she calls to him.)

GIRL.   Lefteris! Eh, Lefteris!

BOY.   Why do you follow me? Go away! Go home!

GIRL.   Mother sent me to call you.

BOY.   The house is for the women. I am going to become like Lambrinos. I will take to the mountains. I can endure this no longer. I want to be free—Free, do you hear? But what can a girl know?

GIRL.   And what do you mean by that?

BOY.   What do I mean? Well, well—Anyone who is on the mountain and kills the foreigners is free. I want to be like Lambrinos.

GIRL.   And where will you find a knife?

BOY.   Here it is! I have it here in my bosom.

GIRL.   You took it from grandfather! I will tell him!

BOY.   I think grandfather saw me take it, but he didn't say anything. He was half-smiling.

GIRL.   Come, let us go home—I won't tell on you.

BOY.   Didn't you hear me? I told you to go away. I am going to the mountains to become a guerrilla fighter.

GIRL.   (*Catching hold of him*) Come, I tell you. Mother is crying. Where will you leave us?

BOY.   I will never return home. I want to kill Sturm! I want to kill Sturm!

GIRL.   (*Begins to cry*) Don't shout because I am afraid.

BOY.   Don't be afraid. From now on, I will take care of you. Tell that to Mother, too. I will take care of you—I have the knife here—I'm going!

(*He vaults over the fence and disappears. The* GIRL *dashes after him, crying convulsively.*)

GIRL.   Lefteris! Lefteris! Come back!

(*The women enter out of breath. The* OLD WOMEN *move slowly. Their clothing is ragged and patched. Some children, boys and girls, are always in the midst of the villagers. The signs of hunger are deeply entrenched on their faces. They resemble ghosts. All are talking among themselves: "How did this happen?" "What is it?" "He has left two orphaned children." "How will his wife endure the suffering?" "Holy Mother, save us from a dishonorable death!"*)

FIRST OLD WOMAN. I have yet to learn, daughter, how it happened.

FIRST YOUNG GIRL. They found weapons concealed in the cave with the secret opening, down in the ravine, close by the big plane tree. It seems they were stolen from the foreigners. And they suspected Liakos, who pretended to be the village idiot. That was why they were not afraid to permit him to work for them. To get to the point, they caught Liakos and put a rope around his neck right there on the spot.

SECOND YOUNG GIRL. They say that the foreigners have decided not to bury Liakos, but to make the villagers file past to look at him for punishment. And because they are afraid that someone might steal the body, they have placed a double and triple sentry on the surrounding hilltops. Not even a bird can approach.

FIRST OLD WOMAN. And weren't they affected by his wife's laments?

FIRST YOUNG GIRL. They kicked her away like a dog, even though she fell at their feet.

FIRST OLD WOMAN. Heavy is the hand of enslavement. Much lighter is the hand of death!

(LIAKOS' *wife enters. With her clothing torn, she is supported by her two children, a boy and a girl, both crying. They seat her in the back, on a slightly higher level. A silence ensues. Suddenly, the two children break into convulsive sobs. The mother allows them to cry for a while, then she embraces them and dries their cheeks.*)

LIAKOS' WIFE. To whom shall I shout out this injustice? To whom?

FIRST OLD WOMAN. Even were you to tear out your lungs, who would hear you, daughter?

LIAKOS' WIFE. Which hand will bring me the head of the murderer?

SECOND OLD WOMAN. No one, daughter. Be patient—

LIAKOS' WIFE. O, my husband, my beloved! What death was reserved for you! How is your wretched body to find rest? Where will it find rest?

(LIAKOS' WIFE *bursts into sobs. The girl sobs with her, while the boy stifles his cries. The women begin a dirge in voices that are barely audible.*)

FIRST YOUNG GIRL. Would to God that I could see the enemy's houses encircled by fire, their land trembling with earthquakes. May the wind which beats without a sound tear their limbs, and may they never find a grave.

SECOND YOUNG GIRL. O, unbearable is the suffering of a tomorrow which cannot be predicted and of a today which is a noose around the throat!

SECOND YOUNG GIRL. To know beforehand what kind of fate the day will bring, what kind of new calamity will come to torture, and never let a tear fall from the eyes—

SECOND OLD WOMAN. All my tears are dry; the sources of my grief are all barren. And I utter not a sound!

FIRST OLD WOMAN. God, lighten the sufferings of the people.

(*The* FIRST WOMAN *of Act I runs in. Other women follow her.*)

FIRST WOMAN. Villagers, eh, you villagers—The Elders are ordering us to remain here in the churchyard. No one is to leave.

(*They all talk at once:* "Why?" "What is happening now?" "What news do you bring?" "Tell us!")

FIRST WOMAN. News has come that the invaders are burning the leading villages, one after the other—

(*An inarticulate cry is heard from the* OLD WOMEN, *which cry gradually fades into:* "O, O—.")

FIRST OLD WOMAN. Speak, daughter; speak!

FIRST WOMAN. I know nothing more. What can I tell you? Only that the foreigners have gone insane. They are on their way here to gratify their shameful fury.

(*An inarticulate cry is heard again from the women, which gradually fades to become an* "O, O—")

FIRST WOMAN. From some words here and there, I gathered that our people, led by Lambrinos, ambushed the foreigners at the ravine of Orias, and there massacred them for sure. Except for three who escaped to bring the news to Sturm, the rest, some fifty of them, were all killed.

LIAKOS' WIFE. (*Seated where she is, she takes off her kerchief and touches the ground three times with her knee in genuflexion*) God be praised for lodging in my house and answering my plea!

SECOND YOUNG GIRL. It would be better to scatter far and wide. Who will prevent them from setting fire to the church and burning us to death?

THIRD YOUNG GIRL. I don't know what to do!

FIRST WOMAN. The Elders must have a serious reason for ordering us to remain here. Who is to prevent the foreigners from setting fire to the village and burning us to death!

(*Cries are heard offstage*: "Yes— Yes—" "Speak— Speak—" "I will tell you the truth—")

FIRST OLD WOMAN. We will wait here with our hopes in God!

SECOND OLD WOMAN. And it is pointless to keep raising our voices!

THIRD YOUNG GIRL. I hold my heart steady—

SECOND YOUNG GIRL. And I close my mouth—

(*The* FIRST WOMAN *suddenly sways from the strain and half-sits on the steps. She speaks in a voice overflowing with grief.*)

FIRST WOMAN. Even I who am as fearful as a child say that we must withhold as long as possible.

(*The* ELDERS *enter. They are tall, thin as skeletons, and resemble Byzantine saints.* KOSMAS *leads them in and he, more than the others, appears to be frowning. The* WOMEN *encircle the* ELDERS *and fasten their eyes on them in agony.*)

FIRST OLD WOMAN. What is happening? Tell me—

KOSMAS. Go and kneel in the church. That is all I can recommend for the moment. And pray to the Sainted Knight for help—

FIRST YOUNG GIRL. They told us that the foreigners are burning the head villages and that they are on their way here—

KOSMAS. Yes, daughter, wherever they pass they leave ashes and cinders behind. Hell itself has regurgitated these men, and they will soon be here. But have no fear—It is within our power to save ourselves.

SECOND YOUNG GIRL. How? I don't see how.

SECOND OLD WOMAN. They told us that more than fifty men were killed in the mountains.

KOSMAS. You heard this right, old woman. They fell into the trap Lambrinos set and were killed—

FIRST WOMAN. Elder, much as I want to keep up courage, I cannot. Do you think perhaps you ought to hide us? If they should come upon us, what safety is there in the church? And furthermore, how am I to blame? How is it my fault?

(*As before, her body sways and she half sits down. Her voice ends in a sob.*)

KOSMAS. Daughter, it is better that the imprisoned man should slide through some unexpected crack in the wall than to wait for the hour when he must be led with drumbeats to the hanging rope. This is what we are now doing so the women can escape.

FIRST OLD WOMAN. Old man Kosmas, I cannot suppress my fears!

KOSMAS. Do not seek to learn more. We who settle the affairs of the village and of our children to whom this land belongs, have thus decided. Whatever befalls us will descend on our heads first. Let whoever escapes remember the people who fell for their sakes. (*Heavy footsteps are heard outside, becoming increasingly louder*) Quick! Into the church! It seems that our hour has come. I hear Sturm approaching.

(*The women enter the church with hasty footsteps, except for the woman who lost her husband. She always keeps her children beside her, one on either side.*)

LIAKOS' WIFE. Let me speak about my husband to the master of the foreigners. I must speak to him. He is obligated to give me permission to bury him—

(STURM *enters with his followers. Their faces are fierce. Even the* ELDERS *fall back a step or two in alarm.* KOSMAS *hesitates for a moment, then he becomes rooted in his place.*)

STURM. I always find you lazy people in the churchyard, always first with words, you spies, you hypocrites—You starve to death so you can say that I am taking your food to force you to bow before my obstinacy. And you attack me, wherever you encounter me; before me, behind me, you set ambushes everywhere. You set fires; and should one of my men drop out of line, annihilation awaits him—Today, I have the proper occasion to reach an understanding with you—What does this woman want?

KOSMAS. Permission to go to the mill—

STURM. The village is under blockade—There is no permission!

KOSMAS. Speak, daughter!

LIAKOS' WIFE. I have only a few words to say—I want to bury my husband—

KOSMAS. She wants the body of her executed husband to put it to rest—

STURM. That thief, that spy, who armed the hands of those murderers with our weapons!

KOSMAS. Our fellow villager, who is still unburied—

STURM. Send this woman away—

LIAKOS' WIFE. Master of the foreigners, your fury has been sated. Now I seek to cover my husband with earth—I want my husband, I tell you—

STURM. (*To the soldiers*) Send her away from here!

(*Two soldiers take hold of her. She eludes them and suddenly rushes at* STURM.)

LIAKOS' WIFE. I spit in your face, Crucifier!

STURM. (*To the soldiers who have again taken her in custody*) Catch her! And now take her to the mill. Once there—to teach this womanly rage what it is to spit on Sturm—you will cut off her tongue.

(*The soldiers pull her away and exit with her. Her sobbing children follow as they look now at the* ELDERS, *now at the foreign soldiers. They are lost in a strange and cruel world.*)

KOSMAS. You first took away the mill. It belongs to her.

STURM. Nothing belongs to her. I am master of the place, and I can dispose of what I want.

KOSMAS. Your soldiers killed her brother ten days ago.

STURM. Her family appears to be vindictive.

KOSMAS. Not any more than others.

STURM. I will kill like a dog any man who defies my orders.

KOSMAS. She lost her mind after what happened to her husband. Otherwise, her actions would have been prudent.

STURM. You are most compassionate toward her, and it appears to me that you are in sympathy with what you just witnessed.

KOSMAS. Do not cut out her tongue. Her dead will remain unmourned.

STURM. I have already told you: my decision is final!

KOSMAS. Why should the blameless suffer?

STURM. You are all to blame. From you down to the last child.

And I see no difference in this guilt. You are all the same, those of you who have gone mad in the mountains and those of you who shape cunning words in the cities.

KOSMAS. If it is a fault to have been born in this country, I tell you plainly that, in our Homeland, man fights against man.

STURM. I see that your audacity is being aroused again. Do you believe that I am unaware of what gives you courage to contradict me so boldly? However, before you fall to your knees to scream for mercy for your villagers, whom you so boastfully protect, it would be better to assist in bringing an end to this rash slaughter while there is yet time. It is in your hands.

KOSMAS. As long as it is in my hands, why should I deny it?

STURM. We will see shortly—You have already learned what has happened to the other villages?

KOSMAS. The smoke has carried the message to me.

STURM. Fifty men are dead at the hands of your spies; my most select troops. Have you learned about this?

KOSMAS. Nothing remains a secret.

STURM. Then, have you no suspicion about the identity of the spy? From where did he come? Where was he taking the secret messages?

KOSMAS. How should I know this?

STURM. And yet, he set out from this village. From here!

KOSMAS. This is the first I hear of this.

STURM. You hear everything for the first time; yet secretly, it is you who sets the projects into motion.

KOSMAS. You have the village under blockade. Which way should I turn? How can I move?

STURM. These are your lands, and it appears that you have many means of sending out messages. Wherever I go, Lambrinos is there before me; wherever I turn, I find him in the passages, waiting to destroy me.

KOSMAS. You fight against one another with weapons. Let who may be killed! Why should we who are in this place interfere?

STURM. You will learn shortly. (*To the soldiers*) Bring the bitch here!

(*Two soldiers exit and return at once to throw* PHOTINE *at* STURM'S *feet. She is thinner, but has a serene face. The girls and old women come out of the church door. Most of them attempt to go near* PHOTINE, *but they are afraid and thus move behind the* ELDERS. *Except for* KOSMAS, *who, from his manner appears to have understood the situation, the other* ELDERS *stand amazed and look at one another in puzzled silence. The women, murmuring and fearful, withdraw to upper stage, as far as possible from the fury of* STURM.)

STURM. Only the truth can save you. Do you hear? If you confess in detail everything you know, you will be saved. But before you open your mouth to give me a string of fairy tales, think carefully, or my fury will break out threefold.

(STURM *straddles* PHOTINE, *who in the meantime has attempted to rise. He pushes her back to the ground. The women cry out*: *"Holy Mother, they will kill her!" "What happened?" "Why have they captured her?" "Where did they find her?"*)

STURM. Eh, you there, women, shut up! Now you here, speak! Explain how you came to be at the place where fifty of my soldiers were killed. And since the village was under blockade, why did you disobey my orders and slide through? Who gave you the secret messages? You are engaged to marry the arch-murderer Lambrinos, are you not?

PHOTINE. I belong to Lambrinos, yes.

STURM. If I catch all the threads of this conspiracy, which for a long time now have been operating behind my back and learning my secrets, as though behind every rock a spy is concealed; if I catch the leaders, then no one will have a thing to fear. Even you will be saved, if you tell me everything you know. You are a simple girl. How could your mind have conceived the idea of spying on my every movement? Someone convinced you and counseled you on what you were to do and how to escape me as you carried whatever you discovered to my enemies. The one who taught you this lesson and implicated you in this plunder is the guilty one—You are about to be killed for the sake of someone else only out of thoughtlessness. As you see, I speak to you with kindness. Now it is your turn to prove to me what there is in your mind—

PHOTINE. I have nothing to say. I don't know.

STURM. Look around at your fellow villagers and consider carefully. Most of the women are your friends. You will be responsible for whatever happens to them. What do they owe you? Why have you anchored yourself in obstinacy and defy your own village? The guilty man pays his debt. He does not allow others to shoulder his guilty deeds. But if the single guilty man is not found, then you will all discharge his debt. And at once, if you do not confess the truth to me!

PHOTINE.   None of the villagers are to blame. No one learned, no one knew what I carried out, of my own accord. I left at midnight and returned at daybreak. Who was to see me, since all the houses were barred? I alone am to blame and no one else—

STURM.   (*To one of his officers*) How many prisoners have you selected as reprisals?

OFFICER.   Thirty!

(*The villagers hear the words with horror. Several women cover their faces with their hands, while one of the women in the back is heard to repeat: "Holy Mother! Holy Mother!"*)

STURM.   For the time being, select twenty more from this group. Show preference for those who stand firmly on their feet—

PHOTINE.   (*Falling at* STURM's *feet*) I swear by your children. No, I tell you. Wait! No one knows a thing!

STURM.   (*Kicking* PHOTINE) Take her away. Stretch her out in the ravine and apply a hot iron to her back. And later, I will come to continue the interrogation. Go; let us not delay!

(*While the* OFFICER *takes two or three steps toward the women,* PHOTINE *looks at him resolutely. Her voice is commanding.*)

PHOTINE.   (*To the* OFFICER) Wait! Don't touch them!

STURM.   (*To* PHOTINE) Have you changed your mind? If so, proceed. Why do you delay? When I have learned all the details, I will take you under my protection, and, so long as you live, you will have nothing to fear.

PHOTINE.   First, swear an oath. The life of every villager will be sacred to you.

STURM.   I have already said so. And now, I am listening. Who involved you in this spying.

PHOTINE.   No one!

STURM.   Shut your mouth, woman of Satan! You are lying!

PHOTINE.   I went to see Lambrinos. I became involved of my own accord—And I carried messages secretly—

STURM.   Who gave them to you? Confess his name.

PHOTINE.   Liakos, the one your men hanged!

STURM.   It is now all the hanged men who will be the guilty ones—You lie—Liakos was an idiot. How could he possibly have dug my grave before my very eyes for such a long time without my suspecting it? No—Wasn't he half-insane? He could not have been worthy of such a deed. It is someone else, some devil, some shrewd man. No, for certain, the hanged man was not the leader of the spies—He was somewhere in the middle of the chain, but never the leader!

PHOTINE.   Only he and no one else! And he had his wits about him! His role was to pretend to be half-insane, and he succeeded in deceiving you.

(KOSMAS *advances, raises* PHOTINE *to her feet, and pushes her aside.*)

KOSMAS.   That is enough, Sturm! Photine is not to blame!

STURM.   Do not worry. The guilty leader will soon fall into my hands!

KOSMAS.   You search in vain!

STURM.   Who is it? Who?

KOSMAS.   It is I.

STURM.   No, no! In spite of the fact that you hatch hatred within you, I believe that you could never have had a hand in this deed. You know how to protect yourself—You are shrewd.

KOSMAS.   You always attack with cunning, and your thoughts bring me unspeakable shame. Stranger, the will of the villagers has made me their leader, not so I can reap easy honors when life flows smoothly but when the storm breaks. And so, from the moment your feet stepped on our soil to enslave me, I became the first, as indeed I have that right, to attack you.

STURM.   Not with words, but with deeds, must you convince me that you are the leader.

KOSMAS.   Ask anyone here for the name of the man who put Liakos to work for you, and you will learn.

STURM.   If you give me the names of your accomplices, I will believe you.

KOSMAS.   Why should I tell you their names when there was no one else.

STURM.   First of all, you are attempting to save this one here by taking all the blame yourself.

KOSMAS.   Yes, because it was I who sent Photine to deliver the last message, in which I told them how they should destroy you, one hour earlier, so that our people can breath again. Certainly, I take all blame myself. When I give an order, not with a whip, but with the free will of everyone, no one can say a word. I dug your grave, and I am proud of it. I spied on you, wherever you

444 INTRODUCTION TO GREEK LITERATURE

turned your footsteps, wherever your soldiers went. And I chose Photine. Here she is before you. Let her tell you.

PHOTINE. I went of my own accord. Every girl would be proud, and I, more than all the others—I, who am to become the wife, of Lambrinos.

KOSMAS. Daughter, come to my arms. Let me kiss you. Your pride brings tears to my eyes.

(*He kisses her on the cheek, then he turns to* STURM *and speaks in a clear voice.*)

KOSMAS. You strike the women and children with deceit, and Photine plunges the knife of shame into your breast. If you are a man who obeys the laws of war, strike me. Your moment has come to show what you are.

STURM. (*While his body quakes with fury*) These two serpents will lead the dance of death. Every one of their relatives, mother, brother, young and old, sick and healthy, will accompany them to repay their frantic stupidity. Thirty from the prison and twenty from those here—Fifty hostages, for the moment, will discharge the inflamed rebellion of these two. And fire will discharge the remainder of the debt.

(STURM's *decision creates an uproar among the villagers. They withdraw with a deep groan. Two or three women fall to the ground as though their feet can no longer sustain them, but at once they rise again.*)

STURM. You are afraid now, I see, eh! And you withdraw so you will not be selected by my men—

FIRST OLD WOMAN. (*Coming forward*) Master of the foreigners, I fall at your feet—

STURM. Go away, before my boot kicks you dead. Instead of groaning, it would be better if you tore apart, with your own hands, those of your people who are responsible for this calamity. The glass containing my vengeance is a deep one.

FOURTH ELDER. (*Coming forward*) Then I fall as one more drop to fill that glass!

STURM. Old man, if you were wise, you would first of all know the value of life—

FOURTH ELDER. I am in a hurry, in case I miss the lesson to which I am listening—

STURM. No, I refuse to accept you. You are trembling and will only put my soldiers to double trouble. You will not remain upright on your feet. Go away!

FOURTH ELDER. Know then that the hanged man was my nephew—

STURM. And what of that?

FOURTH ELDER. He took care of me in his home. I learned all about his actions, and as you know, I often helped him at his work. Anyone you ask will verify this. Judge now, if it is wise that an innocent man should take my place!

STURM. I am making an exception of you, even though those who survive will say that I accepted a bribe from death!

SECOND OLD WOMAN. (*Coming forward*) Though I appear to be an old woman, I stand firmly on my feet. Though I appear to be useless, I am not. What does it matter if it is today or tomorrow? I beg for deliverance to come. Be the Savior.

STURM. Go away, ghost of night!

SECOND OLD WOMAN. As you say, I have always had bad luck.

STURM. You are attempting to spare a living body from death!

SECOND OLD WOMAN. Yes, as you say. It is unjust that a young girl should die and that I should live.

STURM. No. I want you to live. This is your punishment!

(*The* SECOND OLD WOMAN *withdraws, while the* FIRST YOUNG GIRL *stands provocatively before* STURM. *From this point, the crowd of villagers changes from a pathetic one to an almost offensive one. Together, they draw nearer, in obvious fury, which increases slowly and makes them courageous.*)

FIRST YOUNG GIRL. I am just completing my eighteenth year, thus I am paying a heavy price for my place.

SECOND YOUNG GIRL. And I in turn.

FIRST YOUNG GIRL. (*With a cry which is almost hysterical*) Strike me first! Strike!

FIRST WOMAN. I cast my hatred full into your face.

THIRD WOMAN. And I tell you that you should tremble!

FIRST ELDER. The hour is come, Crucifier. The hour is come!

(*The cries become unanimous. Elders, women, and young girls raise their voices: "The hour is come!"* STURM's *fury is so great that both he and his men fall back a step or two.*)

STURM. Shut up, you insane mob. Who is master here, and who are the enslaved? I had heard that you were a perverse race, but my mind never once conceived of what I now see before me. Because your own minds have become unhinged, do you perhaps imagine that I will be swayed by your idiotic words? Hatred is what you will receive in exchange for your hatred! Fire in exchange for your fire. And from now on, the one who dies will be considered victorious. Your village will be surrounded by fire, and let whoever can escape. (*To the soldiers*) Come! I wish to supervise everything.

(STURM *departs with feigned haughtiness. His men follow him with unrhythmical steps. The villagers surround* KOSMAS *and* PHOTINE, *who is beside him.* KOSMAS *stands formally, on ceremony; he takes off his cap and looks at the sky for a long time. Then he speaks in a heavy, formal tone.*)

KOSMAS.   Let it be, God, that one day the conquerors fall into the abyss of your judgment.

(*The villagers take the phrase and convert it into a prayer:* "*Let it be so, God!*" *Then the* THIRD WOMAN, *extending her hands, while all the other women withdraw to give her a place in center stage, says:*)

THIRD WOMAN.   A knight on a white horse! See him! The warrior Saint is appearing. There he is! Now he raises his lance high, and he is rushing from the heavens to strike—Holy One! Holy One! Holy One!

(*The villagers again take the last phrase and repeat it. Many of the women raise their hands in supplication:* "*Holy One, strike!*" *They slowly emerge from their religious ecstasy. Their bodies appear to be thoroughly exhausted. The old women sit where they are. The* ELDERS, *too, sit where they are behind* KOSMAS. *The* YOUNG GIRLS *move behind* PHOTINE. *The children stand in front, perplexed. Some are holding tightly to the hands of their mothers.*)

PHOTINE.   (*Almost a monologue, as though talking to herself*) If all this could be an illusion and a horrible nightmare. And out of the fear which afflicts our hearts, if we should suddenly awaken into light, where our suffering could find relief; that suffering which is about to strangle us.

FIRST YOUNG GIRL. And every morning, as we go to the pump with our pitchers, we would carry back water with which to clean our houses, awakening from a peaceful night.

SECOND YOUNG GIRL. I always like to wear a flowered dress; and rolling up my sleeves, I take the fresh sage broom and soon make my courtyard sparkling clean.

THIRD YOUNG GIRL. I like to hear the cattle bellowing, the roosters crowing on the fences, while I take the basket in my hand and gather fresh eggs. Then I set the table and put out fresh cheese, and bread made from the first crop of wheat, so that our men can satisfy their hunger.

FOURTH YOUNG GIRL. And later to embroider on my dowry, to design crosses and branches, birds and flowers, the good-luck epigrams I learned from the teacher in school—And to pile these articles in my chest, one on top the other, with jasmine to keep them fresh.

PHOTINE. Only until my handsome bridegroom arrives so I can give him children and grandchildren. And may life never, but never, roll to an end—

FIRST OLD WOMAN. And I, twining the wool out on our warm front steps, to direct the spinning wheel to turn and begin to tell its fairy tale—

(ARETE *enters. She appears thinner and taller. She searches around her in a daze.*)

ARETE. A good hour to you, villagers! Daughters, may God's blessings be with you. Tell me, is Photine here by any chance?

(PHOTINE *comes forward as calmly as possible. Her replies reverberate like an echo.*)

PHOTINE. Yes, I am here—

ARETE. May the Holy Mother protect you, my daughter. I lost you since morning, and I did not know where to look for you.

PHOTINE. It is better that you left the house—

ARETE. Speak not of evil, and may God extend a protective hand. I heard that the foreigners will set fire to the vallage, and that they are herding those from the upper village down to the threshing floor. And they told me that perhaps you were involved. It is not true, is it? Tell me! Do not conceal anything from me—

PHOTINE. Your alarm is not justified—

ARETE. I pray to God that it is as you say. You are quick-tempered and I thought that you might have taunted the foreigners. But, daughter, are you crying? What is it?

PHOTINE. The sun is beating on me and has made me dizzy.

ARETE. Come, let us go from here.

PHOTINE. No, no—I must remain here. The foreigners will become angry if I leave.

ARETE. And what do they want of you?

PHOTINE. They told me not to leave.

ARETE. Did they say this to you alone or to everyone?

PHOTINE. (*In a sobbing voice*) Do not ask me—Do not ask me—

ARETE. Your agitation, Photine, tells me a great deal—You, Elders, speak! Has some misfortune enfolded my daughter-in-law from which she cannot escape? Do you refuse to answer me? Old Kosmas, why do you look at me with sealed lips?

KOSMAS. I can tell you only this: Hold your heart firm.

(PHOTINE *falls into the arms of* ARETE *in tears.* ARETE *looks around as though she has received a wound and is aware that everyone has lowered his gaze. She tightens her embrace on* PHOTINE, *who sobs as she speaks.*)

PHOTINE. It was not fated that I should become your daughter-in-law.

(ARETE *stands as though lightning has struck her. She falls to the ground.* PHOTINE *falls with her. Their heads and hands are close together. A silence intervenes. When* ARETE *begins to speak, her voice, clearly lamenting, brings forth a dirge.*)

ARETE. O, my daughter, you inform me of a lamentable wedding, and I hear the dark bridegroom Death approaching. What kind of earth will cover your golden hair? Is it possible that the suns in your eyes will set? What will I tell Lambrinos when he returns?

(ARETE *appears to gain strength from her tears. She rises and pulls* PHOTINE *to her feet. In the meantime,* PHOTINE *has allowed herself to become like a child listening to a lullaby.*)

ARETE. E, Elders, I want my daughter-in-law—I want her! I will tear any man apart with my own hands, if he attempts to take her from me—Why do you stand there looking at me!

PHOTINE. I am afraid of Death, and my entire body is trembling!

FIRST YOUNG GIRL.   Death surrounds me from one hour to the next. Woe is me!

SECOND YOUNG GIRL.   As far from here as possible! Far from here!

(*Cries are now heard: "We are going—We are going!" Led by* ARETE, *with* PHOTINE *following close beside her, the women now advance toward the exit, while* KOSMAS *attempts to stop them.*)

ARETE.   My body endures. Come, let us go!

SECOND WOMAN.   I prefer to kill the murderer rather than be killed by him—

ARETE.   Old-man Kosmas, move over to let me pass.

KOSMAS.   Fruitless labor, women! It will be worse if you leave.

ARETE.   How are we to escape, if we remain here?

KOSMAS.   If you are to remain here—except for those whom Death shall select—someone will be left behind to sing dirges for us. Otherwise, no one will escape. The foreigners have already surrounded the village. And even now, I see smoke rising all around. They have set fire to the village—We are safer here.

(*The villagers draw back as a voice of terror escapes them:* "O, O—")

KOSMAS.   My mind flutters, and I can find no suitable words. There were many men in my family, and now my ancestry is being extinguished. My house was wealthy once, and now it has become cinders. I know what kind of death awaits me. And I, who had a duty to be the first to withhold my tears, now allow them to run from my eyes like a stream. I am crying with you—How can I comfort you, my daughters; you who a short time ago sent prayers on wings to heaven. The black ravens have appeared and are swooping down on us to tear us to pieces. What words can be articulated to raise a hymn to your unjust deaths?

(*The* FIRST OLD WOMAN *begins a stanza as a response and as a dirge. The other women take up the dirge with heavy voices. The cry becomes one. The stage now resembles a funeral procession.*)

FIRST OLD WOMAN.   *To far regions where you travel,*
Become death's tutor, Elder!
Tell him to take what has decayed,
Hands from our youth let him forbear.

KOSMAS. In truth, what is it that man desires from life? A home for warm shelter when the north wind blows; food to nourish his hungry body. He seeks to raise his children so when he dies the thread binding him to the world will not be unraveled. Man seeks never to bow his head!

FIRST ELDER. In our land, those who died in freedom have been the fortunate ones. There is no greater insult to man than to live the life of slavery. You become slave to the enslaved!

(PHOTINE *goes beside* KOSMAS. *She catches his hand and kisses it.*)

PHOTINE. Elder, I ask your forgiveness. My soul has not lost courage, nor has my spirit bowed. Only my heart is about to break. A many-legged viper is crushing it. And the body cannot endure.

KOSMAS. Daughter, your manner gives me courage. Should we happen to be in the same line, hold on to my hand. My knees tremble, and I do not want to appear a coward to the foreigners. We must call forth every bit of secret strength lying dormant in our bodies. Let us hold hands, one with another; a living chain with fifty links. And let us confront the foreign death in such a manner that they will lower their eyes in shame.

PHOTINE. (*Leaves the side of* KOSMAS *and moves beside* ARETE. *She takes her hand and kisses it*) Twofold mother for me, now that you know the path I have taken, give me your blessings— And when, with good luck, Lambrinos returns, tell him to name his first daughter after me—Here, take this florin to buy his wedding wreaths.

FIRST OLD WOMAN. You sparkled, sun-bright morn, as gradually you dawned.
But then came thunder, then came lightning, then came thunderbolt.
And all of a sudden angels warred, all creation darkened . . .

(*As the dirge is completed, loud footsteps are heard and immediately,* STURM *enters, followed by his attendants.*)

The villagers sway like an angry wave. Even the OLD WOMEN *rise to their feet. The women stand behind the* ELDERS. *They confront* STURM *with uplifted heads and an expression of pride.*)

STURM. Which of you is the mother of Lambrinos?

ARETE. (*Stepping forward*) I am!

STURM. You will curse the hour you gave birth to your son. (*To the soldiers*) Take her from here. Let the tigress rot in jail until we have come to terms with the leader of the murderers.

ARETE. And I tell you that Lambrinos will avenge us, and woe to you! Even if you could become a bird to hide, Lambrinos would seek you out to destroy you. (*Taking* PHOTINE *in her arms, she kisses her on the cheeks and forehead in the shape of a Cross*) We will meet in the next world, Daughter. And you, old-man Kosmos, give my regards to my husband and tell him we will meet before long. Fellow villagers, a farewell to you, and may God be with you.

(*A soldier leads* ARETE *away, and they exit.*)

STURM. I thought I would find you on bended knees so my heart could be tempered by your entreaties. But you look on me with contempt. Well, your lying has finally come to an end—Here is the list. Except for the two guilty Elders and this one here—those from the prison and a number of you from this place—fifty in all— You don't even withdraw as you hear me? (*To* KOSMAS) You, there, speak! Have you no argument now concerning your fate? No! Ai! The tumult of your fears has now become sterile. Earlier, the old women fell at my feet and bewailed. What is that which now holds you upright? Not a sound escapes your lips. No! Sturm is not afraid! Even were the blood which has soaked your earth to take the form of Satan, I would continue to kill, if necessary. You can curse me then—I find your curses more natural than being confronted by dumb scarecrows in the middle of the day. Enslaved ones, speak! Sturm commands you! What are you? Men with flesh or hateful ghosts, which my bloody imagination has conjured before me?

THE VILLAGERS. (*In a single voice which appears to be simultaneously a prayer and a hymn*) Hostages!

(STURM *withdraws. The villagers pass quietly before him while the soldiers follow with bowed heads.*)

STURM. (*Remains alone on stage*) The gods of my country are cruel gods. When their eyebrows move, all the world trembles. You primitive spirits of my ancestors, stand beside me; be my assistants. I hear this iron armor in which you have clothed me and sent me for plunder, this holy law, creaking. And these enslaved men frighten *me*, who am the master. Woe is me! I fight against men who are beyond the measure of judgment. In times of need, they are unyielding, and I come to force their heads to bow. No matter how many bullets I plant in their breasts, the wounds open on my own breast; and I am terrified. And while the number of men around diminishes, their dead who fight on are numberless. There, I see them before me. With recognizable shapes, liberated from hunger, they walk upright, and my soldiers aim at them with eyes closed. Are there no boundaries of death here in Greece? Ah, you thrice-accursed sprouts! Confess who your God is so I can extend my arm to strangle the mystery of the resistance. I must destroy my opponent once and for all.

(*Shots are heard offstage.* STURM *is terrified. He bows his head and remains motionless, like a man with a guilty conscience. Then, women, young girls, old men, and children, re-enter with a slow march.* STURM *exits quickly, as though he is being pursued. The villagers walk the width of the stage as though theirs is simultaneously a procession of death and of victory.*)

ACT III

SCENE. *The same place.*

(*It is morning, just at daybreak. Two foreign soldiers and one officer enter. They are not the same warriors of Act I, nor the silent executioners of Act II. These men are frightened. The work has made them dispirited; they are bowed. The* FIRST SOLDIER *is tall and lanky; he has an uneasy expression. The* SECOND SOLDIER, *rather stocky, appears to be fighting something all alone, as though he is conceiving some cunning plan. The* OFFICER *struggles to regain the lost composure of a warrior.*)

FIRST SOLDIER. (*After casting a searching glance around him, he begins the conversation*) Have you ever seen how a scorpion, surrounded by fire, grows smaller and smaller, as though a hot ring clasps him? Then, how he stings and poisons his own head, and finally dies? Have you ever seen such a sight in all your lives? Eh, then, all of us who were dispatched to this front will end like the scorpion. There is no salvation from any direction.

SECOND SOLDIER. Remember how we set out when we received our orders to come down to the Aegean? Greece was a small country and easy to conquer. A game for us. That is what the big brass told us. And now? There she is, Greece upright! She has suddenly become gigantic; she has become a fortress! Wherever you turn, you find a trench; and wherever you find a Greek, you find war!

OFFICER. Friends, in these difficult times, I can only counsel courage—

SECOND SOLDIER. Tell me, what comes of courage?

OFFICER. How can we be saved when fear submerges our hearts? Brothers, let us remember our past glories—

FIRST SOLDIER. Past glories bring me greater terror. All around me, night and day, I discern ghosts parading by. Do you think that all the blood we spilled has become a ghost and seeks retaliation in its turn? I am not afraid to say it: This is a well-deserved settlement!

SECOND SOLDIER. The best thing we can do, comrades, is to separate from the others. I have said this many times, but none of you want to listen.

OFFICER. I refuse to detach myself from the others. Though we are friends, I cannot forget that I am an officer.

SECOND SOLDIER. Once you have turned your back on the war, it matters little if you run on all fours or walk proudly. This is all I have to say to you, friend.

FIRST SOLDIER. You are quite right, quite right. When we are all together, we become the foreign invaders who have destroyed their Homeland. Two or three men, detached from the others, and clothed in rags, we become human beings again. Some sympathetic creatures might give us assistance. If God still has an ounce of compassion for murderers—Who can tell? Maybe something will happen—

SECOND SOLDIER. I am determined to be saved, friend. Thank heaven, I was never considered worthy enough to be granted a commission in the army.

FIRST SOLDIER. And I have a wife and children—

SECOND SOLDIER. Stand firmly! Do not be afraid We will go hand in hand. These people are very strange. They do not persist in hatred. Pay them a compliment, and you see them turn aside like a lamb; and, similarly, insult them, and they become fearless and attack you.

(STURM *enters with a very small retinue. The new arrivals look at the soldiers with obvious mistrust. It is easy to see that there is no sign of brotherhood left between them. Despite signs of fatigue,* STURM *is the same as ever, cruel, merciless to the others and to himself. As he stands looking persistently at the soldiers, one gets the impression that he is determined to strike with a glance. The* OFFICER, *and the two soldiers standing behind him, stand pathetically at attention.*)

STURM.   Why have you three become separated from the others? And why the secrecy and conspiracy? Do you believe that you are deceiving me, as you plan your disgusting games behind my back?

OFFICER.   With all respect, I must say—

STURM.   I know where the thoughts of each one of you go. I know what makes you breathless, and I read your frightened faces quite well— (*A short silence*) For your own good, nonetheless, bear in mind what happened the other day to those who spread traitor-our rumors throughout the army. And each of you will suffer the same punishment, be he brother or son of mine. I feel powerful enough that, were I only permitted, I would leave the entire earth without inhabitants before degrading my Fatherland.

OFFICER.   (*Regaining courage*) Consideration for the Fatherland is the duty of every soldier. There is no sign of treachery.

STURM.   The words of a traitor become bold from the moment he makes up his mind to live. This is what I see.

OFFICER.   Our men have remained under discipline for many years. And even now they wait—

STURM.   (*Approaching him threateningly. He stops abruptly*) What do you mean by "even now"? Is it possible that your men can ever be disobedient?

OFFICER.   (*Alarmed, he takes an apologetic pose. Slowly, he becomes once more the old instrument of execution, while the two soldiers withdraw a few paces*) The position of an army is very difficult in a foreign land—

STURM.   There is no foreign land where the foot of Sturm walks.

OFFFICER.   A land which resists out of vengeance—

STURM.   What of that? Let your vengeance become greater. Suffocate the other vengeance with your savagery. You know the lesson well. Why do you forget it now?

OFFICER.   You have no complaint about me—

STURM.   Never until now. But I see that your thoughts are wavering and that you are being subdued.

OFFICER.   You know very well that I accepted my lot eagerly. My country gave me birth in order to kill me—

STURM. In killing you, it will also honor you—

OFFICER. And the world is amazed at the endurance we have displayed.

STURM. Blot the world from your mind. Pay attention neither to what it says, nor to the curses it utters. The world is friendly only to the one who wins the victory. And the harder you strike, the more the world trembles before your presence.

OFFICER. With all due respect, I wish to know something. What will happen now? What are we seeking? Where are we going? Is it perhaps true that the soldiers of the foreign armies have reached the borders of our Fatherland? Have you any news?

STURM. What does it matter if they have reached our borders? What does it matter if they start fires everywhere? What of that? War takes many turns. The Fatherland will be rebuilt by those who remain alive. You, and these others here. Victory belongs to the last man to stand upright in battle, a battle which has neither beginning nor end. And I will be that last man!

OFFICER. You give my heart confidence. I give my life willingly. Tell me, what must I do?

(*It is one of the rare moments when contentment appears on the face of* STURM. *He has won a difficult battle. Once again, he is the Leader with an indiscernible smile. He climbs higher, and his presence becomes implacable as that of Death. No one can escape him any longer. The two soldiers stand as though hypnotized, waiting for orders.*)

STURM. (*To the* OFFICER) The scattered troops at the ravine must be collected at the mill. And you must lead them. (*To the* TWO SOLDIERS) You two will round up all the villagers and bring them here. Kill anyone who refuses to come! And be quick; time is pressing! (*He looks into the eyes of each of the men*) Each of you to his post. Kill anything that stands in your way, be it God himself!

(*The* OFFICER *salutes and exits. The* TWO SOLDIERS *exit in the opposite direction. The attendants come to stand behind* STURM *and follow him to the exit, a terrible, other-worldly power, which exhibits faith in the fact that war is one of the enduring elements of the world.*

For a time the stage remains empty. The light becomes brighter. The clash of battle is heard in the distance; after a while it ceases. Groups of villagers, young girls, and Elders enter helter-skelter. They appear to be tall, skeleton-like, as though they do not belong to this world. A mixture of voices: "O, God!" "A new misfortune has overtaken us!" "I cannot endure! I cannot endure!" "Listen, there is the clash of weapons again!" "Why have they brought us together here?" "Holy Mother, assist us—" "Where shall I hide? Tell me where to hide." "If I hadn't come, he would have pierced a hole through me, infamous one!" "My legs are aching here—" "The thrice accursed one. Let Death kick him so!" "May God intervene."

The voices, one after another, die out until they blend into a single whisper. The women are, simultaneously, pushed to center stage and ecstatically view LAMBRINOS *on the top step of the church, looking like an Archangel. He is no longer the youth of Act I. He is a mature man. Many women utter his name:* "Lambrinos! Lambrinos!")

LAMBRINOS.   A good hour to you, fellow villagers.

(*The young girls become encouraged; they approach and ask:* "How did you get to us?" "Why have you come here, why?" "O, God, I tremble for your sake!" "Where shall I conceal you?")

FIRST WOMAN.   (*Touches* LAMBRINOS *with her hand while her body takes a supplicating pose*) Go! Go, Lambrinos, or they will kill you!

(*The young girls repeat in supplication:* "Go!")

LAMBRINOS.   Don't talk so loud or Sturm will hear you.

(*A gunshot is heard nearby. The din of battle begins again, like a labored breath, rising and falling. The* SECOND ELDER, *who has become the* FIRST ELDER *of the village since the execution of* KOSMAS, *advances. He stands a step lower than* LAMBRINOS, *while the women all withdraw.*)

FIRST ELDER.   You command us, Lambrinos. Tell us what is going on and what we must do. Listen, the gunshots are near by.

LAMBRINOS.   Those shots come from our people; they are approaching from all sides to surround the foreigners. They have sprouted like ghosts; they are crawling under the bushes and blocking every road to the foreigners. They are attacking everywhere. We will destroy them completely at the mill, and the heifer, by God, will swim in their blood.

SECOND ELDER.   How did you get here?

LAMBRINOS.   I took an oath when Sturm killed our villagers.
I took an oath that I would be avenged with my own hands. That
is why I came.

SECOND ELDER.   What will you do?

LAMBRINOS.   I will tell you briefly. The foreigners are attempting to ease their shameful path by dragging hostages with them.
Once the beast has been wounded, he pounces on everything,
mostly out of fury, before he squirms and dies. So it is with these
people. They collect villagers wherever they pass. There are graves
all along the way. I believe you understand now what Sturm is
planning to do before he leaves the place which has become his
own shameful grave. And rather than increasing the number of
orphans in our Homeland, let me become the one to fall. Thousands
have been restored to life to take my place.

(*The young girls scatter like animals in the fields, animals
which have been struck by lightning. Cries of: "Holy Mother,
watch over us!" "How can I escape; how can I escape?"
"Where shall I hide?" " God—"*)

FIRST WOMAN.   (*Advancing*) May a curse descend on them!

(*The young girls form a group in a semicircle around the* FIRST
WOMAN *and cry out in one voice: "A curse!" The voices finally
become a sob.*)

SECOND ELDER.   How can you interfere with them by coming
into the village? Can it be that you came of your own accord to be
killed?

LAMBRINOS.   Do not worry. I have planned everything. I know
what bait to cast when the right moment comes. Bait which will
catch someone else—not you!

FIRST OLD WOMAN.   There is no advantage to my being saved
from death, and so, with all my body, I tremble for you who stand
there confronting your destiny.

SECOND OLD WOMAN.   It is better that you should go, Lambrinos, before they see you—Why have you come as an animal about
to be slaughtered at their hands? Their hatred for you is deep. Do
not challenge them.

FIRST YOUNG GIRL.   (*Approaches and touches* LAMBRINOS. *Her
motion is full of love and suffering*) Hide, Lambrinos, hide! I, who
see your mother daily at the jail and know her suffering, tell you
to hide. (*Her tone deepens; it is almost a sob*)

LAMBRINOS. (*Barely touching her hair with his hand*) Young maiden, now that a resurrection echoes throughout our Homeland, my hour has come. I am here of my own accord to confront that hour at the church of my village.

SECOND ELDER. I bow before your command. You know better.

LAMBRINOS. Sturm will be here at any moment now. Bear up well. Do not make the final moment appear to be an eternity. Because there the evil has been banished! The sun is rising.

(*In truth, the stage slowly becomes lighter.*)

FIRST YOUNG GIRL. How wonderful it will be to have the sun fall over my heart.

THIRD ELDER. Let me first hear the news, and then may I die.

(STURM *enters with his attendants and the two soldiers. They all have the same expression on their faces. They stand in the same place as at the end of Act I. Behind the* ELDERS, *and among the women, stands* LAMBRINOS *without being visible.*)

STURM. Who is the First Elder?

SECOND ELDER. (*Now become* FIRST ELDER, *advancing*) I am.

STURM. You are the only person who can save this frenzied crowd of villagers from a certain death. Consider well before you reply. Because you have a habit of responding before considering the weight of your words.

SECOND ELDER. I will do what I can.

STURM. Carry a white flag to your people and tell them to clear a path through which I can pass to leave your Homeland without a battle. I will take thirty hostages as security, and I will release them, unharmed, as soon as I have entered the highway that leads to the valley. I give you my word that no one from your village will have a thing to fear, nor will anyone come to harm. My offer, I believe, is a fair one. If you have your wits about you and compassion for your people, you will accept it willingly.

SECOND ELDER. It matters little if I accept your offer.

STURM. I see you hesitate, even though you know that there is no salvation for you.

SECOND ELDER. I stand before you unable to do a thing. These others also stand before you unable to do a thing. There are others who give the orders now. If you had gone without hostages, I would have gone to fall at their feet and soften their hearts.

STURM. I must deal with all of you, thus I execute my orders as suits me best. No. My offer remains unchanged. I do not trust you without hostages beside me. I do not even trust God. I want a living security beside me.

SECOND ELDER. I am hearing such a confession for the first time.

STURM. I revealed the confession out of compassion, so you can be saved.

SECOND ELDER. This is the first time I hear that women and children become shields for warriors.

STURM. Because I am miserly where my men are concerned. They will spill their blood wherever I decide they should spill it. And I have decided now that I shall not lose even half of that blood. I am being frank with you. It is to your benefit and advantage to accept my proposition. Otherwise, even your youngest sprout will fly with the wind. I give you five minutes' time to change your mind. After that, you will have the right to say: "I saved my village."

SECOND ELDER. Ever since the first moment, you have asked me for this same concession; but to no avail. There is a graveyard extending from one end to the other of our Homeland.

STURM. Old man, my Fatherland is also a she-wolf.

SECOND ELDER. Foreigner, she has probably been tamed. In time, this land will also become tamed. Start now, and go!

STURM. Go!

FIRST OLD WOMAN. Go!

(*The villagers suddenly take courage and advance a step or two, crying: "Go!"*)

STURM. So you deny me, in spite of my having spoken the truth calmly. It seems that one can bend steel, but never your infamous obstinacy. However, the freedom which has suddenly gained strength in you, does not terrify me. I will strike with fury against that freedom to my last breath. I command all of you, children, old men, women, to form a circle around my men for safe conduct. And if they dare, let your people make an attempt to attack me! Our march from here will be led by the lioness who gave birth to Lambrinos, so that she may be killed by her own son—

LAMBRINOS. Sturm!

(*The villagers draw aside;* LAMBRINOS *appears and mounts the steps. Behind him stand the* ELDERS *and the women.*)

STURM. (*As his soldiers draw near, ready to fall with him, if necessary*) Who are you? Who is in command here?

LAMBRINOS. I, Lambrinos.

STURM. Did you say Lambrinos? It is impossible for me to believe it—

FIRST YOUNG GIRL. (*Almost hysterically*) He stands before you in one piece, Crucifier!

(*A* silence ensues. The FIRST YOUNG GIRL *returns to her place while the approving exclamations die out. The* SECOND ELDER *turns with severity, and his glance bids them to be silent. From a distance there are continuous sounds of gunshots.*)

LAMBRINOS. And I command you to put down your weapons, that is, if you and your men wish to be saved.

STURM. To be saved, did you say? Did I hear right?

LAMBRINOS. That is what I said, and you heard right. As you know, the resistance forces have you surrounded on all sides. You have fallen; these are your final moments. Your soldiers will depart at any moment now. And then woe to you!

(*The villagers in different voices, which eventually blend into one, cry out furiously: "Woe to you!"*)

LAMBRINOS. Even should wings sprout on your back, it is impossible that you should escape me.

STURM. A kind fortune, I say, has cast you at my feet, and I am wondering where my advantage lies. Let me hear your terms first so I can arrive at a decision.

LAMBRINOS. First, lay down your weapons.

STURM. Your terms are heavy, heavy!—And if I refuse?

LAMBRINOS. No one can escape me—the long hatred will make your blood a stream from which this hatred can drink!

STURM. And if we lay down our weapons?

LAMBRINOS. I will turn you over to the leaders, and let them be your judges.

STURM. And if the villagers do not obey? You said just now that their hatred will be quenched in blood.

LAMBRINOS. My Homeland does not breed wolves. Each villager agrees to the terms—

(*The* ELDERS *shudder where they stand petrified. They nod their heads*: "Yes, yes—" *The women all murmur:*"Go!" "Do not be afraid!" "Yes, yes—" "It is an agreement—")

STURM. And who will guarantee my safety?

LAMBRINOS. I will give you surety. Is that sufficient?

STURM. It is indeed a guarantee, if you are in my hands!

LAMBRINOS. And I have you in *my* hands, do not forget it.

STURM. That is not out of my mind for a moment, nor can it be. Our fates confronted one another from the very first moment. You and me. And we have an open account to settle, as you remember—

LAMBRINOS. By nature, I always pay up and so discharge my debts!

STURM. And I, as well.

LAMBRINOS. Then why the delay? I have no time to lose—

STURM. Yes, but surrender takes time. Meanwhile, let your people cease attacking.

LAMBRINOS. Very well. The Elder here will come with me to prepare the official surrender.

STURM. I agree.

(*The villagers remain amazed. They look from* LAMBRINOS *to* STURM, *who stare at one another with frozen expressions, two antagonistic spirits, incomprehensible within the history of men. The foreign soldiers stand like dumb animals. The women murmur softly.*)

SECOND ELDER. (*To* LAMBRINOS) My son, I am afraid. This sudden reversal frightens me—

LAMBRINOS. I know what I am saying. Go.

STURM. I have been defeated, Old Man, and it is pointless to breed destruction for my men as well.

SECOND ELDER. I thought differently until now.

STURM. Do not consider yourself blessed until you have seen the final outcome.

SECOND ELDER. You are right.

LAMBRINOS. (*To* STURM) Let the doors of the jail be opened at once!

STURM. Yes, but until the official agreement is completed, I am still in command here—I will have the doors of the jail opened and your mother sent here. She has been grieving to see you. (*He turns to leave*) Really, I was under the impression that events would move in one direction, but now they are moving in another.

LAMBRINOS. Now that you are about to go, let me remind you that there is no path through which you can escape.

STURM.   I know it, so do not worry. (*To the soldiers*) Let us go! (STURM *and his bewildered soldiers exit. Behind them walks the* SECOND ELDER, *slowly and with dignity*)

THIRD ELDER.   My son, it is your own life you are exposing, thus I have nothing to say. But all that has taken place here appears strange to me.

FIRST OLD WOMAN.   My son, a man does not take the poisonous snake to his bosom.

LAMBRINOS.   My bait has caught Sturm. That is why I set out and came here alone.

THIRD ELDER.   Yes, but I am afraid that you yourself, Lambrinos, are the bait.

LAMBRINOS.   The longer he takes, caught in the web of his hatred for me, the deeper will he dig his own grave. Two shots, three shots, and he cannot escape.

THIRD ELDER.   What if he breaks his agreement? He is not to be trusted.

LAMBRINOS.   It will be stranger for Sturm to keep his agreement.

THIRD ELDER.   Then I do not follow your meaning.

LAMBRINOS.   I am borrowing time from him, in accordance with the plans I have set; his soldiers will fall, group by group, into our hands. And thus, the Homeland alone will be saved from the pestilence of their departure. In the meantime, he has lost every opportunity to collect you all together. What I have sought I have achieved—

THIRD ELDER.   Very well, and what about Sturm? Is he going to remain inactive?

LAMBRINOS.   He will remain here, dead or alive.

THIRD WOMAN.   God, if I could tear him apart with my own hands! And burn him!

SECOND WOMAN.   Not even his ashes should remain in our Homeland!

FIRST YOUNG GIRL.   And you, Lambrinos? How will you escape?

LAMBRINOS.   Maiden, happiness nourishes me.

FIRST YOUNG GIRL.   My heart flutters to hear it.

LAMBRINOS.   I am going into the church to light a candle—And don't any of you leave. You are much safer in this place.

(*From center stage,* LAMBRINOS *walks up to the door of th church between the* YOUNG WOMEN *and the* ELDERS. *The* YOUNG GIRLS, *half-kneeling, appear to be worshiping* LAMBRINOS. *One would think that the warrior Saint, protector of the village, had descended from the templum.*)

THIRD ELDER. The Creator is making a specter of his beautiful wife in order to secure the bridge which was built in the daytime, only to fall during the night.

FIRST OLD WOMAN. Once, when the howling wolves rushed upon us to tear us to pieces, my deceased husband suddenly grabbed a lamb and threw it at them for food.

THIRD ELDER. No matter how heavy the tear that falls from our eyes, it is not within our power to do otherwise. Digenis always comes to terms with death on the marble threshing floor.

(*The villagers scatter about the stage. High on the steps sit the young girls. The* ELDERS *are at right front. At the back* YOUNG *and* OLD WOMEN *are intermixed. The sound of battle ceases. A young boy bangs two or three times on the plank of wood used as a bell.*)

FIRST WOMAN. The grace of Heaven shines, and I sense a light emerging from within the dark hiding places of my life.

SECOND YOUNG GIRL. Will the hour perhaps ever come when I will not tremble with fear on hearing the flutter of a bird?

FIRST OLD WOMAN. God, grant endurance to the mothers crying for their children. Do not let the fountains of their eyes ever run dry. Put words into their mouths equal to their sorrow, so they can gratify their deep grief.

SECOND WOMAN. The tears in our eyes will become precious as diamonds for those who have been killed.

SECOND OLD WOMAN. O, and where will I find the graves of our people so I can take some oleander and burn incense in a cup to gratify their souls?

THIRD ELDER. Let them become a legend and live within our children and grandchildren to frighten death away.

THIRD YOUNG GIRL. Will the hour perhaps come when life, under the protection of my husband and my pains of childbirth, will roll peacefully until it finally empties into the big river?

FIRST OLD WOMAN. And I, to take my favorite grandchild by the hand and instruct him slowly while his tender hands flutter like wings and his laughter fills all creation.

(ARETE *enters in rags, looking like a ghost. The* YOUNG GIRLS *rise quickly and go to her. The* OLD WOMEN *rise, shaking their heads.*)

THIRD ELDER.   Welcome, Arete!

FIRST YOUNG GIRL.   (*Helping her*) Welcome! Welcome!

SECOND OLD WOMAN.   She has become like a skeleton, poor woman.

THIRD WOMAN.   The dog has kept his word. And he has opened the doors of the jail.

SECOND OLD WOMAN.   I have greater fear now.

ARETE.   Ah, how difficult it is to climb up here. I am not heavy, and yet my feet become rooted as though someone has attached weights to them. (*To the* FIRST YOUNG GIRL, *who is always beside her, holding her up*) Come, daughter; may you have the blessings of God. Guide me to a place where I can sit down. (*She sits at center stage, on the second or third step*) Fellow villagers, forgive my nakedness, but they would not permit me to go home. They pushed me in this direction. It seems that they are playing some evil trick on me. A! It is as though, step by step, I have come up from Hades. My body has rotted in the jail where they threw me, I forget how long ago—

FIRST OLD WOMAN.   It has been a long time ago.

ARETE.   Yes, a time which passes slowly.

FIRST WOMAN.   Come, Aunt Arete. Very soon now all our troubles will be over.

ARETE.   Do not believe it. They are deceiving you. I know them well. That is what they did to me. They would open the doors of the jail: "Come, woman, you can leave now!" But before I could cross the threshold, they kicked me back again. Yes, yes— Even the devils cannot conceive of all the tricks of these foreigners, the thrice-accursed—They would knock on the door at midnight and call out to me: "Are you asleep? Wake up! They have hanged your son—" And they would not even let me cry. They kicked me on the chest until I vomited blood— (*She attempts to rise. The* YOUNG GIRL *is holding on to her, and she helps her to sit down again at a higher level*) I must hide. I must hide! They are plotting some new torture for me. Otherwise, why should they have set me free? "Your son is near the church," Sturm said to me. I searched everywhere along the way. I did not find any dead—

(*Her sobbing tone becomes a lament, the monotonous, bitter and unceasing lament of every mother for her child. The* OLD

WOMEN *and* WOMEN, *murmuring, accompany* ARETE's *lament out of custom. The* YOUNG GIRLS *bend over her.* LAMBRINOS *comes out of the Church with an afflicted appearance. He sees his mother, hesitates as though attempting to recall how she had looked when they had parted three years earlier. He attempts to approach, but holds himself in check. The* WOMEN *withdraw and thus* ARETE *and* LAMBRINOS *are left alone at the top step of the Church.*)

LAMBRINOS.   Hold on, Mother!

ARETE.   Mother? Mother? Who said that?

LAMBRINOS.   I say it. I, your son!

ARETE.   (*As she speaks, she rises and faces him*) Beloved voice! No, do not torture me! Do not! I cannot endure it! Who is imitating the voice of my son?

LAMBRINOS.   (*Heart-broken, he examines the skeleton which is his mother from a closer distance*) No one. I am Lambrinos, and I am standing before you.

ARETE.   Stand against the light so I can see you. O-hou! Tears are running from my eyes, and I cannot see clearly. God, there are no greater torments than those of a mother!

LAMBRINOS.   (*Embracing her*) Have no fear, Mother. It was I who sent Sturm to open the doors of the jail.

ARETE.   Yes, you are my son. My son! (*Dropping her head on the breast of* LAMBRINOS, *she again bursts into her lament*) It has been almost three years since I last saw you, my beloved. Let my fingers touch you. Your hair is like it always was; the curls fall over your forehead— God, there is no joy greater than that of a mother. O, how my hand slides over your cheeks. You have a tender fuzzy growth. You are a little boy, my son. (*The grief she has withheld is suddenly released, and she sobs*)

LAMBRINOS.   Come, do not cry. I want you to be happy now that I have found you.

ARETE.   Yes, my son, I will be happy! I bless the Grace of God which has brought you here— But how does it happen, my son, that they have allowed you to come? And you? How does it happen that you are free among our fellow villagers? And Sturm?

LAMBRINOS.   Do not worry. There is nothing to fear—

ARETE.   The eyes of the wolf sparkled with fury whenever he opened the door of the jail. And so I tremble.

LAMBRINOS.   Mother, when Sturm returns in a little while, I ask this favor of you. Do not let a single tear moisten your eyes.

ARETE. And how am I to blame if the fountains of my eyes start to flow?

LAMBRINOS. I know why I ask you.

ARETE. (*With some strength; with a courage which is strange both to herself and to the others*) From now on I will never heed the words of a man— Though you are creatures of flesh, your fury is quick-tempered like lightning. Though love is born in your hearts, you have no respect for suffering. Though you laugh, as we do, you close your ears to the sound of tears— No, you are my only son! You are the world to me! And I do not know if the whole world is worth your little finger. You were a living creature when I gave birth to you, and I want you alive. Do you hear? And though you are a man, I am still your mother—

(ARETE *suddenly slumps forward and almost sprawls on the top step. The* WOMEN *and* YOUNG GIRLS *draw near her as before.*)

LAMBRINOS. Very well— Very well— Come now, be quiet—

ARETE. O, a stabbing pain suddenly cuts through my heart. Our Photine has been in the ground for almost two years now, my son.

LAMBRINOS. She is in my heart. Nor will she ever leave it.

(ARETE's *body shudders. She takes off her black kerchief and places it on the ground, drawing a deep cry with a voice which is nonetheless steady. The* WOMEN *accompany her in a dirge which breaks through*:)

ARETE. Luminous moon, you who have set, ascend from
            Hades,
            Lambrinos came riding on a steed, with wedding
            wreath to crown you.

(STURM *enters with a few attendants. The* YOUNG GIRLS, *frightened, walk on tiptoe as they go to hide behind the* ELDERS *and* OLD WOMEN.

LAMBRINOS, *leaving his mother's side, advances two or three steps. He breaks away from the villagers.* ARETE's *outstretched hands attempt to hold him back. She rises, wipes away the tears with the back of her hand, holds her head high, and proudly stands at the same level with the* THIRD ELDER.)

STURM. Come, tie the dog's hands behind his back!

(*Two soldiers catch* LAMBRINOS *and begin to tie his hands. The villagers rebel.* ARETE *rushes forward. Cries of "O! O!—" are heard.*)

STURM. If you do not shut up, I will drop you all dead—Stand back! You have nothing to fear from me. This one is enough—

(*The* WOMEN, *instead of withdrawing, advance now, and the* ELDERS *and* OLD WOMEN *simultaneously dash forward. The soldiers stand ready to strike.*)

ARETE. I will tear apart whoever touches my son. No, no! Foreigner, if a drop of milk from woman was poured into your body; if a mother nursed you on her breasts, and you remember how she looked and laughed while you were a baby, you will listen—
STURM. This is no son of a mother. Go away!
LAMBRINOS. Mother, stop your pleading—
ARETE. Foreigner, I fall at your feet. (*She half-kneels*) You came to our Homeland and destroyed my life. You sent Photine to Hades without wings. Take me as your slave; cast me into the fire— O, speak!
LAMBRINOS. Mother, stand tall!
ARETE. Foreigner, you have eyes, you have ears, you have a tongue. You see, hear, and speak. You must be human. All the mothers of the world plead with you. Tell me: Will my son live?
STURM. I will step on his carcass as I fall!

(*Again the* ELDERS *and* YOUNG GIRLS *dash forward.*)

STURM. One more step, and I will strike!
LAMBRINOS. Go back, women! And you, old men! Who can cause me embarrassment in my last moment? Mother, go back—All of you, go back!

(ARETE *is the first to withdraw. Finally, all the others return to their places.*)

STURM. Thus it is that I accept your terms! (*To his soldiers*) Still tighter. There is no compassion here. I said tighter! (*To* LAMBRINOS) From the day I first set foot on your land, you swore to annihilate me. Now it is my turn to discharge my hatred—

LAMBRINOS. You know who discharges a debt today. My people are pulling the knot, and you are being strangled.

STURM. We will see!

LAMBRINOS. I have enclosed you in a sheepfold in the valley. Not even a bird can escape me—

(*From a distance the noise of battle is heard again.*)

LAMBRINOS. The first attack is being launched. And I am drowning slavery in her own blood.

STURM. If you want to save yourself, two feet as you are from your grave, you will send orders to your people to withdraw far away. About noontime, my army will set you free; and, as is proper to a courageous army, they will depart with their weapons. You will remain a hostage in my hands as collatoral to this agreement. If you accept, proceed, because time is pressing.

LAMBRINOS. My resistance forces are at the crossroads, about a hundred feet beyond the village.

STURM. We will both go there. I will lead the way.

LAMBRINOS. Shall we thus write the official agreement?

STURM. As you like. I will be beside you. You and me!

LAMBRINOS. Farewell, fellow villagers!

ARETE. E, where are you going? I am coming with you!

LAMBRINOS. No. Stay here—

ARETE. Not even the distance of a meter will you leave my sight!

FIRST WOMAN. The hand of God, it seems, is guiding you to your Golgotha as you ascend. I kneel before your passing.

(*The* FIRST WOMAN *half-kneels as though worshiping* LAM-BRINOS, *while she bursts into warm tears, which slowly become peaceful, however, without ceasing.*)

LAMBRINOS. Women, everyone must ascend somewhere. Fellow villagers, may God be with you—

(*They exit.* LAMBRINOS *leads the way; his hands are tied behind his back. Sorrowful and yet with proud countenance, he is the Crucified One of Freedom. Behind him walk the two soldiers with heads bowed. Then comes* STURM. *Try as he might to stand proud, he is the image of shame. The other soldiers follow him. And after them comes* ARETE. *Her body has become heavy under the burden of the great sacrifice. The* FIRST YOUNG GIRL *holds her up.*

The escort crosses the width of the stage and exits with slow steps. The young girls and children go up the church steps, where they stand. Near the belfry, on a ledge of the wall of the church, the SECOND YOUNG GIRL *ascends and looks out toward the place where* LAMBRINOS *leads the others. Except for the* ELDERS *and the* OLD WOMEN, *who sit down again, the* YOUNG GIRLS *look either toward the crossroads, in the direction of which the escort is heading, or toward the* SECOND YOUNG GIRL, *whose body is trembling with the same agony as that of the villagers. The noise of battle is continuous, much closer, as though it is just beyond the churchyard.*)

FIRST WOMAN. (*She has now ceased her lamenting and jumps forward wildly*) God, destroy the roots of the wolves!

(*The phrase, which at first is an arhythmical murmur, becomes associated with a simultaneous chorus of anger, suffering, and bitterness.*)

THE VILLAGERS. Destroy the wolves, God!

SECOND YOUNG GIRL. There, I see the accursed Sturm wild with fury—

FIRST OLD WOMAN. When man degenerates, all creation becomes foul—

SECOND YOUNG GIRL. And Lambrinos is hurrying forward with his head high. It is as though the sun has placed a golden crown around his hair.

FIRST OLD WOMAN. The more the heart of men is overpowered by love, the more the world increases.

SECOND OLD WOMAN. Otherwise, man would be nothing, twisting and turning at nothing.

THIRD WOMAN. E, you, young maiden, do not delay. Tell me what you see?

THIRD ELDER. Have they reached the crossroads, daughter?

SECOND YOUNG GIRL. They are just entering the crossroads. There they are, standing at the top. Sturm is raising a white flag.

(*The sounds of battle suddenly cease. The* ELDERS *and the* OLD WOMEN *rise to their feet. The young girls strain their bodies to catch the least sound.*)

SECOND WOMAN. God, let Lambrinos issue the order as Sturm directed him so he can escape.

FIRST OLD WOMAN.   And let the foreigners go to the judgment of God.

(*Within the silence that falls over the villagers, a cry of grief is heard from a woman who falls sprawling to the ground.*)

THIRD WOMAN.   I cannot endure! I cannot endure!

FIRST WOMAN.   Shut your mouth! Do not make a sound!

(*The voice of* LAMBRINOS *is heard offstage:* "Attack! Strike, brothers!")

SECOND YOUNG GIRL.   Lambrinos is ordering them to strike!

(*The voice of* LAMBRINOS *is heard again offstage:* "Strike! Strike me first! I order you—"

The silence is broken, like a clash of swords, by a bullet. Silence again. A second shot, and the sound of battle breaks out furiously. Gradually, the noise fades, indicating that the enemy is being given chase.)

SECOND YOUNG GIRL.   O, they are both sprawled on the ground.

(*The* FIRST WOMAN *is the first to fall on the ground as though she has been struck; then the* OLD WOMEN *follow. The commotion of battle is transferred to the stage. The women come and go. The children climb up the steps; the mothers run after them and grab the children to hide them.*)

SECOND YOUNG GIRL.   They are pursuing the foreigners like ghosts, and the foreigners are leaving. They are leaving! They are being pushed into the ravine. Our people are pursuing them in the direction of the ravine.

(*The* SECOND YOUNG GIRL *jumps to the ground. When she speaks, hers is a heart-rending cry.*)

SECOND YOUNG GIRL.   The wolves are gone, fellow villagers! They are gone!

(*She falls to the ground, weeping loudly. The woman behind her takes the young girl in her arms, and presently the girl's sobbing ceases. Simultaneously, the* SECOND ELDER *enters and stands in the midst of the villagers.*)

THIRD ELDER. I want to know what happened.

SECOND ELDER. It all happened like lightning. What shall I tell you? While Sturm was waiting for Lambrinos to give the signal which would have saved him, Sturm called to one of his captains and ordered him to strike Sturm. The captain refused: "No!" he cried. "Better that we should all be killed than that I should kill you!" I believe you heard Lambrinos at that moment giving his order. "Strike me first!" he shouted and turning suddenly to Sturm, he said: "With my blood I seal your death—" He had barely completed his words when a brother's bullet came from across the way and struck Lambrinos in the heart and he fell.

(*A voice is heard in the distance like the voice of Fate:* "FREEDOM!")

THIRD ELDER. Freedom, they are shouting to us. FREEDOM!

THE VILLAGERS. (*Repeating in a tone of praise*) FREEDOM!

SECOND ELDER. Praise be to God for creating me into life!

(*Simultaneously, four men enter carrying* LAMBRINOS *high. With head held erect, almost proudly,* ARETE *follows. The* FIRST YOUNG GIRL *and the woman who had accompanied her earlier, are on left and right of* ARETE.

The SECOND ELDER *advances to stand beside* ARETE. *The women clear the way. Slowly, they all get into line, and together they climb the steps of the Church. The bell tolls sadly. The sound brings the villagers to life. A youth jumps up, grabs the rope of the bell and tolls louder. A festive call, the* DOXOLOGY, *resounds. The escort enters the Church.*)

THE END

PART III

POETRY

Constantine Cavafis

(1863–1933)

Constantine Cavafis was born in Constantinople in 1863 and died in Alexandria in 1933. Except for three years in England, two in Constantinople, a few months each in Paris and Athens, he spent his entire life in the Alexandria he loved, employed for twenty years as a common clerk in the Department of Irrigation. He wrote only three or four poems a year, published some of them in broadsheets for private use, and not until he was forty-one did he bring out his first book, a slim volume of only fourteen poems, not for sale, reissued five years later with the addition of only seven poems. His main work, collected after his death, totals some forty-six erotic, some forty-one contemplative, and some sixty-seven historical poems. Written on a demotic base, but with a mixture strangely his own from Ancient, Byzantine, and Medieval Greek, his poems (often with a Hellenistic setting) are brief, neither emotional nor lyrical, but dramatic, narrative, objective, realistic, a recounting of facts and episodes in a tone of voice which is dry, precise, deliberately prosaic and, above all, ironic—the undisputed founder and master of modern Greek poetry, and one of the first poets of the modern world.

BIBLIOGRAPHY: *Poems* (Alexandria, Egypt, 1935); *Poems* (1947); *Poems*, 2 vols., (1963) edited by G. P. Savvidhis; *The Poems of C. P. Cavafy* (1951) translated into English by John Mavrogordato; *The Complete Poems of Cavafy* (1961) translated by Rae Dalven.

Ithaca

When you set out on the voyage to Ithaca,
pray that your journey may be long,
full of adventure, full of knowledge.
Of the Laestrygones and the Cyclopes
and of furious Poseidon, do not be afraid,
for such on your journey you shall never meet
if your thought remain lofty, if a select
emotion imbue your spirit and your body.
The Laestrygones and the Cyclopes
and furious Poseidon you will never meet
unless you drag them with you in your soul,
unless your soul raises them up before you.

Pray that your journey may be long,
that many may those summer mornings be
when with what pleasure, what untold delight
you enter harbors for the first time seen;
that you stop at Phoenician market places
to procure the goodly merchandise,
mother of pearl and coral, amber and ebony,
and voluptuous perfumes of every kind,
as lavish an amount of voluptuous perfumes as you can;
that you venture on to many Egyptian cities
to learn and yet again to learn from the sages.

But you must always keep Ithaca in mind.
The arrival there is your predestination.
Yet do not by any means hasten your voyage.
Let it best endure for many years,
until grown old at length you anchor at your island
rich with all you have acquired on the way,
having never expected Ithaca would give you riches.

Ithaca has given you the lovely voyage.
Without her you would not have ventured on the way
She has nothing more to give you now

Poor though you may find her, Ithaca has not deceived you.
Now that you have become so wise, so full of experience,
you will have understood the meaning of an Ithaca.

The City

You said, "I will go to another land, I will go to another sea.
Another city shall be found better than this.
Each one of my endeavors is condemned by fate;
my heart lies buried like a corpse.
How long now in this withering shall my mind remain.
Wherever I turn my eyes, wherever I gaze,
I see here only the black ruins of my life
where I have spent so many years, worn thin and fallen to ruins."

New places you shall never find, you'll not find other seas.
The city still shall follow you. You'll wander still
in the same streets, you'll roam in the same neighborhoods,
in these same houses you'll turn gray.
You'll always arrive at this same city. Don't hope for
    somewhere else;
no ship for you exists, no road exists.
Just as you've ruined your life here, in this
small corner of earth, you've worn it thin the whole world round.

The God Forsakes Antony

When suddenly at the midnight hour you hear
an invisible procession passing by,
with music marvellous, with shouting,
do not then uselessly lament your luck
which now at length gives way, your works
that have failed, your life's plans that have all turned delusion.
Like one for a long time prepared, like a courageous man,
bid her farewell, the Alexandria that is leaving.
Above all, do not delude yourself, do not say that this
was but a dream, that your hearing played you false;
do not condescend to such vain hopes as these.
Like one for a long time prepared, like a courageous man,
as befitting one once worthy of such a city,
approach the window with a steadfast step
and listen deeply moved, not
with the faint-hearted man's entreaties and complaints,
but as a last enjoyment to the sounds,
the marvellous instruments of that occult procession,
and bid her farewell, the Alexandria you are losing.

He Swears

He swears now and again to begin a better life.
But when night comes with its own suggestions,
with its own compromises and its promises;
but when night comes with its own strength
of the body that now craves and seeks, he goes
once more, foredoomed, to the same fatal joy.

Ángelos Sikelianós

(1880–1951)

Ángelos Sikelianós was born in 1880 in Lefkas, one of the Ionian islands, and died in Athens in 1951. For many years he roamed throughout the length and breadth of Greece, confirming his knowledge and mastery of Greek tradition and the demotic tongue. The central action of his life was the formation of the Delphic Festivals in 1927 and 1930. At Delphi, where the Amphictyonic Council (the first League of Nations) used to meet, Sikelianós hoped to found a cosmic center where, through a dedication to a religious view of life without dogma, the nations of the world might meet to insure peace and justice. Aeschylus' *Prometheus Bound* and the *Suppliants* were lavishly mounted, Olympic contests were held on the heights of Mt. Parnassos, Byzantine music was played, Greek demotic songs were delivered and danced, and an international university was planned. The author of nine books of poetry and of seven poetic dramas, Sikelianós was a poet in the grand tradition, a Yeats-like figure, a prophet and seer, a man of high vision and noble actions, one who had assimilated the cultural traditions of his own nation and those of the modern world, a revolutionary democrat and mystic who acted beyond the particular political creeds and religious faiths of the world. His vision was pantheistic and panhellenic, and his poetry, with its wide rhetorical sweep and unequaled command of language, encompassed both the lyric (of which he was a modern master), the philosophic poem, and in his later years, the poetic drama.

BIBLIOGRAPHY: *Consecrated Bread*, Selected Poems (1943, 1961); *The Lyric Life*, 3 vols. (1947); 5 vols. (1965-1968); *Six Poets of Modern Greece* (1961; edited, translated, and introduced by Edmund Keeley and Philip Sherrard).

Sparta

"As if from ambush now for a long time
I've held you in my eye, and from all others
have chosen you as if you were a star;
your countenance has gratified my heart.
Hearken; now let me tightly grasp your hand,
for youth is like a stallion thus subdued;
for one night only shall you lie upon
my bed, and be my own wife's counterpart.

Go; she is small in waist and as compact
in beauty as majestic Helen was;
and fill her generously with your seed.
For one night take her in your strong embrace,
and then uplift my desolate old age
before all Sparta with a worthy son."

See Plutarch's *Life of Lycurgus:* "The old husband of a young woman was permitted to introduce her to a handsome and virtuous young man whom he esteemed, and to recognize the offspring of their generous blood as his own."

Unrecorded

A little beyond the walls of Zion walking
one day somewhat before the set of sun,
Jesus and his disciples came by chance
to that place where for years the town had cast
its rubbish: burnt mattresses of the diseased,
rags, broken crockery, refuse and filth.

And there upon the highest mound of all,
bloated, its legs turned upward toward the sky,
the carcass of a dog lay stretched, from which

at once, as vultures thickly piled on it
took fright at steps approaching, so foul a stench
broke forth, that the disciples as one man,
holding their breath within their hands, drew back.

But Jesus paced his way alone and paused
serenely awhile before that mound of filth,
and gazed upon that carcass, until one
of the disciples, unable to restrain himself,
spoke from afar: "Rabbi, can you not smell
that horrid stench and stand so closely by?"

And he, his eyes not swerving from that sign
on which he gazed, replied: "This horrid stench
does he whose breath is pure breathe even in that
same town from which we came . . . But now with all
my soul do I most marvel at that thing
which issues here from this decay . . . For see
how in the sun the teeth of this dog shine,
now like the hailstone, now like the lily, far
beyond the decay, like a tremendous vow,
reflection of the Eternal, but still more,
the lightning bolt and the harsh hope of Justice."

Thus did he speak; and if they understood
these words or not, together the disciples
followed once more as he went on his silent way.

And now, my Lord, the last of all indeed,
how I do turn my mind on these Thy words,
and wholly in one thought consumed, do stand
before Thee. O grant, even to me, my Lord,
that when I walk beyond the walls of Zion,
and all, from the one end to the other end
of earth are ruins, all are sweepings, all
unburied corpses that choke up the sacred spring
of breath, that in the city or beyond the city,
amid this horrible stench through which I pass,
grant me, my Lord, if only for a moment,
Thine own sublime serenity, that I may pause
unterrified within the midst of carrion
until I also may be given to see

some white spot, like the hailstone, like the lily,
something that suddenly may glow deep in me
out of decay, beyond the world's decay,
as shone the teeth of that dog, O my Lord,
on which Thou gazed at in the setting sun,
and stood and marveled, a tremendous vow,
reflection of the Eternal, but still more,
the lightning bolt and the harsh hope of Justice.

Unrecorded: The title refers to those anecdotes about Christ not admitted in the New Testament or the Apocrypha. This is one of several courageous poems of the Resistance which Sikelianós wrote during the German-Italian Occupation of Greece, and which were secretly circulated in manuscript. The carcass of the dog is a symbol of Greece devastated in the war.

Níkos Kazantzákis

(1883–1957)

Níkos Kanzantzákis was born in Heracleion, Crete, in 1883, and died in Freiburg, Germany, in 1957. He studied law at the University of Athens, philosophy under Henri Bergson at the Collège de France, and literature and art in Germany and Italy. In 1919 he served briefly in the Ministry of Public Welfare, and in 1947 he was appointed Director of Translations from the Classics for UNESCO. The greatest man of letters of modern Greece, Kazantzákis wrote some nine novels (of which *Zorba the Greek, The Greek Passion, Freedom or Death, The Last Temptation of Christ, St. Francis,* and *The Rock Garden* are available in English), five books of travel, sixteen poetic dramas, three philosophical treatises (including *The Saviors of God: Spiritual Exercises,* available in English translation by Kimon Friar), and his great epical poem of 33,333 lines, *The Odyssey: A Modern Sequel,* hailed unanimously as a world masterpiece immediately on its American publication in a translation by Kimon Friar. In addition, he has translated into modern Greek Homer's *Iliad* and *Odyssey,* Dante's *Divine Comedy,* Goethe's *Faust,* Darwin's *Origin of the Species,* and innumerable other books.

BIBLIOGRAPHY: *Odyssey* (1938, 1957, 1960); *The Odyssey: A Modern Sequel* (1958), translated by Kimon Friar; *The Saviors of God: Spiritual Exercises* (1960), translated by Kimon Friar; *Terza Rimas* (1960).

Odysseus and the Cicada

He spoke, then shook his spirit free from dizziness
And leant against the olive tree to plan the seizure;
but all at once he lay stark still with staring eyes
and gazed on the tree's bark where a cocooned cicada
struggled and slowly squirmed to pierce through into light.
Stretched on the ground, Odysseus watched and held his breath.
Like a warm body buried alive, wrapped up in shrouds,
the poor worm twitched to pierce through its translucent tomb
in a mute, heavy war with death, till the Archer stooped
and with his warm breath tried to help the writhing soul.
Then lo! a small nape suddenly slit the shroud in two
and like a budded leaf, soft and curly, poked
a blind, unhardened head in light, swayed gropingly,
then strengthened soon in sun and took on form and color.
It stretched its neck and struggled, crawled from its white sheath,
unglued its soft feet from its belly, clutched with bliss
the tree's gray bark, then slowly stretched its body taut
until its fledgling wings unfurled and shimmered in air.
The honey-pale cicada basked in the shimmering sun,
and the three rubies on its brow burst in three flames
as it plunged deeper still in the world's warmth and scent.
Fixing its glassy, greedy eyes on the tree's foliage,
its soft smoke-silver body overbrimmed with song
yet made no sound, enraptured still by sun and light
and the huge joy of birth as on earth's sill it stood
before it entered, speechless, numb with the world's wonders.
The man of many passions quaked and mutely watched
how the soul pokes through the earth and squirms out of its shroud;
and thus the world, he thought, crawls like a worm to sun,
and thus the mind, in time, bursts like a withered husk
from which there spring, time after time, new finer thoughts
until the ultimate great thought leaps forward: Death.

From *The Odyssey: A Modern Sequel*
—Book IV, 232–264

The Death of Krino

Slim as a switch, pale Krino stood in the shade and waited;
the wild bull danced and leaped about her, women screamed,
and cold and feverish tremors pulsed along their spines,
for the bull gleamed in sun, a mortal, a beast, a god.
From head to toe, like a lean spear, pale Krino swayed
and balanced her unbridled body high on tiptoe,
swinging it right or left to escape the touch of death.
Deep silence in the ring, hearts throbbed in every throat,
all turned to stone, and in the sun there steamed alone
a mortal and a bestial body, like two quivering flames.
The bull lunged swift as lightning, the dust swirled in clouds
as Krino lightly swerved, and the bull crashed to its knees,
but as it rose in fuming rage, the maiden leaped,
grasped both its horns, then balanced, somersalted high,
and lightboned sat astride the brute beast's sweating nape.
The Bull-God stood stock-still, his hooves nailed to the ground,
like blazing firedogs his red eyes rolled in rage
seeking to find some place where he might dash her brains out.
But she had tightly wedged her head between his horns
and glued her back to his, forming one compact body;
the blood throbbed in her veins, the bull's blood throbbed
    in rhythm,
both bodies merged in one immense heartthrob of death,
and the salt waters running down their hot thighs mingled.
But suddenly as the maiden raised her eyes to the sky,
her warm tears welled, then brimmed and tumbled down
    her cheeks
till all at once her heart dropped in the abyss, and vanished.
Her hands lost their firm grip, and her moist temples roared
—it was as though the bowstring snapped which held her spirit—
and as the maiden felt her end draw near, she broke
in bitter wild lament and on the bull's neck swooned.
And the wild beast, as though it felt the maiden's swoon,
spread its hooves wide on earth, gathered its savage strength,
and ah, alas, tossed her lean body high in air.

The crowd turned pale and their dry tongues stuck in their
    throats;
then, as a wild dove wounded in the sky falls tumbling,
crumpled and torn, so on the god's sharp double-ax
raised high on a marble column, Krino fell impaled,
and splattered the bronze cow with her warm brains and
    dripping blood.

From *The Odyssey: A Modern Sequel*
  —Book VI, 571–608

Kóstas Ouránis

(1890–1953)

Kóstas Ouránis (pen name of Neárhos) was born in Constantinople in 1890, and died in Athens in 1953. He began his studies in Náfplion, and continued them later in Constantinople, Paris, and Geneva. As consul, as Secretary of the Ministry of Press and as journalist, he traveled throughout Europe, wrote many travel books, and finally settled in Athens in 1924. He married Eléni Negropónti, one of the foremost literary critics of Greece, best known by her pen name, Álkis Thrílos. Ouránis may be considered as the last of the Greek romantic poets. His poems, written in formal patterns of a lilting music, are windows of escape into the lost paradise of childhood wonders, an escape into memory and nostalgia, an evocation of dream in an elegiac tone of causeless sorrow.

BIBLIOGRAPHY: *Poems* (1953).

I Shall Die One Day on a Mournful
Autumn Twilight

I shall die one day on a mournful autumn twilight
in my cold room where I have lived alone;
in my last anguish I shall hear the rain,
the hollow noise that mounts from the street below.

I shall die one day on a mournful autumn twilight
amid furniture not mine and scattered books;
the street police shall find me in my bed
and bury a man who had no history.

Among my friends who now and then play cards
someone will simply ask, "Has anyone seen
Ouránis? He hasn't been around for days."
Another, playing, will reply, "But he died!"

For a brief moment one will look at the other,
shake his head slowly, sorrowfully, and say,
"Ah, what is man! He was living but yesterday!"
And then renew his playing silently.

Some friend will write in the "small notices"
that "poor Ouránis died abroad untimely,
a youth well-known amid our set, whose book
of poems, just published, showed great promise."

And this will be my life's last epitaph;
only my aged parents, of course, will weep,
hold requiem with many, too many, priests,
with all my friends attending, even my foes.

I shall die one day on a mournful autumn twilight
in a cheap rented room in noisy Paris,
and some "Ketty," thinking I've jilted her for another,
will write to curse me. But I shall be dead.

Stop Sending Now

Stop sending now these signals of alarm,
these shrill wails of the hysterical ship's siren,
and let the wheel run loose in the tempest's hands:
the most dread shipwreck surely is to be saved!

What then? Return to boring Ithaca,
to our cheap joys, our miserable concerns,
to our faithful spouse who weaves her smothering love
round, round our lives like a fine spider's web?

To know once more, beforehand, what tomorrow
will bring, nor feel a single yearning dawn,
until our dreams resemble the fruit once more
that withers away, then rots and falls to earth?

Since we lacked daring (and shall always lack it)
let's rise alone from our smooth, narrow beds
and like free men at the world's early dawn
take to the great, the unfamiliar roads

with a light step like that of a bird on earth
as our souls shiver, leaves in a fine breeze;
let's not at least let this occasion slip
to become the playthings of the savage billows

no matter what the consequence! Grim waves
like tentacles can drag us down the dark depths
or in their sweeping onrush raise us high
aloft—until our foreheads touch the stars.

Kóstas Ouránis

Tákis Papatzónis

(1895–   )

Tákis Papatzónis was born in Athens in 1895. By profession an economist, he became a General Director of the Ministry of Economics, a life-member of the Financial Council of the High Administrative Court, and for many years represented Greece on various economic missions throughout Europe and Cuba. He is now Deputy Chairman of the Commercial Bank of Greece. He published *Selection I* in 1934 and *Ursa Minor* in 1944, but he did not bring out another book until he collected some poems in two volumes in 1962, although enough for four or more volumes lie scattered in various anthologies and periodicals. Greatly influenced not only by Byzantine but also by Roman Catholic doctrines and rituals, Papatzónis is predominantly a religious poet with an inclination toward mysticism and naturalism, tempered by an erotic strain. His poetry gives the impression of being "intellectual," for he makes use of philosophical propositions and axioms, of the language of logic and the abstract. In substance, his poetry becomes transcendent, and ultimately irrational.

BIBLIOGRAPHY: *Selection.* 2 vols. (1962).

The Unlooked-for Theme

Today, after so many crooked byways,
so many detours, so many false leads,
there rises to the surface the great, the unlooked-for theme.
I do not to maintain by this
that I have not hitherto encountered a violet,
or that a rosebush never blossomed before me—
with those all-crimson, those enormous, those flaming
and aromatic roses of May—but it is,
nevertheless, unexpected: it is the antithesis of the cataract
whose roaring tumult the melting snow enlivens;
it is, in the midst of our great wandering through life,
a plateau of pellucid air that bursts into view
up there in the mountains, at a great height,
with a panorama of all the lakes below,
untrembled silver disks with the mists
of Spring and of forests that rise toward God . . . a plateau
of serenity, with Alpine flora, with the opulence
of gardens and even of hothouses
and that pierces the snow, a vegetation entirely
the colors of repose—those lavender tints
or those beautiful yellows—with their offering to you
of the absolute certainty that you have finally touched the heights,
that you are grazing the vast sky.
Something like the antithesis of the cataract. And yet—
how unclear the meanings, how ineffectual, how miserable
      the comparison—
antithetical yet strangely similar to the essence of the cataract!
To the triumphal song of the cataract! And as for the onrush, as
      for the roaring tumult,
as for the strength of the primary element, as for the glittering
      brilliance
in the boiling sun, or as for the foaming spray—
the unlooked-for theme that welled up suddenly
is the theme of the cataract's essence.
It is the theme of *De Profundis*.

The Sluggish of Mind

In passage here a flock of birds
brought us a message from the North, but we turned a deaf ear.

And the Quails in their color of ash reflected the icebergs,
but we were not only deaf—we set snares
and fired upon them and wanted to eat them.
And who? It was we—we who, having awaited
so impatiently the message from the North,
became blind, and not understanding it had come,
fired upon them, wounded them, chased them away.

I do not deny that the flock was transient,
but we neither loved them nor revered their weariness
or their exhaustion; and once they were gone
there fell upon us suddenly a compassion and weight of
    the spirit
for the ungracious act, the evil assault;
and behold, we remained the awkward ones,
the sluggish of mind to discern apparitions,
deserted, with no message from the North,
with our accustomed *mea culpa*
and our profitless self-accusation.

Kóstas Kariotákis

(1896–1928)

Kóstas Kariotákis was born in 1896 in Tripolis (the Peloponnesos), but his father's occupation as mechanical engineer took the family to many parts of Greece, particularly to Haniá, Crete, where Kariotákis spent most of his childhood, his summer holidays, and where he finished high school. As a child he was fearful, timid, sickly, and prone to melancholy and solitude. In 1953 he enrolled in the law school of the University of Athens, took his degree in 1917, but never pursued a career as lawyer. He became, instead, a government clerk posted in various principalities. In order to remain in Athens, he became an employee in the Ministry of Public Welfare, and during his holidays managed to visit Italy, Germany, Rumania, and France. He was again transferred, however, to Patras, and then to "exile" in Preveza where, in a fit of deep melancholy, he put a bullet through his head under a eucalyptus tree. One of the first to be influenced by the French Symbolist school, his poetry is pervaded with a sense of ennui, loneliness, pessimism, and despondency, and though he formed no school, his personality and work were the precursors of modernism and have become ingrained in the Greek poetic temperament.

BIBLIOGRAPHY: *Complete Works.* 2 vols., published poems and translations. Edited by G. P. Savvídhis. (1965).

Only

Ah, all things should have happened as they did!
The hopes and roses should have withered away,
years should have drifted off like little boats
have drifted off and vanished.

And as at eventide we parted once,
many friends thus should have been lost forever.
The place where I grew up as a small child
I should have left one twilight.

The beautiful and simple girls—dear loves!—
life should have taken from me, a quick dance turn.
Even pain, that filled me once with fragrance, should
have weighed down my barren self.

Ah, all things should have happened thus. Only this night
should not have been as lovely as now it is,
nor should the bright stars sparkle there like eyes
that laugh at me and mock me.

Athens

Sweet hour. Athens reclines and gives herself
to April like a beauteous courtesan.
Aromas are voluptuous in the air,
and there is nothing now the soul awaits.

Over the houses evening stoops and lowers
the silver of her eyelids' heavy weight,
and there beyond, the Acropolis like a Queen
wears all the sunset like a crimson robe.

A kiss of light, and the first star explodes.
By the Ilissos a light breeze falls in love
with rose-nymph laurels in their quivering.

Sweet hour of joy and love when the swift wind
of birds that chase each other through the air
beats on a column of the Olympian Zeus.

Optimism

Let us suppose now that we have not reached
the dark blind alley and the mind's abyss.
Let us suppose now that the woods have come
with all the autocratic panoply
of the morning's triumph, with birds, with the sky's light,
and with the sun that here shall pierce them through.

Let us suppose that we are there beyond
in unknown lands far to the West, the North,
that while we toss our coats high in the air
strangers gape at us strangely, soberly,
and that she might receive us tenderly
a Lady has given her servants leave all day.

Let us suppose now that our slim hat's brim
has suddenly widened, that our trousers too
have narrowed and clung tight, that with our spurs'
command a thousand steeds move on their way.
We march on—banners flapping in the wind—
Cross-bearing heroes, saviours of the Saviour.

Let us suppose now that we have not reached
frontiers of silence through a hundred roads,
and let us sing now—may the song resemble
a triumphal trumpet blast, a bursting cry—
that it may entertain the fiery demons
in the bowels of earth, and men in the heights above.

George Seféris

(1900–   )

George Seféris, pseudonym of George Sefariádhis, was born in
Smyrna in 1900 and in 1926 entered the Ministry of Foreign Affairs.
He was formerly the Royal Greek Ambassador to England, and has now
retired. In 1961 he was awarded the William Foyle Poetry Prize in
England, and in 1963 the Nobel Prize in Literature. The author of
eight books of poetry and two of critical essays, he is a poet of evocative
symbols and metaphysical distinctions who has superbly translated
Eliot's *The Waste Land* and other poems. All of his mature poetry is
written in a free verse of great sinuousness, rhythmical yet modulated,
which never rises in tone or diction beyond the "conversation between
intellectual men," as Ezra Pound has it. His is a poetry of understatement
and hesitation, dealing with recurring themes of expatriation and the
disintegration of the modern world. His poetry is brooding and contemplative, precise yet subtle in thought and image. He has often attempted
to define what Greece *is* as a "state of being." Yet in the center of each
poem is the poet himself, looking back into the mythological past of his
country and her symbols, retracing her history, and telling a story which
has the independent validity of imaginative fiction.

BIBLIOGRAPHY: *Poems, 1924–46* (5th ed., 1964); *Cyprus . . .
Where He Prophesied That I . . . .* (1955); *The King of Asine and
Other Poems* (1948; trans. by Bernard Spencer, Nanos Valaoritis, Lawrence Durrell, with an introduction by Rex Warner); *Poems* (translated
and introduced by Rex Warner, 1960); and *Six Poets of Modern Greece*
(1961; edited, translated, and introduced by Edmund Keeley and Philip
Sherrard); *Collected Poems, 1924-1955* (1967, biligual edition) translated, edited, and introduced by Edmund Keeley and Philip Sherrard.

In the Manner of G. S.

No matter where I travel, Greece wounds me.

On Mt Pelion amid the chestnut trees the shirt of the Centaur
slid among leaves to wind about my body
as I mounted the slope and the sea followed me
mounting also like mercury in a thermometer
until we came on mountain waters.
In Santorini, as I touched the sinking islands
and heard a flute play somewhere on the pumice-stone
an arrow suddenly flung
from the confines of a vanished youth
nailed my hand to the gunwhale.
At Mycenae I lifted the huge stones and the treasures of the
    Atridae
and slept beside them at the inn of *The Beautiful Helen of
    Menelaus*;
they vanished only at dawn when Cassandra crowed
with a cock hanging down her black throat.
At Spetsai at Poros at Myconos
the barcaroles nauseated me.
What do they want, all those who say
they may be found in Athens or the Piraeus?
One comes from Salamis and asks whether he "hails from
    Concord Square."
"No, I hail from Constitution Square," replies the other,
    self-satisfied.
"I ran into Yannis and he stood me an ice cream."
In the meantime Greece voyages on
we don't know anything we don't know we are all seamen
    disembarked
we don't know the bitterness of harbors when ships have gone;
we mock those who feel this.

Strange people who say they are in Attica and yet are nowhere;
they buy sugared almonds to get married
hold "beauty-aids" get photographed;
the man I saw today sittting before a backdrop of doves
    and flowers

allowing the hand of the photographer to smooth out the
    wrinkles
left on his face
by all the winged fowl of the heavens.

In the meantime Greece voyages on and keeps on voyaging
and if "we see the Aegean flowering with corpses"
they are of those who wanted to catch the great liner
    by swimming
those who wearied of waiting for ships which cannot set sail
the ELSIE the SAMOTHRACE the AMBRAKIKOS.
Now as night falls the ships whistle in the Piraeus
they whistle and keep whistling but not a single capstan stirs
not a single wet chain glistens in the last declining light
the captain stands enmarbled in his white and gold.

No matter where I travel, Greece wounds me;
screen of mountains archipelagoes bald granite.
The ship which voyages is named AG GONY 937.

—*Aboard the Avlis, waiting to sail.*
Summer, 1936.

NOTES

G. S.: George Seféris
Mt Pelion . . . centaur: The most wise and just of the Centaurs, Chiron,
lived on Pelion, a range of mountains in Thessaly where the timber
was felled with which the ship *Argo* was built. Chiron was the teacher
of most of the Greek heroes, and was accidentally struck by Heracles
with a poisoned arrow. Although immortal, he chose not to live, and
bequeathed his immortality to Prometheus. Zeus placed him among the
stars as Sagittarius. The word "shirt" connects this passage with another
centaur, Nessus, who, in carrying Deianira, wife of Heracles, across
a river, tried to outrage her. Heracles shot him with an arrow. The
dying centaur told Deianira to take some of his blood with her as a
certain means of preserving the love of her husband. Fearing that she
might one day be supplanted, Deianira steeped a garment of Heracles
in the blood. But the blood had been poisoned by the arrow, and the
poison penetrated into Heracles' limbs when he wore the garment. He
wrenched it off, but it stuck to his flesh, and with it he tore away whole
pieces from his body.

The Inn . . . Menelaus: Such an inn actually exists on the approach to Mycenae, where you may be served a light meal by the two brothers who run the place, named Agamemnon and Orestes.

Spétsai, Póros, Myconos: The first two are islands in the Aegean near the Peloponnesian coast. Myconos is one of the Cyclades.

"Hails . . . Constitution Square": Concord Square is, roughly, the Times Square or Picadilly Circus of Athens. Constitution Square is the main square of the city surrounded and environed by the House of Parliament, the various embassies, the best hotels and smart shops. Seféris has his characters speak partly in the purist tongue, and he comments on how such ragtags of elegant expression have been taken over by the common people in their daily diction. The difference is impossible of translation.

Sugared almonds: At Greek weddings and baptisms sugar-covered almonds are always passed out to the guests.

"Beauty-aids": Seféris uses, ironically, an ancient Greek word *(lykythos)*, meaning a casket for unguents, cosmetics, etc.

Ambrákikos: Named after the Ambracian Gulf, now the Gulf of Arta, part of the Ionian Sea, between Epirus and Acarnania.

AG GONY: The letters are so separated in the poem to denote how they were painted on either side of the prow. Also, the first two letters in Greek constitute the abbreviation for saint: ʌr. Most Greek ships are named after a patron saint.

"we see . . . corpses": A herald, reporting the homecoming of Agamemnon, tells how only the king himself had escaped the storm that raged the previous night. "But when the radiant light of the sun arose, we beheld the Aegean flowering with corpses of Achaean men and the wreckage of ships."—Aeschylus, *Agamemnon*, 658–660. In his poem Seféris quotes from the ancient Greek.

Our Own Sun

This sun was yours and mine: we shared it
who suffers behind the golden silk who dies?
A woman was shrieking striking her dry breast: "Cowards,
they have taken my children and torn them to pieces, you were the
    ones who killed them
watching with curious expression the glowworms at evening,
abstracted in a blind meditation."
The blood was drying on the hand dyed green by a tree
a warrior was sleeping clutching a lance that brightened his side.

The sun was ours, we could see nothing behind the
     golden embroideries
later the messengers came breathless and dirty
stammering incomprehensible syllables
twenty days and nights across sterile lands and nothing but thorns
twenty days and nights of feeling the horses' bellies dripping
     with blood
stopping not even for a moment to drink rainwater.
You told them to rest first and speak afterwards, the light
     had dazzled you.
They expired saying: "There is no time," touching a few rays
     of the sun;
you kept forgetting that no one ever rests.

A woman was howling "Cowards," like a dog in the night
she must once have been as beautiful as you
with a moist mouth, with veins alive under the skin
with love.

This sun was ours; you kept all of it, you did not want to
     follow me
and it was then I learned about these things behind the gold
     and the silk;
there is no time. The messengers spoke truly.

Stratis the Mariner by the Dead Sea

"At times you may see in chapels erected on legendary
sites the relevant passage from the Gospel quoted in
English, and below: THIS IS THE PLACE, GENTLEMEN!"
     —Letter from Stratis the Mariner, from Jerusalem.

Jerusalem, ungoverned city,
Jerusalem, city of refuges.

On the road sometimes at noon
you may see on the asphalt gliding
a flock of black leaves scattered—
Migrating birds pass by under the sun
but you don't raise your head.

Jerusalem, ungoverned city!

Unknown tongues of Babel,
with no relation to the grammar
the *Lives of the Saints* or the *Psalter*
which they taught you to spell out in autumn
when fishing boats were tied to the quays;
unknown tongues glued to ravaged lips
like burnt-out cigarette butts.

Jerusalem, city of refugees!

But their eyes all speak the same word,
not the Word that became man—God forgive us—
nor voyages to see new lands, but
the dark train of escape where infants
are fed on the filth and sins of parents
and the middle-aged feel the chasm
growing wider between the body
that straggles behind like a wounded camel
and the soul with its inexhaustible courage, as they say.
There are also the ships in which they voyage
bolt-upright in the hold like bishops
embalmed, to anchor any evening
on the sea's bottom gently amid the seaweed.

Jerusalem, ungoverned city!

> To the River Jordan
> three monks brought
> and tied to the bank
> a red sailing boat.

Three from the Holy Mountain
sailed for three months
and bound to a branch
by the bank of the Jordan
a refugee's offering.
For three months they hungered
for three months they thirsted
for three months they slept not,
they came from Mt Athos
they came from Salonika
the slave-driven monks.

We are all like the Dead Sea
many fathoms below the level of the Aegean.
Come with me that I may show you the place:

In the Dead Sea
there are no fish
there is no seaweed
nor any sea urchins
there is no life.
There is nothing living
that has a belly
to suffer hunger
that nourishes nerves
to suffer pain,
THIS IS THE PLACE, GENTLEMEN!

In the Dead Sea
the wages of scorn
are no one's merchandise,
nobody cares.
Heart and thought
grow stiff in salt
that is bitter, and join
the mineral world.
THIS IS THE PLACE, GENTLEMEN!

In the Dead Sea
are friends and enemies
wife and children
and relatives,
go and find them.
They're in Gomorrah
down at the bottom
extremely happy
in not expecting
a single message.

GENTLEMEN,
      let us continue our tour
many fathoms below the level of the Aegean.

July, 1952

NOTES

Stratis the Mariner: A fictitious character who appears in several
   poems by Seféris.
bolt-upright . . . embalmed: The bishops of the Greek Orthodox
   Church are buried seated upon their thrones.

George Thémelis

(1900–   )

George Thémelis was born on the island of Samos in 1900, studied literature at the University of Athens, and has been teaching in the high schools of Salonika since 1930. He is the author of ten books of poetry and of several books of essays and the translator into modern Greek of *Prometheus Bound* and *Oedipus the King*. In 1955 he was awarded the Second, and in 1961 the First State Award in Poetry. Essentially a metaphysical poet, Thémelis explores the esoteric country of the spirit, the individual conscience, and in so doing emphasizes less man's agony and disintegration and more man's progress from struggle to hope, from death into birth, affirmation, and salvation.

BIBLIOGRAPHY: *Naked Window* (1945); *Men and Birds* (1947); *The Return* (1948); *Odes by Which to Remember Heroes* (1949); *Escort* (1950); *Conversations* (1953); *The Orchard* (1955); *The Face and the Image* (1959); *Mona Plays* (1961); *Chiaroscuro* (1961); and *The Fishing Net of Souls* (1965).

Appearance

When you seek your features in some transparency,
When as you turn a corner you encounter a stranger,
It is another face which makes its appearance.

On opening a room locked up for a long time,
With a certain impatience which makes your hand tremble,
(Your heart beating faster for fear it won't come in time)
With a certain nervousness which, as it touches
Your secret chords, has made you an instrument of music—
You hear, as you turn the key, a certain resonance
As though all your personal compartments were being unlocked
    at the same time.

As you enter, you are seized by the breathing of a
    certain desolation.
The noise of naked feet, of gestures over all things . . .

Someone must be there who hastens now to disappear,
(You came upon him perhaps in an hour of sleep or nakedness. . .)
As though from a sense of guilt behind some kind
    of masquerade. . . .)

(The garment is the contrivance of a certain sin. . .
When guilt erupts on our face like a rash,
That we might hide ourselves from glances and become invisible,
Playing a game: present-absent. . .)

Walking down the very frequented streets of a city,
(In particular during the night hours of an autumn day)
With a revealing nuance on the calm horizon)
Gazing on faces that press behind each other in a crowd,
Nothing strikes your gaze but fragments, smashed
    mirror reflections,
As though from some other face behind these faces.

You may come in time to see the reflection
In the gaze of a child who looks at you and falls silent.
In the passing of a girl in the light.
In the long awaited return of one long absent in foreign lands.
In the face of an unknown man who looks at you
As he searches his memory to find you.
(You have seen him somewhere—you have met
    him somewhere. . .)

From encounter to encounter, from gesture to gesture.

He moves the lips of lovers and makes them tremble.
He is present in their night encounter.
He appears in their faces and makes them glow.

He stoops over us, passes beyond us, enters our sleep
Causing our souls to shudder and remember,
Astonishing invasion of beauty, cleft of light.

Sometimes he will manifest himself face to face
He will lean over our petrified lips to kiss us. . .

(Do not throw away those old mirrors which held your form.)

Pray in the dark and love music.

Passing

Passing amid familiar walls, we hear the sound. . .

We don't know if it comes from our steps or those of another
Which at one time dragged behind us and now follow us. . .
We don't know if we are the musicians or the instruments,
If it is we who are walking, looking behind us
At our long shadows—or perhaps it transposes us
As though we were its hanged ones on some tree
(Or, it may be, in a cistern or an old mirror)
Falling from garden to garden, from corridor to corridor,

Like another face—other faces, one merging into the other,
Like the worlds of a poem which is continued
With interruptions, relapses, and a coherence of images. . .
Or reflections—shadowy lights on a blackboard.

Before every blackboard there is a child
(Just as there is an ideal face before every gaze
Or a luminous meteor before every expectation. . .

(For this reason, when night falls we grow cold and are
    gripped with fears. . .
For this reason, when we meet, we leave a trail of phosphorus,
One seeking the other, an encounter in the night. . .)

The blackboards open with a secret lock in back:
(All things have secret folds and places)
They present photograph frames, coffers, or empty boxes. . .

Within every frame there is a landscape.
Within every coffer there is a buried secret.
Within every empty box a probable doll
With glass eyes and crossed hands.

Zoë Karelli

(1901–   )

Zoë Karelli, born in 1901 in Salonika, received the tutorial education of a girl of good family according to her class and period, married at the age of seventeen, and then attended courses in philosophy at the University of Salonika. She has two sons. The author of ten books of poetry and three of poetic drama, she has translated and published, with an explanatory essay, Eliot's *Family Reunion*. For Mrs. Karelli, love of the word itself is a primary element of poetry; for her, the strength of life lies in the strength of the words which express it. Unfortunately, her puns, her play on words in assonance, consonance, and syntax are mostly lost in translation. Her themes are almost exclusively concerned with the split in personality of the man of sensibility tormented to find his integrity, to create ties of continuity and cohesion in a world of spiritual disintegration. In 1955 she was granted the second State Award in Poetry for *Cassandra and Other Poems*, and has also been given the "Palms Academiques" by France.

BIBLIOGRAPHY: *The March* (1940); *Season of Death* (1948); *Fantasy of Time* (1949); *Of Solitude and Arrogance* (1951); *Etchings and Icons* (1952); *The Ship* (1955); *Garden Legends* (1955); *Antitheses* (1957); *The Mirror of Midnight* (1958).

Worker in the Workshop of Time

As he wrought the shape,
a worker, a blower of glass,
felt his love profoundly
for that material
into which he blew his breath.
At times crystal or like pearl,
mother-of-pearl, precious ivory
or opal with misty colors
drifting toward azure.
All these were materials that became shapes,
erotic shapes for whatever exists
within time.

The shape, receptacle of time,
enclosed it erotically,
an offering to time,
expectation and acceptance both,
that form which is an embracement of time,
the singular shape which he wrought
out of his own essence,
his own imagination.

But as his material hand
caressed the final shape afterward,
he understood the materiality of time
as his own hand
together with the shape
and the precious, erotic material
were transformed into the diaphanous meaning of time.
All together,
but particularly he.

Presences

You will remain very much alone,
—quietness of the fragile movement,
anxiety of perception—
that the presences may come.

Do not be afraid,
the dead never die;
even the most humble and forgotten
exist, and when you are very much alone
they come near you
invested with the mystic silence
of the irradicable,
the incomparable presence of man.

Kiss of Silence

Kiss of silence, icy
pleasure in the well of warm conversation,
your seal is an indelible mark,
the blossoming of another world, the voice of a whisper
that terrifies, mystic
fragrance that tears the living
entrails apart, promise
that no one knows,
and all the power of life
prepares your entire imagination.

You are not yet the expectation
of nonexistence. You are the integral,
the only difference, that superb
immobility which possesses
perfect Love, and is possessed.

Andréas Embirícos

(1901-   )

Andréas Embirícos, whose family of international shipowners and shipbuilders come from the island of Andros, was born in Rumania in 1901. He worked in the London offices of the Byron Steamship Company (owned by his family) between 1921 and 1925, but gave up his shipping career and went to Paris where he studied psychoanalysis under Dr. René LaForgue and became a member of the surrealist group headed by André Brêton. Later, he founded the Greek group of psychoanalysis with the late Marie Bonaparte and others, and published two books of poetry as the first surrealist poet of Greece. Those acquainted with psychoanalysis can easily discern a cohesion in his surrealist images, and recently, without departing from the seemingly dislocated world of fantasy, he has been writing in a more pellucid manner. Between 1945 and 1951, he completed an as yet unpublished two-thousand-page erotic novel called *The Great Eastern*, after the first liner to cross the Atlantic.

BIBLIOGRAPHY: *Poems* (1962); *Writings or Personal Mythology* (1960. Published as *Amour Amour*. Translated by Nikos Stangos and Alan Ross, with drawings by Minos Argyrakis, 1966).

Light on a Whale

The original form of woman was the braiding of two dinosaur necks. Times changed after that, and woman also changed shape. She became much smaller, more fluid, more adapted to the two-masted (in some countries three-masted) ships that sail above the calamities of life's struggles. Woman herself sails on the fish-scales of a cylinder-carrying dove of long trajectory. Times change, and in our time woman resembles the chasm of a fuse.

Spring as Always

Covering the waves of the spear-conquered town with her
    red dress
At first small and then large
She ascends to the top of the tower
And seizes the clouds and presses them to her bosom
Perhaps there was never a sorrow greater than hers
Perhaps no whisper ever fell more incandescent on the surface
    of a face
Perhaps there was never exposed to the comprehension of man
    an exhibition more extensive
Exhibition more varied more comprehensive than the story
    of this confession told by the clouds
Cut here and there by guillotines
Warm drops fall to the ground
The hillock formed on the principal spot of this fall
Swells and rises still
No tax can be so heavy as one such drop
No diamond more heavy
No suitor more passionate
Bright are the fringes of the hill and they gleam in the sun
On the summit a basin is waiting
It is full to the brim
And from its water a very small and very lovely girl emerges
Our hope for the morrow.

The Euphrates

It is true that complete solitude is difficult to bear and that the desert is parched and tyrannizing. But, but, and yet again but (as in Islam's "Il Allah," or the Christian's "God will provide," or as in the lofty thoughts of the godless), no sweat, no thirst will exhaust the secret Euphrates which even in the desert, even within and beyond silence, within and beyond every solitude and every complaint irrigates all things always, its source as invisible as the great unstructured light (its own source invisible) that illuminates everything to eternity, everything, everything, even the most minute as well as the most ecstatic, the most imperishable, the never-setting, the great, foaming universe.

George Thomas Vafópoulos

(1904–   )

George Thomas Vafópoulos was born in Gevgeli, a town near the Yugoslavian border, in 1904. He completed his high school studies in Salonika, and for a while studied mathematics at the University of Athens. From 1939 to 1963 he directed the Municipal Library of Salonika, and in that capacity was invited by the British Council to visit Great Britain in 1951, and by the United States Department of State to visit America in 1957. He is the author of seven books of poetry and of a poetic drama. He has been influenced not by surrealist devices, but by the insistence of that school on the subconscious and on unknown forces drawn from the spirit of the times. His poetry, the result of a dual tension, a dialogue between the two parts of his severed self, is the expression of painful experiences which range from a desperate love of life to the inevitable acceptance of death, the tragedy of the solitary man. He was awarded the First State Award for Poetry in 1966.

BIBLIOGRAPHY: *The Roses of Myrtale* (1931); *Esther* (1934); *The Offering* (1938); *The Offering and Songs of Resurrection* (1948); *The Floor and Other Poems* (1951); *The Vast Night and the Window* (1959); and *Death Songs and Satires* (1966).

The Night

When midnight strikes, do not hasten
to open the window. At that hour
people are returning home from the theater,
and virgins make love in dark corners.

When midnight strikes, it is not night.
The uniforms of the generals dance with arrogance
and the frocks of the officials bow low
before flowering, empty muslins.

When midnight strikes, it is day.
And your own eyes cannot bear such light
nor even the lighted faces of men.

You must endure much. And when you have made certain
that all have entered the wardrobes, that the melodies
have curled up to sleep in the instruments,
then you may open the window with care and gaze
at the light of the stars: it is another light.
Or accept the slap of the hurricane: it is another slap.

And if suddenly your eyes discern
a certain shadow in the thick darkness
—a thief who has broken into the pavilion,
a mother who is waiting for her drunken son,
a doctor who is leaving a dead man's house—
do not hasten to close the window.

What you have seen is not man.
It is the spectre of the vast night
and which is called sin, love, or duty.
In that hour it was simply seeking shelter.

Lean into the darkness of this well
which is measured by the depth of your conscience
and give your hand to the night's spectre.
Then quietly close your window once more
before men fling open their own windows.

The Return of the Satyrs

On the leaves, Lydia, where last night's rain dropped all her tears
there moves an inexpressible, most grave tranquillity.
One might say that the spirit of an ancient pastoral god
has blessed and magnified the forest with his old glory.

Who says that the glory of ancient days has gone, that all flutes
and shepherds' pipes in the forests of Arcady are silent?
Lydia, my dear, come close—Pan still lives in these woods,
and the blood of his Satyrs threatens to burst in our veins.

The Mask

You existed within me before I existed.
Protoplasmic cell that voyaged in my forefathers,
changing your clothes after every death.
If I had not the prudence to bolt
all doors and shut all windows
perhaps I would have lost the possibility of knowing you.

Now you can slip out of my skin with safety
the way a hand emerges from a glove,
and you can sit opposite me in an armchair.
But first I must light the lamp
that I may see my face
in this mirror you carry about with you.

It would have been impossible to recognize you,
you old rascal, in this disguise you wear,
could I not guess at you: that stiff collar
is exactly like the one my father wore.
I think it's with this very watch chain I played
whenever I climbed up my grandfather's knees.
And this tailcoat of yours accompanied many a funeral.

I must pluck away your scales. I must unpeel you
to your deep marrow that I might find my roots
that are tightly entwined around my own death.
Monster, dragging about you the death of each of my deaths!
Reptile, tightly entwined around the root of time!

I would open the door for you, if only I could bear
such emptiness. The empty sack
which now I am, I would bind up tightly
if only it could fill with itself again.

Take off, at least, this fearful mask.
Wipe off the thick dust from your mirror.
In the safety of this solitude
I could even confront Medusa's head.
But hush! I think someone is knocking on the door.
Hurry up, dress yourself and slip back into my skin.
Safety, it is clear, must be sought elsewhere.
Let's put it off, to another time.

—Yes, Dr. Wagner, you may come in now.

NOTE: Wagner is the assistant in Goethe's *Faust,* and symbolizes
the pedantic man who looks logically at all things. Here too, as in *Faust,*
he knocks on the door and enters.

Alexander Báras

(1906–   )

Alexander Báras was born in Constantinople in 1906 and completed his high school studies there. After the Asia Minor defeat of Greece by Turkey in 1922, he spent three years in Cairo, but returned to Constantinople in 1925 where, until 1966, he was employed in the Royal Greek Ministry of Foreign Affairs, and served in that capacity in Athens during 1948–49. He was among the first Greek poets to write in free verse and to unburden his poetry of decorative imagery, though he still retains some exotic imagery phrased with clarity, evocative of disillusion and nostalgia.

BIBLIOGRAPHY: *Poems, 1933–1953* (1954).

The *Cleopatra,* The *Semiramis,* and The *Theodora*

Once every week,
on a specified day,
and always at the same hour,
three beautiful ships,
the *Cleopatra,* the *Semiramis,* and the *Theodora,*
set sail from the wharves
at nine o'clock
for Piraeus always,
for Brindisi and for Trieste
always.

Without maneuvers or meanderings
or hesitation
or fruitless shrieking of sirens
they turn their prows toward open waters,
the *Cleopatra,* the *Semiramis,* and the *Theodora,*
like certain well-bred persons
who leave a salon
without insipid and unnecessary
handshaking.

They set sail from the wharves
at nine o'clock,
for Piraeus always,
for Brindisi and for Trieste
always—whether it's cold or whether it's hot.

They go
to soil the azure waters
of the Aegean and the Mediterranean
with their smoke.
They go to scatter their lights
like topazes on the water
at night.
They go
always with people and with luggage. . .

The *Cleopatra,* the *Semiramis,* and the *Theodora*
for years now

make the same voyage
arrive on the same day
leave at the same hour.

They resemble white collar workers
who have become such time machines
that an office door
might fall down in a heap
if for one day even
it does not see them passing below.

(When the road is the same always
what does it matter if it crosses an entire Mediterranean
or goes from one house to another neighborhood?)
The *Cleopatra*, the *Semiramis*, and the *Theodora*
for a long time now and for many years
have felt the tyranny of boredom,
pacing always on the same road,
tied up always in the same harbors.

If I were a shipmaster,
yes—*si j'étais roi!*—
if I were a shipmaster
on the *Cleopatra*, the *Semiramis*, the *Theodora*,
if I were a shipmaster
with four golden stripes,
abandoned on this same line
for so many, many years,
I would climb to the fourth deck
in the middle of the sea
on a night of full moon,
and with my official uniform,
with my golden stripes
and my golden decorations,
—although I could hear music
playing from the salons of the first class—
I would describe a most harmonious curve
in the water
from the fourth deck
thus dressed in all my gold,
like a shooting star,
like a hero of unaccountable death.

George Sarandáris

(1917–41)

George Sarandáris was born in Constantinople in 1917, but was raised in Italy between the ages of two and sixteen, where his father's business took him. He attended the law school of the University of Bologna, and between 1929 and 1931 lived in Montaponne, and in Macerata at whose university he took his degree in law. He came to Greece in 1931 for his military service and remained there, with infrequent trips to Italy, until his death in 1941, aged twenty-four, from the hardships he suffered as a common soldier in the Albanian war. He never practiced law, but, living on a small income, gave himself completely to poetry and philosophy. Of a cultivated and candid nature, he wrote in an unrhymed free verse of condensed imagery and size, metaphysical in intent, pellucid in meaning, yet with evocative overtones, and became one of the forerunners of modern poetry in Greece, experimenting both in existentialism and in anti-novel prose. Hundreds of his poems in Greek, Italian, and French still remain unpublished.

BIBLIOGRAPHY: *Poems.* Edited by George Marinakis (1961). *Poems in Italian and French.* Edited by George Marinakis (1961).

Bride

Joy comes to us as a bride,
The first rains burst in bloom.
Nightingales strike up a dance in our neighborhood;
Thoughts turn into gold
And gold all conversation;
Poets and girls
Memorize kisses;
Someone arrives at the festival panting
And it is Time with a flute.

Friendships

The beloved sky
So ingenuous, so naive,
Annoys us with its dazzling light;
It will not forgive us
For falling so eagerly in love
With life.

Melissánthi

(1910–   )

Melissánthi, pseudonym of Hebe Skandhalákis, was born in Athens in 1910. She received her diplomas from various institutes in Athens for the study of English, French, and German, and has since translated much from these languages, in particular from Robert Frost and Emily Dickinson. Author of nine books of poetry and a play for children, she received the award of the Athens Academy of Arts and Sciences in 1936 for *Return to the Prodigal,* and the Palamas Award in 1946 for *Lyrical Confession.* An essentially lyrical poet, she suffered a religious crisis and turned to an expression of metaphysical agony which nonetheless emphasizes her belief in man and his ability to realize his basic goodness and love.

BIBLIOGRAPHY: *Insect Voices* (1930); *Prophecies* (1931, 1940); *Flaming Bush* (1935); *Return of the Prodigal* (1936, 1938); *Hosannah* (1939); *Lyrical Confession* (1945); *The Season of Sleep and Wakefulness* (1950); *Human Shape* (1961); *The Barrier of Silence* (1961); *Selection* (1965).

Stage Set

A draft must have been blowing for hours
because we could see the stage sets swaying.
A colored partition made of cloth
flapped for a moment strongly
and then would suddenly droop, crumpling again.
As we turned to look
a hand grasped and was shaking
a wooden, hollow sky.
"Its stars have become unglued!
Look! They're falling!" a few shouted.

Now you could discern in the far depths
the worm-eaten scaffold.
Some stars got stuck on the windowpanes,
on the shopwindows in the center of town, like
    instant pictures.
They clung wherever they could, here and there,
but most fell into the void
and a few drifted and hooked themselves
on the hanging carcasses of pigs. In a little while
an unimaginable wind began to blow.
It ravaged in the streets where
the heaped fruit were now tumbling.
It seized every variety of merchandise
and hurled them about forcefully.
Everywhere it uprooted signs.

The enormous scaffold creaked and leaned.
It lurched here and there
as they set it up and tore it down,
leaving holes of darkness in the ceiling.

Finally a new sun rose high
—the cardboard had sunk somewhat here and there,
the gold-leafed paper had flaked at the edges—

The crowd now poured into the streets to make purchases,
fragrance of spice rose from the Supermarkets,
and a wrenched sign informed us:
"Various costumes for rent here."
Many had already donned different masquerades.

And a few asked themselves in a low voice:
"How does it happen that so many ghosts
walk in the market place at high noon?"

Atonement

Every time I sinned a door half opened, and the Angels
who in my virtue had never found me beautiful,
tipped over the full amphora of their flower souls;
every time I sinned, it was as though a door had opened,
and tears of sweet compassion dripped among the grasses.
But if the sword of my remorse chased me from heaven,
every time I sinned a door half opened, and though men
thought me most ugly, the angels thought me beautiful.

Yánnis Rítsos

(1909–   )

Yánnis Rítsos, born in Monemvasia, a town of the Peloponnesos, in 1909, fell ill at the age of eighteen months of tuberculosis and spent many years in various sanatoriums. His heritage is a tragic one, for both his mother and elder brother died of tuberculosis and his father and sister died insane. Because of his left-wing activities, he spent the years 1948–52 in various detention camps in Greece. The author of twenty-three books of poetry, three volumes of *Collected Poems* (1961-64), of two plays and a poem for dance, he won the State Award in Poetry for 1956 for *Moonlight Sonata*.

BIBLIOGRAPHY: *The Window* (1960); *The Bridge* (1960); *Testimonies* (1963); and *Twelve Poems for Cavafis* (1963).

Guilty Conscience

At noon they spread their lunch on cool vineleaves—
olives, bread, tomatoes, salt—half-starved,
they didn't hear or see, they chewed. Only the stranger
was not hungry and did not eat, but gazed
at the meadow streaming in the sun, embittered
because he was not hungry. Then he took his
jackknife, which had never cut bread,
and on the bark of a fig tree carved a large hand.

Perhaps this empty hand could later hold
the entire field with its harvesters and their straw hats.

The First Sensual Delight

Proud mountains, Killidromon, Oeta, Othrys,
dominating rocks, vineyards, wheat fields and olive groves;
here they have dug quarries, the sea has withdrawn;
the heavy fragrance of bulrushes burnt by the sun,
and the resin dripping in thick drops. A large
descending evening. There by the bank, Achilles,
not yet an adolescent, as he held his ankle
in tying his sandal, felt that singular sensual delight.
For a while he paused and gazed abstractedly at the water's
     refractions. Then
he went to the ironmongers and ordered his shield—
he knew precisely its shape now, its scenes, its size.

Under Suspicion

He locked the door, looked behind him distrustingly,
and thrust the key in his pocket. It was then they arrested him.

They harassed him for months. Until, one evening, he confessed
(and this was demonstrated) that the key and the house
were his. But no one could understand
why he had hidden the key. And so,
though he was proved innocent, he remained suspected by all.

Degrees of Emotion

The sun sank, rose-red, orange. The sea,
a dark bluegreen. Far away, a boat—
a black, wavering speck. Someone
jumped to his feet and shouted: "A boat! A boat!"
The others in the coffee house left their chairs and ran to look.
Truly, it was a boat. But the one who had shouted,
guilty now under the angry gaze of the others,
lowered his head and said in a low voice: "I lied."

Builders

Have you seen those who build out of instinct
and those who build professionally
and the third who build to avenge themselves against death
and those who build consciously, with resolution?

Both these and the others stop from time to time,
wipe their plastered hands on their blue jeans,
wipe away their sweat, and weep.
They do not wipe their eyes.

In this way, moreover, the mortar knits better.
And this proceeds much beyond their purpose.
Because of this, all builders dream at night
of that unknown, that invisible "beyond,"
and every morning they build the "here" a bit better.

Nikos Engonópoulos

(1910–   )

Nikos Engonópoulos, born in Constantinople in 1910, ranks as the foremost surrealist painter in Greece and in the Biennial Exhibition of Modern and Fantastic Art in Venice in 1954 was represented by seventy-four canvases. But he is also the author of eight books of poetry. His main effort is toward self-expression, no matter what the means: if he finds himself without colors, he will turn to words; if without words, to action. Paints, words, action are for him the mediums of a single expression. He believes that the more personal a work of art, the more universal its significance; that the fundamental thing is the responsible presence of a man in a work of art, which is the expression of loneliness. Though he has a profound sense of and love for tradition, he understands that what was revolutionary and fertile in one generation may become reactionary and stifling in another, that traditions and institutions inevitably decay. He therefore believes in revolution in the name of tradition.

BIBLIOGRAPHY: *Do Not Speak to the Conductor* (1938); *The Pianos of Silence* (1939); *Seven Poems* (1944); *Bolivar: A Greek Poem* (1944, 1962); *Return of the Birds* (1946); *Eleusis* (1948); *The Atlantic* (1945); *In a Blossoming Greek Language* (1957); *Do Not Speak to the Conductor and The Pianos of Silence* (1966).

Mercurius Bouas

He kneels and opens the chest, and as with one hand he holds
the cover, with the other he rummages and searches within.
—What do you have there? I ask him.
He turns:
—*Lettere d'amore,* he replies.
And then:
—Don't they interest you?
But of course . . . if they're about love affairs, I answer.

Then very slowly, with extremely careful movements, he
begins to take out different things, one by one, and to show
them to me.

First he draws out and shows me various velvet materials,
piles of disheveled bolts, some embellished and others in mono-
tone colors. Then a rotted mattress, and finally he lets go of the
cover and brings out a corpse, well preserved, of a dead man, and
lays it down on the floor. That which was particularly interesting
about this corpse, however, was the glossy and dazzling whiteness
of its skin, as well as its unruly hair and its long martial mustache.

Psychoanalysis of Phantoms

> *. . . and have not charity, I am become*
> *as sounding brass, or a tinkling cymbal.*

As the ship of love enters the harbor at night it is received
by the mysterious music of the wilderness. Everywhere the waters
fill with flowers of all kinds and of all colors, and a white row of
naked women wait for us at the pier. All are ready, at our first
gesture, to wear immediately the red uniforms of divers. Not, however, to descend into the depths of the sea, but only to come and
wait for us, perhaps for many hours, tirelessly, affectionately, at
the entrance of the subterranean station. We, naturally, arrive
unexpectedly, waving our large wings and shouting words in-
coherent and beautiful. Then the quietness of the country land-

scape suddenly becomes more noticeable, and thus from the darkness, from the fields, men dressed in black emerge, who are like comets, and upright pianos with their white keys, who are stars. Flags flutter in the wind, at regular intervals machine guns resound and children sing. In our ears we hear the prophetic names of the women we might have loved. Also the name of a city: Sinope. I, however, do not fear death, because I love life.

NOTE: *and have . . . cymbal*: The First Epistle of Paul the Apostle to the Corinthians, XIII,i. *Sinope*: Ancient Greek city on the Black Sea.

Poetry 1948

this age
of civil strife
is not an age
for poetry
or similar things:
when something
is
to be written
it is
as if
it were written
on the other side
of death
announcements

this is why
my poems
are so bitter
(and when, indeed, were they not?)
and why they are
—above all—
so
few

Alexander Mátsas

(1910–   )

Alexander Mátsas, born in Athens in 1911, studied political science and Ancient Greek at Oxford and entered the Greek diplomatic service in 1934. He served in various posts in Egypt, London, Paris, The Hague, and Rome, was Royal Greek Ambassador to Turkey, Iran, and Pakistan, and until recently was Royal Greek Ambassador to the United States. He has published three books of poetry (the first written in French) and three poetical dramas on ancient themes, of which two—*Clytemnestra* and *Croesus*—have been produced by the State Royal Theatre of Athens in 1957 and 1963, respectively. The multiplicity of human nature, the successive metamorphosis of the individual in character and personality under the stress of circumstance and time, seem to Mátsas the most striking element in life. Sleep and love are an escape into time. Because he believes that communion with life is best attained through the world of the senses, his poetry is often a lament on the passage of time and the dispersal of the body. For Mátsas poetry is a precise art yet permeated with suggestive disintegrations under which precise meaning crumbles away and vague unanswered questions of death and decay obtrude.

BIBLIOGRAPHY: *Poems* (1946); *Poems* (1964).

Adventure of Psyche

While her beautiful vestments decline
with the rich ecstasy of the flesh,
the Soul pursues tirelessly her great adventure,
hidden behind a thousand illusions,
hidden behind hours, days, years,
      hidden behind yourself.

Like the gleaner who timidly follows the harvesters,
she gathers much that on your way you despised,
behind actions, behind words, behind thoughts,
      behind labor and sleep.

With these fragments she shapes the powerful figures
which rule the inexorable firmament of Myth,
always uncapturable, but ever so close
that you feel their breathing and their command
      behind the scenery.

Thus you may sometimes recapture the outcast
Soul, in some abyss of silence or some tear;
when the body unexpectedly shivers under a breath
      of life, from the lips of death.

Diver

The trap door of myth has suddenly opened again,
the soil, which seemed so solid, has suddenly receded like a marsh,
and now you sink, a diver holding for weight
this head you had buried and which turned to marble
in the shallow graves of oblivion.

You will find no mercy on the lips nor in the glance
of the head of stone with the thousand faces
which go on changing, uncapturable, in the depths;
and which sometimes take the relentless visage
of repudiated slaves.

Don't hope for absolution, don't expect mercy
for the statues that claim life
from the idols that don't forgive apostasy
from the ghosts demanding justice,
in the starry depths of the soul.

However artful you might have been in your negotiations
whatever security you might think you acquired
they will lay ambush to your vigil and your sleep:
behind the mirrors of the universe, behind Time
you will find the stone face of reproach.

Odysseus Elytis

(1912–   )

Odysseus Elytis, pseudonym for Odysseus Alepoudhélis, was born in Heracleion, Crete in 1912, of a well-known industrial family, and studied law and political science at the University of Athens. In the period between 1940 and 1941 he served as a second lieutenant on the Albanian front in the Greek-Italian war. In 1938 he represented Greece at the eleventh International Congress of Writers at Geneva, and in 1950 at the first International Congress of Art Critics in Paris. He has spent many years in France and several months touring the United States in 1961 under the auspices of the State Department. The author of five books of poetry, his work marks the joyous return to nature, to summer and the sea, to the blaze of the noonday sun over the Aegean, to the praise of adolescence and its sentiments. His second book was entitled *Sun the First,* as one might refer to an emperor. Though his poetry is rhythmical in effect, he is more interested in the plastic use of language and imagery, both of which still reflect his earlier preoccupation with surrealism. His experience on the Albanian front during the war brought greater depth and sobriety to his poetry and resulted in one of the best elegies written about the war. He was awarded the State Award in Poetry in 1960 for *Worthy It Is.*

BIBLIOGRAPHY: *Orientations* (1940, 1961); *Sun the First* (1943); *Heroic and Elegiac Song for the Lost Second Lieutenant of the Albanian Campaign* (1945); *Worthy It Is* (1959); *Six and One Regrets for the Sky* (1960).

Body of Summer

A long time has passed since the last rainfall was heard
Above the ants and the lizards
Now the sun burns endlessly
The fruit-trees paint their mouths
The pores of the earth very slowly open
And besides the trickling and syllabic waters
A huge plant stares into the sun's eye.

Who is this who sprawls on the far beaches
Stretched on his back, smoking the smokesilver olive leaves
Crickets warm themselves in his ears
Ants scurry to work on his chest
Lizards glide in the long grasses of his armpits
And through the seaweed of his feet a wave lightly passes
Sent by that small siren who sang:

"O naked body of summer, burnt
And eaten away by oil and salt
Body of rock and the heart's tremor
Great fluttering in the willow's hair
Breath of basil on the curly groin
Filled with starlets and pine-needles
Profound body, vessel of day!"

The slow rains come, the pelting hail,
The shores pass, flogged by the claws of the wintry wind
That with savage billows lowers in the sea-depths
The hills plunge into thick cloud udders
But behind all this you smile unconcernedly
And find again your deathless hour
As once more you are found on the beaches by the sun
And amid your naked vigor by the sky.

The Autopsy

Well, it was found that the gold of the olive root had dripped into the leaves of his heart.

And because of the many times he had kept vigil close by a candlestick, waiting for dawn to break, a strange ardor had gripped him to the marrow.

A little below the skin, the cerulean line of the horizon in a hue intense, and ample traces of azure in the blood.

It seems that the cries of birds, which in hours of great loneliness he had learned by heart, had all burst out together, so that it had not been possible for the knife to penetrate to any great depth.

Probably the intention sufficed for the Evil

Which he confronted—it is evident—in the terrifying posture of the innocent. His eyes open and proud, the whole forest still moving on his unblemished retina.

In his brain nothing but a shattered echo of the sky.

And only in the conch of his left ear, a few grains of delicate, extremely fine sand, as in seashells. Which indicates that many times he had plodded by the sea, utterly alone, with the withering grief of love and the roar of the wind.

And as for those flakes of fire on his groin, they showed that in truth he had moved time many hours ahead whenever he had merged with a woman.

We shall have early fruit this year.

This Wind That Loiters

This wind that loiters and gapes in the quince trees
This insect that sucks the grapevines
This stone that the scorpion wears next to its skin
And these wheat-stalks on the threshing floors
That play the giant to small barefoot children

Images of the Resurrection
On the wall that the pine trees scratched with their fingers
This whitewash that bears all noons on its back
And the cicadas the cicadas in the ears of the trees

Huge summer of chalk
Huge summer of cork
Red sails slanting in the squalls
Bleach-blond creatures on the sea-bottom, sponges
Accordions of the rocks
Sea-perch from the fingermarks of the awkward fisherman
Proud reefs on the fishing lines of the sun

One, two: no one shall tell us our fate
Three, four: we shall tell the sun's fate ourselves.

Nikiphóros Vrettákos

(1911–   )

Nikiphóros Vrettákos, born in Sparta in 1911, worked as a common laborer in Athens until he was given a post in the Ministry of Labor. The author of twenty-one books of poetry, he is a pure singing voice, writing spontaneously without much attention to form, impelled by an almost naïve religious devotion and a deep sentiment for the ills of downtrodden humanity. His hatred of injustice and his desire to better the world often leads him to moralize in the midst of song. Christian and democratic in his views, he believes and asserts in his poetry that art must be the expression of love and goodness, that these form the beauty of civilization as a higher ordering of human relations, a kind of divine law, a "brightness of man's soul" which is that brilliant element called the "deathlessness of art." He has twice won the State Award for Poetry: in 1940 for *The Grimaces of Man,* and in 1956 for *Poems, 1929–1951.*

BIBLIOGRAPHY: *Poems, 1929–1951* (1955); *To Robert Oppenheimer* (1954); *Time and the River* (1957); *My Mother in Church* (1957); *Royal Oak* (1959); *The World's Depth* (1961); *Autobiography* (1961).

To a Friend

The sun is setting. Its rays hang across from me like a harp.
I see your hands growing longer, ready to play me
a song. Your hands, which you forgot in that place where
we had been sitting by the sea. Your hands which you forgot
amid the wildflowers one morning as we sat on the grass.
Which you left on my table, and though I ran after you,
I could not find you. You had vanished on the crossroads
    of the world.

Your hands which you forgot on my forehead,
as preoccupied God forgets his streams. Your hands
which you forgot on my verses,
as you listened to them breathing like the small
breasts of Mangalís, that night when above her she had placed
the icon of St. Mary to watch over her,
at her side the nurse with the white blouse.
Your hands which you forgot on my life,
tied with a seablue ribbon, and which now
I keep in my trembling bag where
there is nothing more than my father's
blessing and a few odds and ends, more than enough for me
as I cut my way through the eternal rain, bareheaded,
half way through our century, to create
a smile for those to come.

Your hands which you forgot, and which now
I shall never give back to you—I shall never return them to you
throughout the unending century. At this time
I am thinking of leaving for my village. There is
a church there. As you enter, to the right,
you will find an angel without hands, painted
about two hundred years ago. I shall give him your hands.

The Other Morning

When I got up the other morning,
Jenny had thrown the window shutters wide open
to the blue horizon. She was wearing her new
rose-colored dress which glittered
like the emerald sea at daybreak. Her hair tumbled down
over her shoulders like a small
golden waterfall.
                       Dante was playing
his harmonica, and one would say that his fingers
dripped with music and water into his
mother's soul. Helen also came
to the house in the afternoon and brought three flower pots,
our roses for tomorrow. I wandered about, I looked,
I found the papers on my table sympathetic,
the idea of war improbable.
No sort of coffin could possibly fit into the universe.
Indeed, I wanted to write to the world:
If even I talk to you about
such things, know this: I will refer to a coffin
filled with sun.

The Flowering Dogwood

We could see since morning there would be an excess of light
      that day.
It was then spring. And the dogwood in flower.
Their blossoms seemed like wellsprings filled to overflowing.
Appearing on the high slopes, they descended and foamed white
under the sun like thrashing river waters,
The light their blossoms emitted had such force
that you stood beside them speechless, hesitating to
      approach them.
And when I stretched out my hand, broke a branch
and offered it to you, God then illuminated

his most beautiful day in the world. The foliage dripped
    with gold.
All creation above shook wholly and lost its rhythm.
The houses took small steps in the light,
and as the zepher blew, flowers from your cheeks
and your garments fell to the ground.
Looking about you, speechless, you asked me
if the world, if beauty, if colors, if love had any limits.
And I denied you—everything around me gestured no.
Because on your breast you had placed the small branch
of the dogwood and it glittered endlessly. Because the sun
had cut off the shadows of the trees, and the stone
had become light, the wind light, time light. Because
all the world about us had turned to Easter and to love.

Níkos Gátsos

(1915–   )

Níkos Gátsos was born in a small village in Arcadia and took his
degree from the School of Letters at the University of Athens. From
early childhood he grew up in the heroic traditions of his countryside,
made vivid for him by the ballads and folksongs of the region. He is
the author of only one longish poem, *Amorgós,* but it has had a disproportionate influence among the writers of his generation. In *Amorgós,*
the practice of surrealism, the rhythms of the Bible, and the traditions
of Greek folk ballads were combined for the first time in a strange,
arresting, and elegiac manner. Profoundly influenced by the Ionian
philosopher Heracleitos, Gátsos believes that the essence of life and
art is to be found in nothing static, but in in eternal flux. In the broodiing
long lines of his lamentations, however, there is always to be found the
sprig of basil or rosemary, symbols of hope and resurrection, joyful
melancholy.

BIBLIOGRAPHY: *Amorgós* (1943; 1963); *Six Poets of Modern Greece*
(1961; edited, translated, and introduced by Edmund Keeley and Philip
Sherrard).

543

From Amorgós

How much I loved you only I know
I who once lightly touched you with the eyes of the Pleiades
And embraced you with the mane of the moon and danced with
    you on the summery plains
On the hewn stubble and ate cut clover together
O Dark Enormous Sea, the multitudinous pebbles about your
    throat, the multi-colored shingle in your hair
A vessel sails into the bay, a rusty millstone groaning
A tuft of blue smoke within the rose of the horizon
Exactly like the wing of a crane throbbing;
Armies of swallows await the brave men to offer them welcome
Arms rise up naked with anchors engraved near the armpits
The cries of children entwine with the birdsongs of the West Wind
Honeybees buzz in and out of a cow's nostrils
The kerchiefs of Kalamáta are waving
And a distant bell dabbles the sky with bluing
Like the sound of a small gong traveling amid the constellations
So many centuries fled.
From the souls of Goths and the domes of Baltimore
And from lost St. Sophia, the renowned cathedral.

But who are those who watch with unwavering eyes and serene
    faces from the top of the highest mountains?
This dust-storm in the air is the echo of what conflagration?
Can it be Kalívas fighting or it is Levendoyánnis?
Is it a clash perhaps between the Germans and the people
    of Máni?
No, it is neither Kalívas fighting nor Levendoyánnis
Nor is it a clash between the Germans and the people of Máni.
Towers are guarding in silence a princess turned phantom
The tops of cypress trees companion a dead windflower
Shepherds with reeds of linden serenely sing their songs
    of morning
A stupid hunter fires on the turtle doves
And an old windmill, forgotten by all
Mends by itself its rotting sails with a needle of dolphin bone
And descends from the hillsides with a favorable northeaster

As Adonis descended the paths of Mt. Chelmos to say
    good-evening to Gólfo.

Year after year have I struggled with hammer and ink, O my
    tormented heart
With gold and fire to stitch you an embroidery
The hyacinth of an orange tree
A blossoming quince to console you
I who once lightly touched you with the eyes of the Pleiades
And embraced you with the mane of the moon and danced with
    you on the summery plains
On the hewn stubble and ate cut clover together
O Dark Enormous Solitude, the multitudinous pebbles about your
    throat, the multi-colored jewels in your hair.

Tákis Varvitsiótis

(1916–   )

Tákis Varvitsiótis was born in Salonika in 1916, studied law at the University of Salonika, and is a practicing lawyer. He is the author of six books of poetry, of which *The Birth of Spring* was awarded the poetry prize by the Group of Twelve for 1960. He has also been honored for his poetry by the Municipality of Salonika. Deeply influenced by French and Spanish symbolist poetry, of which he is a translator, he writes in a lyrical vein of great purity and delicacy, an almost childlike innocence, a dreamlike translucence.

BIBLIOGRAPHY: *Leaves of Sleep* (1949); *The Winter Solstice*, together with *The Wooden Horse* and *The Spelling Book* (1955); *Epitaph* (1951); *The Birth of Springs* (1959); *The Veil and the Smile* (1963).

The Testimony of the Mirror

On its face it puts to sleep
The flowing light of a candle
But within itself, much deeper,
It discovers many things
That sing

(But all things sing
When within ourselves we lock up
Something of their spirit)

And these things are
The crystals of dreams
Remnants of wings
And snow
Much snow

And these things are
The plaster hands of girls
Hair that grows pale
Multiple reflections
Eyes winking

And within it deeper still
A certain lethal coldness
A strange hard eyelid
That strains and stretches continuously
To guard its one and only
Quivering, watery eye.

To Federico García Lorca

What has become of our faces?
What has become of our kisses?
Where can the gold of the hours be
On which our memories will roll?
Has a yellow cornflower sprouted perhaps
On his closed mouth?
What mournful birds of the tempest
What dreadful stage curtains
Pursue us still?

On the banner of your sleep
The tympanum of a windflower leans.
Green stars fall into the sea
To commit suicide,
The glassy fear
Lies in ambush in our veins.
Your blood has turned to iodine
And colors
The wintry windowpanes of your absence.

In the hallways of ice
The lilies dance
In the satin winds
Resplendent horsemen are hidden
Who smell of jasmine and dream.

A frightened girl
Dissolves into music
An eyelash on the threshold of death
Will not reach its springtime.
The sky buries
Its dead dolls.

A memory made of spikenard and ashes
Binds the hands of our tender lives.
Why do the seashells fall silent?
Why don't the children sing?
We have destroyed all plants and animals.
The women have dressed themselves in all the tears
And all the lights have been forgotten
In the cemetery of mist.

My voice, my own,
My everlasting friend,
Who emerge from rock
Wearing three carnations
And three wounds,
Dressed in the smoke of my nostalgia,
Buried in the South Wind,
Benumbed reflections of nightingales.

Burning flute
On the lips of sleep,
Of snow,
Of fresh innocence,
Of grass under the new cornstalks,
On the lips of time
With its crimson colors.

Date Due

MAY 11 '71					

889.08
G433   68726

AUTHOR
Gianos, Mary P.

TITLE
Introduction to modern Greek liter-

889.08   68726
G433

Gianos, Mary P.
Introduction to modern Greek literature.